THE MUSICIAN'S GUIDE WORKBOOK AND EAR-TRAINING FOURTH AP® EDITION

THE MUSICIAN'S GUIDE

Workbook and Ear-Training

FOURTH AP® EDITION

Paul Murphy
Muhlenberg College

Joel Phillips
Westminster Choir College of Rider University

Elizabeth West Marvin
Eastman School of Music

Jane Piper Clendinning
Florida State University College of Music

W. W. NORTON & COMPANY
Independent Publishers Since 1923

W. W. Norton & Company has been independent since its founding in 1923, when William Warder Norton and Mary D. Herter Norton first published lectures delivered at the People's Institute, the adult education division of New York City's Cooper Union. The firm soon expanded its program beyond the Institute, publishing books by celebrated academics from America and abroad. By midcentury, the two major pillars of Norton's publishing program—trade books and college texts—were firmly established. In the 1950s, the Norton family transferred control of the company to its employees, and today—with a staff of five hundred and hundreds of trade, college, and professional titles published each year—W. W. Norton & Company stands as the largest and oldest publishing house owned wholly by its employees.

Printed in the United States of America

Fourth Edition

Editor: Christopher Freitag
Assistant editor: Julie Kocsis
Development editor: Meg Wilhoite
Project editor: Michael Fauver
Managing editor, College: Marian Johnson
Managing editor, College Digital Media: Kim Yi
Copyeditor: Jodi Beder
Proofreader: Debra Nichols
Media editor: Steve Hoge
Media assistant editor: Eleanor Shirocky
Production manager: Stephen Sajdak
Design director: Rubina Yeh
Designer: Marisa Nakasone
Music typesetting and page composition: David Botwinik
Manufacturing: LSC Communications: Owensville

ISBN: 978-0-393-44250-2

W. W. Norton & Company, Inc., 500 Fifth Avenue, New York, NY 10110
www.wwnorton.com

W. W. Norton & Company, Ltd., 15 Carlisle Street, London W1D 3BS

2 3 4 5 6 7 8 9 0

Contents

Ear-Training

Part I Elements of Music

Part II Diatonic Harmony and Tonicization

Part III Chromatic Harmony and Form

Preface

The Musician's Guide series is the complete package of theory and aural skills materials that covers everything students need to know for the AP® exam. The AP® theory textbook discusses music that will be relevant to every musician, while the AP® *Workbook & Ear-Training* volume provides ideal practice for the dictation questions on the AP® exam, and the AP® *Sight-Singing* volume features all the material students need for the sight-singing portion of the exam. With each revision, we hear from many colleagues around the country about what works best for their students, and we are proud to retain these features while introducing something new to each edition.

This *Workbook & Ear-Training* volume is comprised of two parts. The Workbook is designed to provide hands-on, minds-engaged assignments for students to complete in or outside of class, as the teacher chooses. Assignments are arranged in chapter order so that students will have enough information to complete the first homework assignments on a given topic even if only the first part of that chapter has been covered. Assignments include fundamental skills such as chord spelling, style compositions—from melody writing to figured bass to composing music in complete small forms—and music analysis. Many chapters ask for short, prose responses to questions about the music being studied. By practicing each new skill from a variety of perspectives, students will have a better and more well-rounded understanding of music theory.

The Musician's Guide takes a spiral approach to learning, in which the Anthology's core repertoire is revisited from chapter to chapter as new concepts are introduced; the Workbook continues this approach, revisiting Anthology scores in a series of analytical explorations, as well as introducing additional compositions. We hope that by examining aspects of these works through analytical methods, students will gain a rich understanding of the music presented in the Anthology.

The *Ear-Training* section is distinctive in three significant ways. First, no other source offers hundreds of carefully selected works from a wide array of musical literature in a way that seamlessly corresponds to written skills, sight-singing, and rhythm reading. Second, since the inception of the *Musician's Guide* series, a primary goal has been to present literature from composers whose works are historically underrepresented. The Fourth Edition's literature significantly expands that gender, ethnic, racial, and geographical diversity with the addition of dozens of works, almost none of which have appeared in any pedagogical forum. Many of those works appear exclusively in *Ear-Training*. Third, our approach to skills acquisition emphasizes meticulous attention to scaffolding and sequencing.

Ear-Training is divided into twenty-three chapters that align with both *Sight-Singing* and *The Musician's Guide to Theory and Analysis*. Thus, instructors will find it easy to plan for class and to coordinate aural skills with conceptual understanding. All audio examples are available online. Students access audio for all of the examples as well as the Aural Skills InQuizitive activities by going to digital.wwnorton.com/auralskillsiq2ap and registering with the code inside their text or included as part of Total Access.

Each chapter begins with specific learning objectives and key concepts that emphasize listening strategies. ***Try it*** exercises—short, self-led, self-evaluated dictations—reinforce chapter concepts and prepare students to succeed with longer excerpts from the literature. Answers for all ***Try it*** exercises appear in the Teacher's Edition and in an appendix of the Student Edition.

The Fourth Edition of *Ear-Training* improves **Contextual Listening** activities in three significant ways. First, we added numerous works by a broad range of composers from diverse geographical regions. Second, each of the hundreds of exercises has been recast to make it more accessible to novice listeners. Initial exercises prepare students to tackle the specific problems presented in the work from literature, and the redesigned Workspace makes taking dictation much easier and more methodical. Third, the quality of the recordings has been improved, all playback levels normalized, and many new recordings appear, some debuting literature never heard by modern audiences.

Each chapter's **Contextual Listening** exercises progress from easiest to most challenging. The structure of every exercise guides students through listening in a step-by-step process. Annotated scores and answers to all **Contextual Listening** examples appear in the Teacher's Edition.

Contextual Listening exercises feature Workspaces, where students work from the outside inward in a strategic process that results in accurate notation of what they hear. Students might begin by notating meter and rhythm on a single staff, to which they then assign solfège syllables or scale-degree numbers. They then map this information onto notes on the staff to complete accurate transcriptions. Targeted analytic questions guide students through the process and deepen conceptual understanding.

Assessing and Assigning Contextual Listening

Contextual Listening assignments develop strategic thinking. The more students practice, the better their skills. To encourage regular practice, many teachers score these exercises holistically (e.g., 2-1-0; good, fair, redo). Students can focus on the main concepts without chasing perfection. Conversely, if time permits, allowing students to redo assignments until they earn the top score is a great way to encourage more practice.

- Because **Contextual Listening** exercises move from easy to challenging, teachers can match assignment demands to the skill level of each student.
- Consider completing the initial exercises during class to prepare students to finish the **Contextual Listening** on their own.
- **Contextual Listening** assignments can make good partner work, particularly if students have complementary skill strengths.
- Especially for longer or more complex works, consider assigning and checking one portion before continuing.

Applying Solfège Syllables and Scale-Degree Numbers

All singing systems have merit, and choosing *some* system is far superior to using none. To reinforce musical patterns, we recommend singing with movable-*do* solfège syllables and/or scale-degree numbers, but we provide a summary explanation of both the movable- and fixed-*do* systems in Chapter 1 to help students get started. (A quick reference for diatonic and chromatic syllables also appears at the front of this volume.) For solfège in modal contexts, we present two systems in Chapter 9, one using syllables derived from major and minor, and one using relative (rotated) syllables.

Applying a Rhythm-Counting System

Many people use some counting system to learn and perform rhythms—in effect, "rhythmic solfège." For example, a rhythm in $\frac{2}{4}$ meter might be vocalized "du de, du ta de ta" (Edwin Gordon system), or "1 and, 2 e and a" (McHose/Tibbs system), or "Ta di Ta ka di mi" (Takadimi system). We leave it to the discretion of each instructor whether to use such a system and which to require.

Our Thanks to . . .

A work of this size and scope is helped along the way by many people. We are especially grateful for the support of our families and our students. Our work together as coauthors has been incredibly rewarding, a collaboration for which we are sincerely thankful. We also thank Joel Phillips (Westminster Choir College) for his many important contributions—pedagogical, musical, and personal—to our project, and especially for the coordinated aural-skills component of this package, *The Musician's Guide to Aural Skills* with Paul Murphy (Muhlenberg College), who has become a key member of our team.

For subvention of the recordings, we thank James Undercofler (director and dean of the Eastman School of Music), as well as Eastman's Professional Development Committee. For audio engineering, we are grateful to recording engineers John Ebert and John Baker. For audio production work, we thank Glenn West, Christina Lenti, and Lance Peeler, who assisted in the recording sessions. We also thank our colleagues at both Westminster Choir College and the Eastman School of Music who gave of their talents to help make the recordings. The joy of their music making contributed mightily to this project.

We are grateful for the thorough and detailed work of our prepublication reviewers, whose suggestions inspired many improvements, large and small: Erin Perdue Brownfield (East Ascension High School), Tracy Carr (Eastern New Mexico University), David Davies (Texas A&M University-Commerce), Amy Engelsdorfer (Luther College), Stefanie Harger Gardner (Glendale Community College, AZ), William Heinrichs (University of Wisconsin-Milwaukee), Ronald Hemmel (Westminster Choir College), Jennifer Jessen-Foose (Cedar Grove High School), Kimberly Goddard Loeffert (Oklahoma State University), Ryan Messling (Prairie High School), David Parker (Bob Jones University), Brian Parrish (Parkway West High School), Richard Robbins (University of Minnesota Duluth), Jennifer Russell (Northern Arizona University), Janna Saslaw (Loyola University), and Heather Thayer (Henderson State University). For previous editions, reviewers have included Michael Berry (University of Washington), David Castro (St. Olaf College), Melissa Cox (Emory University), Gary Don (University of Wisconsin-Eau Claire), Jeff Donovick (St. Petersburg College), Terry Eder (Plano Senior High School), Jeffrey Gillespie (Butler University), Bruce Hammel (Virginia Commonwealth University), Melissa Hoag (Oakland University), Rebecca Jemian (University of Louisville), Charles Leinberger (University of Texas-El Paso), David Lockart (North Hunterdon High School), Robert Mills (Liberty University), Daniel Musselman (Union University), Kristen Nelson (Stephen F. Austin State University), Shaugn O'Donnell (City College, CUNY), Tim Pack (University of Oregon), Scott Perkins (DePauw University), Ruth Rendleman (Montclair

State University), Sarah Sarver (Oklahoma City University), Alexander Tutunov (Southern Oregon University), and Annie Yih (University of California at Santa Barbara).

We are indebted to the staff of W. W. Norton for their commitment to this project and their painstaking care in producing these volumes. Most notable among these are Chris Freitag, who has capably guided this edition with great enthusiasm; Meg Wilhoite, who served as development editor; Justin Hoffman, who steered the second and third editions with a steady hand; and Maribeth Anderson Payne, whose vision helped launch the series with great aplomb. Michael Fauver was project editor of the volume, with assistance from copyeditor Jodi Beder and proofreader Debra Nichols. We appreciate the invaluable assistance of media experts Steve Hoge and Eleanor Shirocky. Julie Kocsis was assistant editor, David Botwinik was typesetter, and Stephen Sajdak was production manager.

Joel Phillips, Paul Murphy, Elizabeth West Marvin, and Jane Piper Clendinning

Elements of Music

NAME ________________________________

Pitch and Pitch Class

ASSIGNMENT 1.1

I. Identifying letter names from the keyboard

A. Count letter names above the pitches labeled on the keyboard (e.g., 3 above C). Be sure to count the given note (C-D-E). Write the letter name of the new pitch (E) on the appropriate key and in the blank provided.

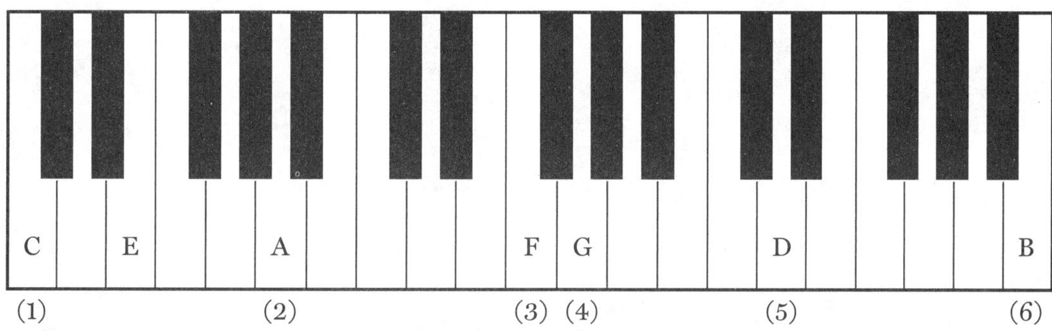

(1) 3 above C ___E___ (2) 4 above A ________ (3) 4 below F ________

(4) 6 above G ________ (5) 3 above D ________ (6) 3 below B ________

B. Write the letter name for each numbered white or black key in the blank. Choose either enharmonic name for black keys.

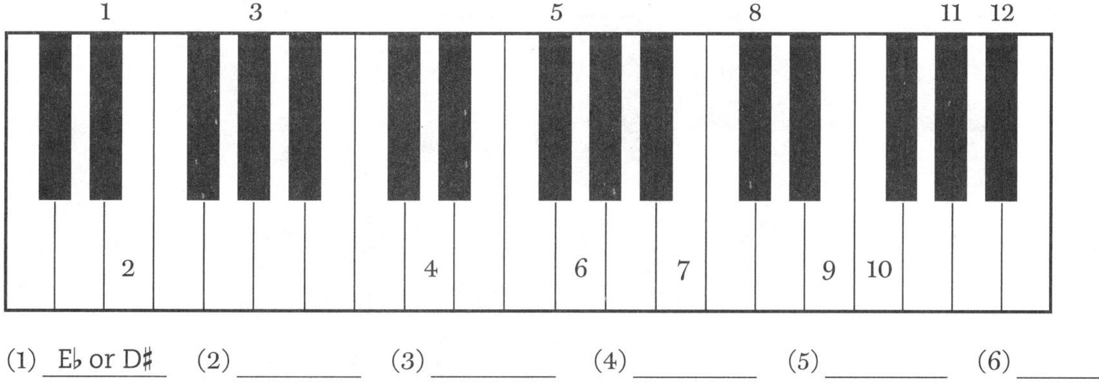

(1) E♭ or D♯ (2) ________ (3) ________ (4) ________ (5) ________ (6) ________

(7) ________ (8) ________ (9) ________ (10) ________ (11) ________ (12) ________

II. Identifying whole and half steps at the keyboard

Locate each pair of pitches on the keyboard below in any octave. Write their names on a white key or above a black key. Then, in the blank provided, write W (whole step), H (half step), or N (neither).

(a) A♯–B ___H___ (b) F–E ______ (c) G♭–A ______

(d) B♭–C ______ (e) G♯–G♮ ______ (f) D♭–C♭ ______

(g) F♯–G♯ ______ (h) E–F♭ ______ (i) G♭–G♮ ______

(j) B–C ______ (k) G–A♯ ______ (l) C♯–D♯ ______

(m) E♭–E♮ ______ (n) A–B ______ (o) A♭–G♭ ______

(p) B♭–C♯ ______ (q) E♭–F ______ (r) A♭–A♮ ______

III. Enharmonic pitches

Circle any pair of pitches that are *not* enharmonic.

(a) F♯–G♭ (b) B𝄪–C (c) A♯–B♭ (d) C♭–B (e) G𝄫–F (f) D–E𝄫

(g) E♯–F♭ (h) A𝄫–G (i) D𝄪–E (j) C𝄪–D (k) B♭–C𝄫 (l) A𝄪–B♭

NAME ______________________

ASSIGNMENT 1.2

I. Identifying whole and half steps at the keyboard

In each exercise below, start with the key indicated and move your finger along the path of half and whole steps given. In the blank, write the name of the pitch where you end.

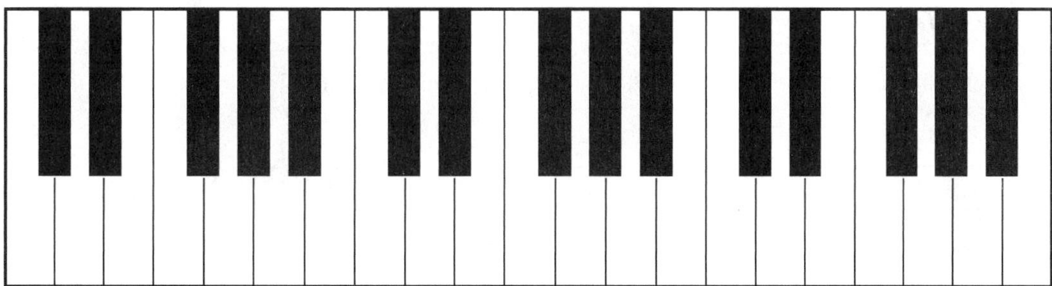

(a) Begin on C: down W, down H, down W, up H, up H = ___A___

(b) Begin on E: up W, up H, up W, down H, up W, up W = ________

(c) Begin on F♯: down W, down W, up H, down W, down H, up W = ________

(d) Begin on A♭: up W, up W, up W, down H, up W, up W = ________

(e) Begin on C♯: down W, up H, up W, up W, up H, up H = ________

(f) Begin on B: up H, up H, down W, down H, down W, down W = ________

(g) Begin on D: up H, down W, down W, down H, down H, up W = ________

(h) Begin on E♭: down W, down W, down H, down W, up H, up H = ________

II. Staff notation

Write the letter name of each pitch in the blank below.

A. Treble and bass clefs

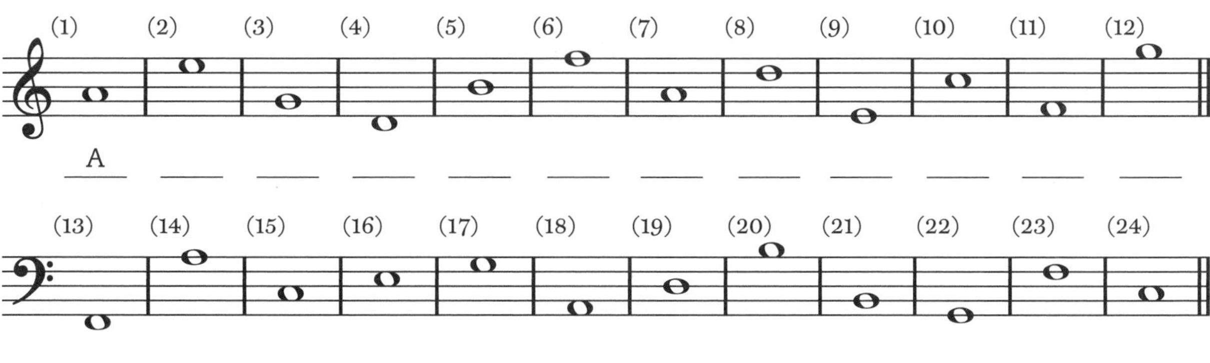

B. Alto and tenor clefs

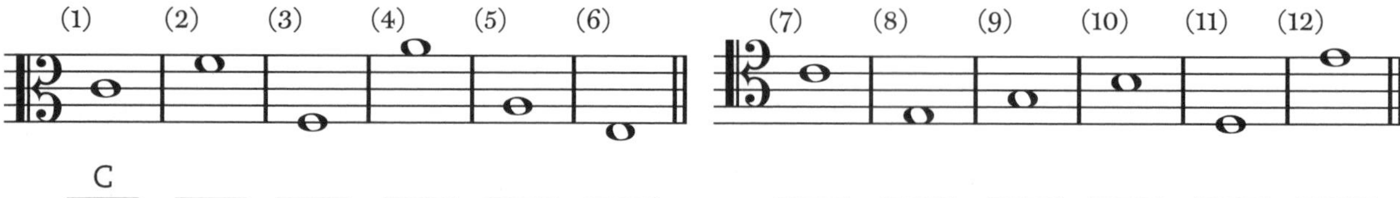

III. Half and whole steps from staff notation

For each pitch pair below, write W (whole step), H (half step), or N (neither) in the blank.

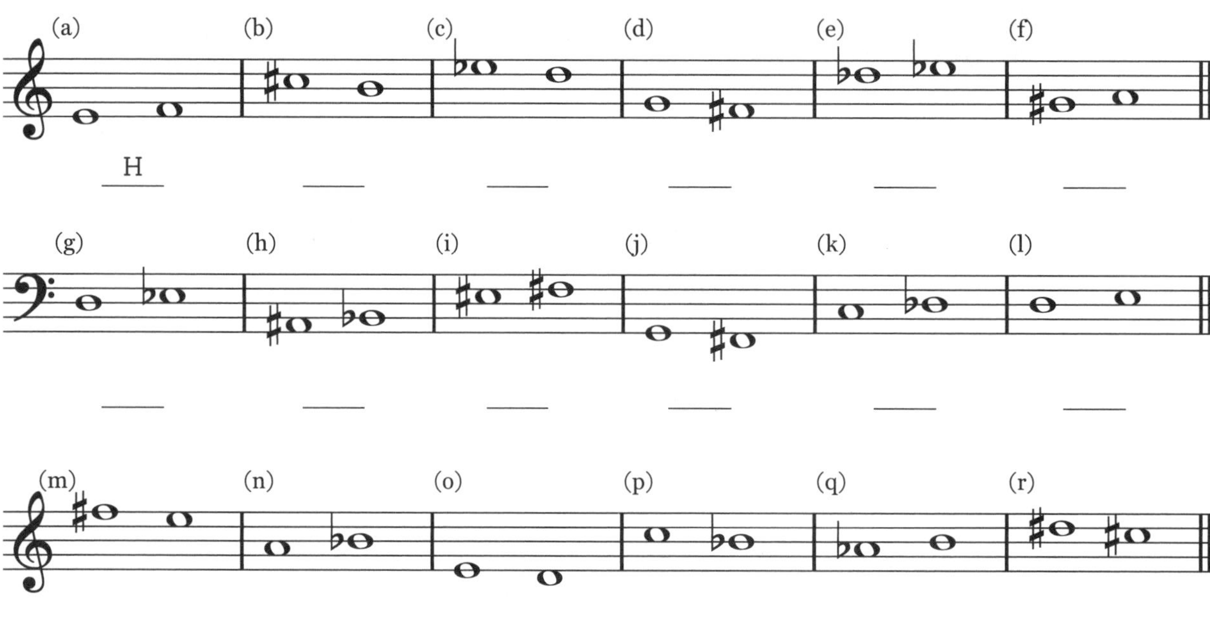

IV. Analysis: Half and whole steps in melodies

Write W (whole step), H (half step), or N (neither) in the blank below the circled pitches.

A. Charles Ives, "The Cage," m. 2 (vocal part)

Note: Accidentals apply only to the note immediately adjacent.

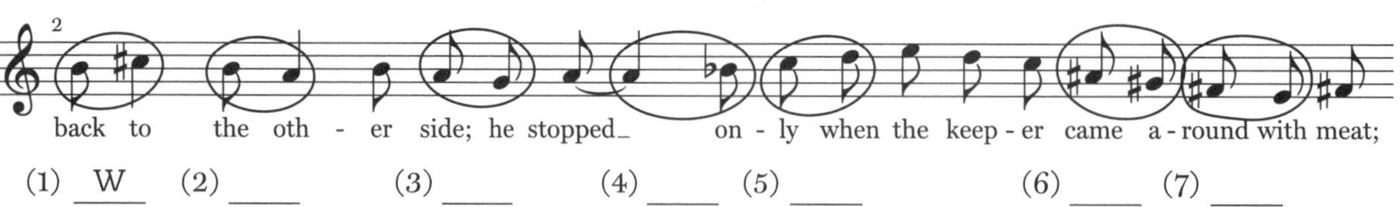

B. J. S. Bach, Minuet, from Cello Suite No. 1 in G Major, mm. 25–30

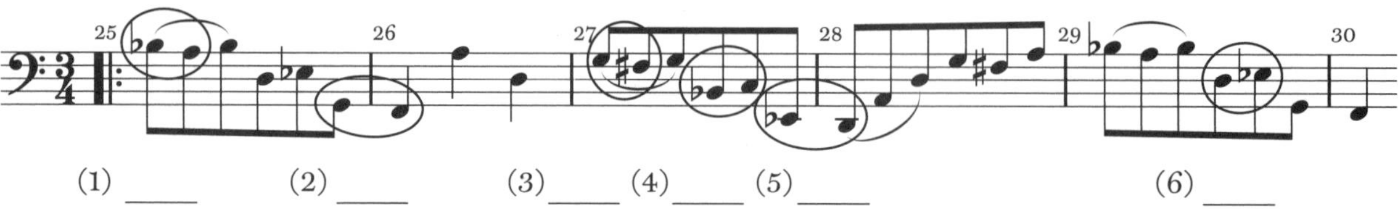

ASSIGNMENT 1.3

I. Writing whole and half steps on the staff

For each given note:

- Draw a stem to make a half note; be sure that the stem is on the correct side of the note and extends in the correct direction.
- Write a second half note a whole or half step above or below the given note, as indicated by the arrow.
- Choose a spelling for the second note that has a different letter name from the given pitch.

II. Identifying pitches with and without ledger lines

Write the letter name of each pitch in the blank provided.

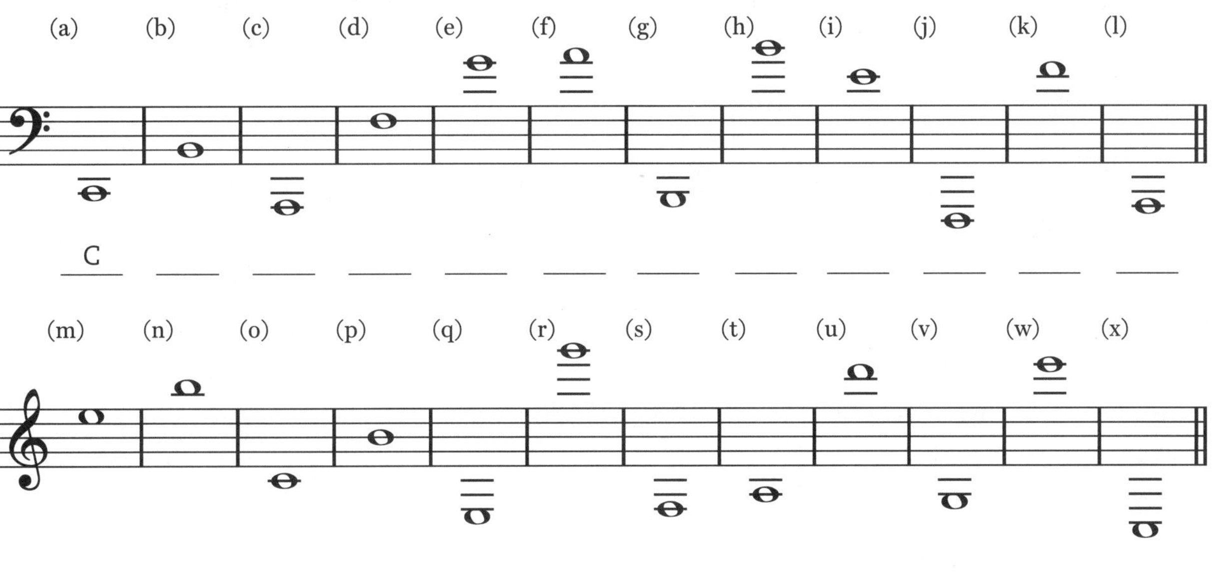

III. Identifying pitches in C clefs

For each pitch on the left, label every pitch with the correct letter name and octave number in the blank. Then write the C-clef equivalent notation on the right. Don't change the octave.

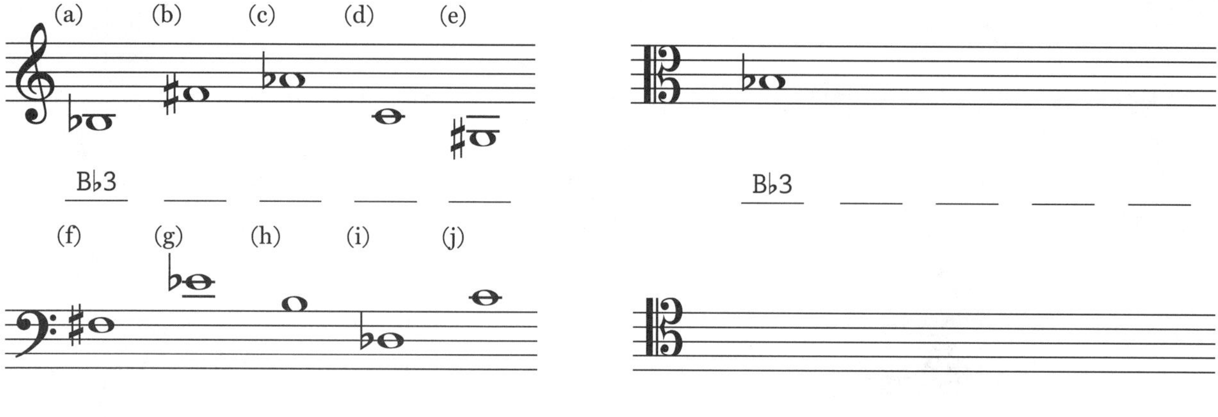

IV. Analysis

In the following melodies, write W or H for each bracketed pair of pitches in the blank below.

A. Joel Phillips, "Blues for Norton," mm. 20–24 (bass line)

B. Louise Farrenc, Trio for Flute, Cello, and Piano, Op. 45, mvt. 3, mm. 5–9 (flute only)

C. Scott Joplin, "Pine Apple Rag," mm. 1–4 (right hand)

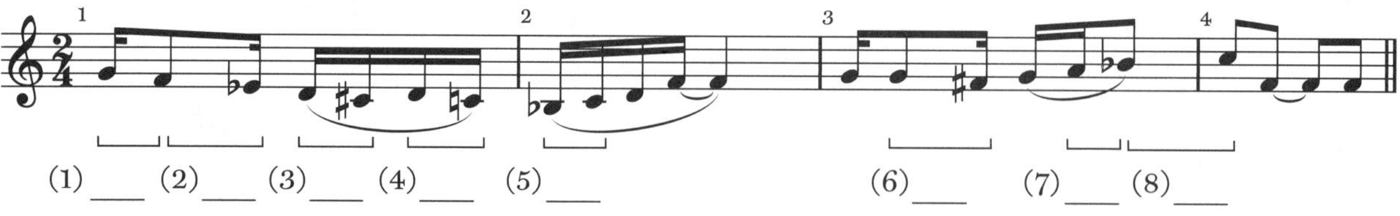

D. Willie Nelson, "On the Road Again," mm. 11–14

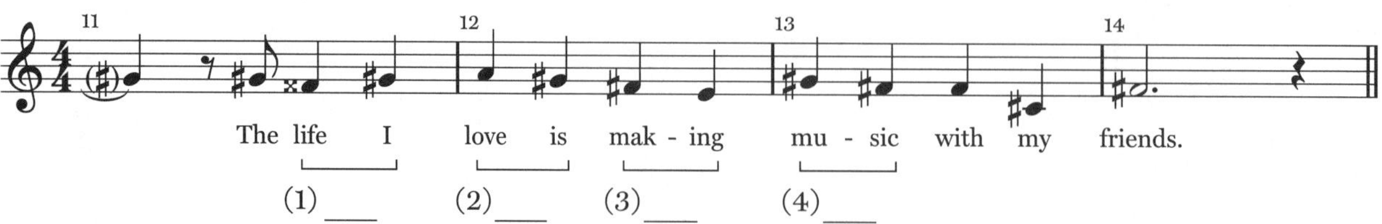

ASSIGNMENT 1.4

I. Identifying pitches in mixed clefs

Write the letter name and octave number of each pitch below.

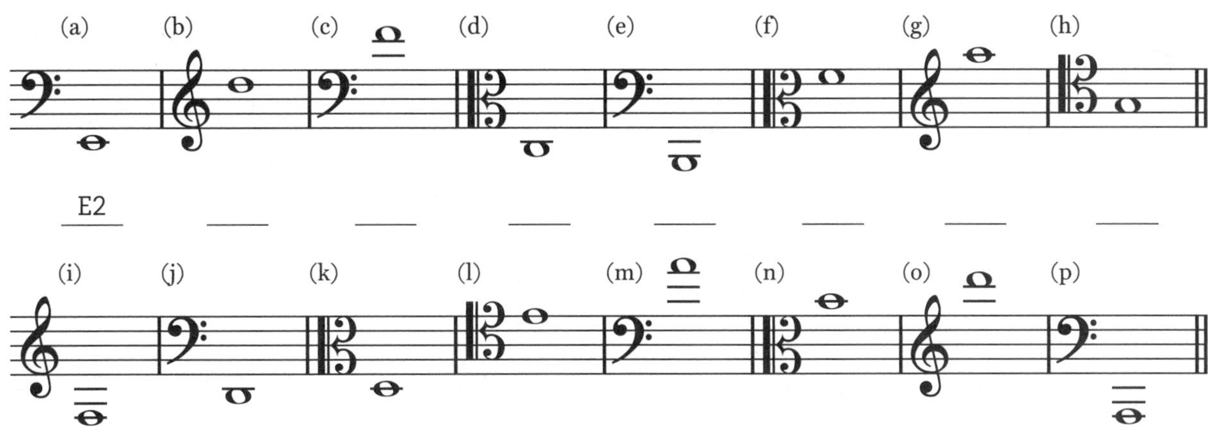

II. Writing half and whole steps in mixed clefs

In the following exercises, choose a spelling that has a different letter name from the given pitch.

A. Write a whole step above each given note.

B. Write a whole step below each given note.

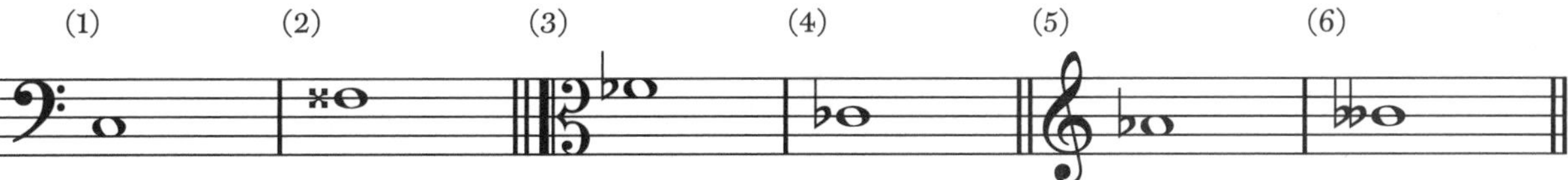

C. Write a half step above each given note (remember to use a different letter name from that given).

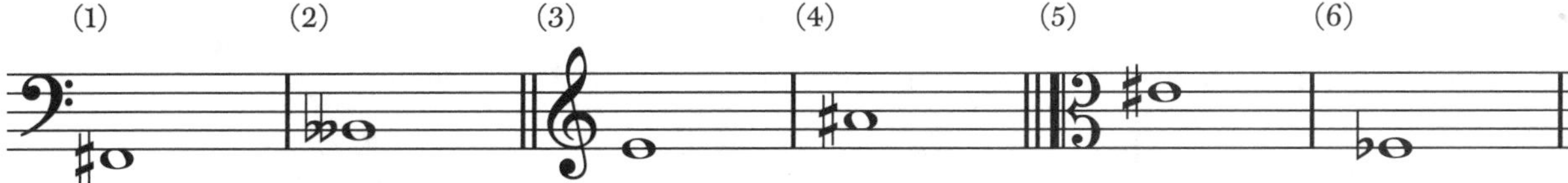

D. Write a half step below each given note (remember to use a different letter name from that given).

III. Identifying pitch and register in musical contexts

In the excerpts below, write the letter name and octave number of the circled pitch in the blank that corresponds with the numbers marked on the score.

A. Haydn, Menuetto and Trio, from String Quartet in D Minor, Op. 76, No. 2 (*Quinten*), mm. 1–11

(1) F5 (2) ______ (3) ______ (4) ______ (5) ______

(6) ______ (7) ______ (8) ______ (9) ______ (10) ______

B. Clara Schumann, Romanze, Op. 21, No. 1, mm. 5–8

(1) E5 (2) ______ (3) ______ (4) ______ (5) ______ (6) ______

ASSIGNMENT 1.5

I. Arranging

Rewrite each excerpt on the blank staff provided, according to the individual instructions. Use ledger lines as needed. Remember to change the stem direction where necessary in the new octave. Copy note heads, stems, and other symbols as shown (you'll learn more about them in Chapter 2).

A. John Tavener, "The Lamb," mm. 3–4

Rewrite two octaves lower in the bass clef.

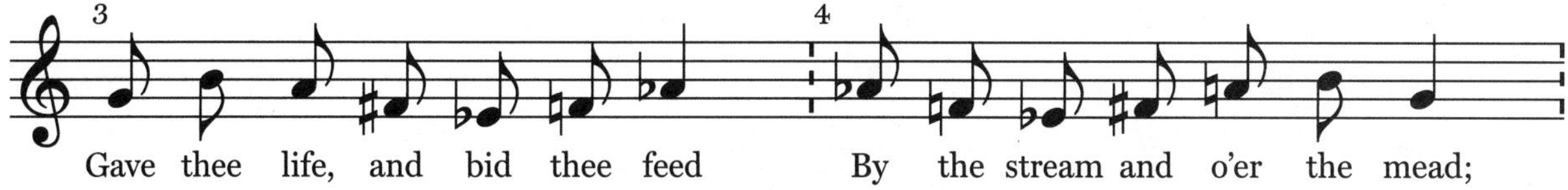
3
4
Gave thee life, and bid thee feed
By the stream and o'er the mead;

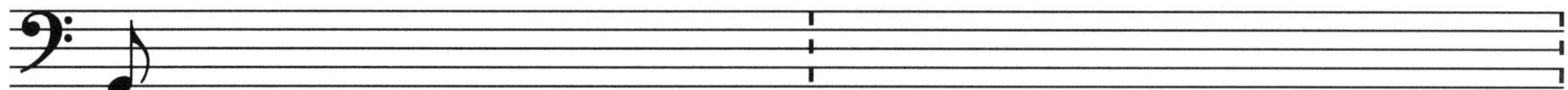

B. Henry Purcell, "Music for a While," mm. 21–22

Rewrite this line for bassoon in the tenor clef; don't change the octave.

21
22

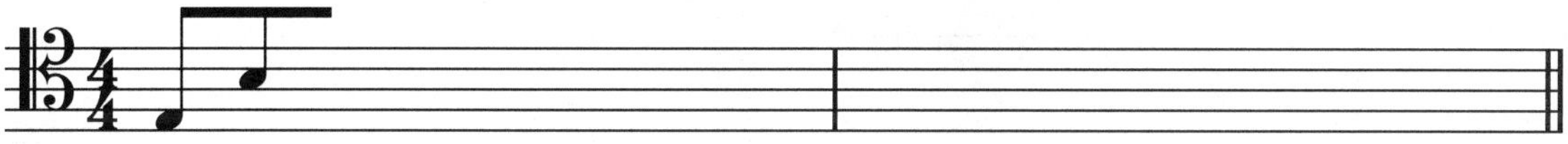

C. Haydn, Concerto in D Major for Corno di caccia and Orchestra, mvt. 1, mm. 1–4

Rewrite this viola part for violin in the treble clef; don't change the octave.

1
2
3
4

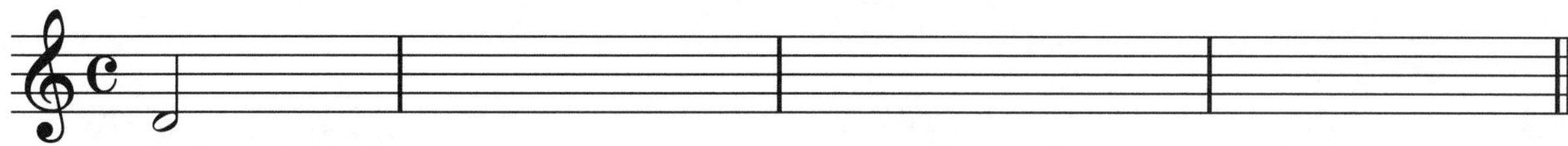

II. Composing melodies

On the staves below, compose two melodies of mostly whole and half steps in any musical style you choose.

- Choose a different "home" pitch for each melody. Begin and end on this note.
- Write at least ten pitches for each, using only adjacent letter names (e.g., B–C or G–F♯–E).
- Write two to three times as many whole steps as half steps.
- Notate all accidentals, even naturals.
- Notate your melody with rhythm if you wish, or use filled and hollow note heads as shown below (hollow note heads last twice as long as filled).
- Add dynamic indications for the performance of your melody.

Sample melody 1

Sample melody 2

A. Melody 1

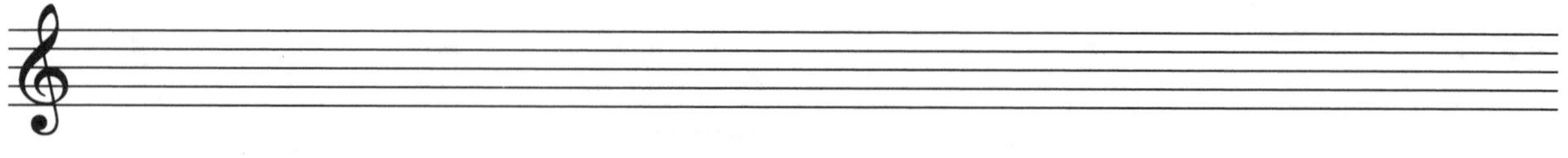

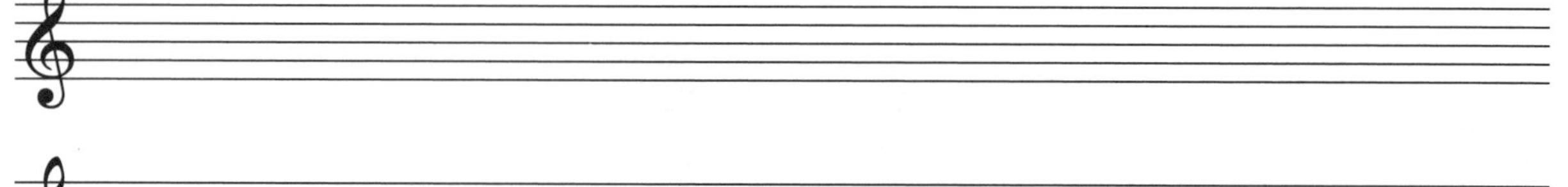

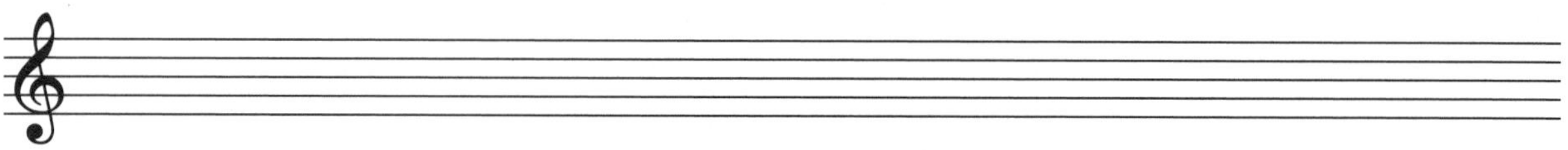

B. Melody 2

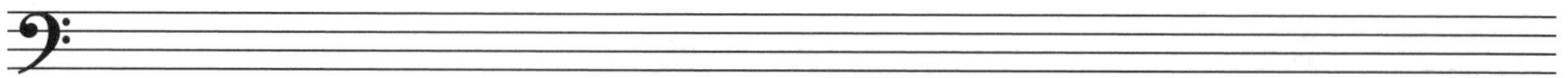

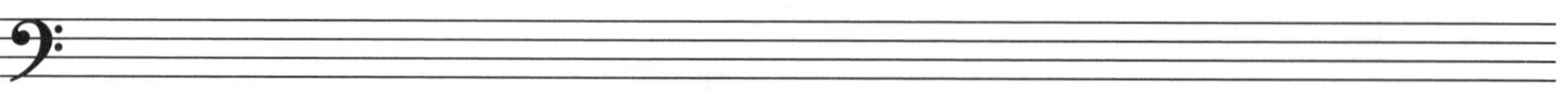

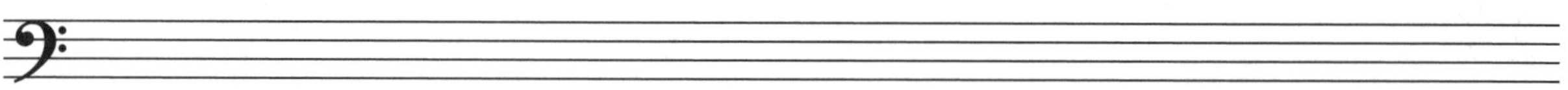

Simple Meters

ASSIGNMENT 2.1

I. Notation basics

A. Circle any notation errors on the left, then renotate the entire exercise correctly on the right.

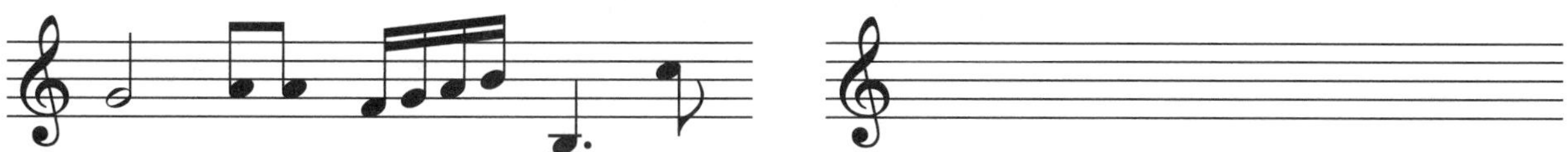

B. For each rhythmic value or rest notated on the first staff, notate the corresponding rest or note on the second staff. When you notate pitches, write the correct rhythmic value for any pitch you choose.

II. Identifying meter

Write the meter signatures and meter type (e.g., simple duple) for each of the following melodies.

A. J. S. Bach, Minuet, from Cello Suite No. 1 in G Major, mm. 25–32

Meter: __________ Meter type: ______________________________

B. Clara Schumann, "Liebst du um Schönheit," mm. 3–6

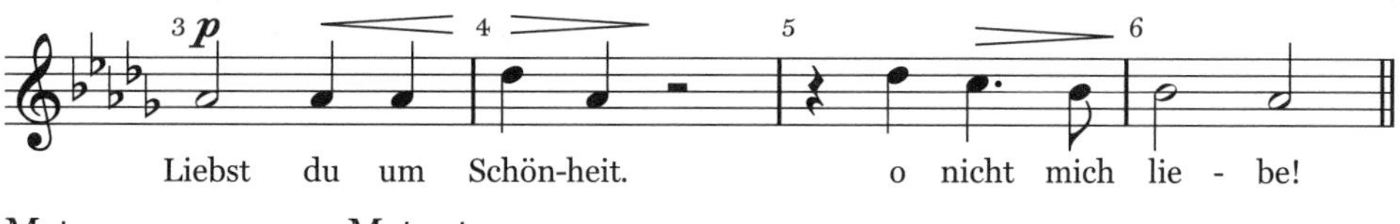

Meter: __________ Meter type: ______________________________

C. W. A. Mozart, Sonata in F Major, K. 332, mvt. 1, mm. 1–9

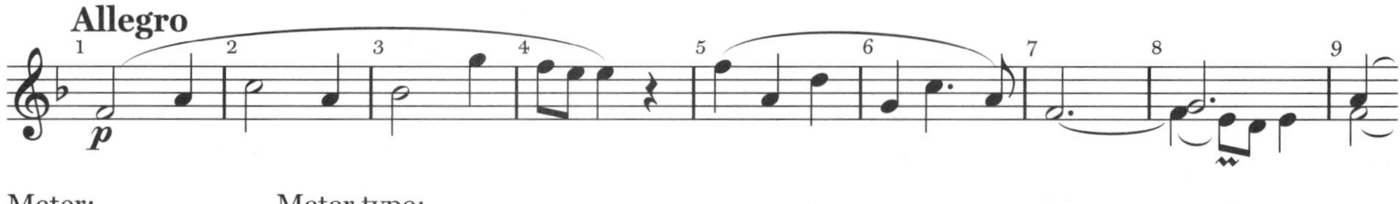
Allegro
p

Meter: _________ Meter type: ____________________________

III. Counting rhythms

For each rhythm provided, add the missing bar lines and write the counts below the score. Then perform the rhythm.

A.
1 (2) 3 &
B.
C.
D.
E.

F. Pentz, Ørsted, Allen, Bieber, Levin, Sheeran, Scott, and Meckseper, "Cold Water," mm. 10–13 (the last measure is incomplete)

feel you're sink-ing, I__ will jump right o - ver in - to cold, cold wa - ter for you.___

G. Tesfaye, Bangalter, Homem-Christo, McKinney, Walter, and Quenneville, "Starboy," mm. 30–31

Le-gend of the Fall took the year like a ban - dit. Buy my ma a crib and a brand-new wag - on;

ASSIGNMENT 2.2

I. Understanding dots

Write the appropriate note value in each empty box of the chart provided.

𝅗𝅥.	=	𝅗𝅥	+	♩
♩.	=	♩	+	
	=	♪	+	𝅘𝅥𝅯

𝅝.	=	𝅝	+	
𝅗𝅥.	=		+	♩
♩.	=		+	♪

II. Counting rhythms with beat subdivisions

A. Add the missing bar lines to each rhythm, and write the counts below. Then perform the rhythm.

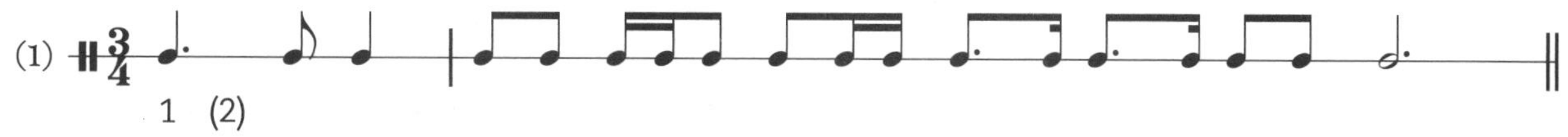

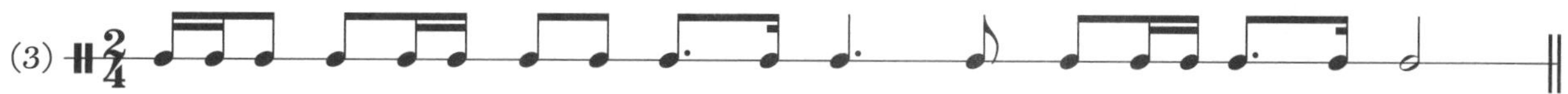

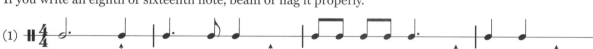

B. At each position marked by an arrow, add one note to complete the measure in the meter indicated. If you write an eighth or sixteenth note, beam or flag it properly.

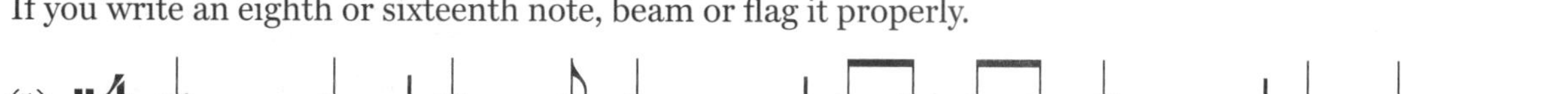

III. Counting rhythms with rests

Rewrite each rhythm on the blank staff provided, supplying the missing bar lines and correcting the beaming to reflect the beat.

D. Robert Schumann, "Im wunderschönen Monat Mai," from *Dichterliebe*, mm. 5–10

Recopy the melody, changing the beaming to reflect the beat and supplying bar lines. The melody begins with an anacrusis and ends with an incomplete measure as shown. Do not recopy the text.

ASSIGNMENT 2.3

I. Beaming to reflect the beat

Rewrite each of the following rhythms with correct beams that reflect the beat unit. Add the counts beneath the rhythm, and read the rhythm aloud.

II. Counting rhythms with dots and ties

Rewrite the following rhythms with dots in place of tied notes. Be careful to beam your answers correctly. Write the counts beneath the rewritten rhythm, with the beat number in parentheses if there is no corresponding note above it.

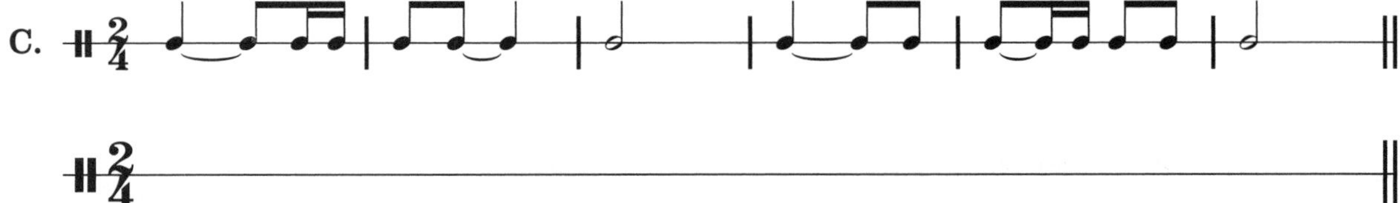
C.

III. Syncopation

Syncopated rhythms are widespread in music written for popular songs, the movies, and musical theater. In each of the following tunes, draw an arrow above the staff that points to a syncopation, and write the counts for the entire rhythm beneath.

A. Horner, Mann, and Weil, "Somewhere Out There," from *An American Tail*, mm. 27-28

27
28
it helps to think we might be wish - in' on the same bright star.
a 1 & a

B. Shania Twain and Mutt Lange, "You're Still the One," mm. 13-16

13
14
15
16
They said, "I bet they'll ne-ver make it." But just look at us hold-ing on.

C. Lin-Manuel Miranda, "How Far I'll Go," from *Moana*, mm. 6-9

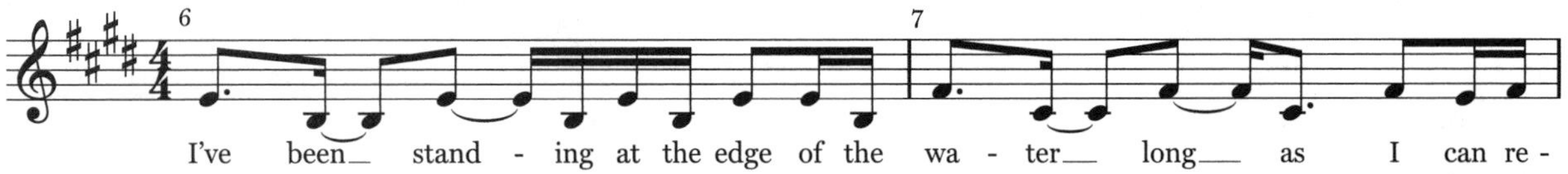
6
7
I've been stand - ing at the edge of the wa - ter long as I can re -

8
9
mem - ber, nev - er real - ly know - ing why.

D. Moore, Mac, and McDaid, "What About Us?," mm. 56-58

56
57
58
Are you read - y?
I'll be read - y.
I don't want con - trol, I want to let go.

ASSIGNMENT 2.4

I. Reading meter signatures

A. Fill in the empty boxes in the chart with a meter or note value.

METER TYPE	METER	BEAT UNIT	BEAT DIVISION	FULL BAR DURATION
Simple duple	2/2	𝅗𝅥	♩ ♩	𝅝
Simple duple			♫	
Simple triple	3/8			
Simple triple				𝅝.
Simple quadruple		𝅗𝅥		𝅜
Simple quadruple	4/4			

B. Write the meter signature and meter type (e.g., simple duple) for each of the given works.

(1) Arcangelo Corelli, Preludio, from Trio Sonata in D Minor, Op. 4, No. 8, mm. 3–9 (bass)

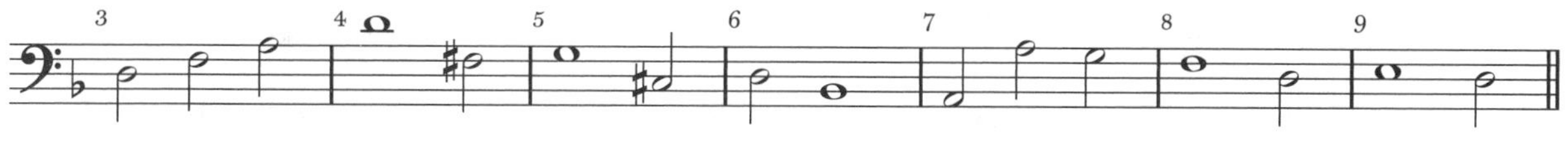

Meter: 3/2 Meter type: ______________________________

(2) Orlando Gibbons, Song 46, mm. 1–4 (last measure is incomplete)

Meter: __________ Meter type: ______________________________

(3) Domenico Scarlatti, Sonata in G Major, L. 388, mm. 1–6

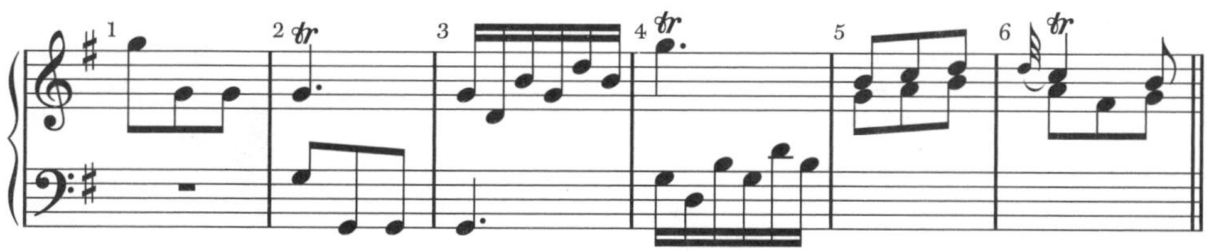

Meter: __________ Meter type: ______________________________

II. Reading and writing in different meters

A. At each position marked by an arrow, write the appropriate note value. If you write an eighth or sixteenth note, beam or flag it properly.

B. Renotate the following rhythms with ties instead of dotted notes.

(1)

Renotated

(2)

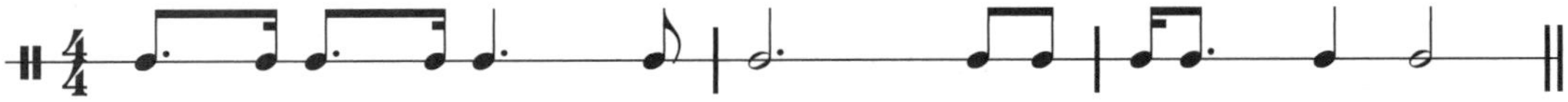

Renotated

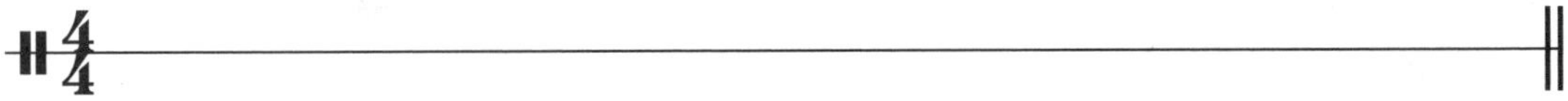

(3)

Renotated

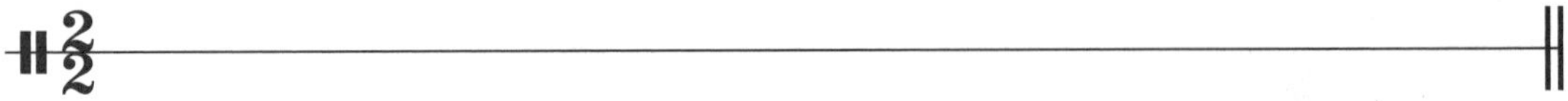

(4)

Renotated

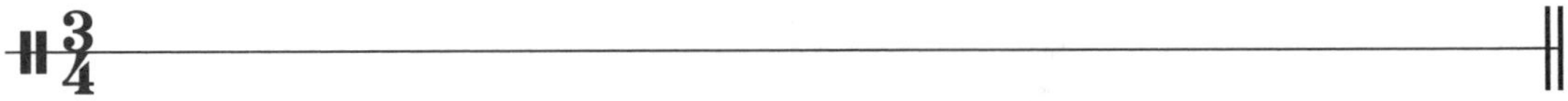

ASSIGNMENT 2.5

I. Understanding meter signatures

For each meter given, write the beat unit on the staff (on any line or space), and the meter type (duple, triple, or quadruple) in the blank.

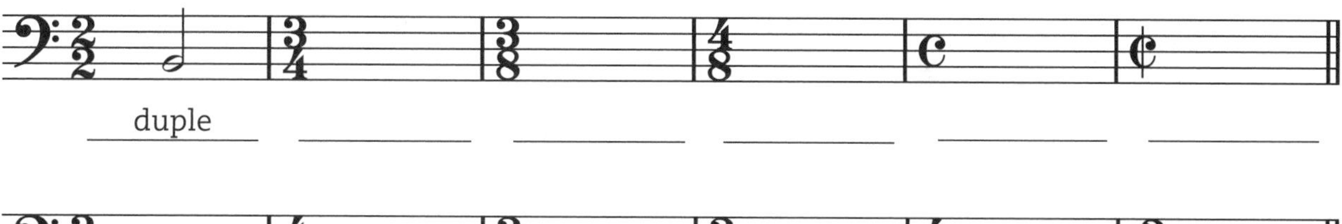
duple

II. Writing in different meters

A. Renotate Schumann's melody (not the text) on the blank staves, in $\frac{3}{4}$. When beaming the rhythms, use modern ("instrumental") style rather than vocal notation. The last measure is incomplete.

Robert Schumann, "Widmung," from *Myrthen*, mm. 18–25 (melody)

18
19
20
21
Du bist vom Him - mel mir be - schie - den. Dass du mich
22
23
24
25
liebst, macht mich mir wert, dein Blick hat mich vor mir ver - klärt,

Translation: You are granted to me from heaven. That you love me makes me worthy, your gaze has transfigured my view of myself,

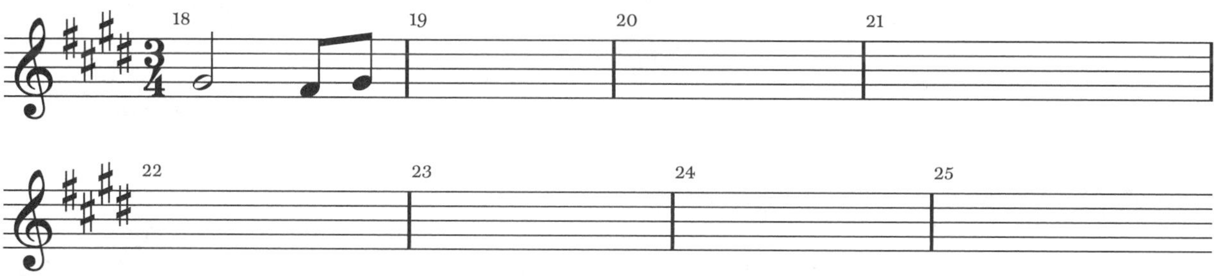
18
19
20
21
22
23
24
25

The piano part at the beginning of the song (in a different key) repeats the same rhythm multiple times. Renotate measure 1 in $\frac{3}{4}$ meter.

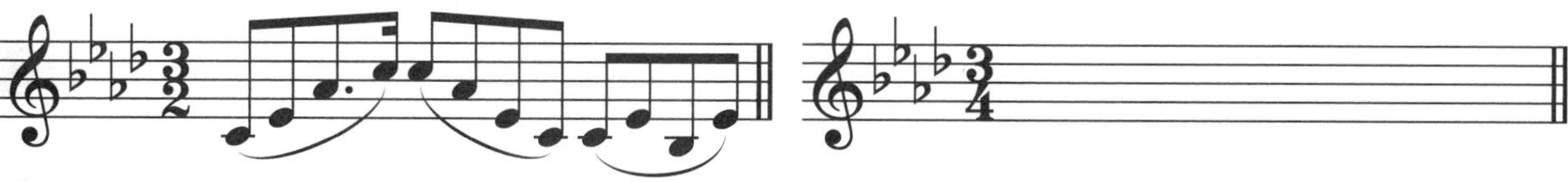

B. Renotate the following rhythms without ties. Then perform each rhythm.

C. Complete the following rhythms by adding one or two rests in any position marked by an arrow. Then perform each rhythm.

NAME ______________________

ASSIGNMENT 2.6

I. Anacrusis notation

Each of these melodies begins with an anacrusis. What note value (or note value plus rest) should the composer use to fill the final measure of the composition (not shown) to balance the anacrusis? Write this value in the blank provided.

A. J. S. Bach, Passacaglia in C Minor, mm. 1–7

Final note value: ____________

B. Haydn, Scherzo, from Piano Sonata No. 9 in F Major, mm. 1–4

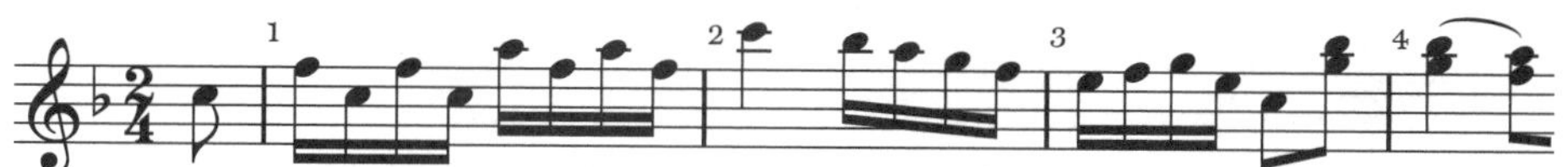

Final note value: ____________

C. "Wayfaring Stranger," mm. 1–4

Final note value: ____________

D. Don McLean, "American Pie," mm. 1–3

Final note value: ____________

II. Composing a rhythmic round

On your own paper, compose a rhythmic round in four parts to perform with classmates.

- Begin by performing the following round as an example, with classmates divided into four groups. Each group starts at the beginning, entering when the preceding group reaches rehearsal number 2, and performs to the end (like "Row, Row, Row Your Boat"). Each unit of the round is consistently two measures long.
- On your own paper, compose an eight-measure round, using this one as an example. Each musical unit should be two measures. Each of the four groups joins the round after the preceding group reaches measure 3.

- Compose the rhythms and text together. Try using geographical names, names of classmates, buildings on campus, or a message you want to convey. (For a more complex example, listen to Ernst Toch's *Geographical Fugue*).
- Build in ties and syncopations. Use rhythms that emphasize different beats or parts of the beat, and add contrasting dynamic markings to each line to create an interesting musical effect in performance.

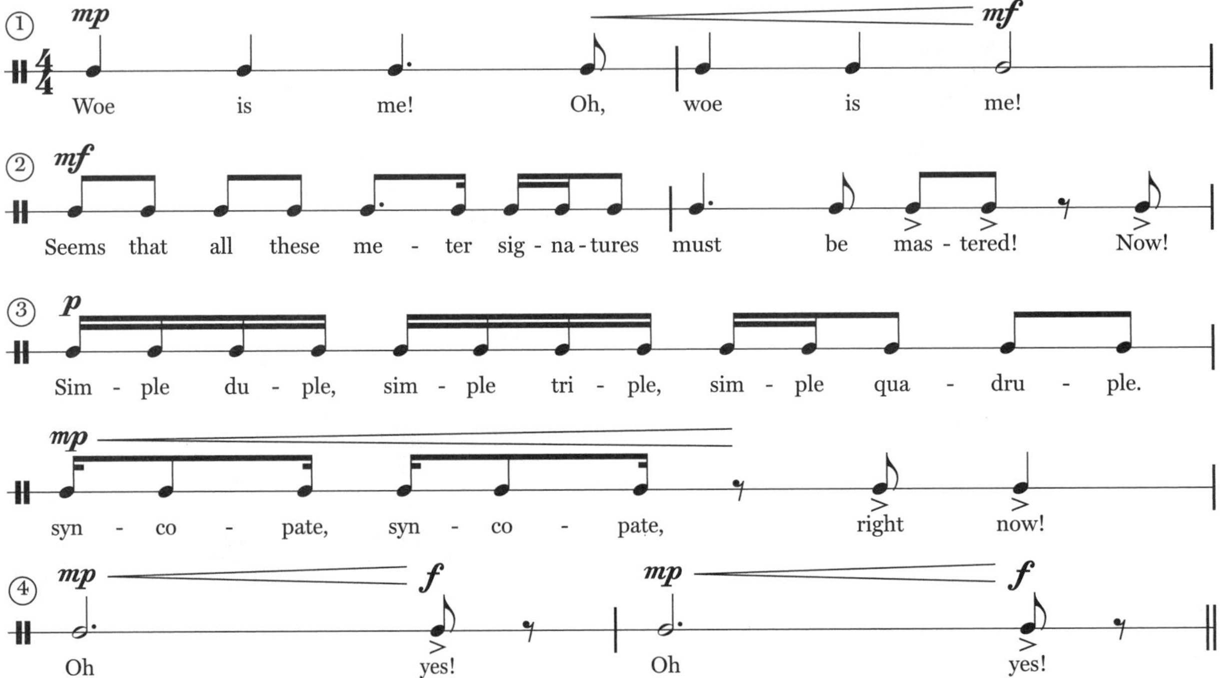

III. Analysis

Listen to Kern's song "Look for the Silver Lining" (Anthology 54), and consider the effect created by the change in meter. Insert the appropriate counts for the song's melody in the two excerpts shown.

Jerome Kern and Bud DeSylva, "Look for the Silver Lining," mm. 3–4

mm. 12–14

How does the change in meter affect the mood and character of each section?

NAME ____________________

Pitch Collections, Scales, and Major Keys

ASSIGNMENT 3.1

I. Writing scales

A. Beginning on the pitch given, build an ascending major scale by adding flats or sharps where needed, following the correct pattern of whole and half steps. Label the whole and half steps as shown.

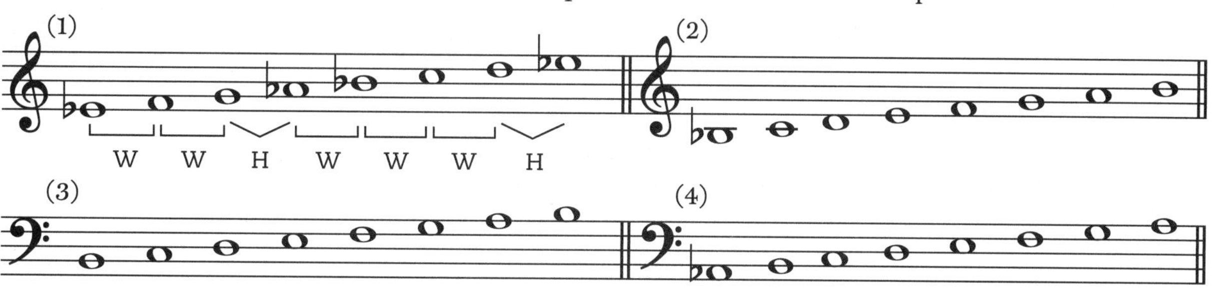

B. Write the major scales indicated, beginning with the specified pitch.

(1) D4 ascending

(2) F♯4 ascending

(3) A♭3 descending

(4) E♭3 ascending

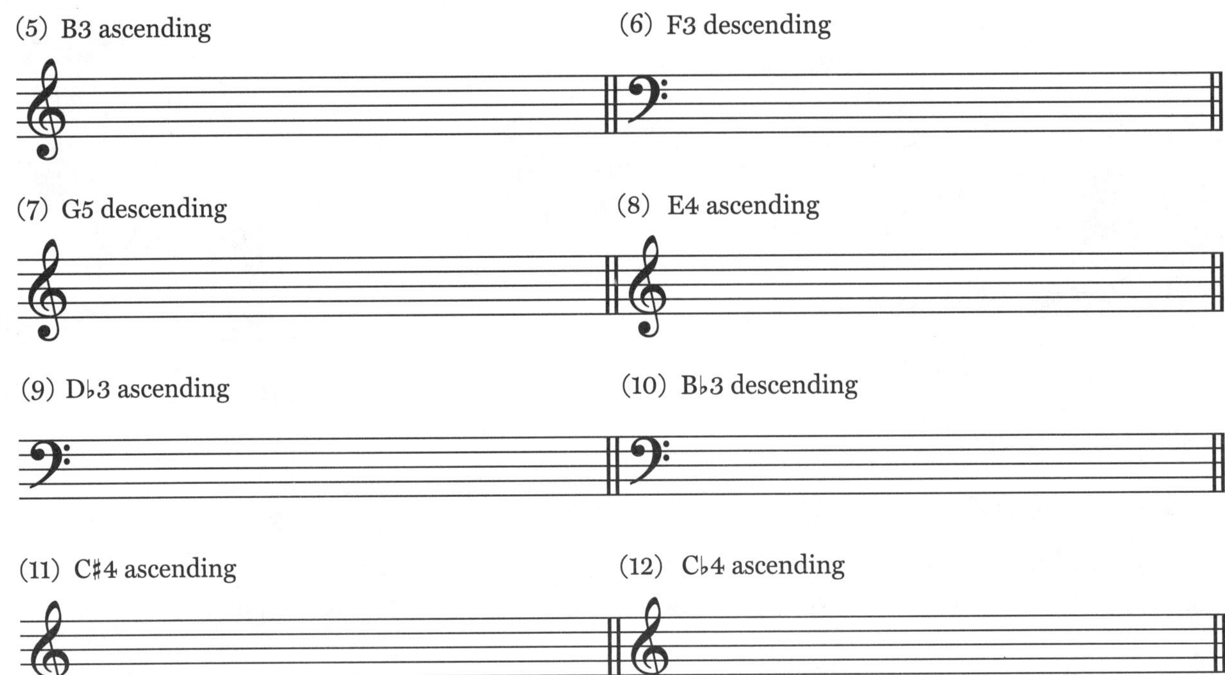

C. Write chromatic scales, using the following steps.

- Write a major scale with hollow note heads, ascending or descending as specified, starting with the given pitch.
- Label each pitch with its scale-degree number, and mark whole and half steps. Leave a space between the whole steps to add a note between.
- Then fill in half steps (with filled note heads) as needed to make a chromatic scale.

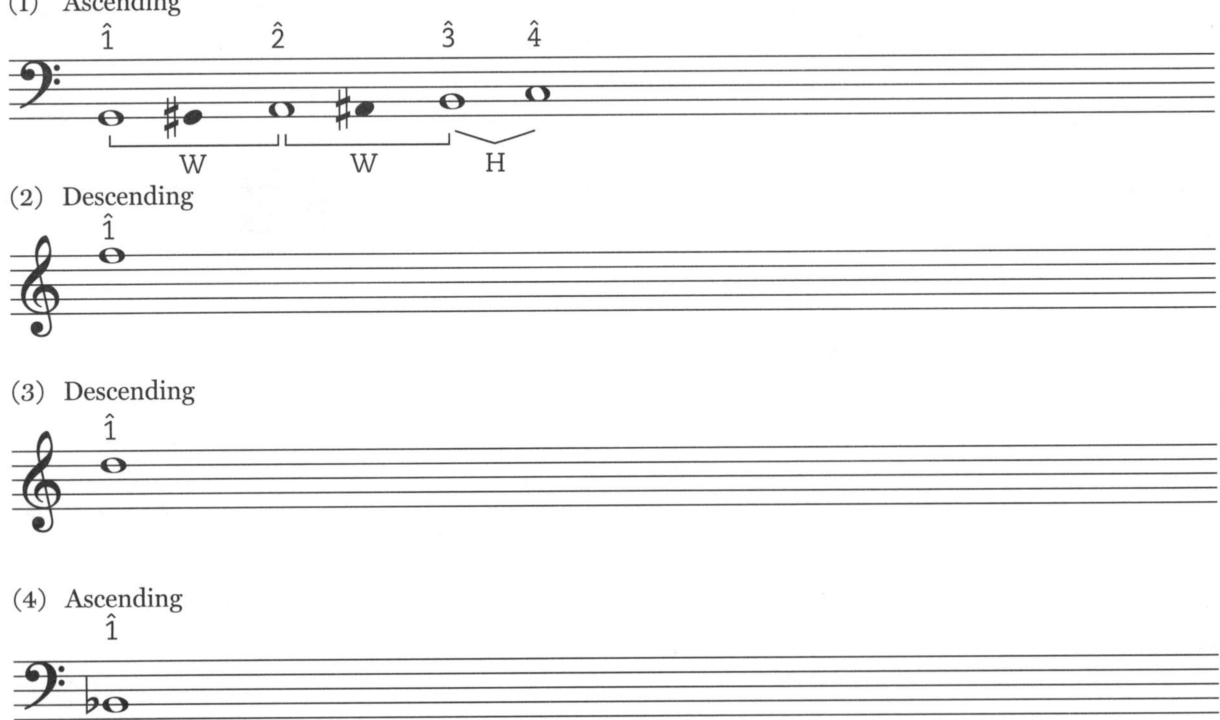

NAME ______________________________

ASSIGNMENT 3.2

I. Key signatures

A. On the following staves, write the key signature for each major key indicated. Be sure that the sharps and flats appear in the correct order and octave.

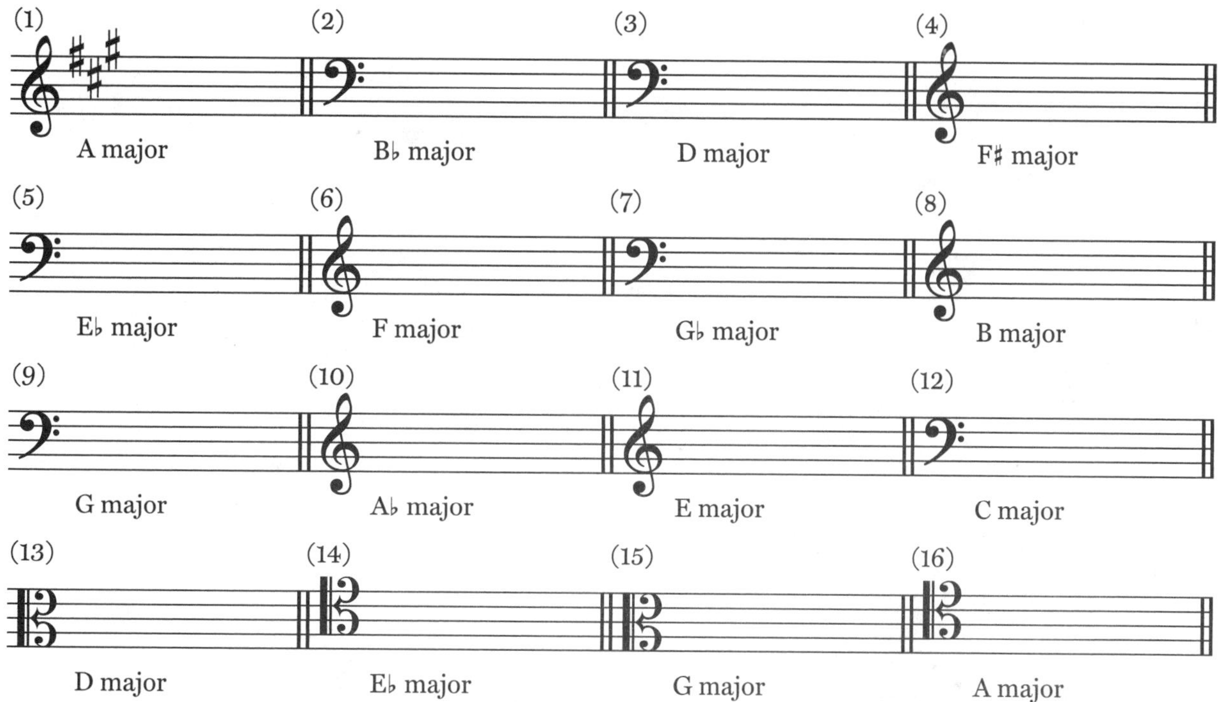

B. Identify the name of the major key associated with each of these key signatures.

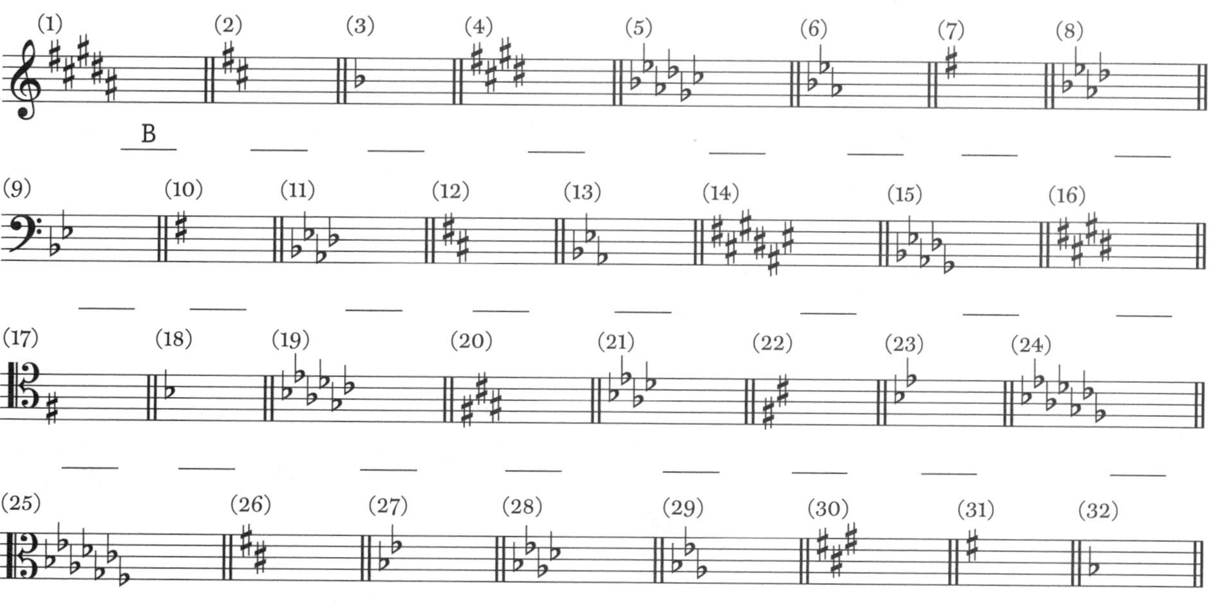

II. Scale-degree analysis of melodies

For each melody (1) write the name of the key in the blank below the melody, then (2) write the appropriate scale-degree numbers or solfège syllables (first letter only) above each note. Finally, sing the melody with scale-degree numbers or solfège.

A. "Shenandoah," mm. 1–10

Key: ____________________

B. Richard Rodgers and Oscar Hammerstein, "The Sound of Music," mm. 9–15

Key: ____________________

C. Fanny Mendelssohn Hensel, "Die Mainacht," mm. 15–17

Translation: I wander sadly from bush to bush.

Key: ____________________

ASSIGNMENT 3.3

I. Scale and scale degree

A. Given the scale degree notated on the left, write the major scale to which it belongs. Begin by writing whole notes on each line and space, then fill in the necessary accidentals. Write the scale-degree number or name beneath the given note in your scale, to check your answer.

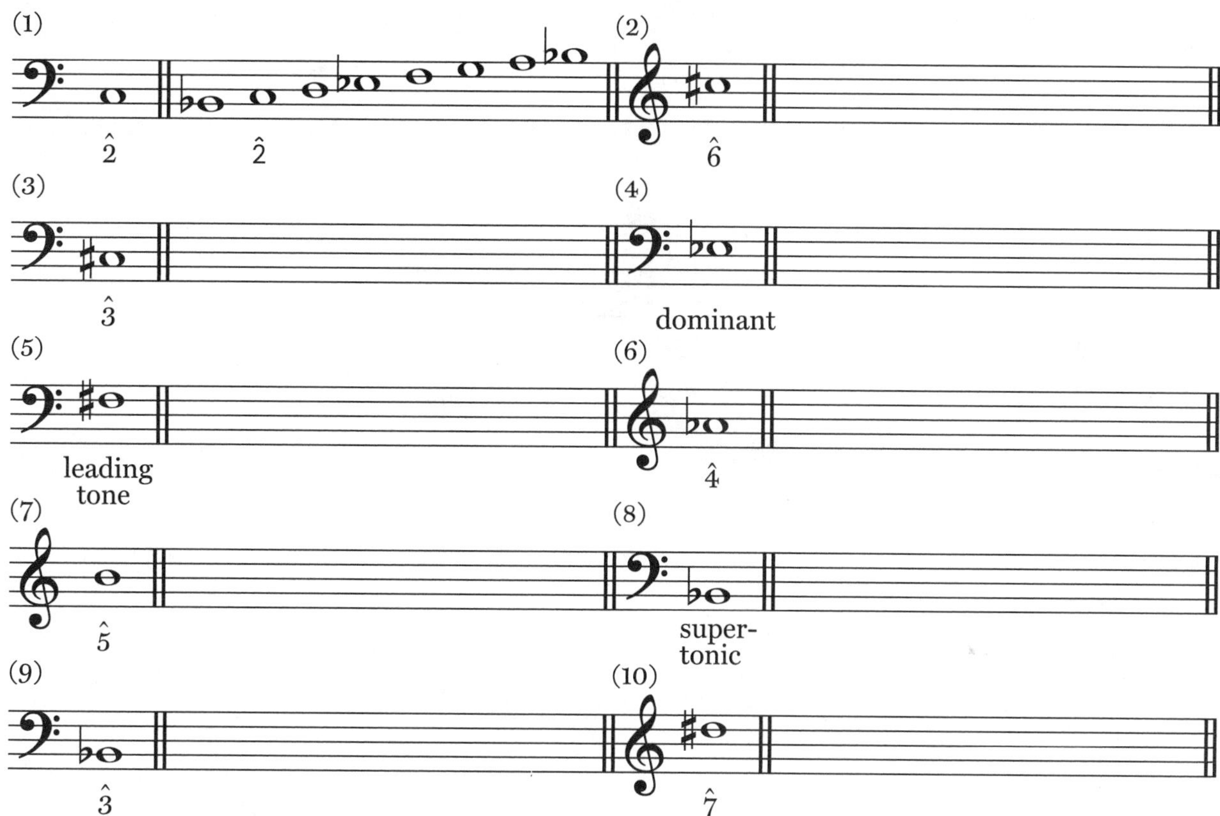

B. Complete the table by writing the requested major key, scale degree, or pitch name.

	MAJOR KEY	SCALE DEGREE	PITCH
(1)	E	$\hat{7}$	
(2)		supertonic	C♯
(3)	F♯		C♯
(4)	E♭	$\hat{3}$	
(5)		$\hat{4}$	G♭
(6)		leading tone	A

	MAJOR KEY	SCALE DEGREE	PITCH
(7)	F	subdominant	
(8)	D	leading tone	
(9)		$\hat{4}$	F♯
(10)	B	$\hat{5}$	
(11)	C	mediant	
(12)		$\hat{6}$	F

II. Scale and key analysis

Each of the following pieces features a prominent scale or scale segment. Write the scale or segment with accidentals on the staff below. In the blank, specify whether the scale is chromatic or major. If major, name the tonic.

A. W. A. Mozart, Piano Sonata, K. 333, mvt. 1, mm. 8–10

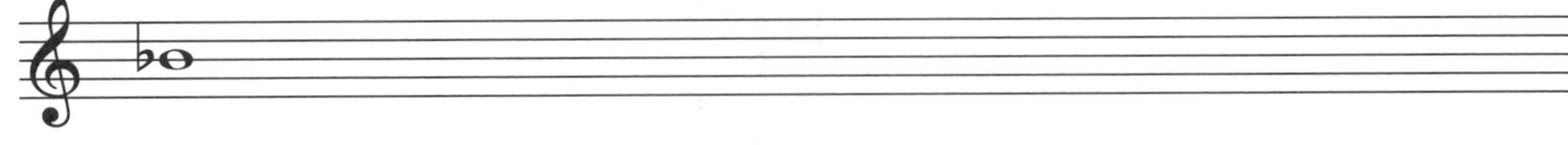

Scale type or major key: ____________________

B. Scott Joplin, "The Ragtime Dance," mm. 61–64

Scale type or major key: ____________________

C. Handel, Chaconne in G Major, mm. 49–51

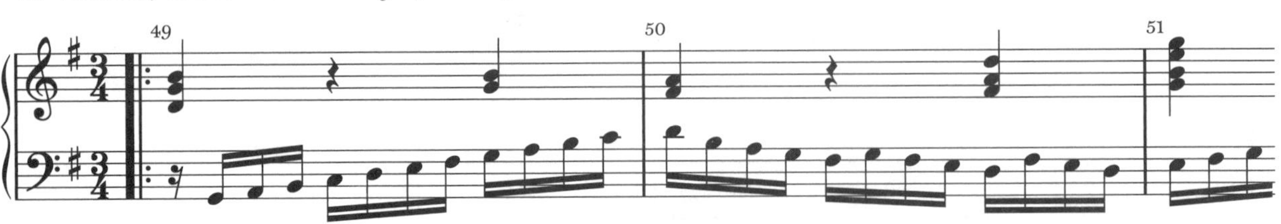

Scale type or major key: ____________________

ASSIGNMENT 3.4

I. Key signature review

A. Identify the major key indicated by each key signature.

B. Write the key signature for each major key specified. Place sharps or flats in the correct order and octave.

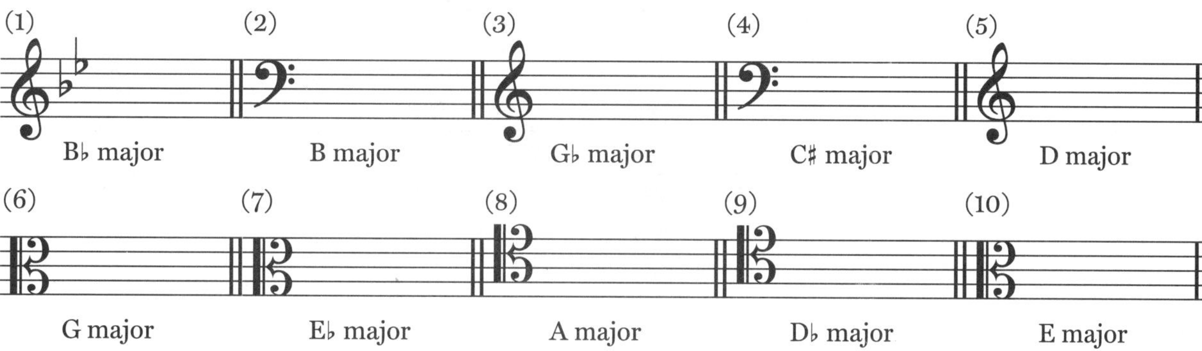

II. Identifying scale degrees

A. Write the note on the staff indicated by the major key and scale degree.

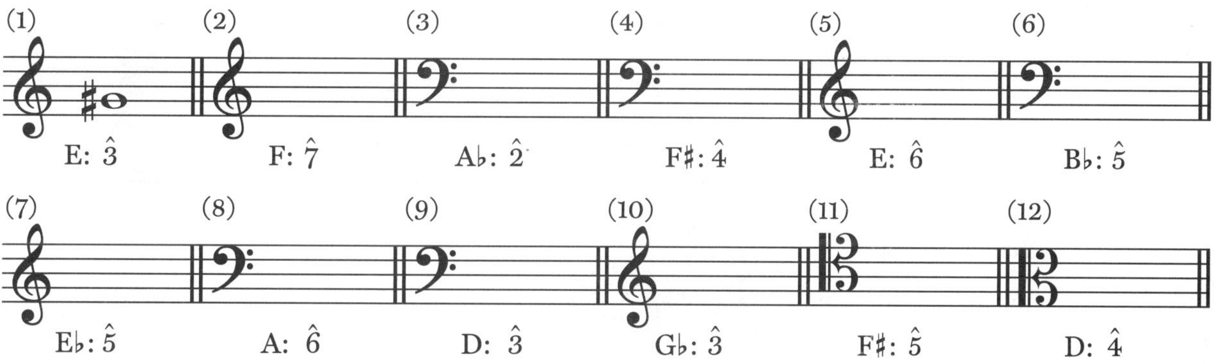

B. Each of the following sequences of scale degrees and solfège syllables represents a well-known melody. An underlined symbol shows a pitch below the tonic.

- On the top staff, write out the major scale specified, and label with scale degrees or solfège.
- Use these labels to write out the melody (with correct key signature) on the lower staves. (Rhythm is optional.) If you know the name of the tune, write it in the blank provided (optional).

(1) A major

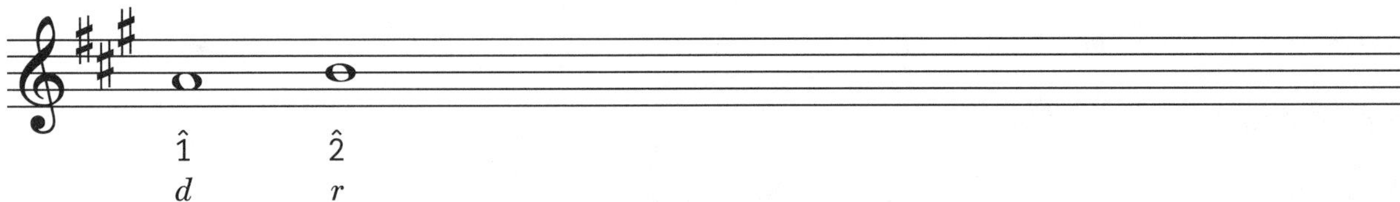

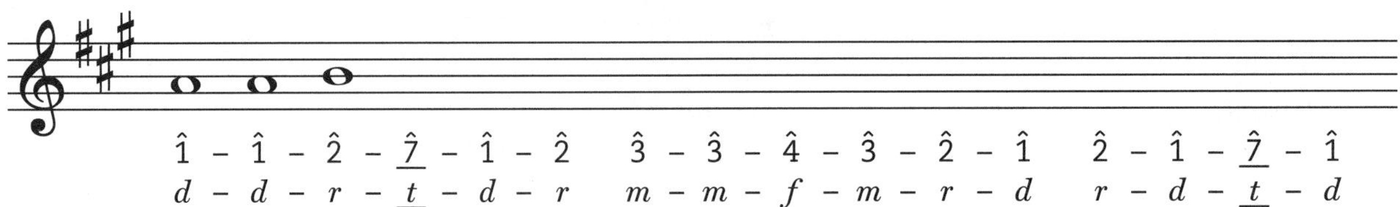

Name of melody: ______________________________

(2) B♭ major

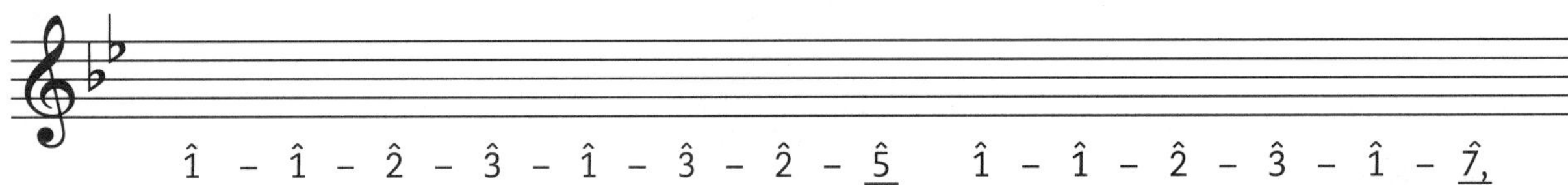

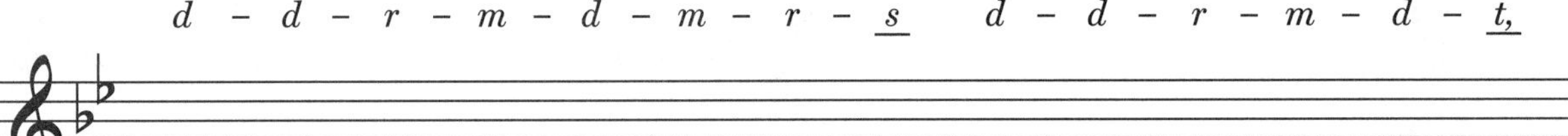

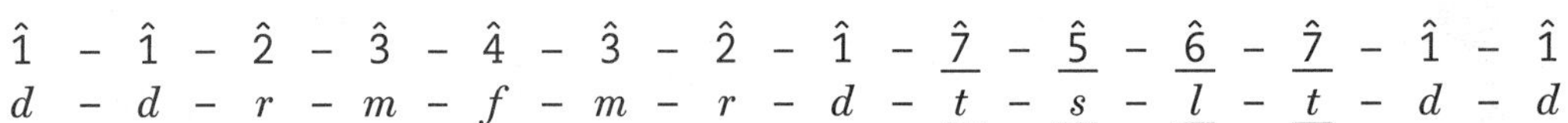

Name of melody: ______________________________

III. Pentatonic scales

Write the following major pentatonic scales (1̂-2̂-3̂-5̂-6̂, or *do-re-mi-sol-la*).

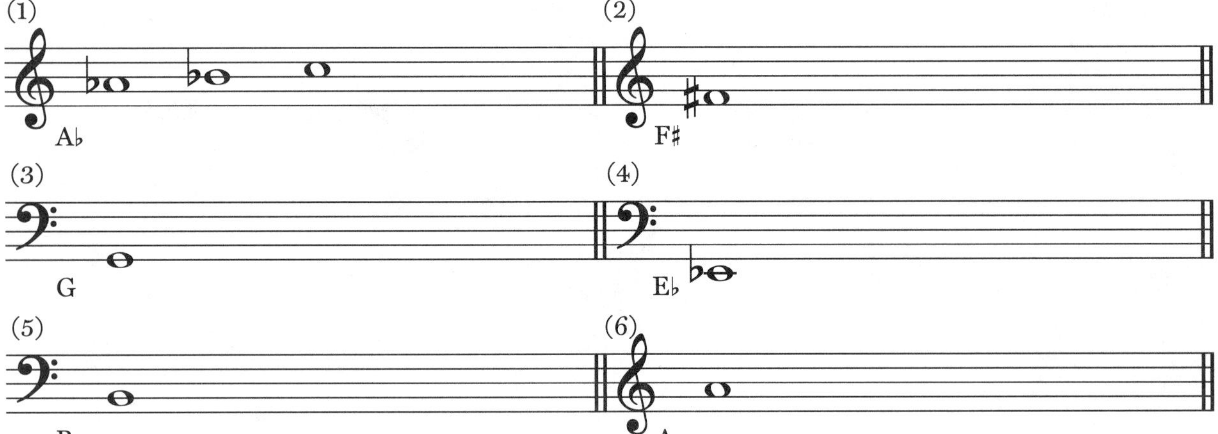

NAME ____________________

ASSIGNMENT 3.5

I. Scale review

Write the scales requested, beginning with the given pitch. Add accidentals before each note as needed, rather than using a key signature.

A. Scales ascending and descending

(1) Major

(2) Chromatic

(3) Major

(4) Chromatic

(5) Major

B. Scales either ascending or descending

(1) Major pentatonic, ascending

(2) Major, descending

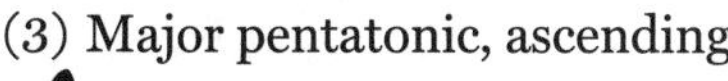

(3) Major pentatonic, ascending

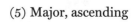

(4) Major pentatonic, ascending

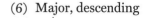

(5) Major, ascending

(6) Major, descending

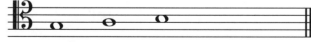

II. Analysis of scale type

Look at the key signature and melodic cues from the beginning and end of each given melody to determine the key. Write the name of the major key (or "not major") in the blank. If major, label the scale degrees of each note below the staff to confirm that they fit well in the key you have chosen.

A. "Hush, Little Baby," mm. 1–8

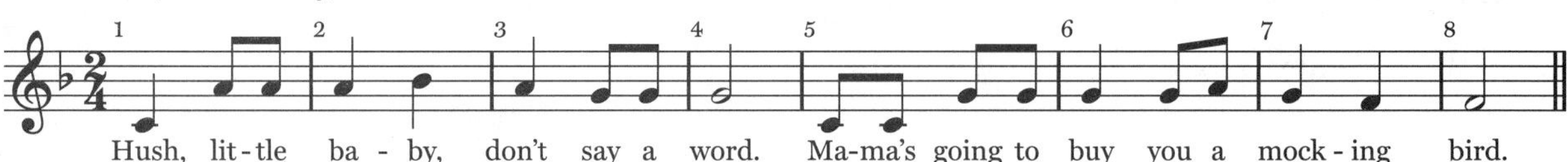

Key: ____________________

B. Franz Schubert, "Der Lindenbaum," from *Winterreise*, mm. 9–12

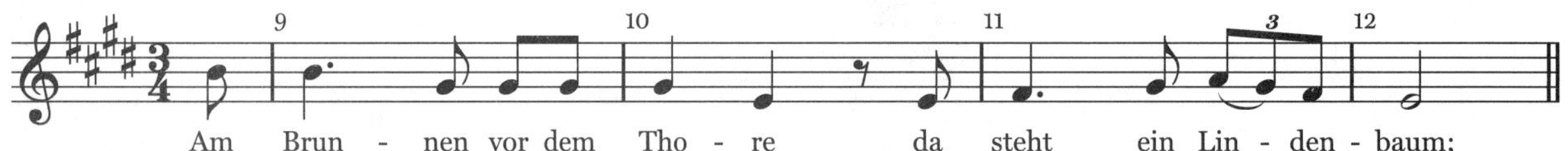

Translation: At the well in front of the gate there stands a linden tree;

Key: ____________________

C. Gabriel Fauré, "Après un rêve," mm. 44–47

Translation: O mysterious night!

Key: ____________________

D. Mendes, Warburton, Geiger, and Harris, "There's Nothing Holdin' Me Back," mm. 5–8

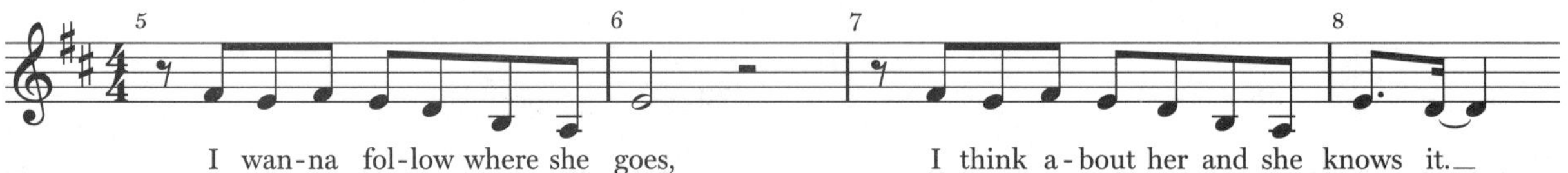

Key: ____________________

E. W. A. Mozart, Kyrie eleison, from *Requiem*, mm. 1–5 (bass part)

Key: ____________________

NAME ________________________________

Compound Meters

ASSIGNMENT 4.1

I. Understanding simple and compound meter signatures

A. From the information given, complete the following chart.

METER TYPE	METER	BEAT UNIT	BEAT DIVISION	FULL BAR DURATION
Compound duple	6/4	𝅗𝅥.	♩ ♩ ♩	𝅝.
Compound duple			♪♪♪	
Simple triple				𝅗𝅥.
Compound triple	9/4			𝅝‿𝅗𝅥.
Simple quadruple		♪		
Compound quadruple	12/16			

B. Each of these melodies is taken from a keyboard prelude in J. S. Bach's *Well-Tempered Clavier*, Book I. Provide the correct simple or compound meter signature, then write the meter type (e.g., compound triple) and beat unit (e.g., ♪.) in the blanks provided. (The final measure of the excerpt may be incomplete.)

(1) Prelude in A Minor, mm. 1–4 (left hand, m. 4 is incomplete)

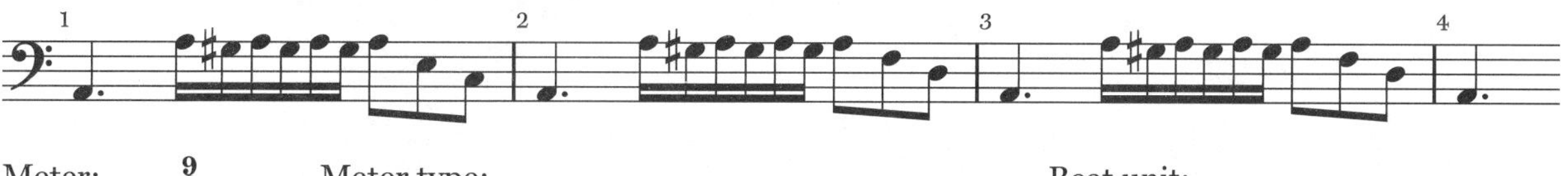

Meter: 9/8 Meter type: ______________________ Beat unit: ________

(2) Prelude in A♭ Major, mm. 1–5 (right hand)

Meter: ________ Meter type: ______________________ Beat unit: ________

(3) Prelude in G♯ Minor, mm. 1–4 (right hand)

Meter: ________ Meter type: ______________________________ Beat unit: ________

(4) Prelude in C♯ Minor, mm. 1–4 (right hand)

Meter: ________ Meter type: ______________________________ Beat unit: ________

(5) Prelude in E♭ Minor, mm. 1–4 (right hand)

Meter: ________ Meter type: ______________________________ Beat unit: ________

(6) Prelude in E Major, mm. 1–3 (left hand)

Meter: ________ Meter type: ______________________________ Beat unit: ________

(7) Prelude in C♯ Major, mm. 1–7 (right hand)

Meter: ________ Meter type: ______________________________ Beat unit: ________

(8) Prelude in F Major, mm. 1–2 (left hand)

Meter: ________ Meter type: ______________________________ Beat unit: ________

NAME ____________________

ASSIGNMENT 4.2

I. Understanding simple and compound meter signatures

For each meter signature given, fill in the missing information.

METER	METER TYPE	BEAT UNIT	BEAT DIVISION	BEAT SUBDIVISION
9/8	Compound triple	♩.	♪♪♪ (beamed)	six beamed sixteenths
6/4				
12/16				
3/2				
9/4				

II. Compound meters with ♩. beat units

A. At each position marked by an arrow, add one note value that completes the measure in the meter indicated. Then write the counts below the staff.

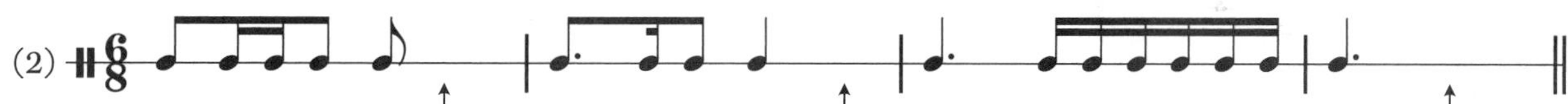

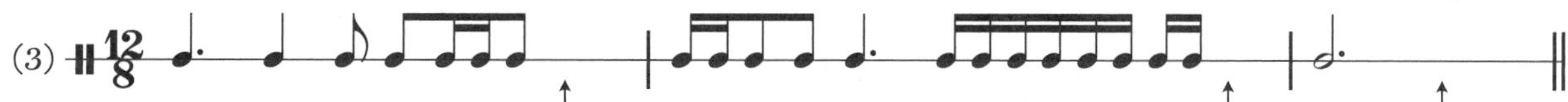

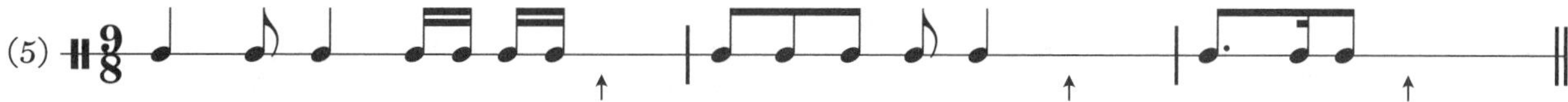

B. Rewrite the following rhythms with correct beaming to reflect the beat. Practice the rhythms on "ta" or counting syllables. Be prepared to perform them in class.

(1) 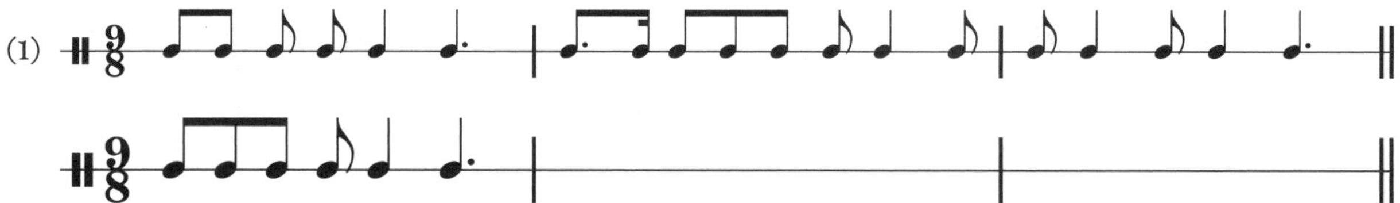

(2) 

(3) 

(4) 

(5) 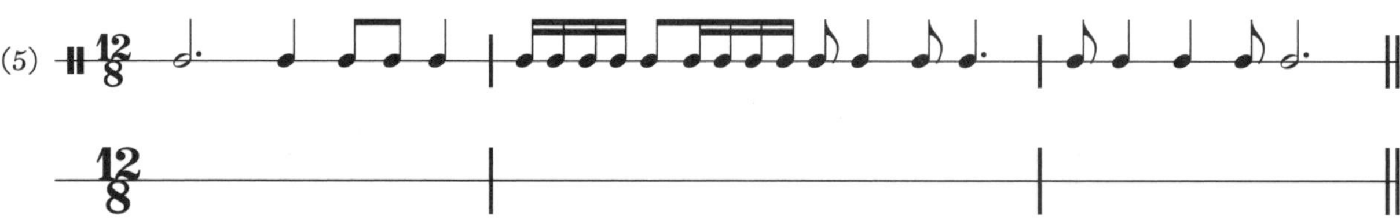

(6) 

ASSIGNMENT 4.3

I. Understanding compound meters

For each melody, provide the missing bar lines that correspond with the meter signature given. The final measure may be incomplete.

A. Beethoven, String Quartet in F Major, Op. 18, No. 1, mvt. 2 (cello part, adapted)

B. Fanny Mendelssohn Hensel, "Schwanenlied," Op. 1, No. 1 (adapted)

C. Béla Bartók, String Quartet No. 2, mvt. 1 (cello)

II. Understanding rests

At each position marked with an arrow, add one rest to complete the measure in the meter indicated. Write the counts below the rhythm; enclose counts in parentheses if they fall on a rest.

III. Beaming to reflect the meter

Vocal music, especially in older editions, is often written with flags that correspond to syllables of the sung text. Copy the vocal lines on the blank staves (without text), replacing flags with beams to reflect the meter and beat unit instead. Copy the rests exactly.

A. Handel, "How beautiful are the feet of them," from *Messiah*, mm. 5–9

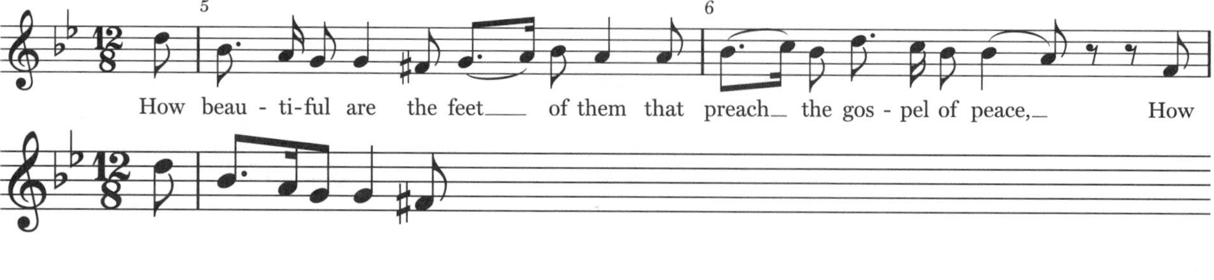

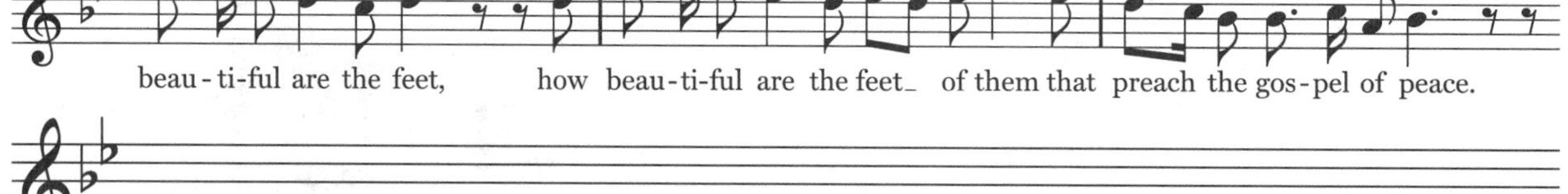

B. W. A. Mozart, "Lacrimosa," from *Requiem*, mm. 9–10 (soprano part)

Translation: Mournful that day

C. Robert Schumann, "Ich hab' im Traum geweinet," from *Dichterliebe*, mm. 10–13 and 15–17

Translation: Still flowed down my cheeks. I wept in my dream, I dreamed that you left me.

ASSIGNMENT 4.4

I. Compound meters with 𝅗𝅥. and 𝅘𝅥𝅮. beat units

A. Write counts beneath each melody. Then rewrite the melody (not the words) in the meters indicated. Use proper beaming and stem direction. Some of the examples end with an incomplete measure.

(1) Fanny Mendelssohn Hensel, "Die Mainacht," mm. 4–6

mf
1. Wenn der sil - ber - ne Mond durch die Ge - sträu - che blinkt.

Translation: When the silvery moon beams through the shrubbery.

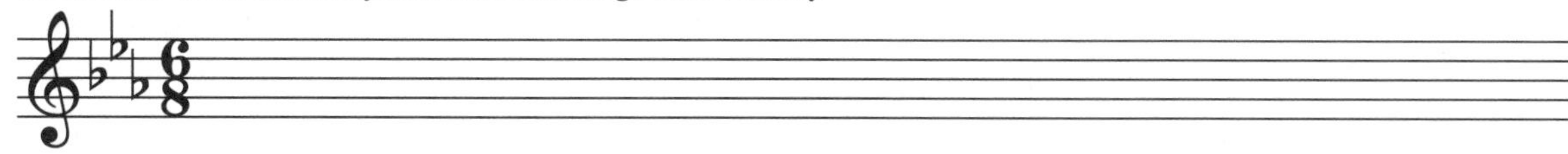

(2) "The Pretty Girl Milking Her Cow," mm. 3–4

And as I walk'd out for my pleas-ure I saw a maid milk - ing her cow;

(3) "When Johnny Comes Marching Home," mm. 1–4

When John - ny comes march - ing home a - gain, Hur - rah! Hur - rah!

(4) Ralph Vaughan Williams, "The Call," mm. 3–6

p
Come, my Way, my Truth, my Life: Such a Way, as gives us breath:

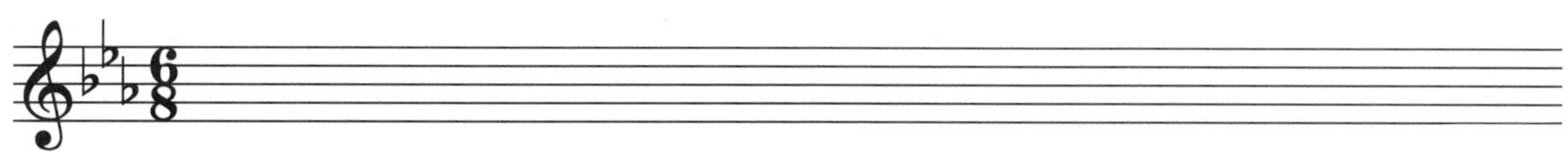

B. At each position marked by an arrow, add one note value to complete the measure in the meter indicated. Remember to subtract the value of an anacrusis from the final bar.

II. Rhythmic duets

Compose a second line to go with each of the following rhythms. Write notes and rests that complement (and don't overpower) the first line. Make sure that each measure is complete. Prepare your duet for performance with a classmate.

ASSIGNMENT 4.5

I. Reading and writing triplets

A. In each of these rhythms, provide the missing bar lines that correspond with the meter signature given.

B. Renotate each of these rhythms, and insert a triplet in place of the bracketed beat. Write the counts beneath your answer. Then perform the rhythm you have written.

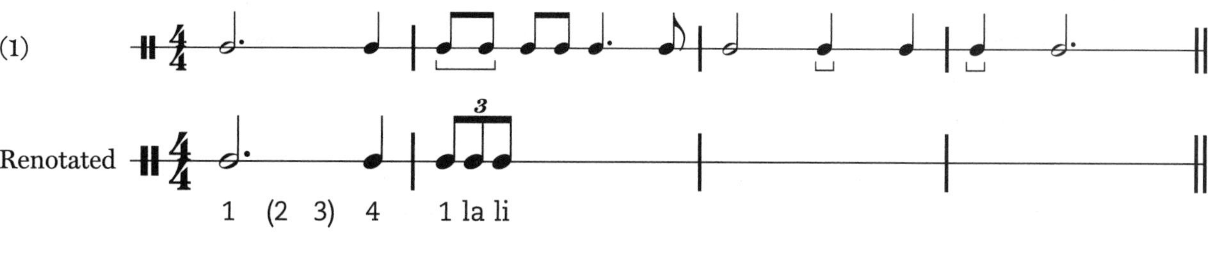

II. Syncopations

A. Rewrite each rhythm, adding ties or accent marks to create syncopations. Be prepared to perform each syncopated rhythm.

(1)

(2)

B. Compose a syncopated compound-meter rhythmic round for performance with classmates. Begin by performing the following three-part round as an example. Divide into three groups; each new group begins when the previous group has reached ②. In your composition:

- Write three lines of two measures each.
- Make the three lines distinctive, including rhythms that emphasize different beats or offbeats for contrast.
- Add a text and contrasting dynamics and accents in each line to create an interesting and musical effect in performance.
- Circle each syncopated pattern.

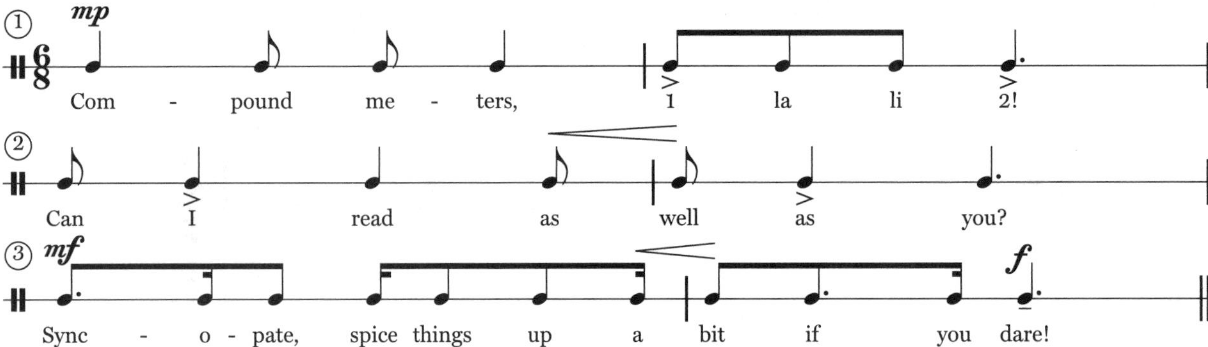

Your composition:

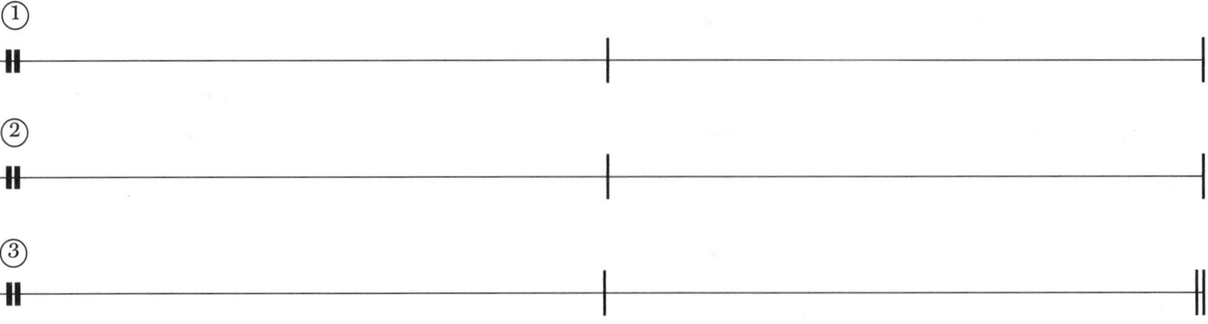

ASSIGNMENT 4.6

I. Analysis

Name the meter type for each excerpt. Then, below the staff write the counts where indicated. Finally, answer the question below the excerpt with one or two sentences.

A. Handel, "Rejoice greatly," from *Messiah* (soprano part, alternate version), mm. 9–14

9
10
11
Re-joice, re - joice, re-joice great - ly,
Counts: (1 2) li 3 (4) li
12
13
14
re-joice great - ly, O daugh - ter of Zi - on,

Counts:

Meter type: ____________________

How does this setting differ from the one in your anthology (Anthology 41a)? Which version do you think is simpler to sing, and why?

B. Franz Schubert, "Erlkönig," mm. 15–19

15
16
17
18
19
Wer rei - tet so spät durch Nacht und Wind?
3

Counts for bass clef:

Translation: Who rides so late through night and wind?

Meter type: ____________________

With so many triplets, Schubert might have chosen to write the piano accompaniment in what compound meter?

Meter: ________

On the staff, write the vocal part for measures 15-19 in that compound meter.

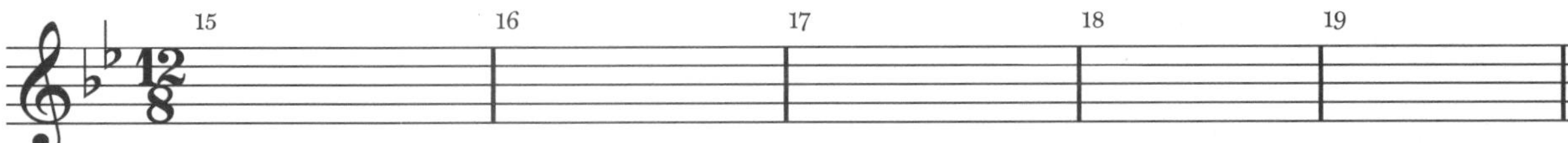

C. Gabriel Fauré, "Après un rêve," mm. 5-8

Write the counts for the melody line above the staff.

Counts (voice):

Translation: I dreamed of happiness, ardent mirage.

Meter type: ______________________________

What rhythmic device describes the relationship between the two hands in measure 7? ____________________

D. Clara Schumann, Romanze, Op. 21, No. 1, mm. 27-30

For this excerpt, no counts are required; answer the questions that follow.

Although not marked explicitly, what type of note values are in the alto voice? ____________________

The small number between the staves in measure 27 marks the quarter notes in the tenor voice as what type of rhythm? ____________________

What rhythmic device describes the relationship between the two hands in measure 27? ____________________

NAME ______________________

Minor Keys and the Diatonic Modes

ASSIGNMENT 5.1

I. Writing minor scales

A. For each major key requested, write the key signature and major scale in the left column. Circle scale degree $\hat{6}$. Then, in the right column, write the major scale's relative natural minor and name it, as shown.

(1)

E major

Relative minor: C♯ minor

(2)

B♭ major

Relative minor: ______

(3)

D major

Relative minor: ______

(4)

A♭ major

Relative minor: ______

(5)

B major

Relative minor: ______

(6)

G major

Relative minor: ______

B. On the left, build the natural minor scale specified by adding flats or sharps in front of the pitches given. On the right, write the key signature of the relative major, and name the key. Then write the complete major scale.

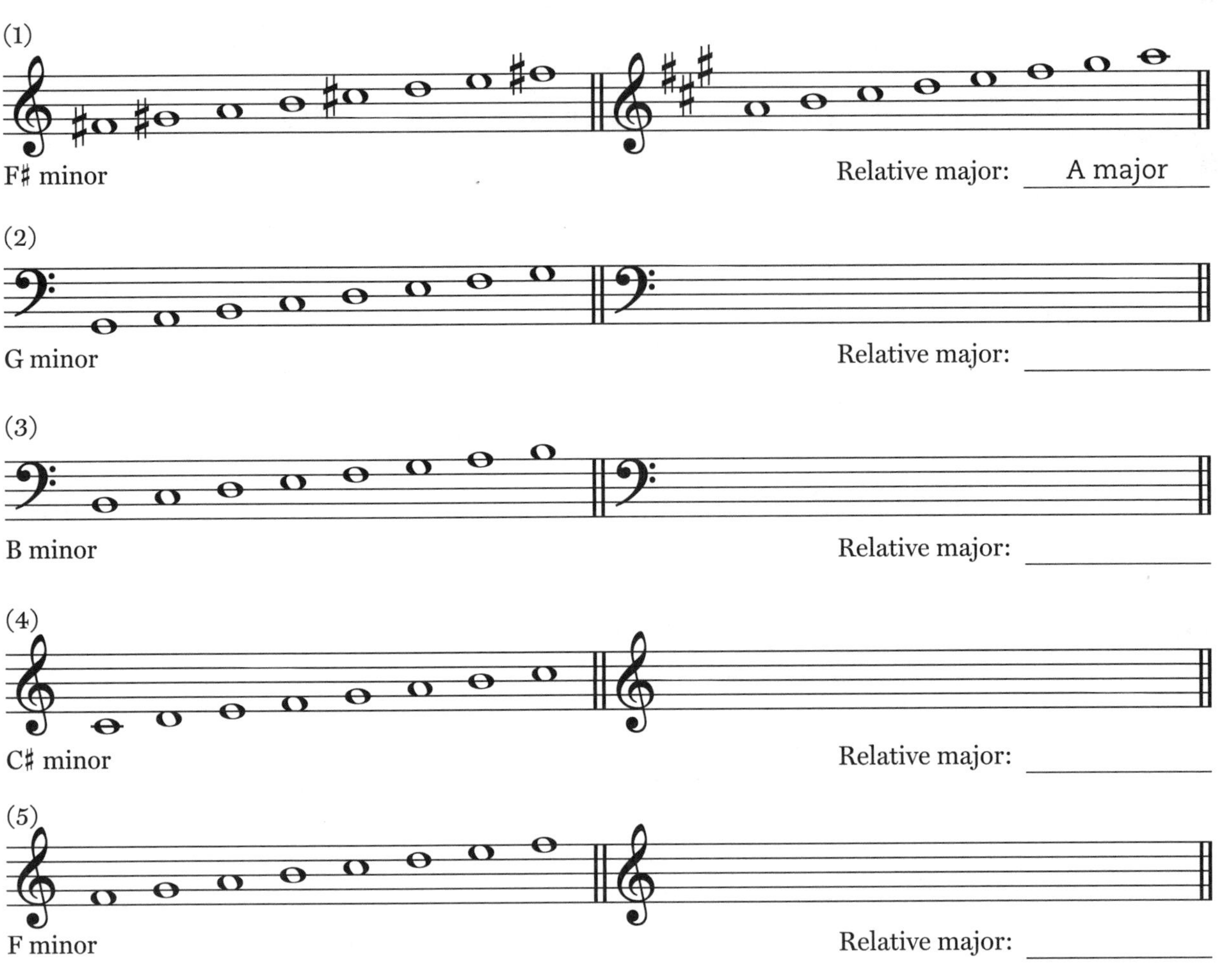

II. Identifying relative and parallel keys

Fill in the blanks, identifying the key or key signature.

(a) Relative minor of E♭ major: C minor

(b) Parallel major of E minor has how many ♯s? ____________

(c) Relative major of F minor has how many ♭s? ____________

(d) Relative minor of D major: ____________

(e) Relative major of D minor: ____________

(f) Parallel major of F♯ minor has how many ♯s? ____________

(g) Relative minor of B♭ major: ____________

(h) Relative major of F♯ minor has how many ♯s? ____________

NAME ______________________

ASSIGNMENT 5.2

I. Key signatures

A. For each key signature given, identify the major and minor key, as shown. Use a lowercase letter for minor keys.

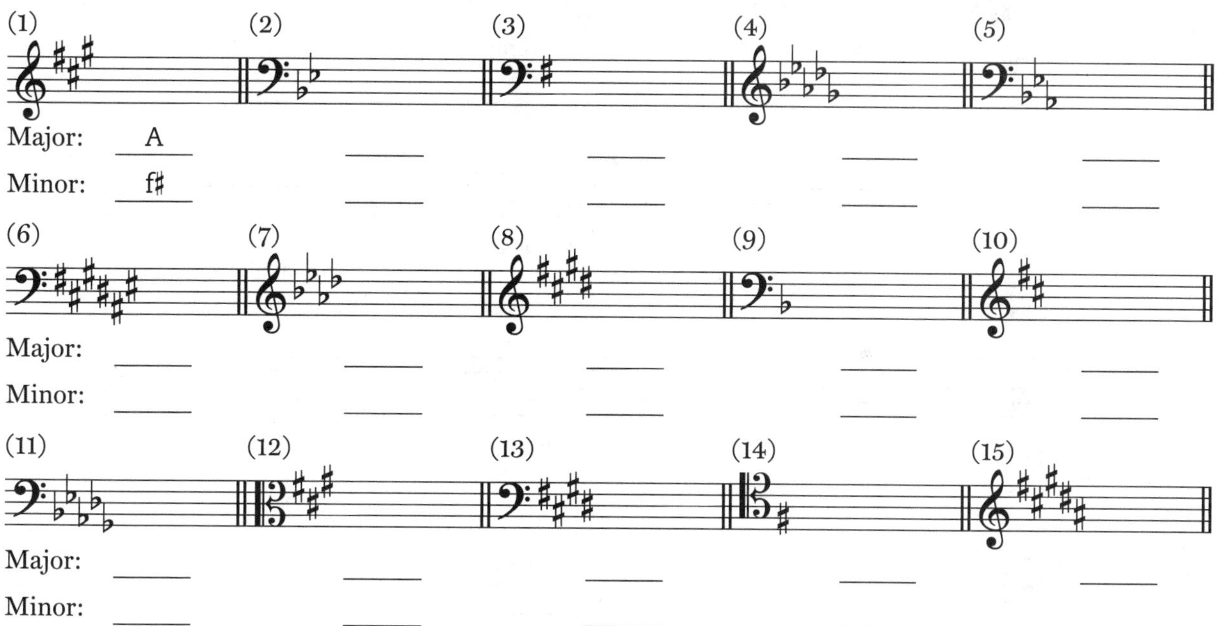

B. Write the requested key signature.

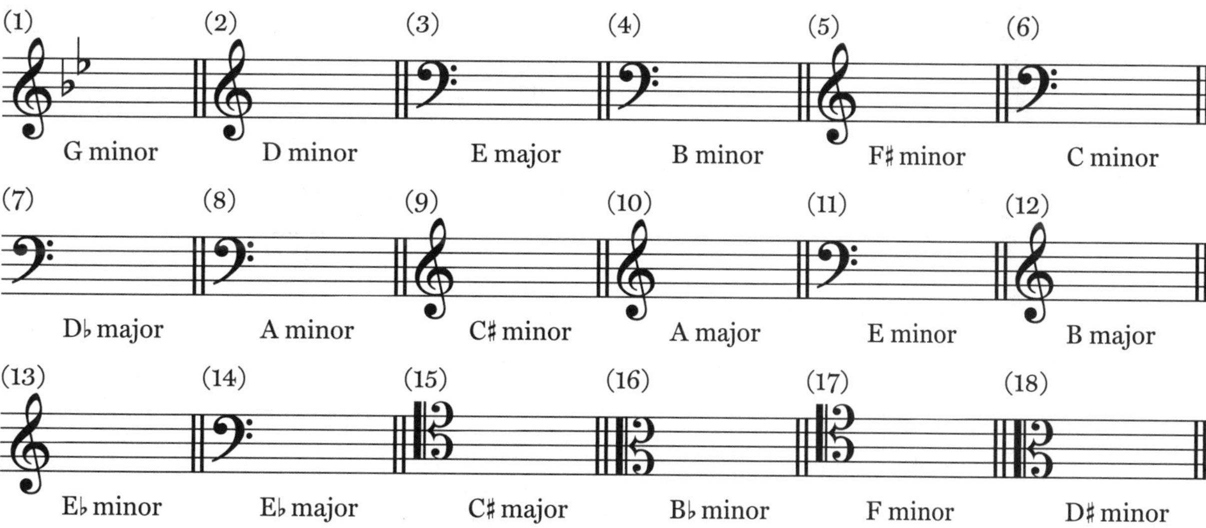

II. Scale degrees in minor

A. Given the scale degree labeled on the left, write the minor scale to which that pitch belongs. Use natural minor, unless the raised submediant or leading tone is requested (indicating melodic or harmonic minor); in these two cases, indicate in the blank which scale type you've written.

B. Complete the table by writing the pitch, scale degree (number or name), or key requested.

KEY	SCALE DEGREE	PITCH
(1) B minor	supertonic	
(2) E minor	$\flat\hat{3}$	
(3)	$\flat\hat{6}$	D♭
(4)	leading tone	G♯
(5) F♯ minor		A
(6) C♯ minor	subdominant	

KEY	SCALE DEGREE	PITCH
(7)	subtonic	C
(8) E♭ minor	$\hat{4}$	
(9)	raised submediant	C♯
(10) C♯ minor	leading tone	
(11) B minor		F♯
(12)	subtonic	E♭

ASSIGNMENT 5.3

I. Forms of the minor scale

On the blank staves provided, write the correct key signature for each minor key indicated. Then write the scale requested, ascending and descending, altering scale degrees $\hat{6}$ and $\hat{7}$ as needed. Include accidentals for any notes needing them, both ascending and descending.

(a) C♯ harmonic minor

(b) F melodic minor

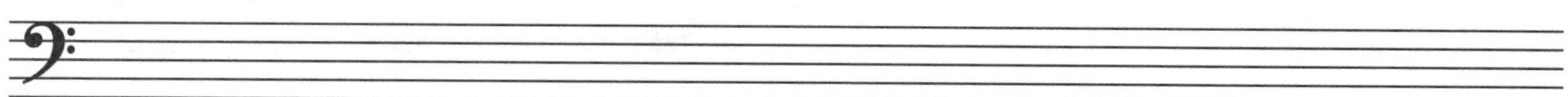

(c) G♯ harmonic minor

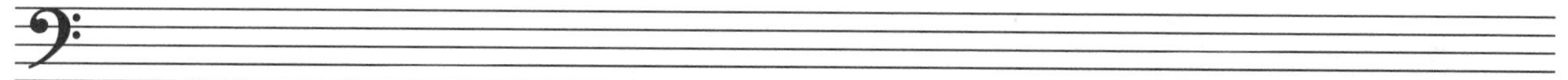

(d) E melodic minor

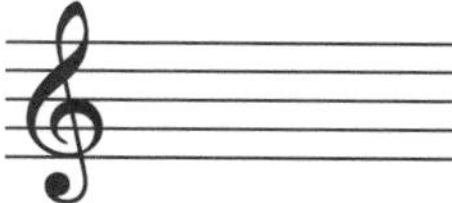

(e) B♭ natural minor

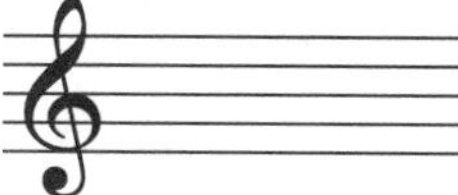

(f) D melodic minor

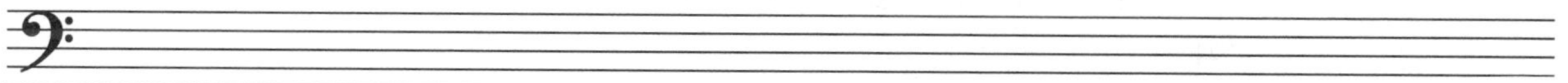

(g) G harmonic minor

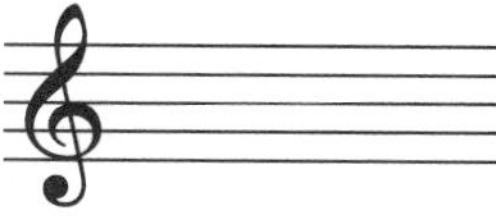

(h) D♯ natural minor

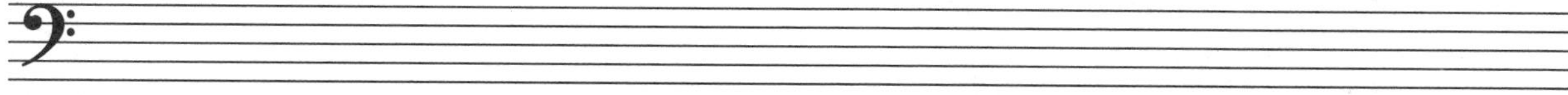

II. Scale and scale-degree analysis

Each of the following excerpts features a prominent scale or scale segment. Name the major or minor key. If minor, specify the type of minor scale (e.g., melodic minor). If a minor melody omits $\hat{6}$ (or $\flat\hat{6}$), assume that the missing scale degree conforms to the key signature (without an added accidental).

A. Jean Baptiste Loeillet, Sonata, Op. 3, No. 10, mvt. 4, mm. 1-4

Key: ______________ Scale type (if minor): ______________

B. Handel, Chaconne in G Major, mm. 53-56

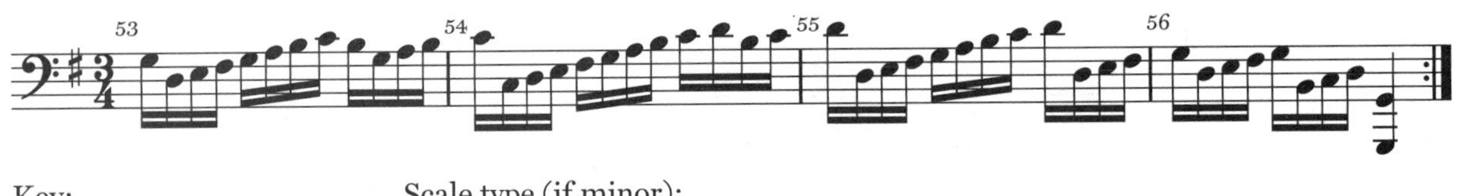

Key: ______________ Scale type (if minor): ______________

C. W. A. Mozart, String Quartet in D Minor, K. 421, mvt. 1, mm. 5-8

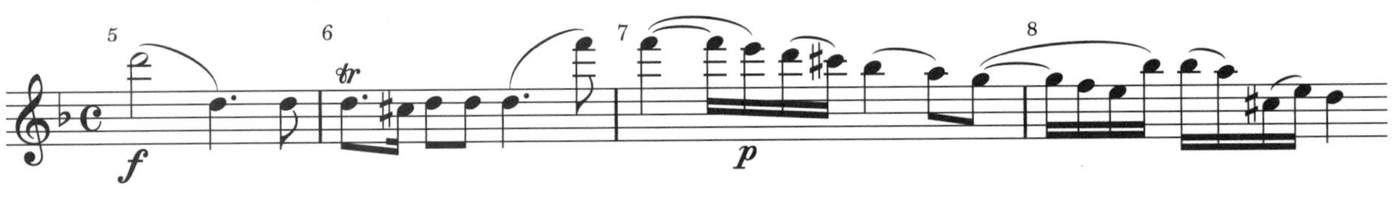

Key: ______________ Scale type (if minor): ______________

D. Elisabeth-Claude Jacquet de la Guerre, Sonata No. 2 for Violin and Continuo, mvt. 3, mm. 1-4

Key: ______________ Scale type (if minor): ______________

E. Arcangelo Corelli, Sarabanda, from Violin Sonata in E Minor, Op. 5, No. 8, mm. 21-24

Key: ______________ Scale type (if minor): ______________

III. Finding parallel and relative keys

For each pair of excerpts in the previous exercise, circle the appropriate relationship.

(a) Handel and Corelli	relative keys	parallel keys
(b) Loeillet and Jacquet de la Guerre	relative keys	parallel keys
(c) Mozart and Jacquet de la Guerre	relative keys	parallel keys

NAME ______________________________

ASSIGNMENT 5.4

I. Writing melodies from scale degrees

Each sequence of solfège syllables and scale-degree numbers given represents a minor-key melody. An underlined syllable or number indicates a pitch *below* the tonic. On the first staff, write the scale specified (along with the key signature), and label it with solfège and scale-degree numbers. Then use these to write the melody on the second staff (rhythm is optional). If you know the name of the tune, write it in the blank.

A. D natural minor

$\hat{1}$ $\hat{2}$ $\flat\hat{3}$

do re me

$\hat{1}$ $\hat{1}$ $\hat{5}$ $\hat{5}$ $\hat{4}$ $\flat\hat{3}$ $\hat{2}$ $\hat{1}$ $\underline{\flat\hat{7}}$ $\hat{1}$ $\hat{2}$ $\flat\hat{3}$ $\hat{4}$ $\hat{5}$

do do sol sol fa me re do *<u>te</u>* *do re me fa sol*

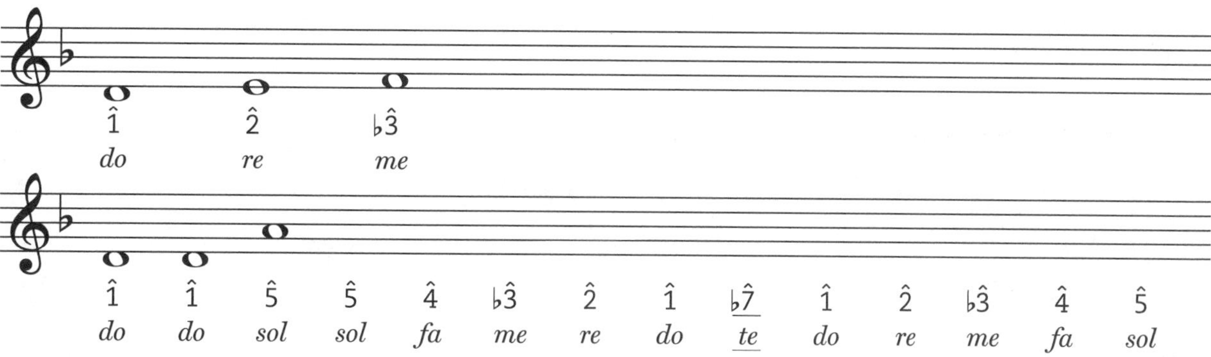

Name of melody: ______________________________

B. F harmonic minor

$\underline{\hat{5}}$ $\flat\hat{3}$ $\flat\hat{3}$ $\hat{2}$ $\hat{2}$ $\flat\hat{3}$ $\flat\hat{3}$ $\hat{1}$ $\underline{\hat{5}}$ $\underline{\hat{5}}$ $\underline{\hat{7}}$ $\underline{\hat{7}}$ $\hat{1}$

<u>sol</u> me me re re me me do <u>sol</u> <u>sol</u> <u>ti</u> <u>ti</u> do

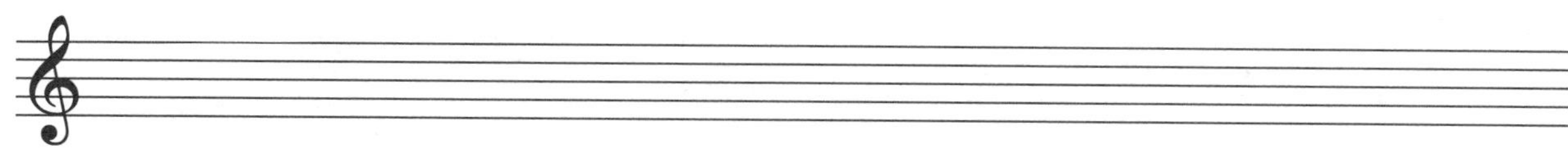

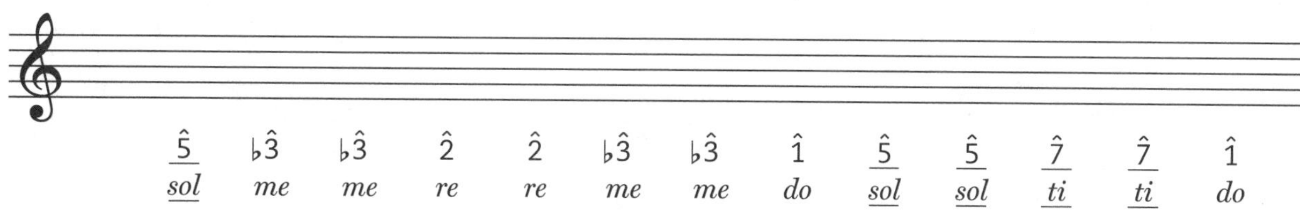

Name of melody: ______________________________

C. C♯ natural minor

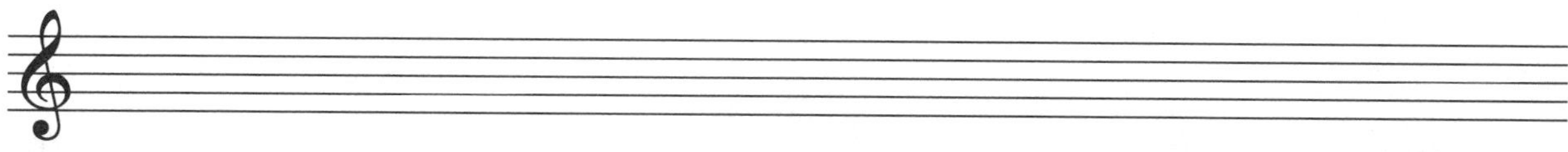

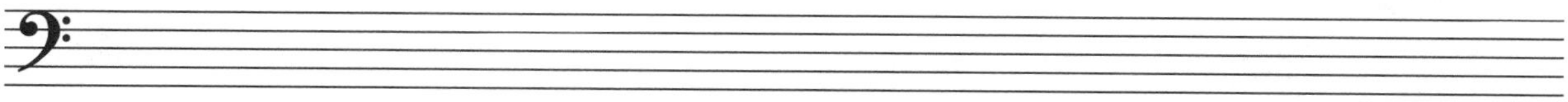

$\hat{1}$ $\underline{\hat{5}}$ $\hat{1}$ $\hat{1}$ $\hat{1}$ $\hat{2}$ $\flat\hat{3}$ $\hat{2}$ $\flat\hat{3}$ $\hat{1}$ $\underline{\flat\hat{7}}$ $\underline{\hat{5}}$ $\underline{\flat\hat{7}}$

do <u>sol</u> do do do re me re me do <u>te</u> <u>sol</u> <u>te</u>

Name of melody: ______________________________

II. Analyzing keys in musical contexts

For each Bach invention:

- Write the key in the blank provided.
- For each bracketed portion of the melody, write the scale type suggested by the melodic line.

A. J. S. Bach, Invention No. 2, mm. 1–2

Key: ______________

B. J. S. Bach, Invention No. 11, mm. 1–3

Key: ______________

C. J. S. Bach, Invention No. 13, mm. 1–3

Key: ______________

D. J. S. Bach, Invention No. 7, mm. 1–3

Key: ______________

E. In a sentence or two, explain how the melody for Invention No. 7 (shown in part D) does not conform to the scale types considered in this chapter.

NAME ______________________________

ASSIGNMENT 5.5

I. Writing pentatonic scales

Write the pentatonic scales requested (ascending form only).

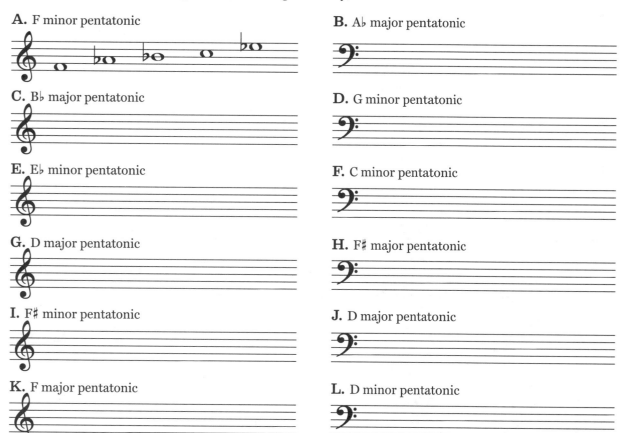

A. F minor pentatonic

B. A♭ major pentatonic

C. B♭ major pentatonic

D. G minor pentatonic

E. E♭ minor pentatonic

F. C minor pentatonic

G. D major pentatonic

H. F♯ major pentatonic

I. F♯ minor pentatonic

J. D major pentatonic

K. F major pentatonic

L. D minor pentatonic

II. Composing a melody

On your own paper or on these staves, compose a folklike melody in a minor or minor-pentatonic key. Take the melodies in the chapter as examples. Notate your tune in treble or bass clef, simple or compound meter. Use a key signature and add accidentals for $\hat{6}$ and $\hat{7}$, if needed. Use scale segments where possible, keeping the melody simple enough that you can sing it.

III. Review: Writing mixed types of scales

Write the following scales as specified, starting from the given pitch. Write accidentals before each note (rather than writing key signatures).

A. Major, ascending

B. Natural minor, descending

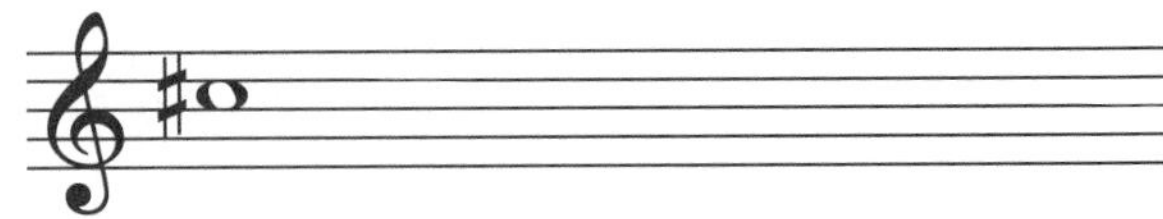

C. Melodic minor, ascending and descending

D. Harmonic minor, ascending

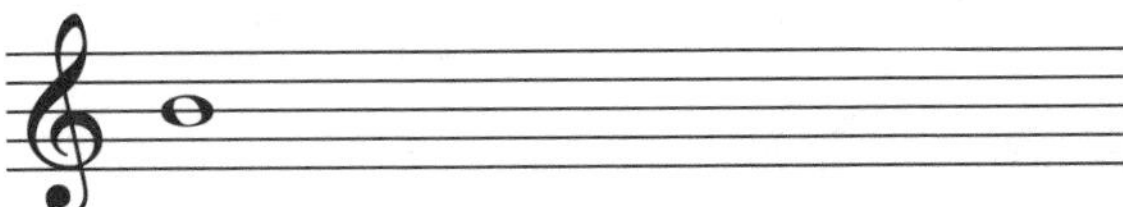

E. Harmonic minor, descending

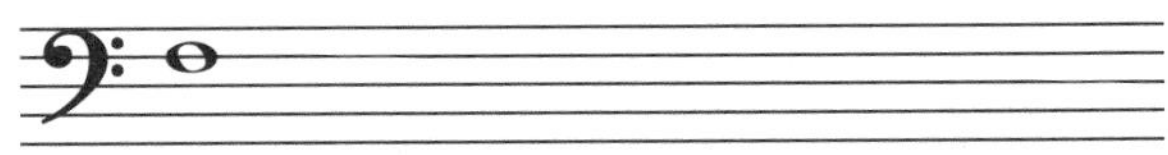

F. Chromatic, ascending and descending (use context of a C♯ major scale)

G. Major, descending

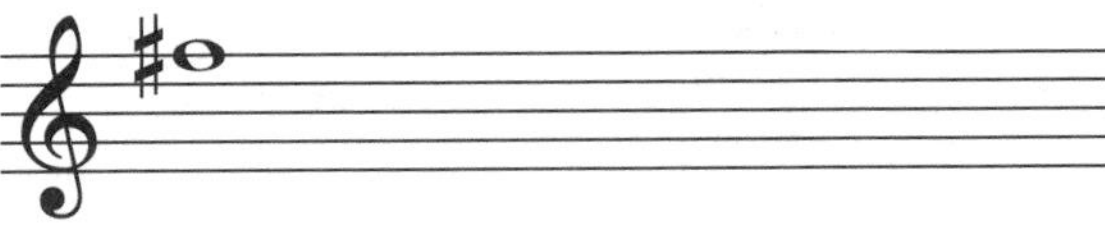

H. Harmonic minor, descending

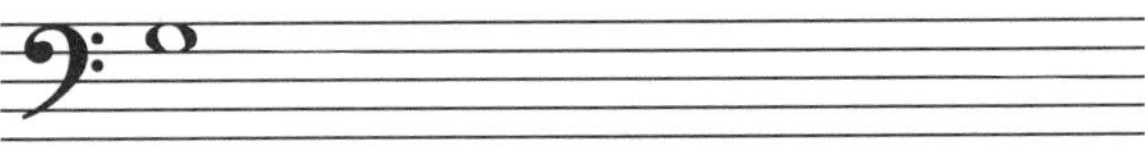

I. Natural minor, descending

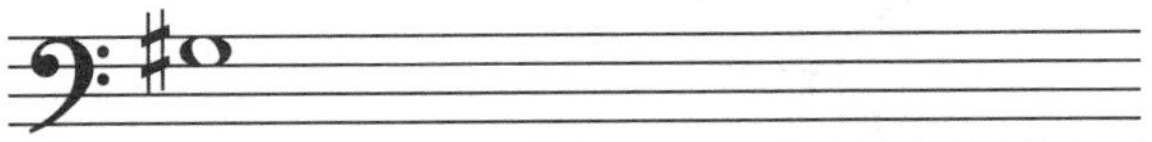

J. Major pentatonic, ascending

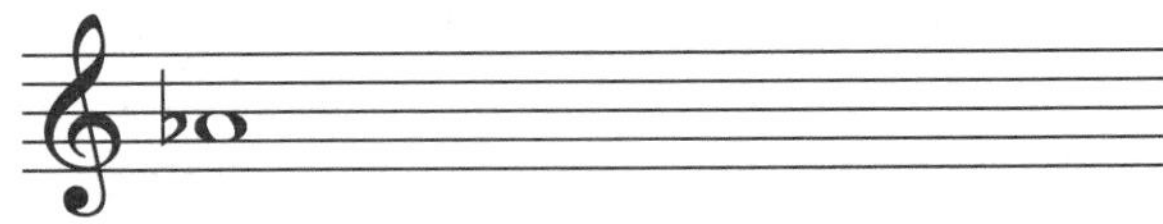

K. Minor pentatonic, ascending

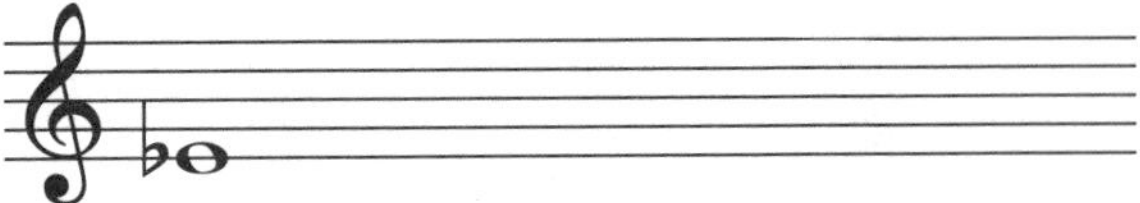

L. Minor pentatonic, ascending

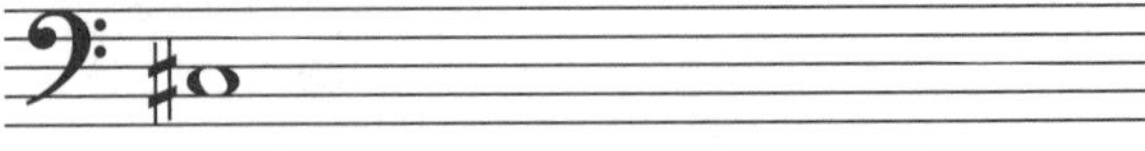

NAME ______________________

ASSIGNMENT 5.6

I. Writing the diatonic modes

A. As scales: Beginning on the given pitch, write the mode requested, adding accidentals before the pitches as needed.

(1) C Phrygian

(2) F♯ Dorian

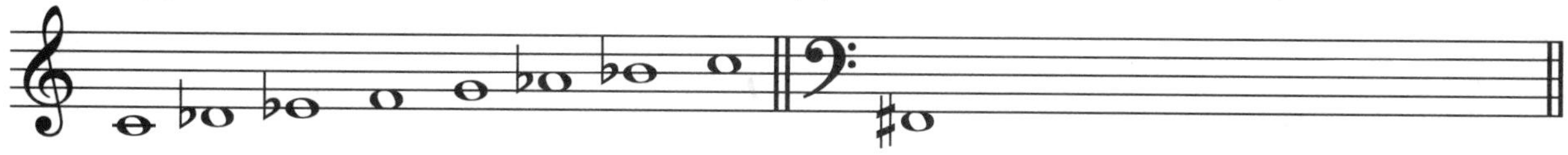

(3) F Mixolydian

(4) B♭ Lydian

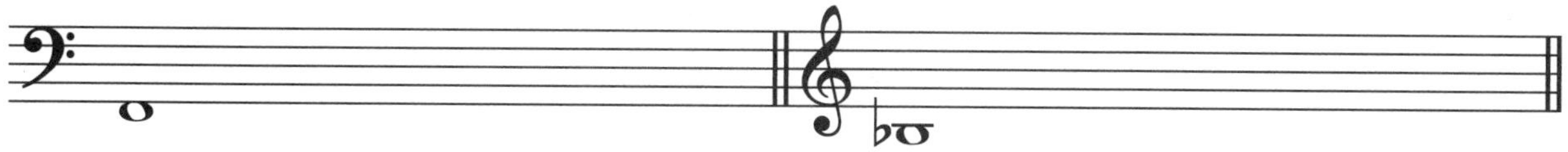

(5) E Dorian

(6) A Phrygian

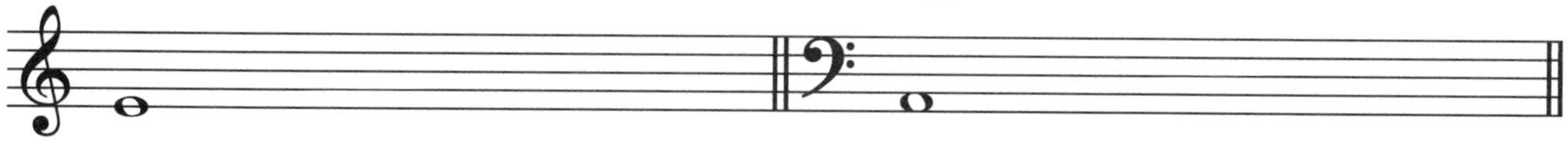

(7) A♭ Lydian

(8) D Mixolydian

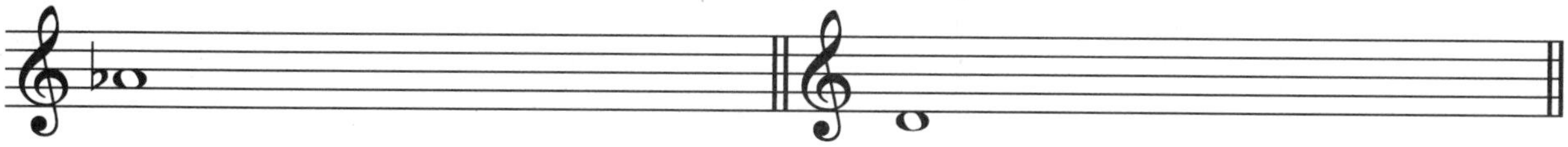

(9) C♯ Dorian

(10) B Lydian

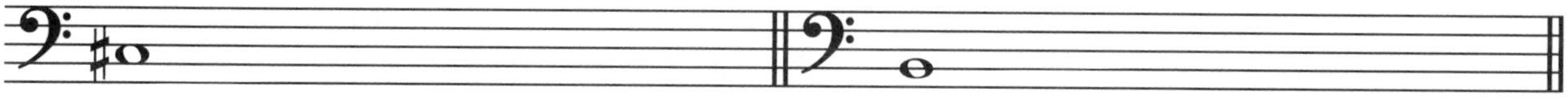

B. With key signatures: Write the correct key signature for the mode requested.

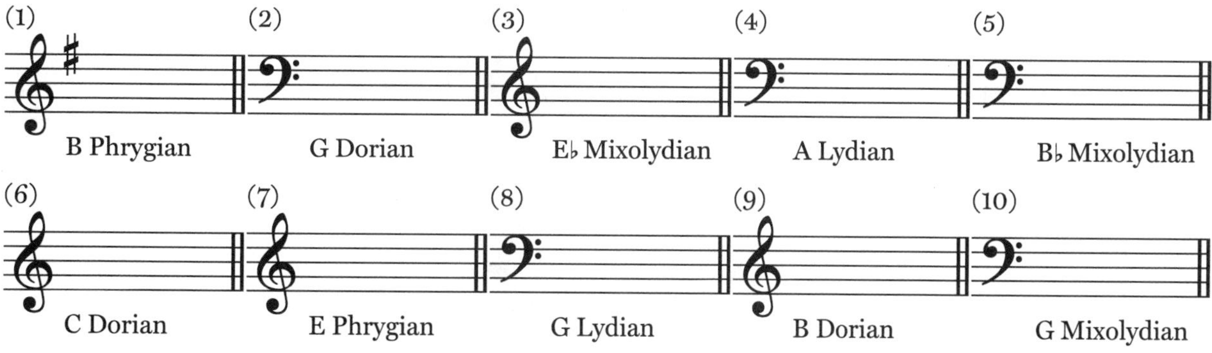

II. Analyzing pentatonic and modal melodies

Play or sing each of these melodies. Then, on the blank provided, indicate the mode (e.g., G Phrygian).

A. "Pange Lingua" (Sarum plainchant, abridged)

Pan - ge lin - gua glo - ri - o - si, Cor - po - ris my - ste - ri - um
Fruc - tus ven - tris ge - ne - ro - si, Rex ef - fu - dit gen - ti - um.

Translation: Sing, my tongue, the mystery of the glorious body, the fruit of the noble womb, the King of nations poured out.

Mode or scale: ___________________

B. A. Young, M. Young, and Johnson (AC/DC), "Back in Black," mm. 5–6

Hint: the key signature here is misleading.

5
6
Back in black, I hit the sack, I've been too long, I'm glad to be back.

Mode or scale: ___________________

C. Tomás Luis de Victoria, "O magnum mysterium," mm. 5–9

5
6
7
8
9
et ad - mi - ra - bi - le sa - cra-men - - - - - - - - tum,

Translation: And wonderful sacrament.

Mode or scale: ___________________

D. "Swallowtail Jig," mm. 1–8

1
2
3
4
5
6
7
8

Mode or scale: ___________________

NAME ____________________

6 Intervals

ASSIGNMENT 6.1

I. Identifying interval size

A. Write the number that represents the size of each interval in the blank below.

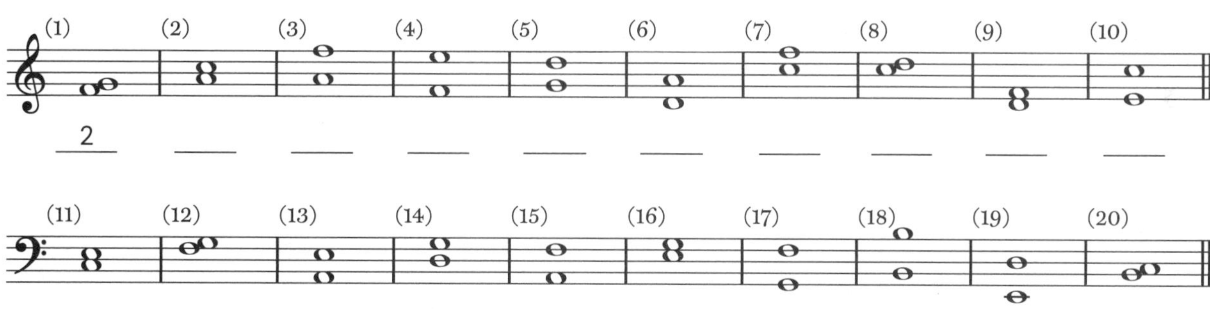

B. In the numbered blanks that correspond with each circled melodic interval, write the interval size.

W. A. Mozart, Piano Sonata in C Major, K. 545, mvt. 1, mm. 1–4

C. The circled intervals given may be simple or compound. In the first row of blanks, write the simple-interval size (e.g., 3 not 10). In the second row, write a C for any compound interval and an S for any simple interval.

Anonymous, Minuet in D Minor, from the *Anna Magdalena Bach Notebook*, mm. 9–16 (right hand)

II. Writing interval sizes

Write a whole note on the correct line or space to make each interval size specified. Don't add sharps or flats.

A. Write the specified melodic interval above the given note.

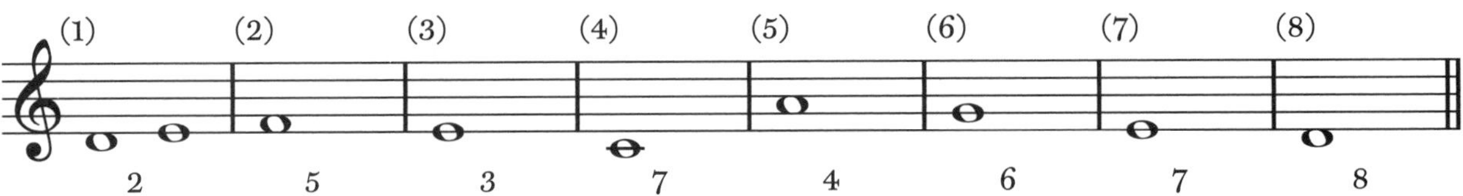

B. Write the specified melodic interval below the given note.

C. Write the specified harmonic interval above the given note.

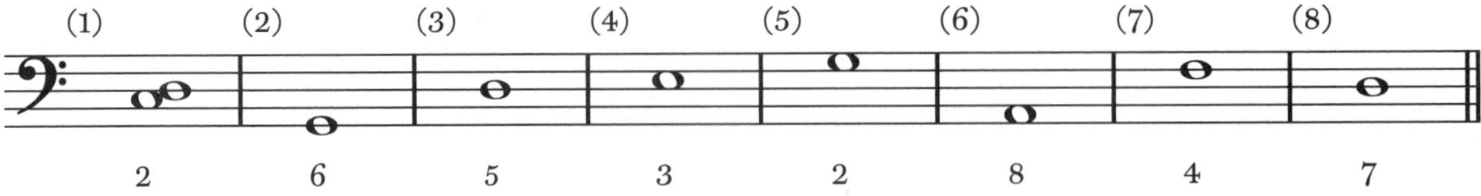

D. Write the specified harmonic interval below the given note.

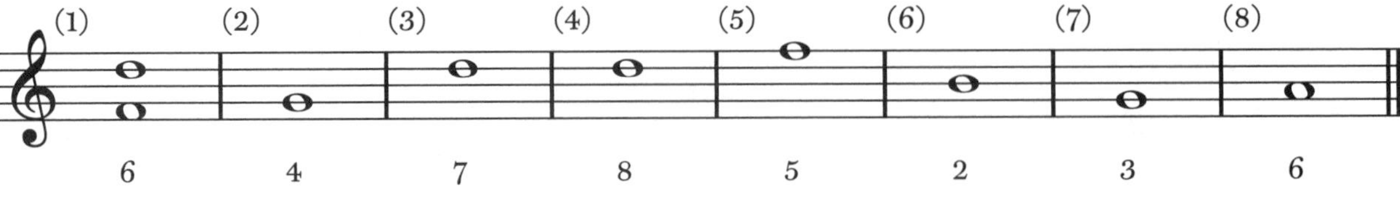

NAME ____________________

ASSIGNMENT 6.2

I. Identifying intervals

A. For each harmonic interval, write the size and quality.

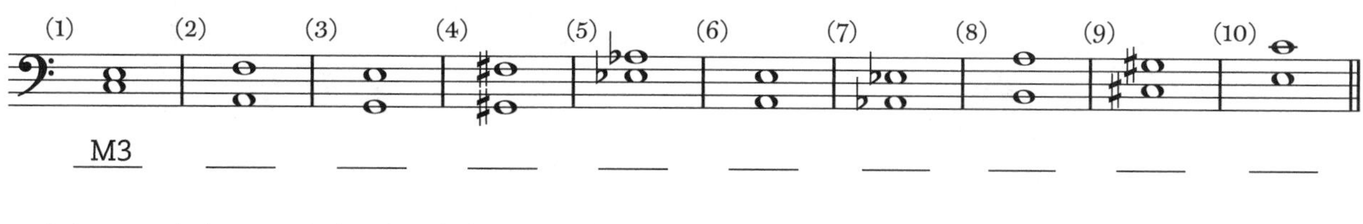

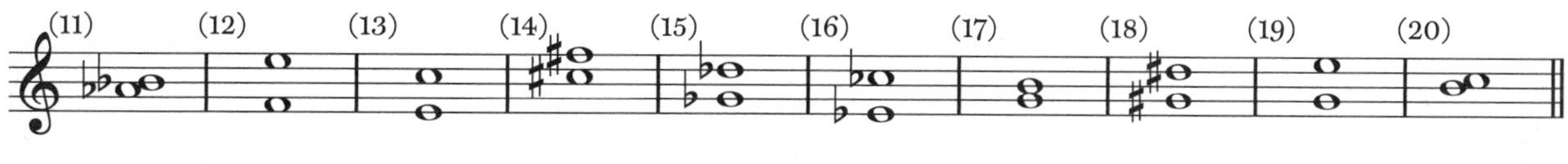

B. For each circled interval, write the size and quality in the corresponding blank. (You identified the size of these intervals in Assignment 6.1.)

W. A. Mozart, Piano Sonata in C Major, K. 545, mvt. 1, mm. 1–4

(1) M3 (2) ________ (3) ________ (4) ________

(5) ________ (6) ________ (7) ________ (8) ________

(9) ________ (10) ________ (11) ________ (12) ________

C. In the blanks provided below the staff, write the size and quality of each major, minor, or perfect melodic interval. Circle any interval that is not one of these qualities and place an "X" in the corresponding blank.

Béla Bartók, Suite, Op. 14, mvt. 2, mm. 17–24

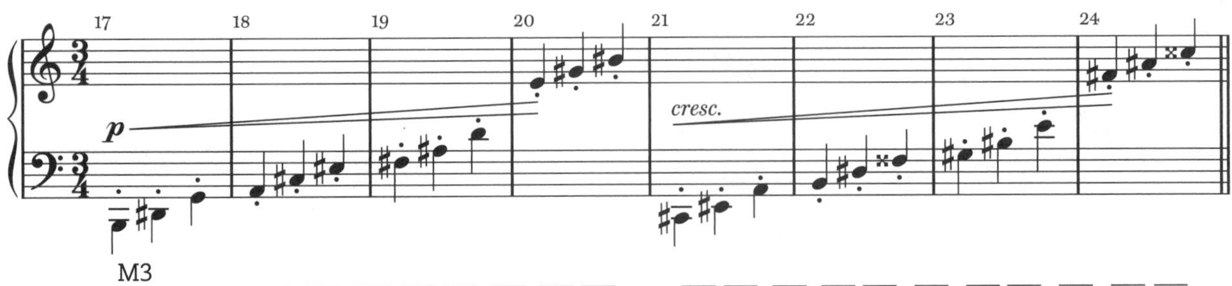

II. Writing intervals

A. Write the following harmonic intervals, as whole notes, above the given pitch.

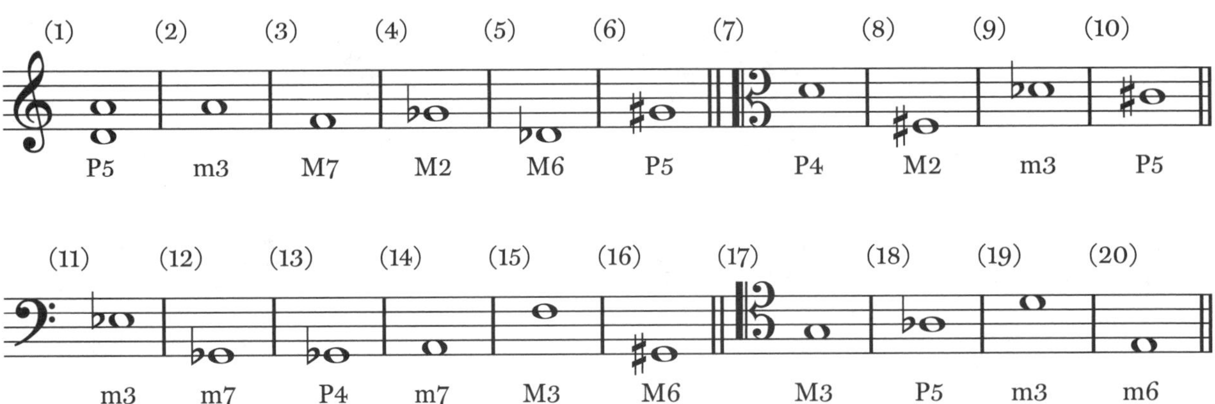

B. Write the following melodic intervals, as whole notes, above the given pitch.

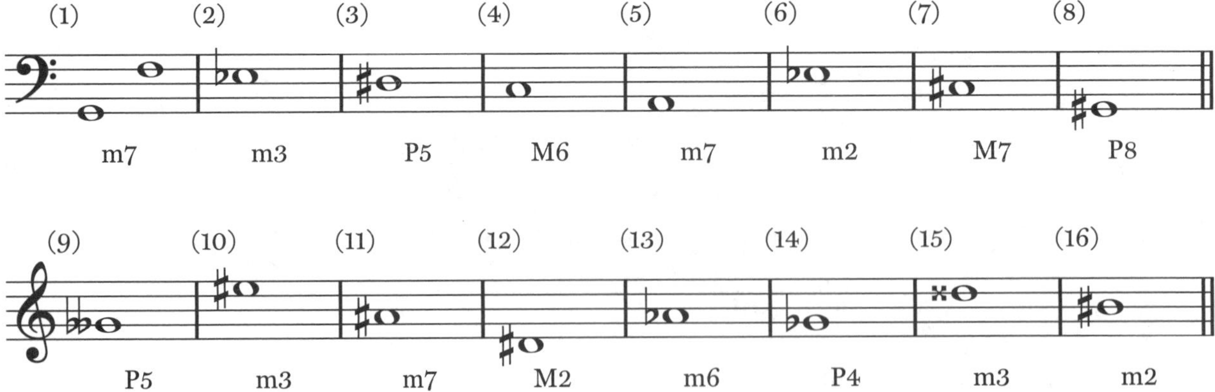

ASSIGNMENT 6.3

I. Writing major, minor, and perfect melodic intervals

A. Write the melodic intervals, as whole notes, above the given pitch.

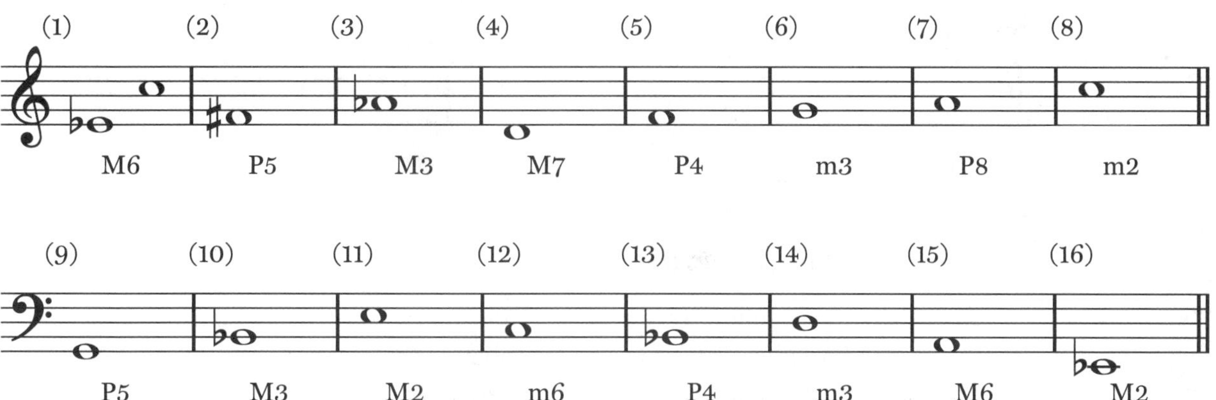

B. Write the melodic intervals, as whole notes, below the given pitch.

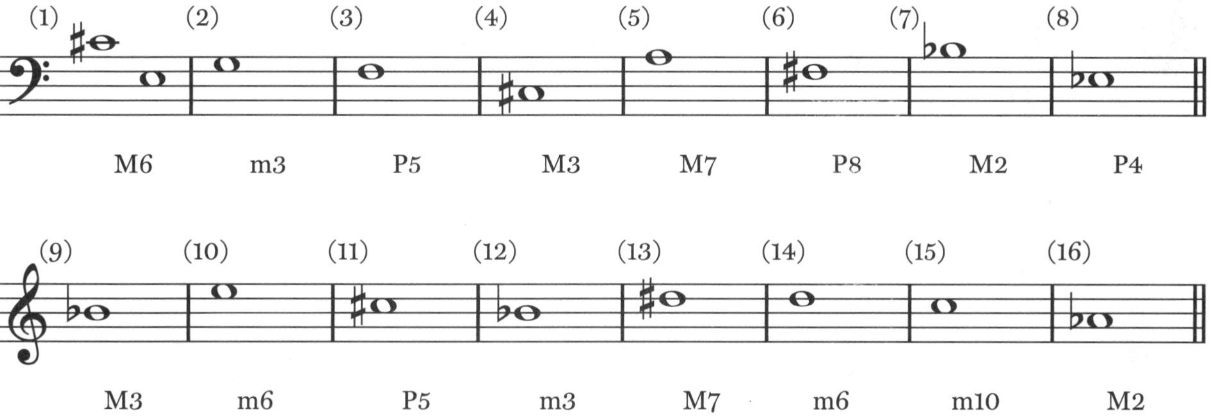

II. Writing major, minor, and perfect harmonic intervals

A. Write the harmonic intervals, as whole notes, above the given pitch.

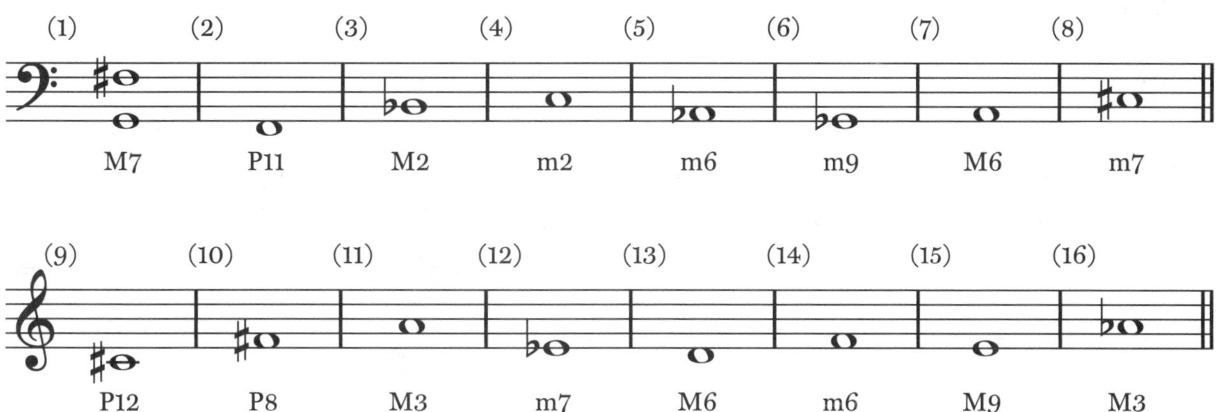

B. Write the following harmonic intervals, as whole notes, below the given pitch.

(1) (2) (3) (4) (5) (6) (7) (8)
m7 M6 M10 m2 P4 M10 m3 P11

(9) (10) (11) (12) (13) (14) (15) (16)
m7 P12 M3 M7 m3 M3 m9 P5

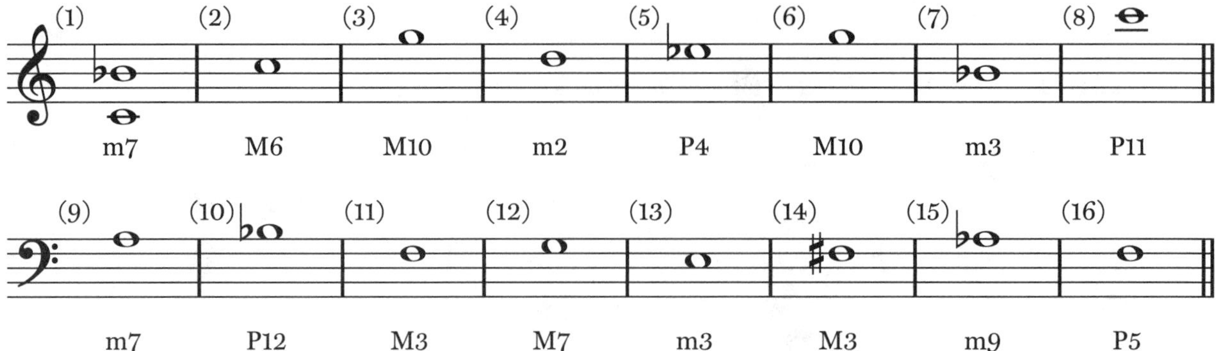

III. Writing melodies from intervals

Starting with the given pitch, write the following series of melodic intervals. The labels and arrows above the staff indicate the interval and whether it should be written above or below the previous note. When finished, play or sing the pitches to determine which song you have notated. Write the name of the song (if you know it) in the blank.

A.

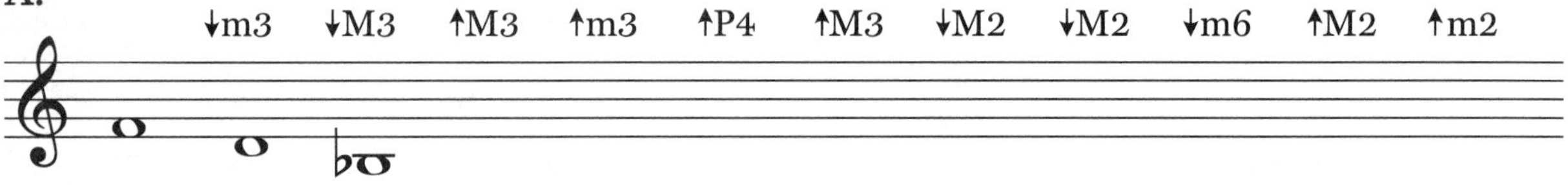

↓m3 ↓M3 ↑M3 ↑m3 ↑P4 ↑M3 ↓M2 ↓M2 ↓m6 ↑M2 ↑m2

Song title: ______________________________

B.

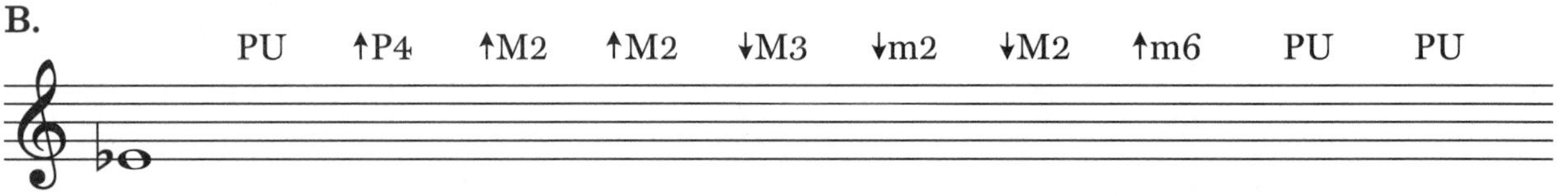

PU ↑P4 ↑M2 ↑M2 ↓M3 ↓m2 ↓M2 ↑m6 PU PU

Song title: ______________________________

C.

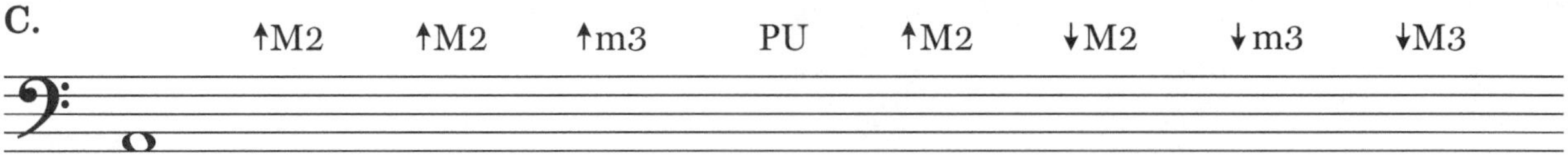

↑M2 ↑M2 ↑m3 PU ↑M2 ↓M2 ↓m3 ↓M3

Song title: ______________________________

D.

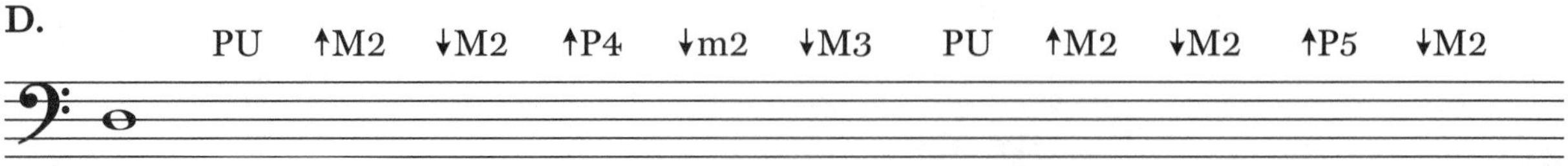

PU ↑M2 ↓M2 ↑P4 ↓m2 ↓M3 PU ↑M2 ↓M2 ↑P5 ↓M2

Song title: ______________________________

NAME ______________________________

ASSIGNMENT 6.4

I. Interval inversion

A. For each given interval, rewrite the second pitch, then write the first pitch up an octave. Label both intervals.

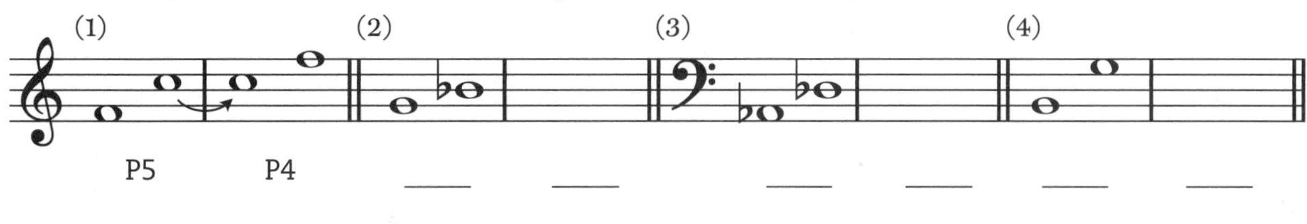

B. Invert each given interval as in part A, but this time rewrite the second pitch, then write the first pitch *down* an octave. Label both intervals.

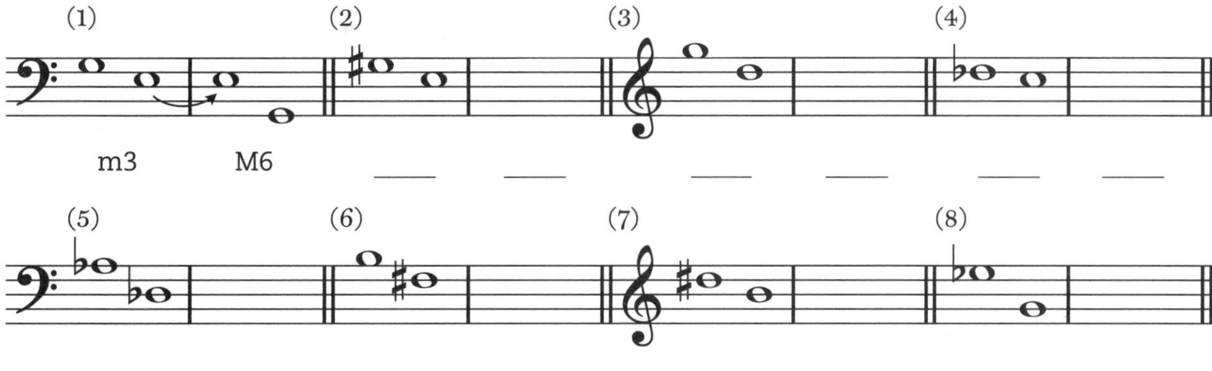

II. Writing augmented and diminished intervals

A. Harmonic intervals: First write the major, minor, or perfect interval requested, *above* the given note. Then copy the *bottom* note in the blank measure, and raise or lower the *top* note to create the interval specified.

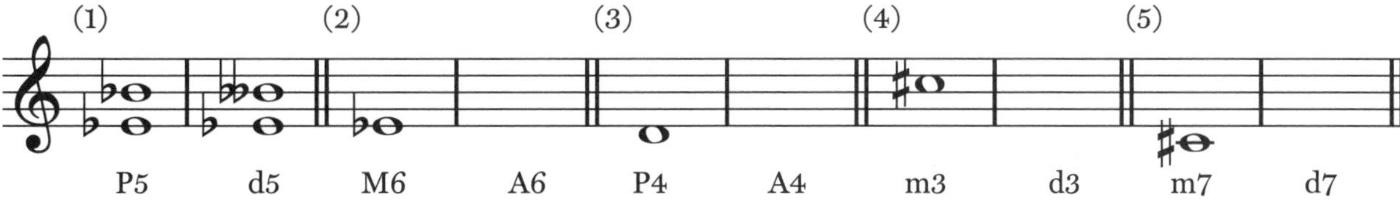

B. Melodic intervals: First write the major, minor, or perfect melodic interval requested, *below* the given note. Then copy the *top* note in the blank measure, and raise or lower the *bottom* note to create the melodic interval specified.

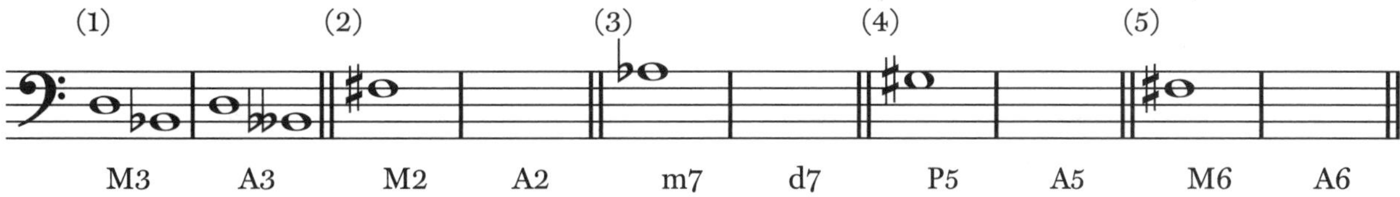

III. Identifying intervals in the context of a key

A. Listen to this melody. Then write the size and quality of each melodic interval below the staff in the blanks provided. Don't forget to check the flats from the key signature.

Beethoven, Piano Sonata in C Minor, Op. 13 (*Pathétique*), mvt. 2, mm. 1–8 (right hand)

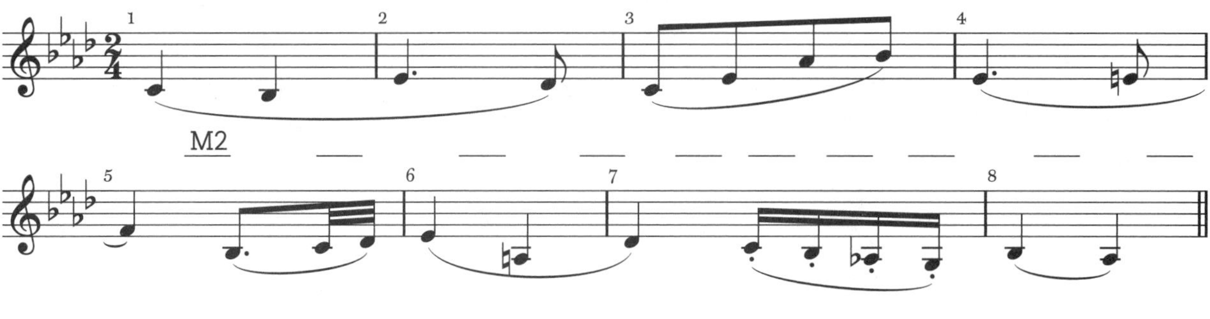

B. Listen to the following passages. Identify the harmonic intervals between the voices shown, labeling as simple intervals even if they are compound. In the second row of blanks label the interval type by writing P (perfect consonance), I (imperfect consonance), or D (dissonance).

(1) Beethoven, Piano Sonata in C Minor, Op. 13 (*Pathétique*), mvt. 2, mm. 1–8

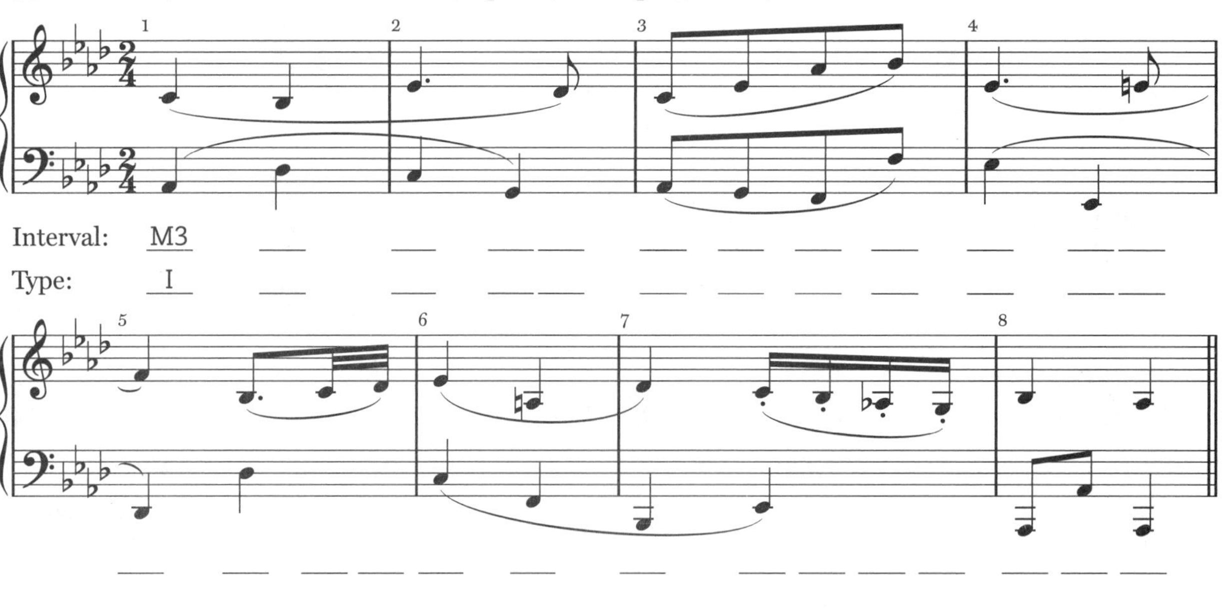

(2) "St. Anne," mm. 1–4 (soprano and bass)

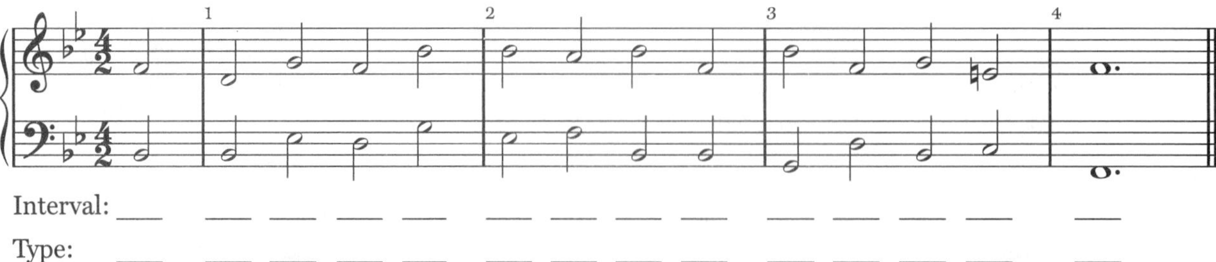

ASSIGNMENT 6.5

I. Writing diminished and augmented intervals

A. Write the specified harmonic interval above the given note.

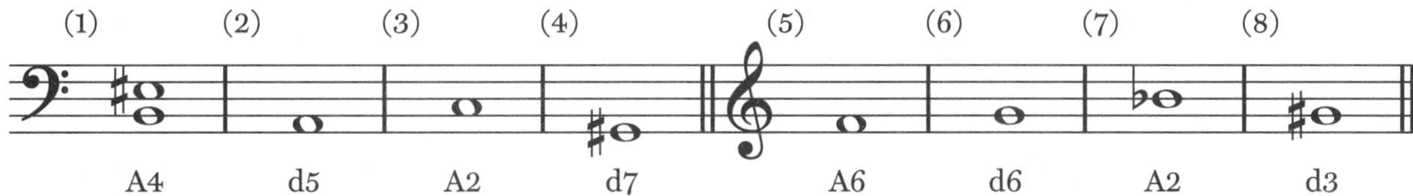

B. Write the specified harmonic interval below the given note.

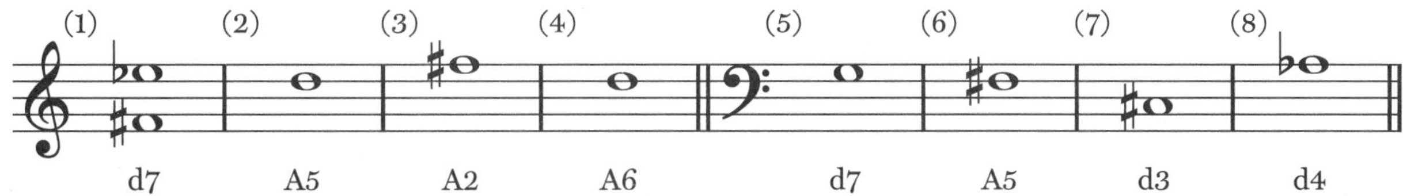

II. Writing enharmonically equivalent intervals

For each given interval, write two intervals beside it that sound the same but are spelled differently. Label each interval in the blank provided.

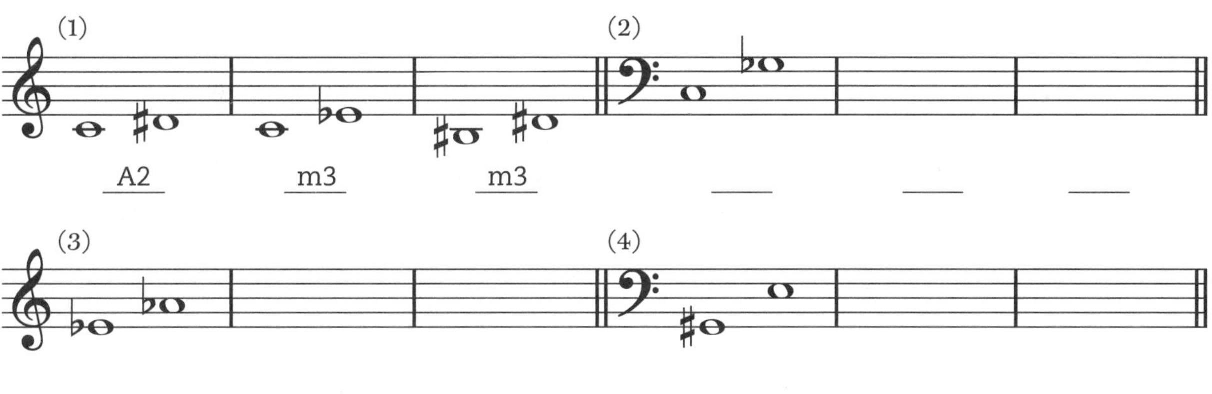

III. Writing all interval types

A. Write the specified melodic interval above the given note.

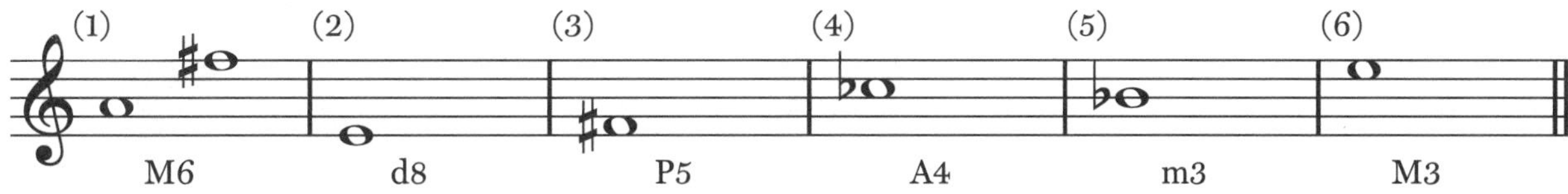

B. Write the specified melodic interval below the given note.

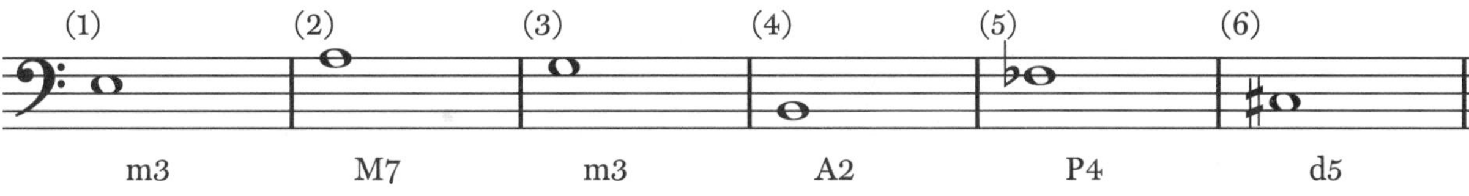

C. Write the melodic interval above or below the given note as specified.

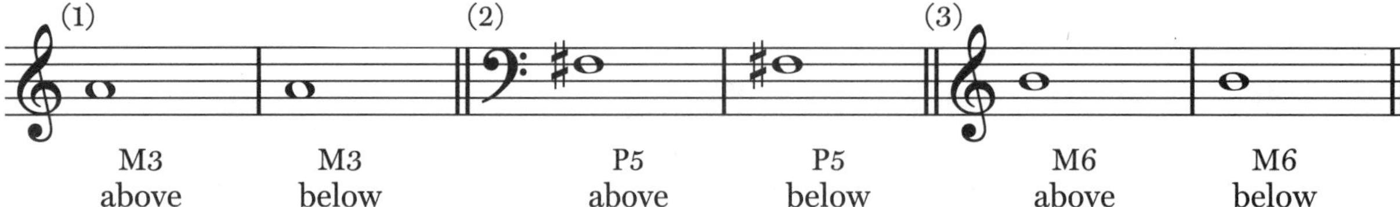

IV. Identifying intervals in a key context

A. For each circled and numbered harmonic interval, write its size and quality (e.g., m6) in the corresponding blank. Remember to include the sharp from the key signature.

J. S. Bach, "Aus meines Herzens Grunde," mm. 1-4

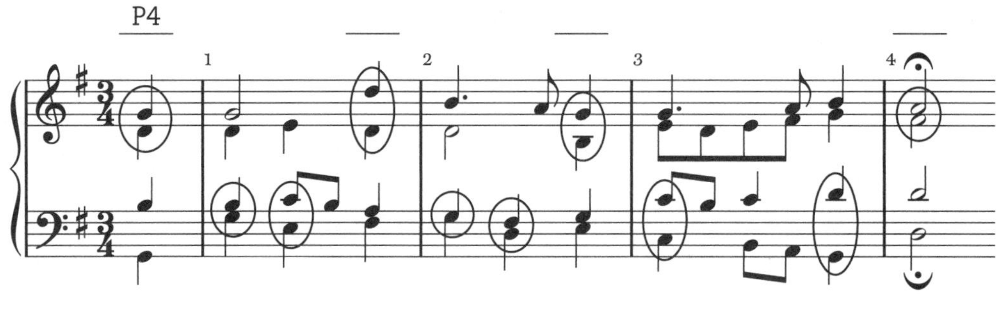

B. For each circled melodic interval, write its size and quality in the blank below the staves. Remember to include flats from the key signature.

Arnold Schoenberg, "Erwartung," from *Vier Lieder*, Op. 2, No. 1, mm. 1-5 (melody)

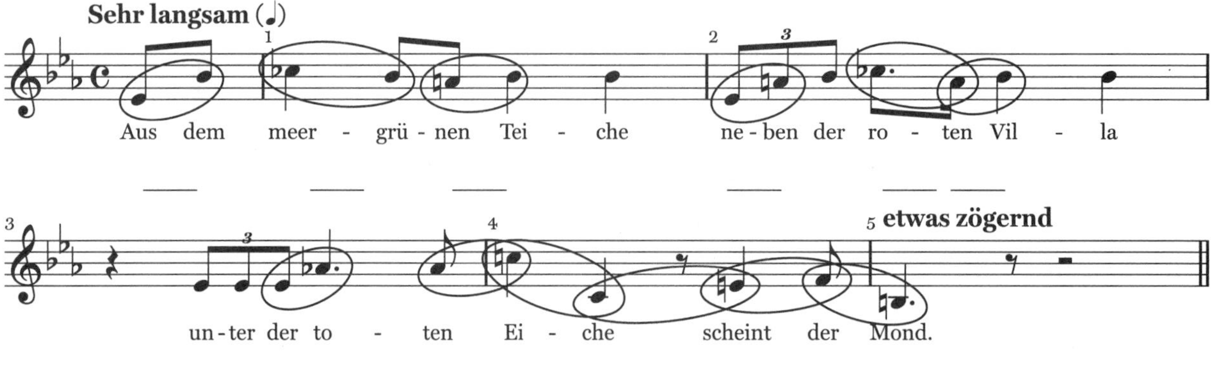

Translation: From the sea-green pond next to the red villa under the dead oak shines the moon.

ASSIGNMENT 6.6

I. Identifying all interval types

Identify the size and quality of the following intervals. In the second row of blanks, label each interval P (perfect consonance), I (imperfect consonance), or D (dissonance).

II. Writing all intervals

A. Write the following harmonic intervals, as whole notes, below the given pitch.

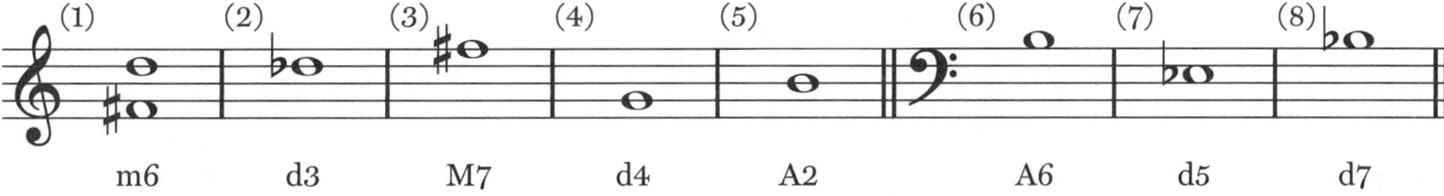

B. Write the following harmonic intervals, as whole notes, above the given pitch.

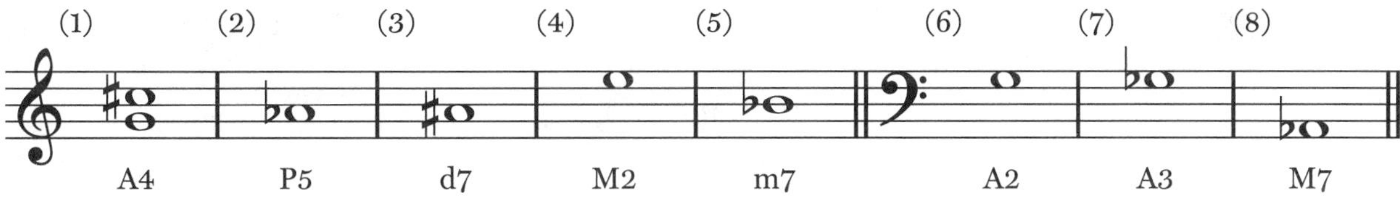

C. Write the inversion of each given harmonic interval, as whole notes, on the staff beneath. Write the name of each interval in the blank provided.

Inversion:

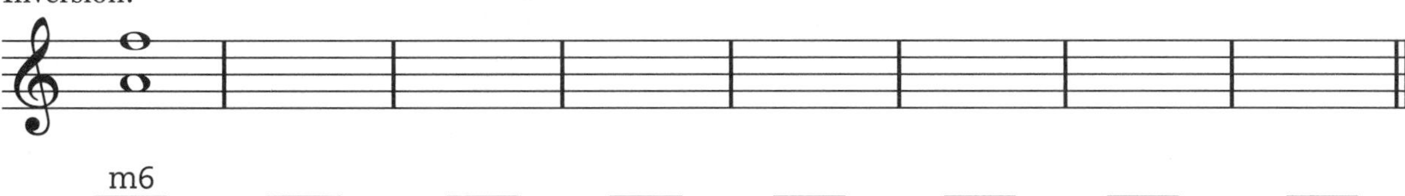

III. Melodic analysis: Two melodies by Charles Ives

A. Begin by playing the pitches of each melody on a keyboard or on your own instrument. (Don't worry about the rhythm.) Then label each melodic interval in the blanks provided. Circle any augmented or diminished interval. Ignore small (grace) notes.

(1) Charles Ives, "November 2, 1920," mm. 8–10

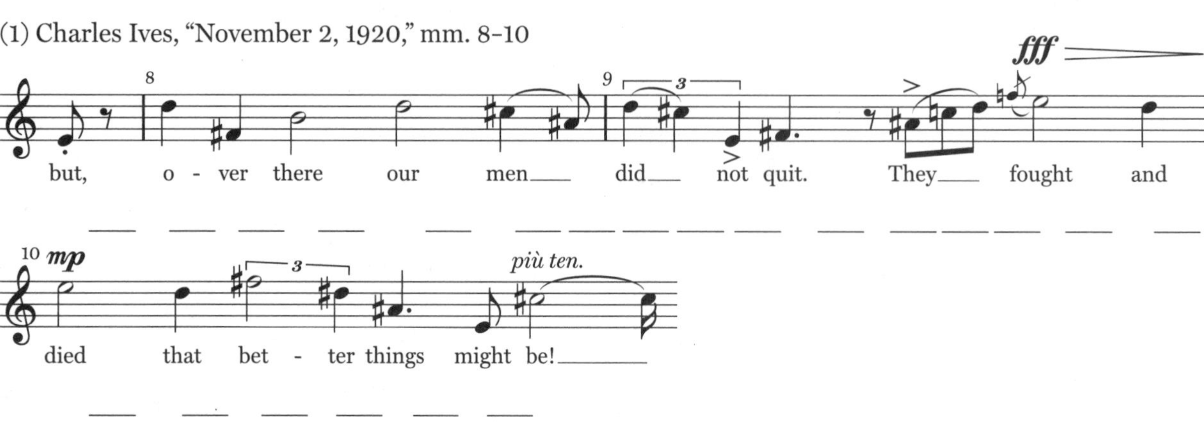

(2) Charles Ives, "The Rainbow (So May It Be!)," mm. 4–8

B. For class discussion, or in a paragraph (as assigned by your teacher), consider Ives's vocal-writing style. What types of melodic intervals do you find? How do they fit into a mode or scale? What challenges would a singer face in preparing these melodies for performance?

NAME ______________________

Triads

ASSIGNMENT 7.1

I. Writing scale-degree triads

Notate the requested scale in whole notes (ascending only), adding any needed accidentals. Above each scale degree, write a triad, again adding the necessary accidentals. In minor keys, use the leading tone from harmonic minor to spell the chords built on $\hat{5}$ and $\hat{7}$. Then in the blank, identify each triad's quality as M (major), m (minor), d (diminished), or A (augmented).

A. Major scales

D: M ____ ____ ____ ____ ____ ____

E♭: ____ ____ ____ ____ ____ ____ ____

B. Harmonic minor scales

g: m ____ ____ ____ ____ ____ ____

e: ____ ____ ____ ____ ____ ____ ____

II. Triad quality

Identify the quality of each triad as M (major), m (minor), d (diminished), or A (augmented) in the blank.

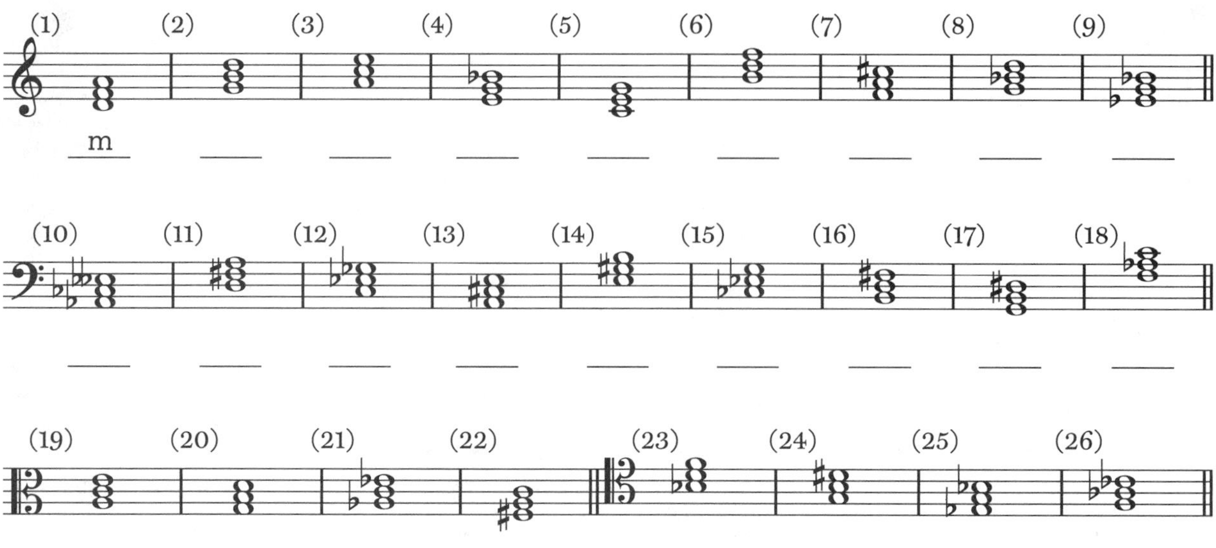

III. Identifying triads in a musical context

For each chord (with the exception of eighth-note chords), write the triad in root position on the treble-clef staff in whole notes. Then label the root and quality for each chord in the blanks beneath.

"St. Prisca," mm. 1–4

ASSIGNMENT 7.2

I. Identifying major and minor triads

Identify the root and quality of each given triad. Write uppercase letters for major triads (F♯) and lowercase for minor triads (f♯).

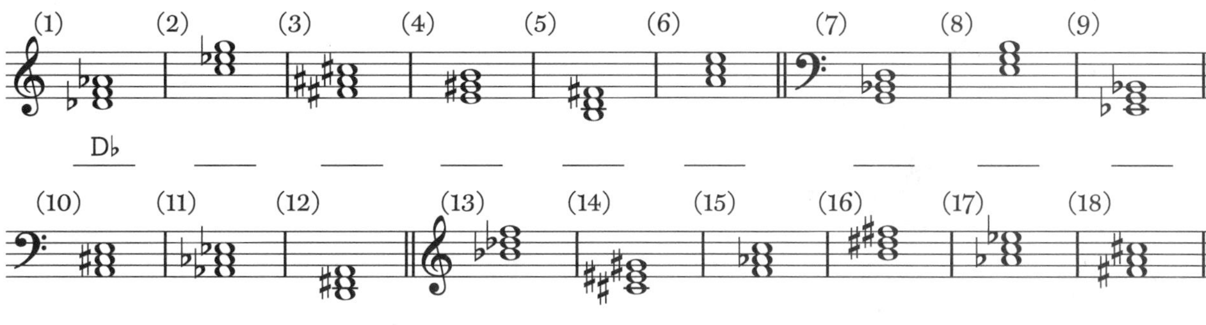

II. Spelling all triad types

A. Rewrite each major triad, adding or subtracting accidentals to create the chord quality specified. Do not change the given root.

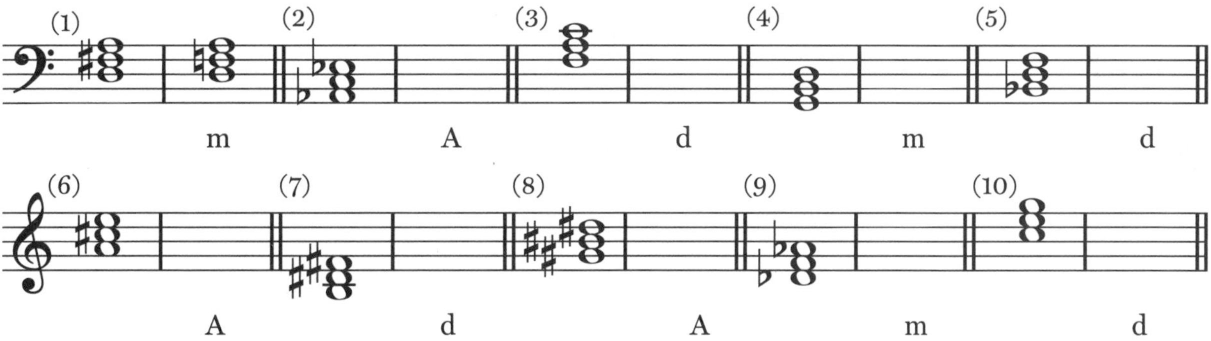

B. Consider each given pitch to be the root of a triad. Write the remaining pitches to create the quality specified.

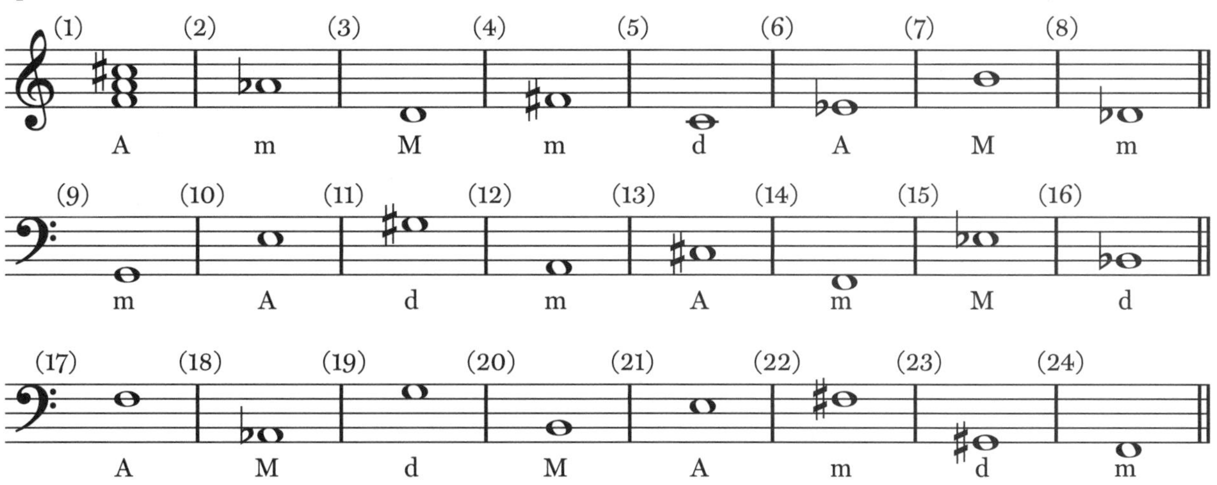

III. Identifying triad types in musical context

In the top row of blanks, identify the root of the chord, which may or may not be the lowest pitch. In the bottom row, write M, m, d, or A to show its quality. Determine chord quality from the keyboard part, rather than the solo lines. Ignore any circled note in the keyboard part.

A. Claude Debussy, "Fantoches," from *Fêtes galantes*, mm. 12–13

Root: ____ ____ ____ ____

Quality: ____ ____ ____ ____

B. Louise Farrenc, Trio for Flute, Cello, and Piano, Op. 45, mvt. 3, mm. 135–140

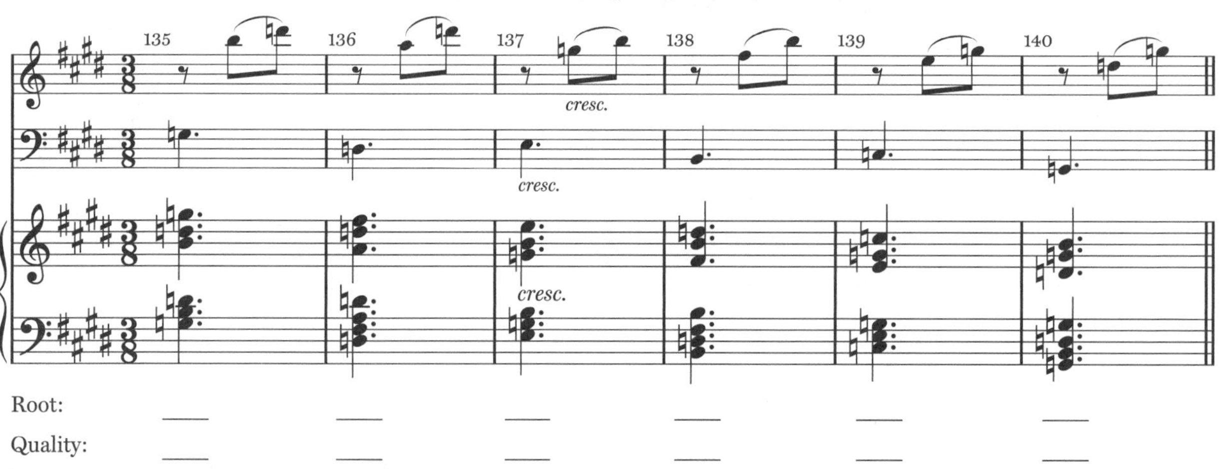

Root: ____ ____ ____ ____ ____ ____

Quality: ____ ____ ____ ____ ____ ____

C. Henry Purcell, "Thy hand, Belinda," from *Dido and Aeneas*, mm. 7–9

Root: ____ ____ ____ ____ ____ ____

Quality: ____ ____ ____ ____ ____ ____

ASSIGNMENT 7.3

I. Writing triads in a key

Write triads in root position above the given roots, using whole notes. Don't write accidentals except in minor keys, where you should use the leading tone to spell the chords built on $\hat{5}$ and $\hat{7}$. In the blanks, identify the triads, using uppercase or lowercase Roman numerals and the symbols ° and ⁺ to show their quality and position in the scale.

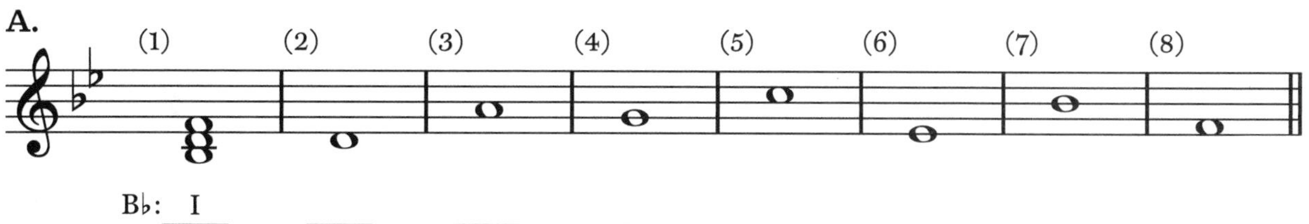

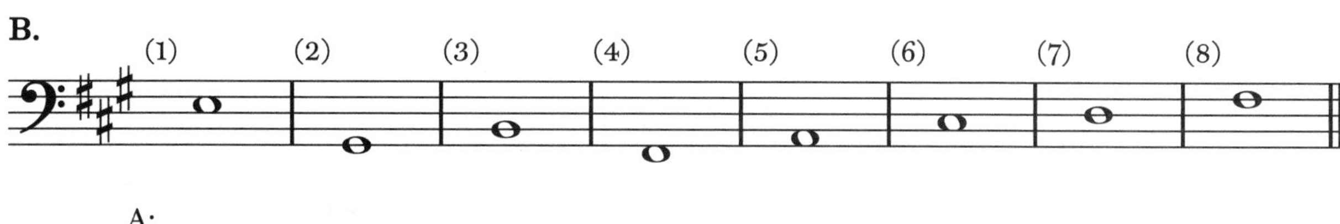

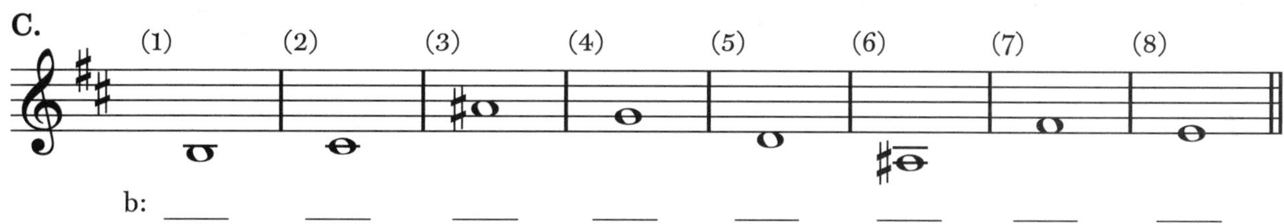

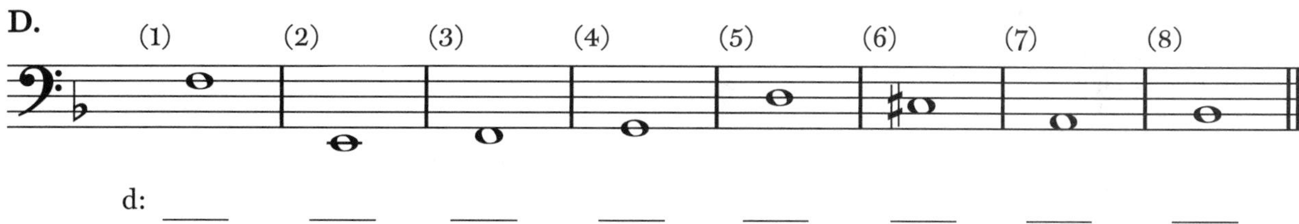

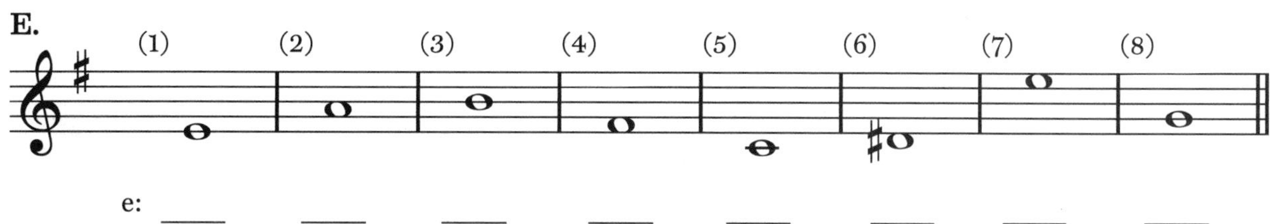

II. Identifying triads in musical contexts

For each chord, write the triad in root position (whole notes) on the blank staff. Ignore any circled notes. In the blanks beneath, identify the triad with an uppercase or lowercase Roman numeral to show its quality and position in the key. (You need not specify inversions.)

A. Johann Pachelbel, Canon in D Major, mm. 3–4

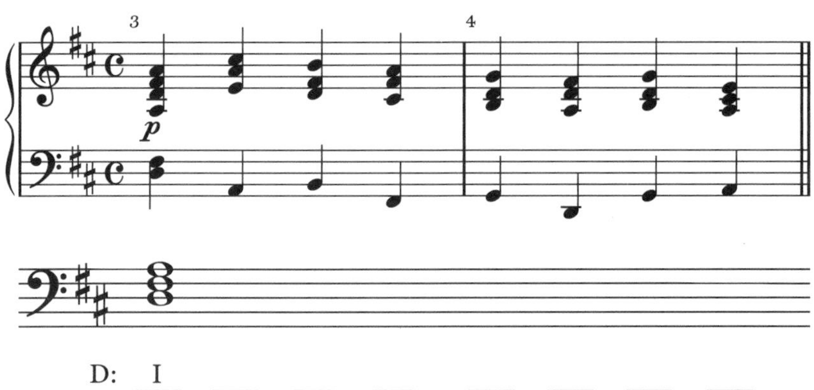

D: I ___ ___ ___ ___ ___ ___ ___

B. Johann Crüger, "Nun danket alle Gott," mm. 1–4

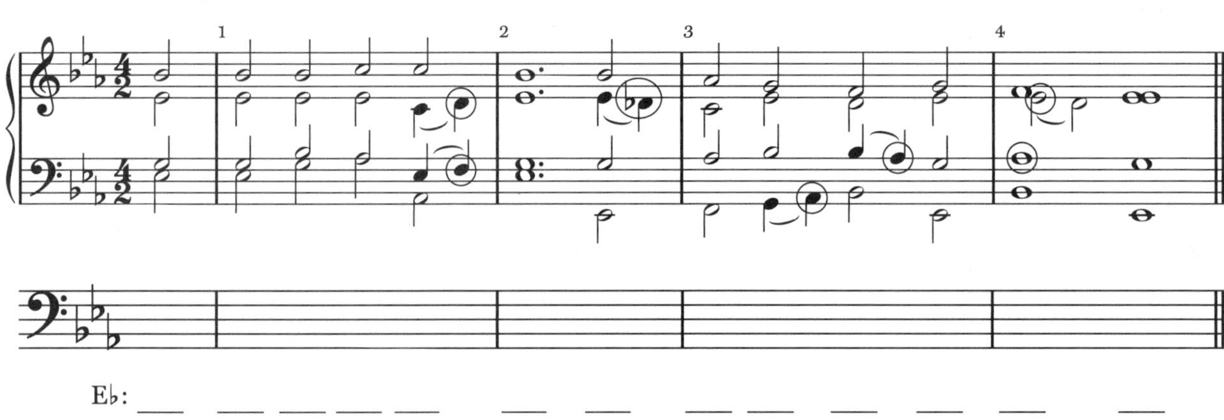

E♭: ___ ___ ___ ___ ___ ___ ___ ___ ___ ___ ___ ___ ___

C. "Old Hundredth," mm. 1–6

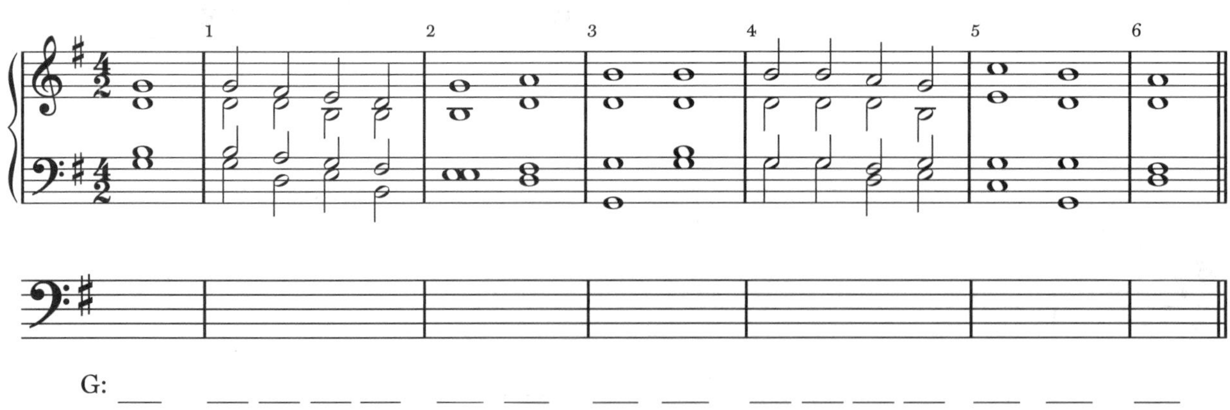

G: ___ ___ ___ ___ ___ ___ ___ ___ ___ ___ ___ ___ ___ ___ ___ ___

ASSIGNMENT 7.4

I. Identifying triad root, quality, and inversion

In the top row of blanks, identify the chord root and quality (e.g., D or d). In the second row, identify the position or inversion (root, 1st, or 2nd).

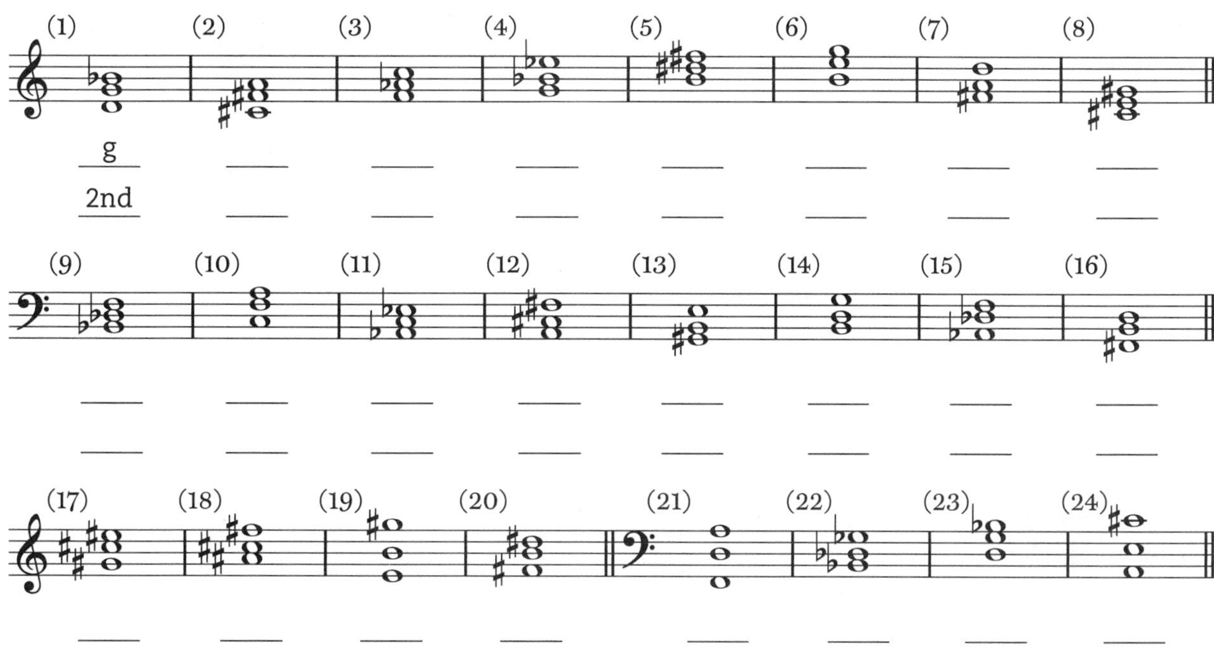

II. Identifying triads in a musical context

For each chord (with the exception of eighth-note chords), write the triad in root position on the treble-clef staff (using whole notes). In the top row of blanks, write each chord root and quality. In the second row, identify the position or inversion (root, 1st, or 2nd) of that chord in the musical excerpt.

"St. George's Windsor," mm. 1–4

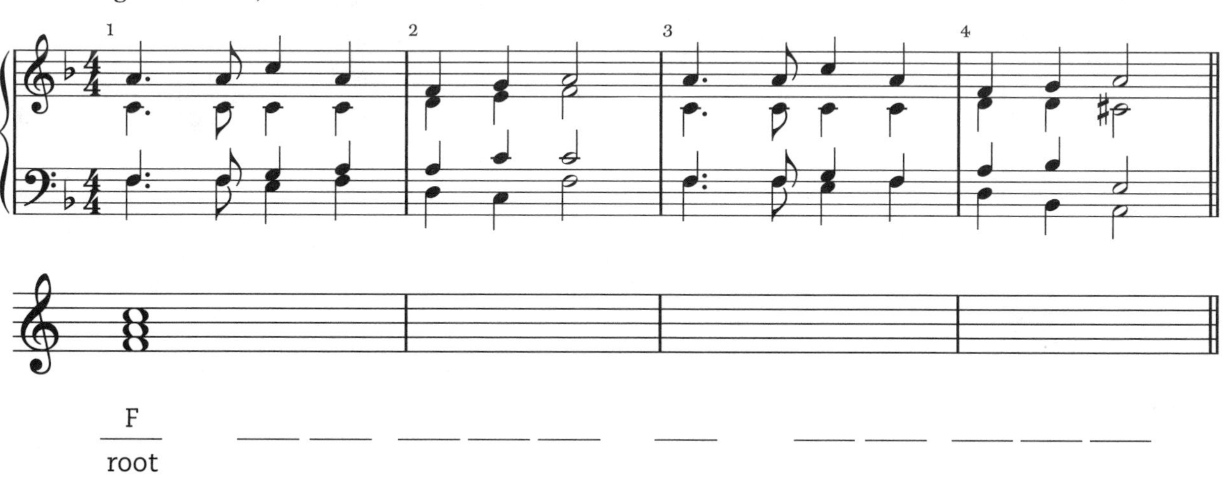

III. Identifying triads and inversions in musical contexts

For each of these excerpts, in the positions indicated by the blanks, write the triads in root position (whole notes). Ignore any circled notes. Identify the triad with an uppercase or lowercase Roman numeral (to show its quality and position in the key) and figures (to show its inversion) in the blank below the staff.

A. Thomas Tallis, "If ye love me," mm. 1–4

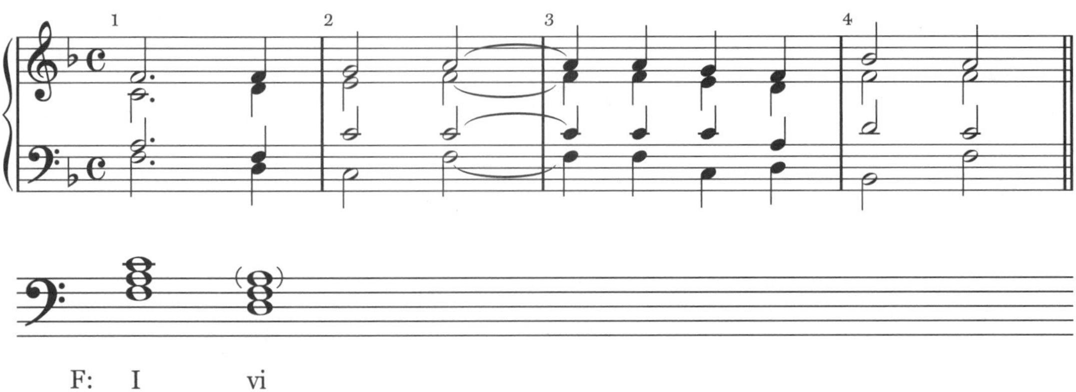

B. Robert Schumann, "Wilder Reiter," from *Album for the Young*, mm. 1–3

C. "Chartres," mm. 1–4

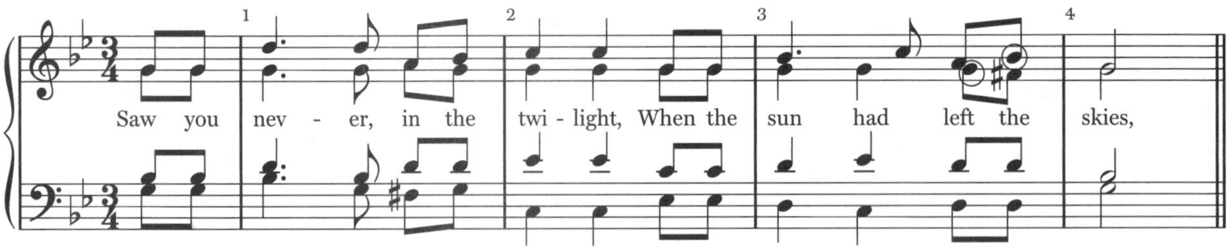

g: i

ASSIGNMENT 7.5

I. Identifying triads from figured bass

On the treble-clef staff, write the triad indicated by the bass and figures. Use half notes stacked in thirds. In the blank below the staff, write the Roman numeral reflecting the triad's position and quality in the given key. For inverted triads, also write the inversion (e.g., IV6).

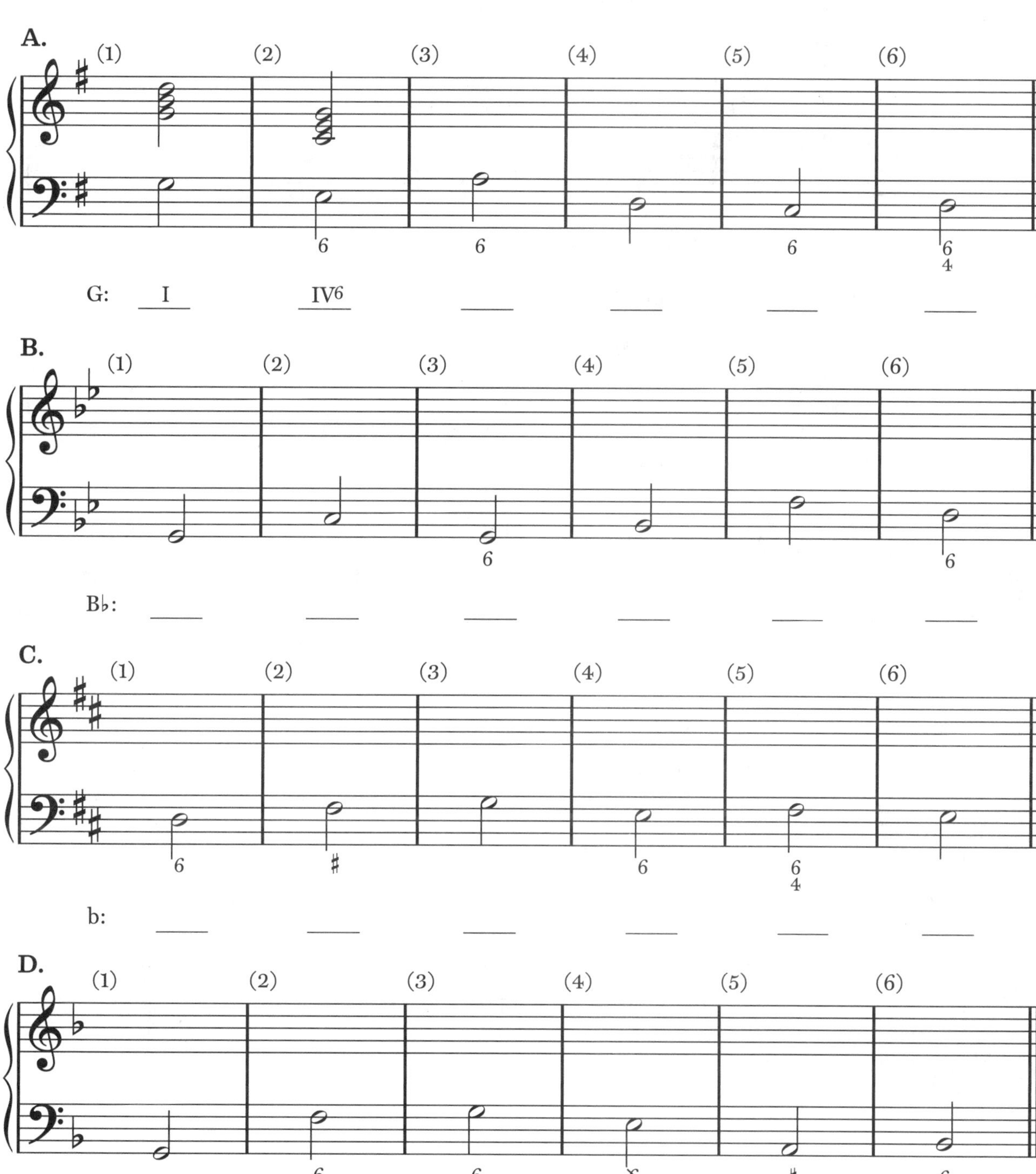

II. Review: Spelling isolated triads

Fill in the other notes of each triad, adding accidentals as needed to make the correct quality. Don't change the given pitch.

A. Each given pitch is the root of a triad.

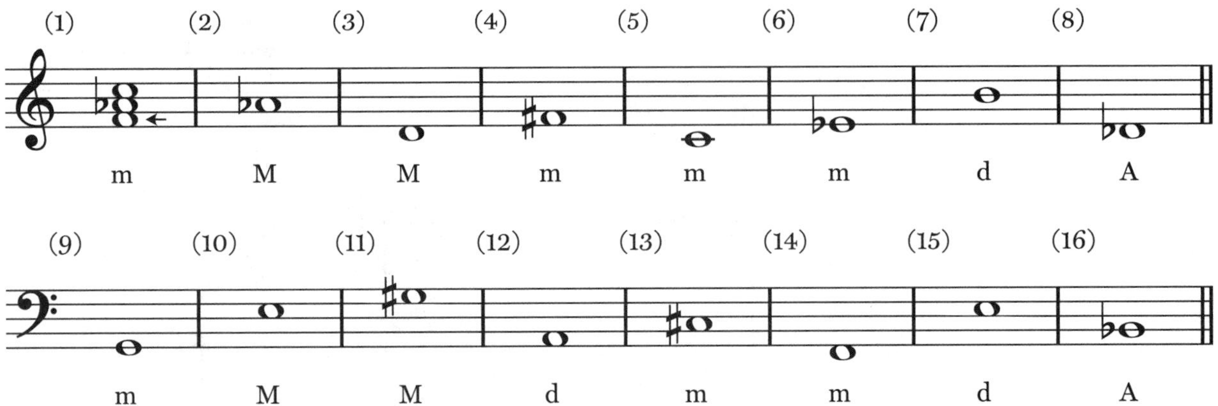

B. Each given pitch is the third of a triad.

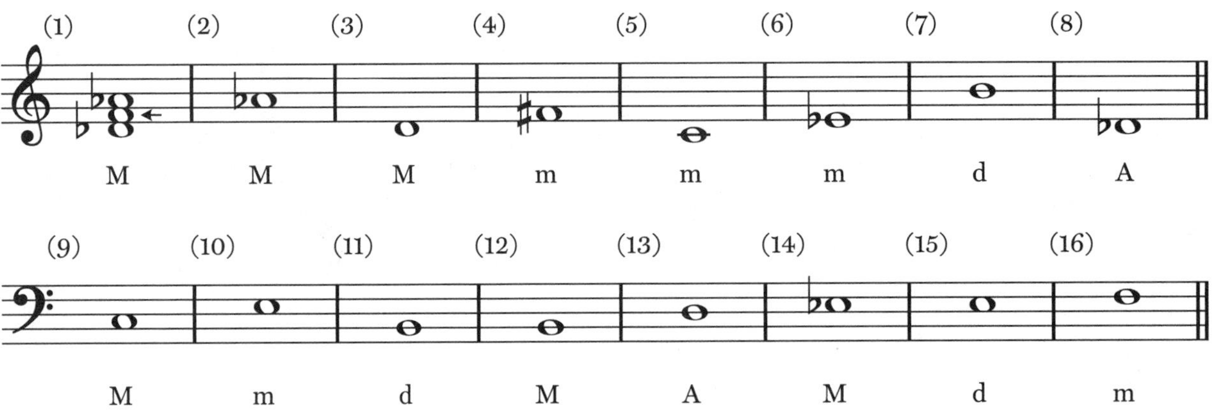

C. Each given pitch is the fifth of a triad.

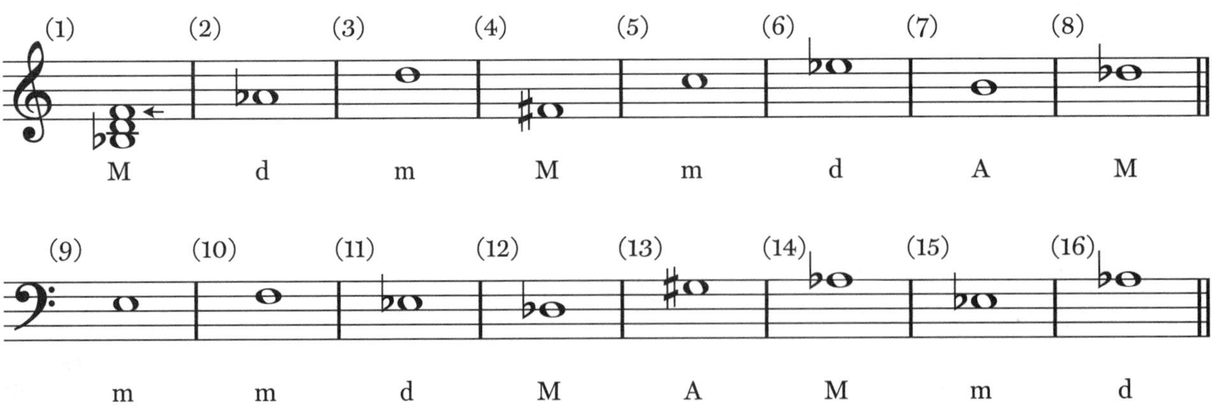

NAME ______________________________

ASSIGNMENT 7.6

I. Writing triads from chord symbols

Write the triads indicated in root position, in whole notes. Include all needed accidentals for the correct triad quality.

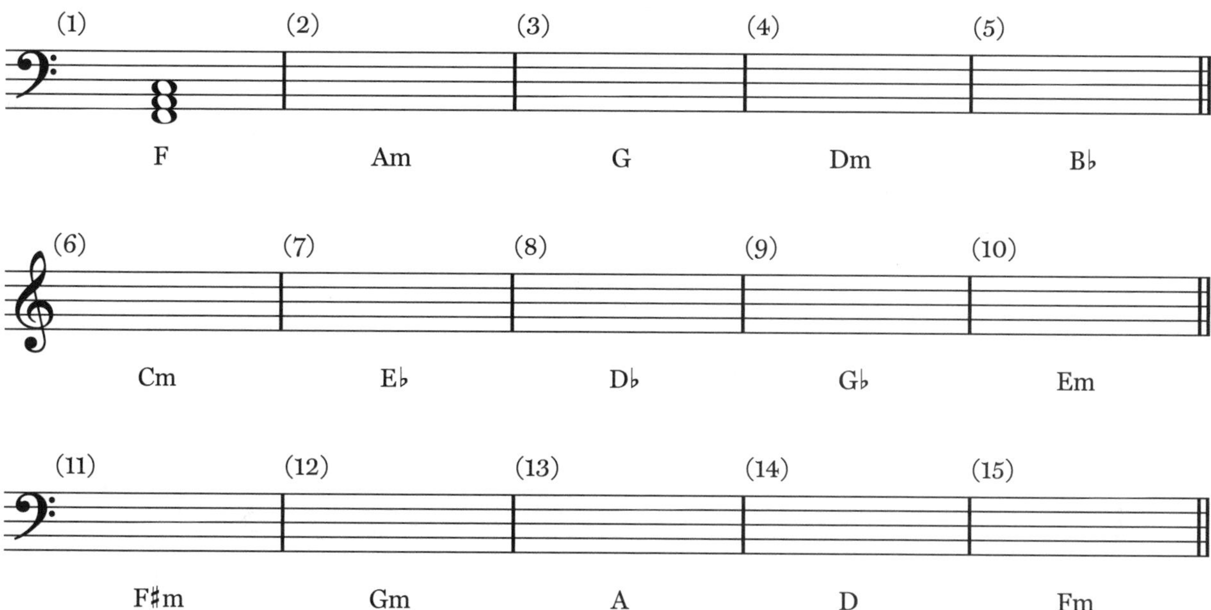

II. Identifying triads

Identify the quality and root of each triad using chord symbols (e.g., Gm, F). Don't specify any inversion.

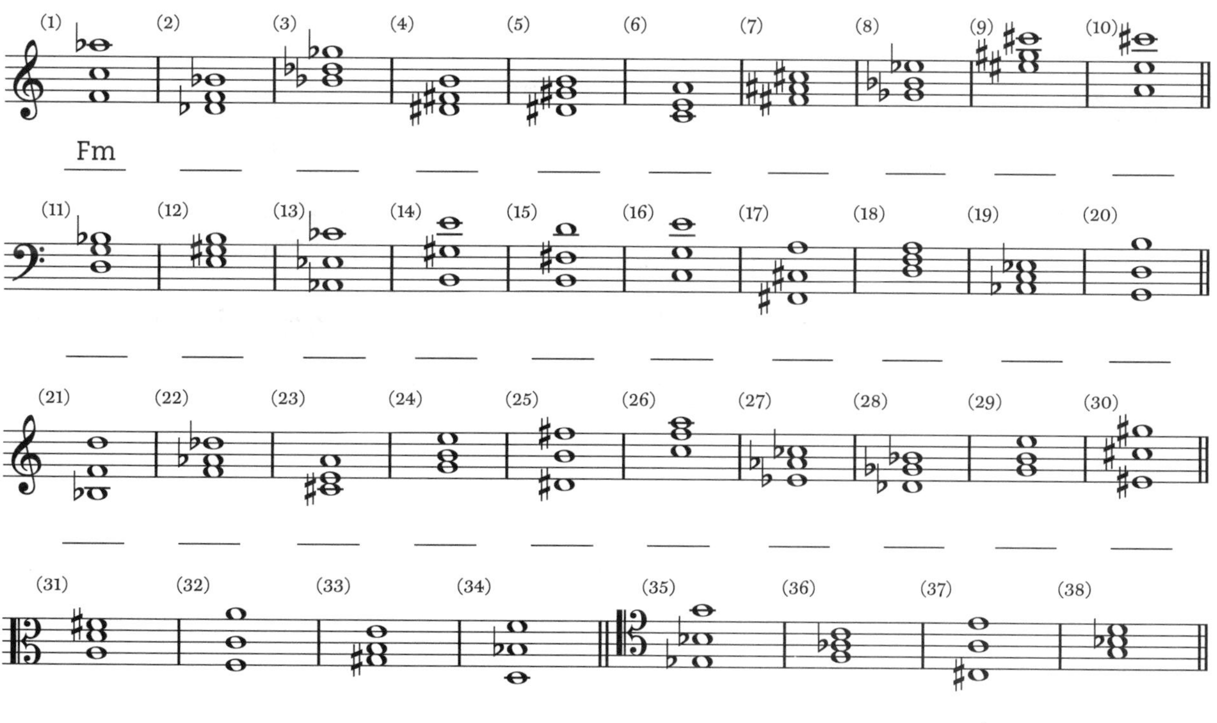

III. Analysis with chord symbols

For each song, examine the notated piano accompaniment to identify the chords used (one chord per measure). Then write the appropriate popular-music chord symbol above the staff in the blanks provided. Use slash notation for any inverted triad. Ignore any circled pitches.

A. Mendes, Harris, and Geiger, "Treat You Better," mm. 45–48

B. Ryan Tedder, "Secrets" (as sung by OneRepublic), mm. 5–8

NAME ____________________

8 Seventh Chords

ASSIGNMENT 8.1

I. Writing seventh chords above a scale

Notate the requested scale in whole notes (ascending only), adding any needed accidentals. Above each note, write a seventh chord with the necessary accidentals for that key. In minor keys, use the leading tone for the chords on $\hat{5}$ and $\hat{7}$. In the first row of blanks, identify the seventh-chord quality as MM7, Mm7, mm7, ø7 (half-diminished), or °7 (fully diminished). In the second row of blanks, write the Roman numeral.

A. F major

Quality:	MM7	mm7	mm7	___	___	___	___
Roman numeral:	I^7	ii^7	iii^7	___	___	___	___

B. A minor

Quality:	___	___	___	___	___	___	___
Roman numeral:	___	___	___	___	___	___	___

C. F♯ minor

Quality:	___	___	___	___	___	___	___
Roman numeral:	___	___	___	___	___	___	___

D. G major

Quality:	___	___	___	___	___	___	___
Roman numeral:	___	___	___	___	___	___	___

II. *Identifying scale-degree seventh chords*

A. Root-position chords

In the first row of blanks, provide a Roman numeral that reflects the correct seventh-chord quality in the given key. In the second row, write the chord quality (e.g., Mm7, ø7).

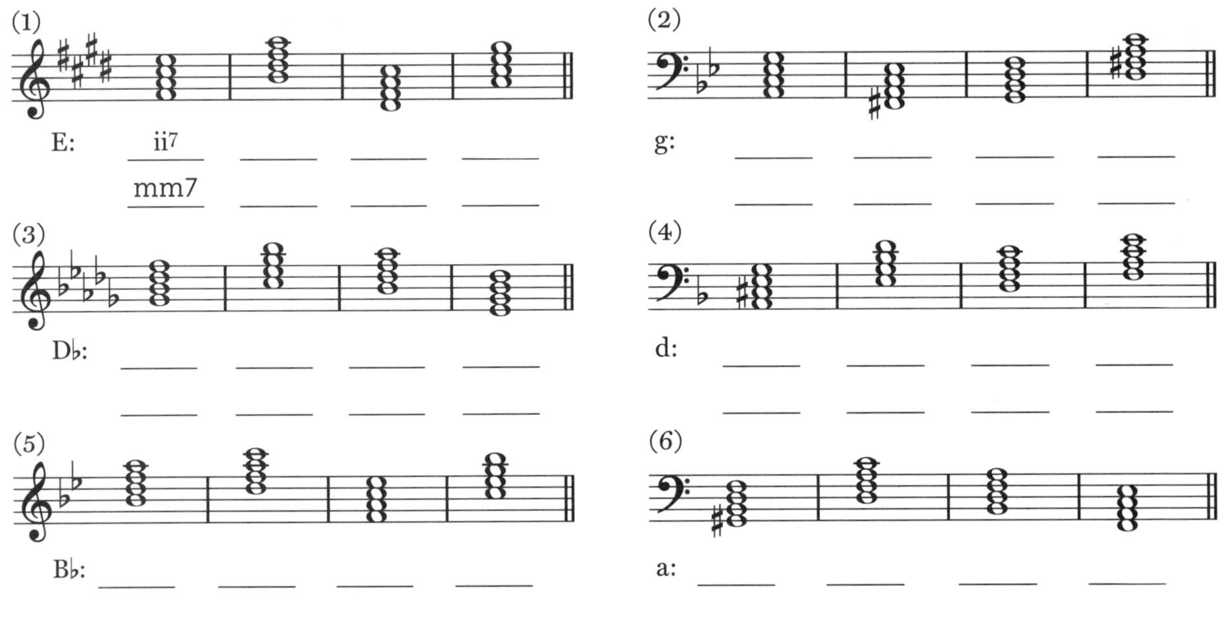

B. Chords in inversion

Provide a Roman numeral and figures $^6_5$, $^4_3$, or $^4_2$ for each given seventh chord.

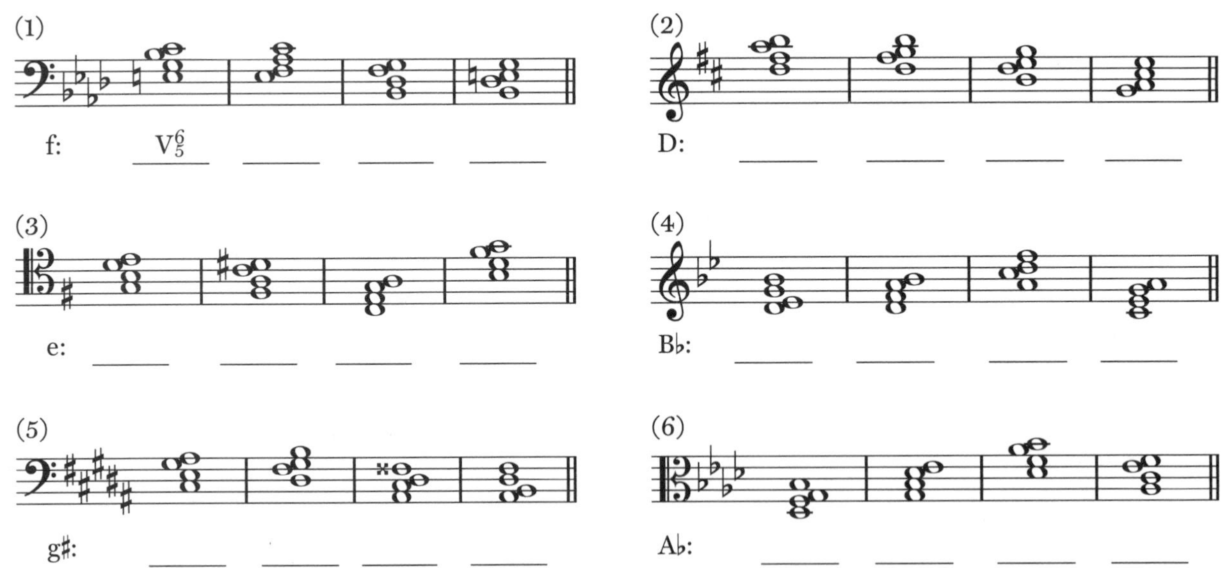

ASSIGNMENT 8.2

I. Writing scale-degree seventh chords from Roman numerals

A. Write each of the following root-position seventh chords. Provide the key signature, and add accidentals to make the correct quality. For minor keys, use the leading tone for the chords on $\hat{5}$ and $\hat{7}$.

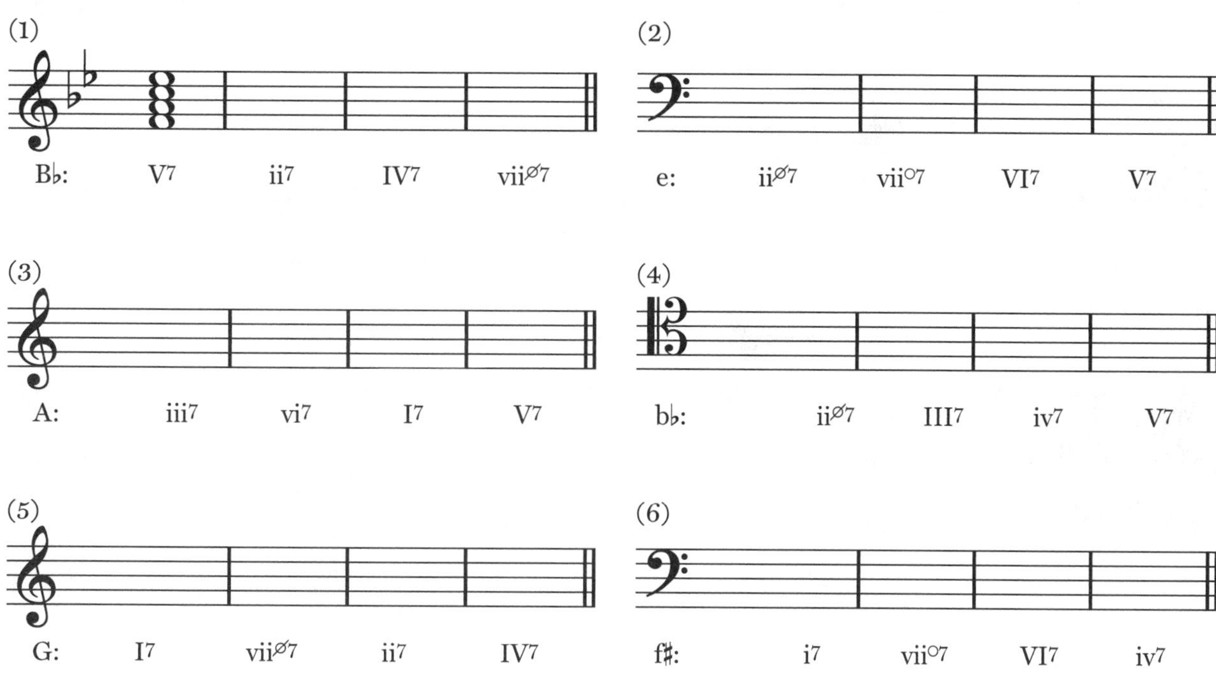

B. Write each seventh chord in the key and inversion specified. Provide the key signature, and add accidentals to make the correct quality. For minor keys, use the leading tone for the chords on $\hat{5}$ and $\hat{7}$.

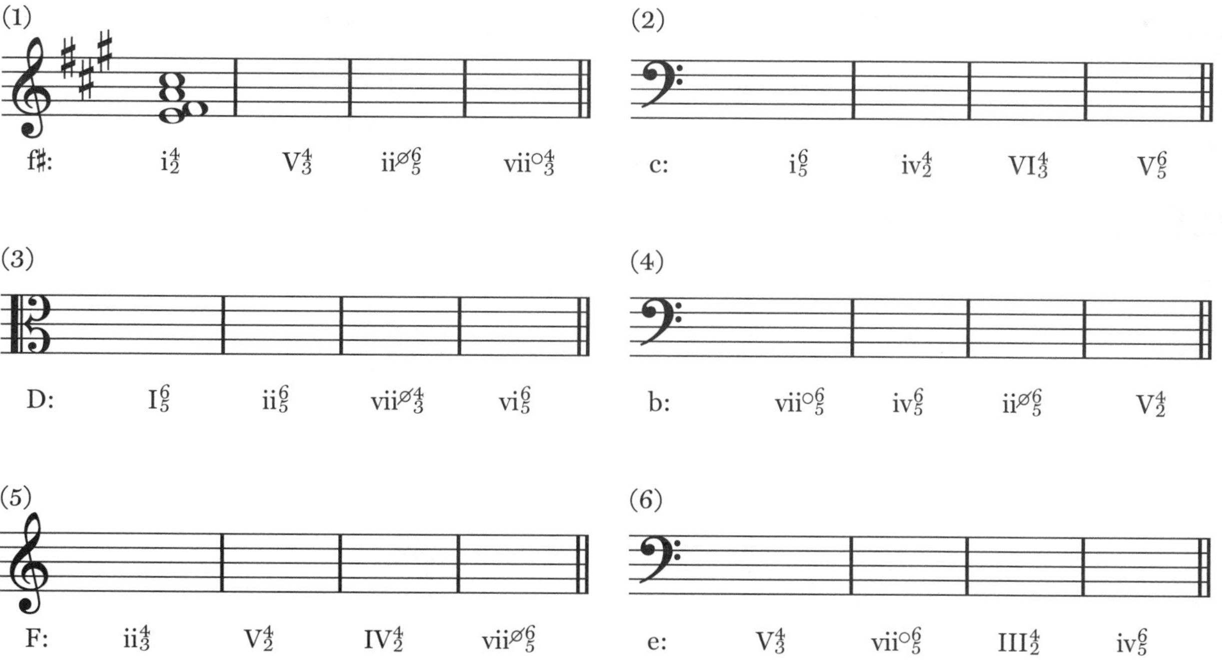

II. Analyzing seventh chords in musical contexts

In the blanks provided, write the chord quality and inversion (e.g., Mm7, $^{ø6}_{5}$, etc.) of each triad or seventh chord. When identifying chord quality, be sure to check the key signature and any accidentals.

A. J. S. Bach, Prelude, from Cello Suite No. 2 in D Minor, mm. 1-8

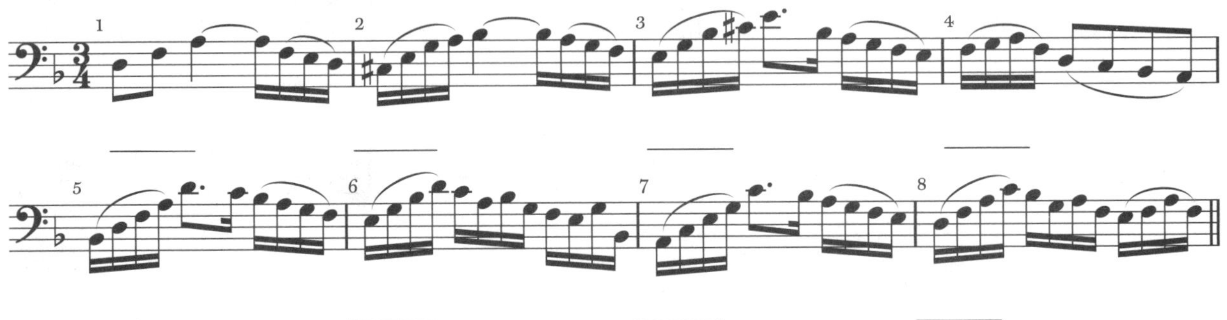

B. Felix Mendelssohn, "Aber der Herr sieht es nicht," from *Elijah*, No. 5, mm. 68-73

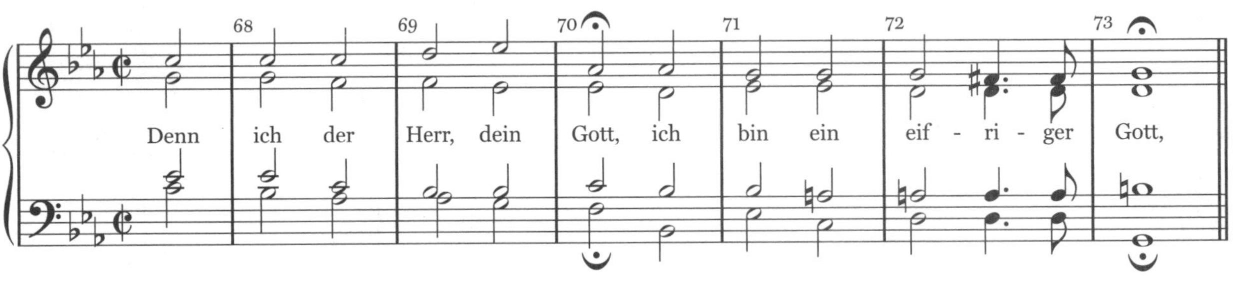

Translation: For I the Lord your God, I am a jealous God.

C. Johannes Brahms, Ballade in G Minor, Op. 118, No. 3, mm. 15-17

The middle voices are rhythmically offset. Circles have been added to help you identify chord tones.

NAME ____________________

ASSIGNMENT 8.3

I. Identifying isolated seventh chords

A. Roman numerals

Write the appropriate Roman numeral and figures for each seventh chord in the given key.

(1)

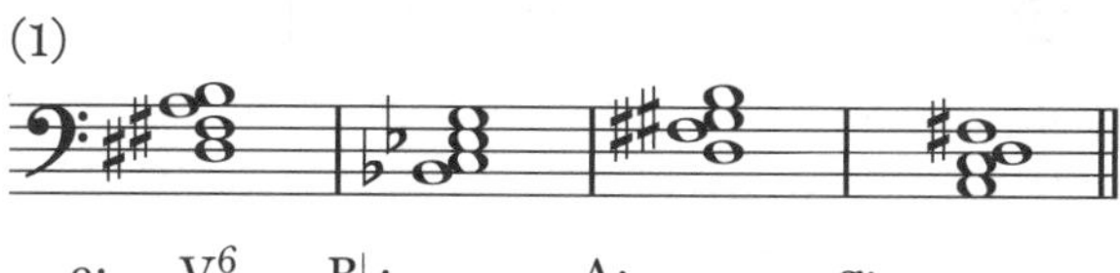

e: V^6_5 B♭: ______ A: ______ g: ______

(2)

d: ______ B♭: ______ d: ______ F: ______

(3)

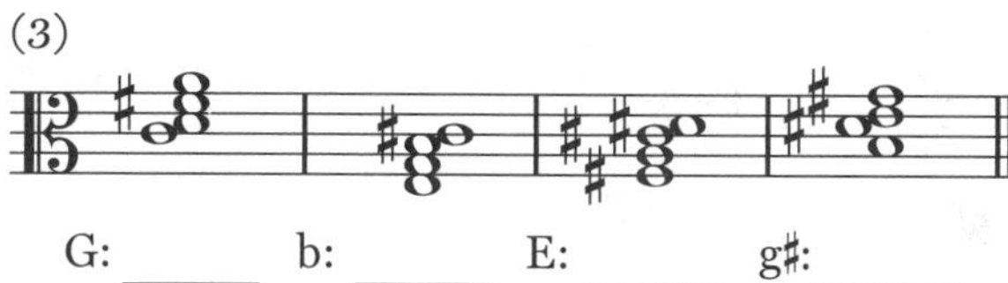

G: ______ b: ______ E: ______ g♯: ______

(4)

c: ______ A♭: ______ f♯: ______ f: ______

(5)

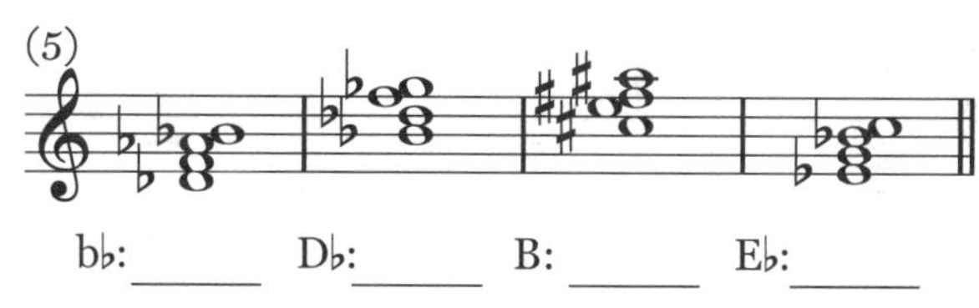

b♭: ______ D♭: ______ B: ______ E♭: ______

(6)

a: ______ D: ______ c♯: ______ G♭: ______

B. Chord quality

Write the chord quality (e.g., mm7, °7) for each seventh chord.

(1)

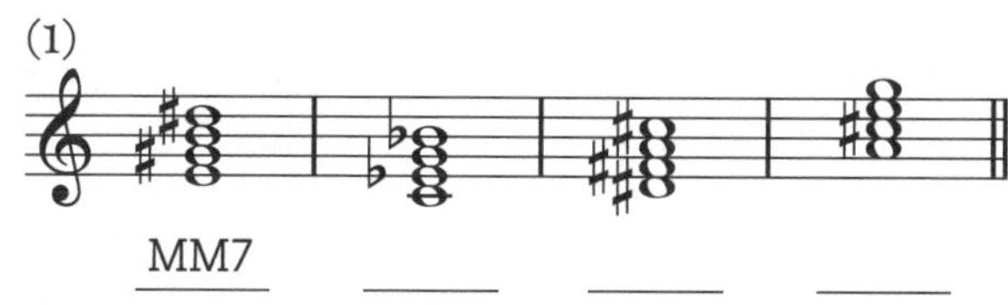

MM7 ______ ______ ______

(2)

______ ______ ______ ______

(3)

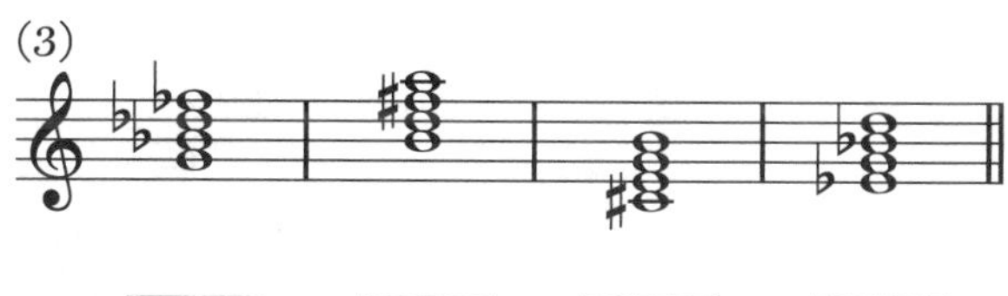

______ ______ ______ ______

(4)

______ ______ ______ ______

(5)

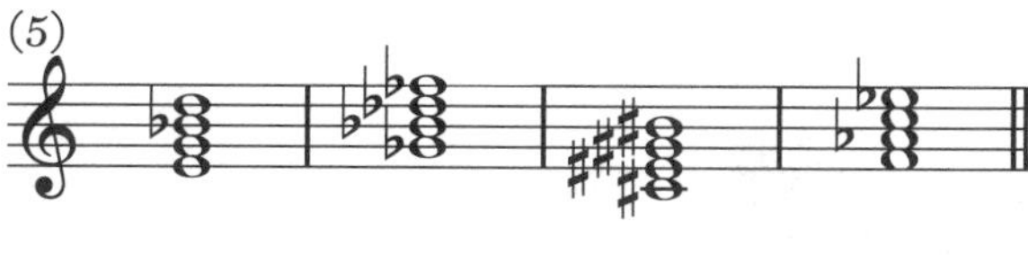

______ ______ ______ ______

(6)

______ ______ ______ ______

II. Writing isolated seventh chords

Write the seventh chords specified, given (A) the key and Roman numeral or (B) the root and chord quality. Spell with accidentals rather than key signatures.

A. Key and Roman numeral given

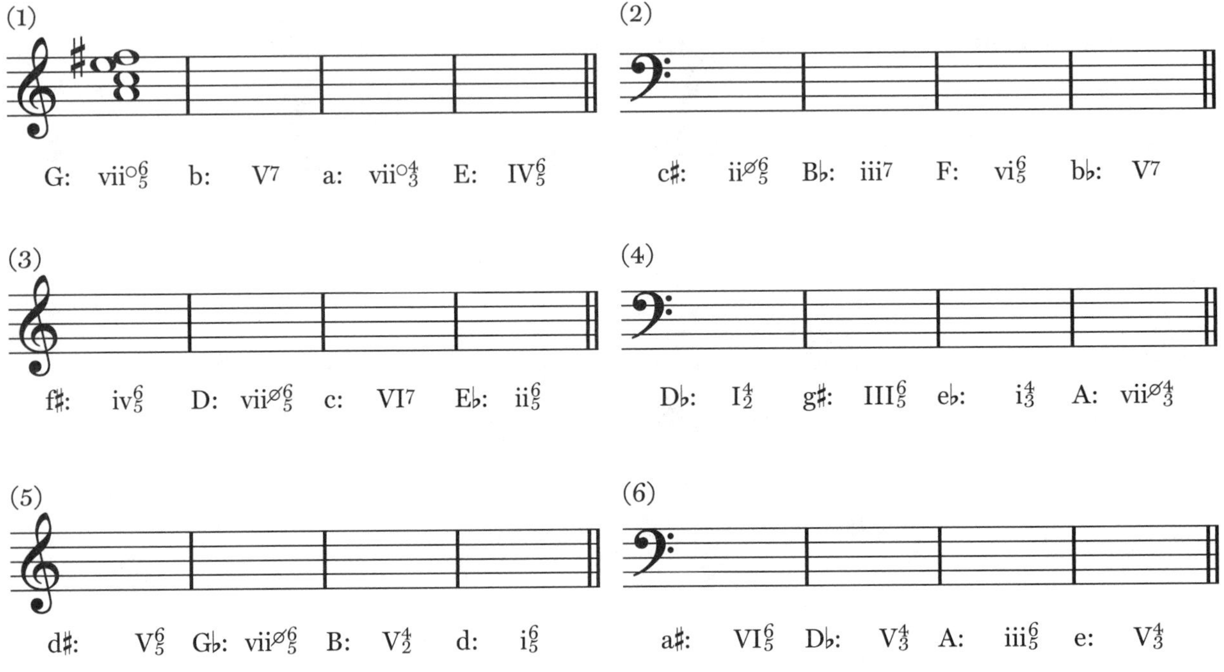

B. Root and chord quality given

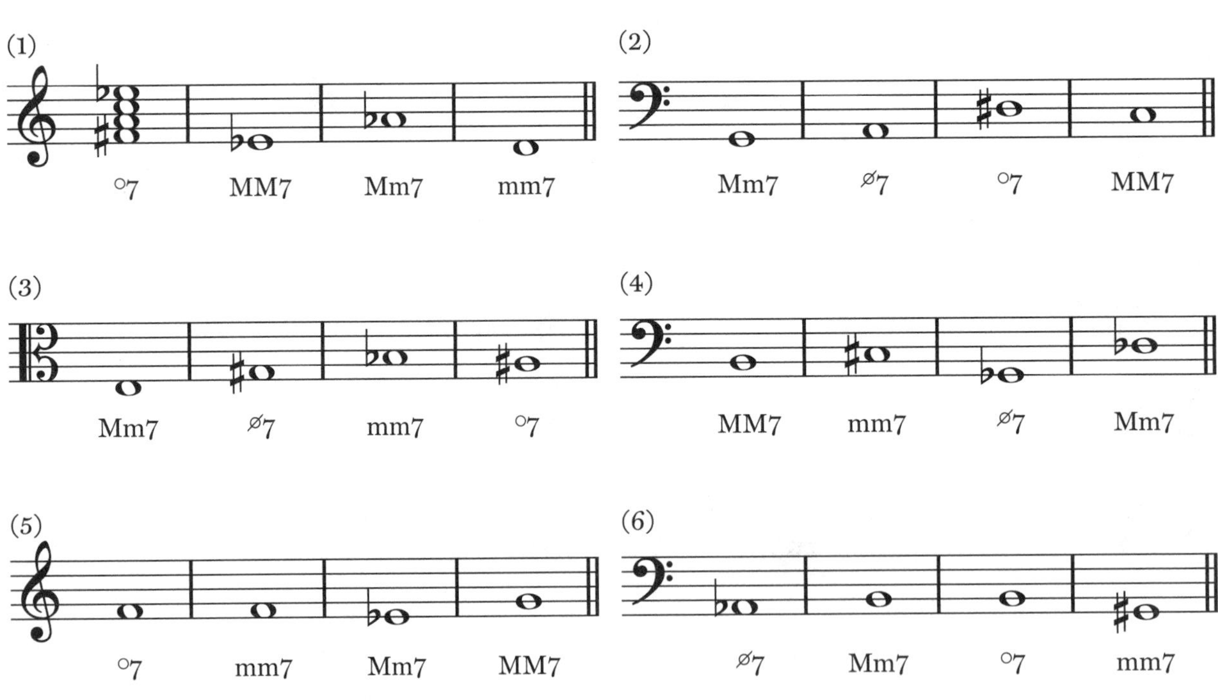

ASSIGNMENT 8.4

I. Writing chords from a lead sheet

"Rich and Rare" (traditional Irish melody), arranged by Joel Phillips

Examine each chord symbol in the following lead sheet. Write the chords on the staff underneath each measure, using dotted-half, half, and quarter notes, in the correct inversion.

II. *Triads and seventh chords from lead-sheet symbols*

Write each chord requested in four parts in keyboard style (in quarter notes)—three parts in the right hand and one part in the left. Include any accidentals needed to make the correct chord quality. If slash notation is used (e.g., F/A), put the proper chord member in the bass. Check that each seventh-chord member is present; for triads, double the bass note.

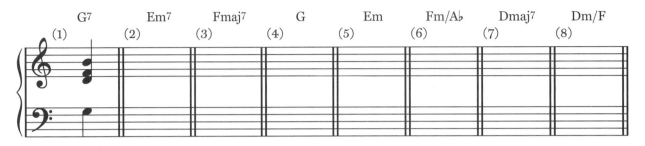

(1)	(2)	(3)	(4)	(5)	(6)	(7)	(8)
G7	Em7	Fmaj7	G	Em	Fm/A♭	Dmaj7	Dm/F

(9)	(10)	(11)	(12)	(13)	(14)	(15)	(16)
A♭7/C	Fm7	Gmaj7	E♭	A	Cm	B♭/D	F

(17)	(18)	(19)	(20)	(21)	(22)	(23)	(24)
A7	Gm7	A♭maj7	C♯m7(♭5)	F♯°7	A♭7/G♭	B♭7	D♯°7

(25)	(26)	(27)	(28)	(29)	(30)	(31)	(32)
B♭7/D	Am7	Cmaj7	Em7(♭5)	A°7	C♯7	B°7	F7/A

NAME ____________________

ASSIGNMENT 8.5

I. Spelling isolated seventh chords

Fill in the other notes of each seventh chord, adding accidentals as needed to make the correct quality. Don't change the given pitch.

A. Each given pitch is the root of a seventh chord.

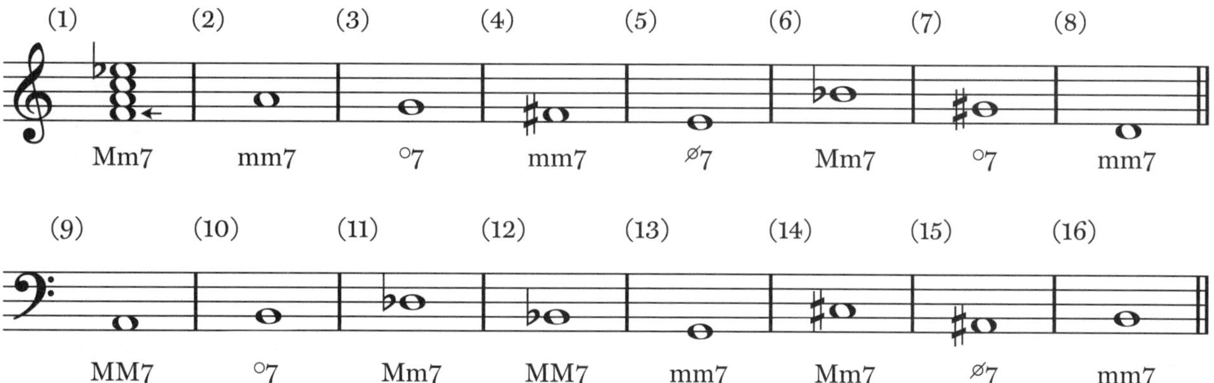

B. Each given pitch is the third of a seventh chord.

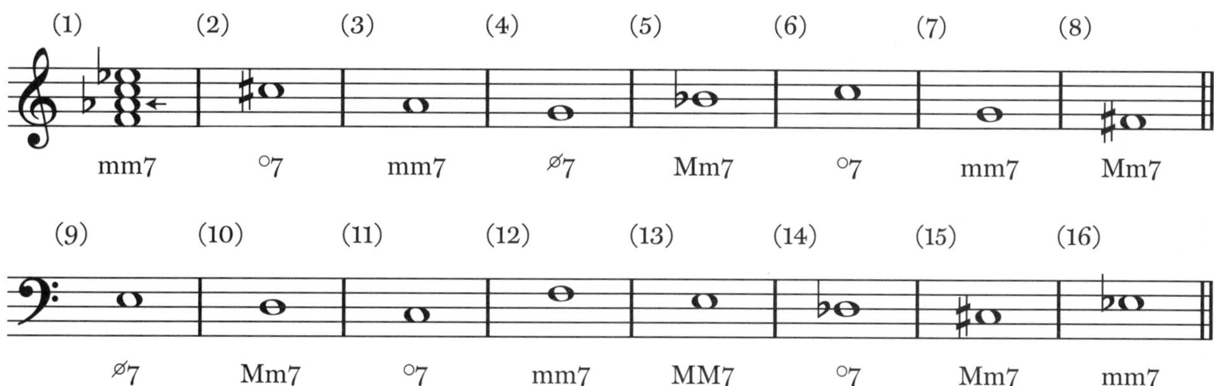

C. Each given pitch is the fifth of a seventh chord.

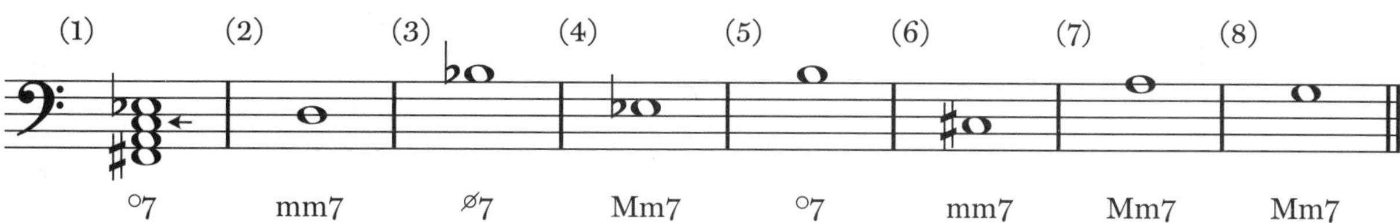

D. Each given pitch is the seventh of a seventh chord.

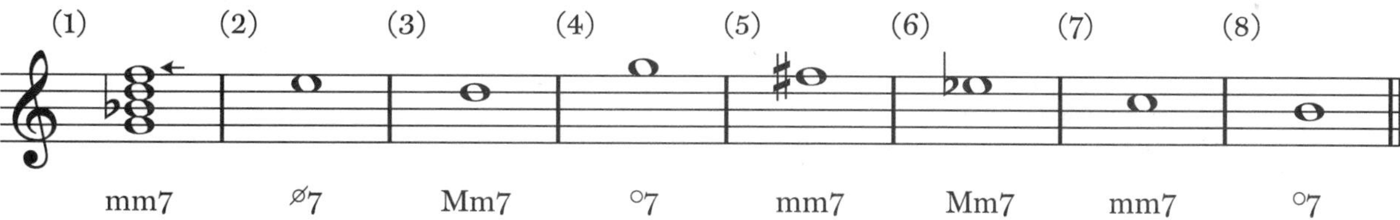

II. Analyzing seventh chords in musical contexts

Johannes Brahms, "Tageweis von einer schönen Frauen," from *28 Deutsche Volkslieder*, mm. 5–8
Identify two chords per measure by writing a chord symbol above the staff and a Roman numeral (with inversion) in the blanks provided. Ignore any circled notes.

Translation: My heart is raging for your charms, don't drive me to despair my lady

III. Instrumentation and score reading

Write the Roman numerals below the staff for measures 13–14, when the horn first enters.
What part of the first chord does the horn play in measure 13? Circle one: root third fifth

Beethoven, Symphony No. 6, mvt. 1, mm. 8–16

NAME ______________________________

ASSIGNMENT 8.6

I. Analysis: Chord quality and Roman numerals

A. Identify the chord quality of the circled chords in the blanks below the staff.

Marc Shaiman and Scott Wittman, "Good Morning Baltimore," from *Hairspray*, mm. 5–12 (ignore Gs in m. 12)

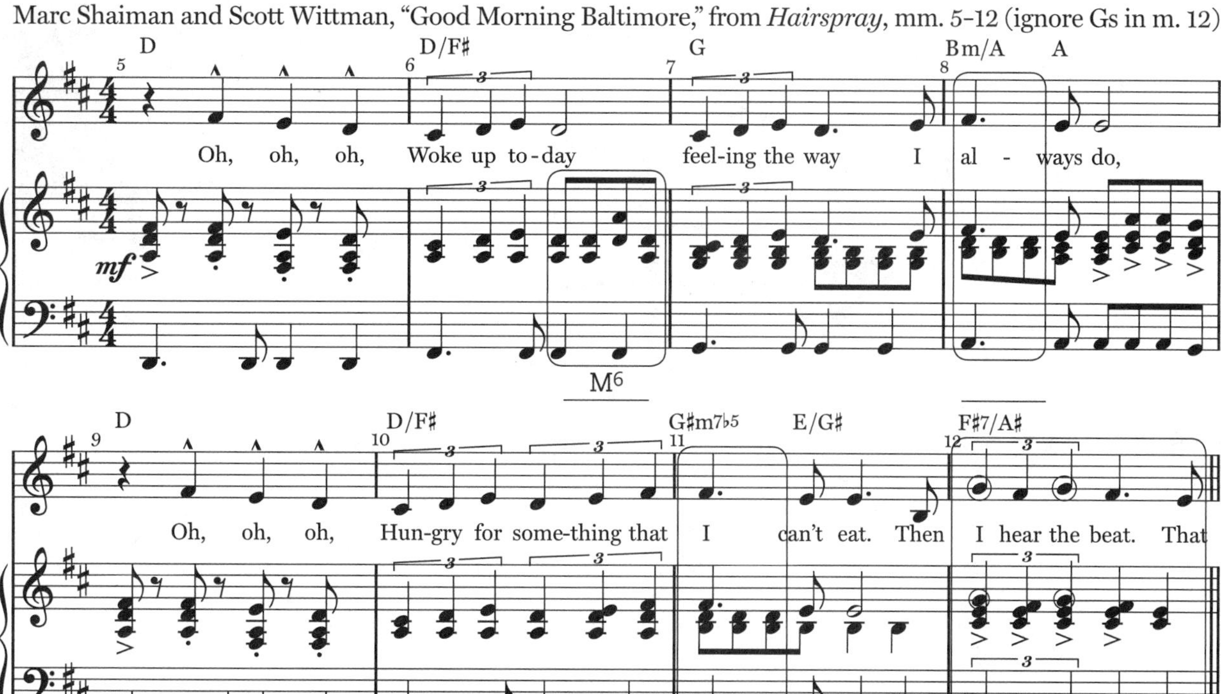

B. In the blanks provided, identify the harmonies by writing chord symbols above the staff and Roman numerals with figures below the staff. Ignore measure 40.

Frédéric Chopin, Étude, Op. 10, No. 1, mm. 39–44

II. Instrumentation and score reading

Listen to the recording of this excerpt, paying attention to the instruments that are playing or doubling the melody. Consult Appendix 5 in your textbook for the exact transposition of each instrument.

Gustav Holst, Second Suite in F for Military Band, mvt. 4, mm. 41–44

For each of the following pairs of instruments, circle the interval at which the melody is doubled in measures 42–44.

A. The piccolo and oboe are doubled in

thirds sixths octaves double octaves

B. The oboe and E♭ clarinet are doubled in

unison thirds sixths octaves

C. The oboe and 1st B♭ clarinet are doubled in

unison thirds sixths octaves

D. The flute and 1st B♭ clarinet are doubled in

unison thirds sixths octaves

E. The oboe and 2nd B♭ clarinet are doubled in

unison thirds sixths octaves

NAME ______________________________

9 Connecting Intervals in Note-to-Note Counterpoint

Common Counterpoint Errors Checklist

Keep this page in your notebook or workbook to use for Assignment 9.4 and to check your work for errors. Your teacher may also identify errors in your part writing with the letters given here.

Opening:

A. Opening harmonic interval is not PU, P8, or P5.
B. Opening does not establish the tonic harmony.

Closing:

C. Closing harmonic interval is not P8 or PU.
D. Incorrect interval approaching the close (must be 6-8, 10-8, or 3-U) or a missing leading tone.
E. Leading tone does not resolve to tonic.

Harmonic intervals:

F. Parallel octaves or contrary octaves (includes P8-PU, PU-P8, and PU-PU).
G. Parallel fifths or contrary fifths.
H. Too many parallel imperfect consonances (3 or 6).
I. Too many perfect consonances.
J. Dissonant interval not allowed in strict species.

Soprano or bass line:

K. Melodic line is static: repeats notes or circles around one note.
L. Leap or skip is not set with a step in the other part.
M. Melodic leap not preceded and followed by stepwise contrary motion.
N. Dissonant melodic interval (e.g., leap of m7, M7, d5, A4, or A2).
O. Leap or skip in the upper part into an octave or a fifth (may also create hidden octaves or fifths).
P. Too little contrary motion.
Q. Counterpoint line lacks a single high (or low) point.

Traditional *Cantus Firmus* Lines

Use these *cantus* lines for practice in class and as assigned by your teacher for additional homework for Chapters 9 and 10. Each can serve as the upper or lower part.

Cantus firmus 1 (Fux, adapted)

Cantus firmus 2 (Jeppesen)

Cantus firmus 3 (Schenker)

Cantus firmus 4 (Fux)

Cantus firmus 5 (Kirnberger)

Cantus firmus 6 (Kirnberger)

Cantus firmus 7 (Fux)

Try writing your own *cantus firmus*, starting on $\hat{1}$ and ending with $\hat{2}$–$\hat{1}$. Make a pleasing contour, using mostly steps, but also include some skips or one leap for interest and to make the *cantus* more challenging for those composing a counterpoint.

NAME ____________________

ASSIGNMENT 9.1

I. Melodic and harmonic intervals in counterpoint

In each of the following completed first-species settings:

- Label the harmonic intervals between the staves.
- Mark with a bracket any skip or leap in the counterpoint or *cantus*.

In the chart below the counterpoint:

- Indicate where (measure numbers) and in which part each skip and leap appears.
- Indicate whether there is a step, skip, leap, or repeated pitch in the other part at that point.
- Label the type of motion between parts at that point.

A. *Cantus firmus* 5 (Kirnberger) in a first-species setting

CF5
U
CPT

MEASURES	PART	SKIP OR LEAP?	SKIP/STEP/LEAP IN OTHER PART?	TYPE OF MOTION
1–2	*cantus*	leap	step	contrary

B. *Cantus firmus* 5 (Kirnberger) in another first-species setting

CF5
CPT

MEASURES	PART	SKIP OR LEAP?	SKIP/STEP/LEAP IN OTHER PART?	TYPE OF MOTION

C. *Cantus firmus* 5 (Kirnberger) in a first-species setting

1 2 3 4 5 6 7 8 9

CPT

CF5

MEASURES	PART	SKIP OR LEAP?	SKIP/STEP/LEAP IN OTHER PART?	TYPE OF MOTION

II. Evaluating Counterpoint

Answer the following questions about the three *cantus* settings provided in part I, or be prepared to discuss them in class.

A. What challenges are presented by the first half of the *cantus*? What about the second half? What considerations are important to keep in mind in setting this *cantus*?

B. Listen carefully to each setting. Name at least two strengths and two weaknesses of each. Which do you think is the best setting? Explain.

C. What are other ways this *cantus* may be set? Be prepared to discuss other options for setting notes 1–4 and 5–9.

ASSIGNMENT 9.2

I. Opening a counterpoint

Set each of the following *cantus firmus* openings (the first four notes) in two different ways. Write in the harmonic interval numbers, and label any skips or leaps. If you like, use the optional tables to identify letter names of the possible consonant intervals. At the beginning of A, for example, the consonances below the first note C4 are C (8), A (3), F (5), and E (6), shown in the column below that note; since this first note should be set with an octave, C (bold) has been chosen. You may eliminate other potential intervals as you make selections, by marking any that would create parallel octaves or fifths; also cross out any d5s.

A. *Cantus* as upper part

(1) CF5

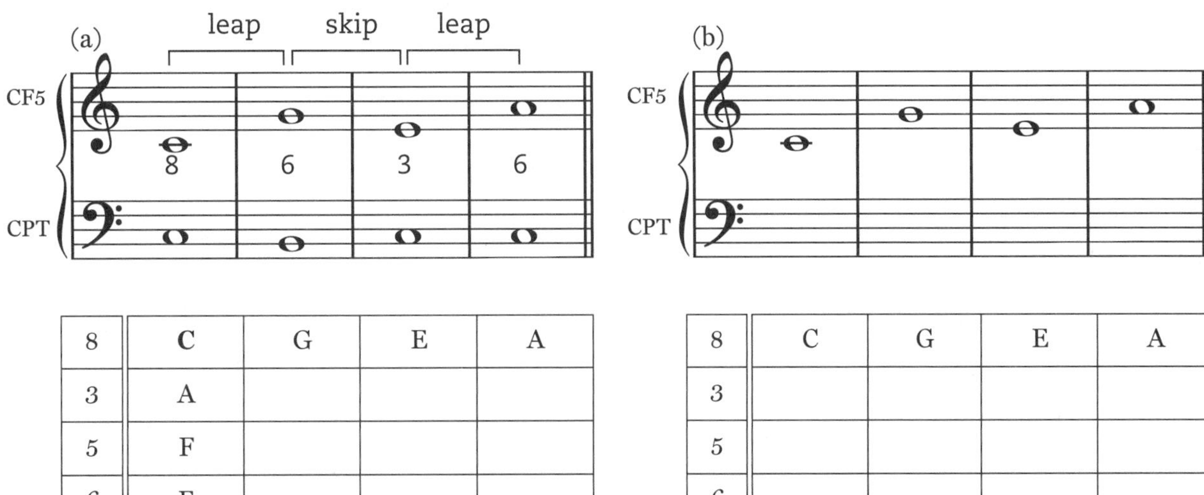

(a)

8	**C**	G	E	A
3	A			
5	F			
6	E			

(b)

8	C	G	E	A
3				
5				
6				

(2) CF6

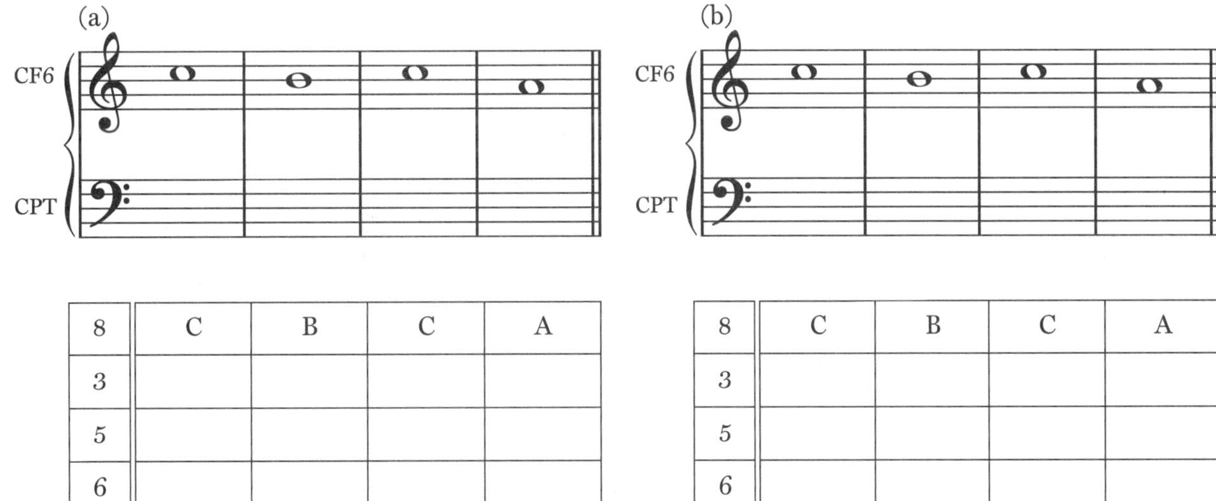

(a)

8	C	B	C	A
3				
5				
6				

(b)

8	C	B	C	A
3				
5				
6				

(3) CF7

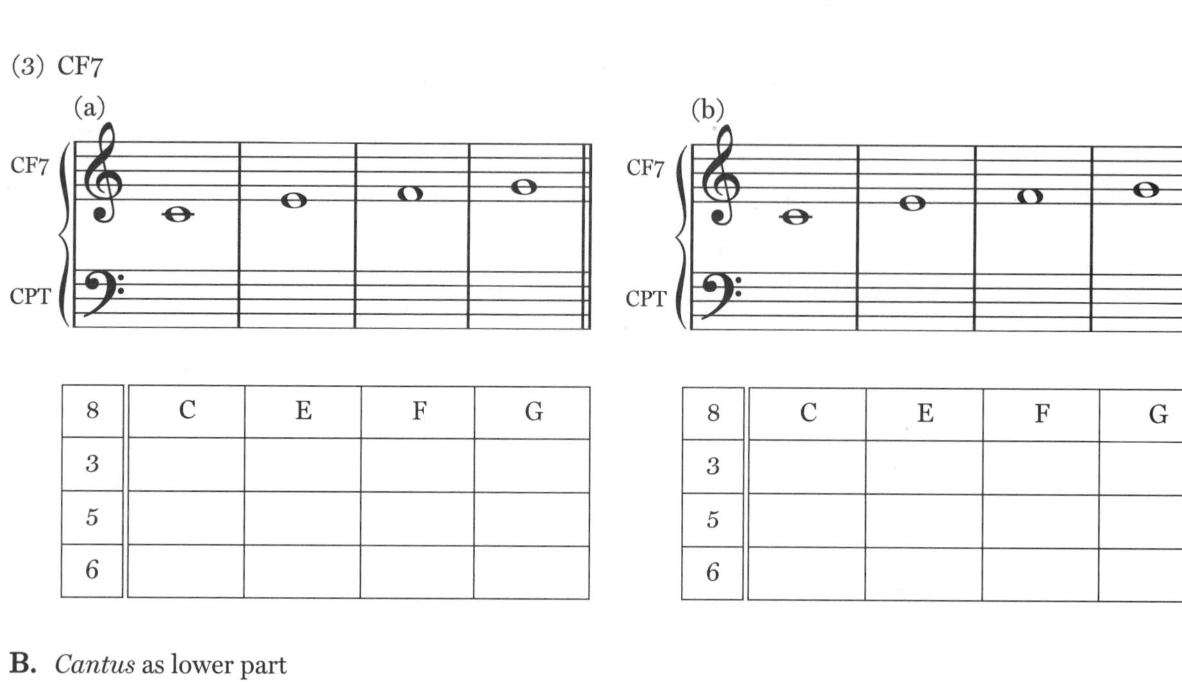

8	C	E	F	G
3				
5				
6				

8	C	E	F	G
3				
5				
6				

B. *Cantus* as lower part

(1) CF5

6				
5				
3				
8	C	G	E	A

6				
5				
3				
8	C	G	E	A

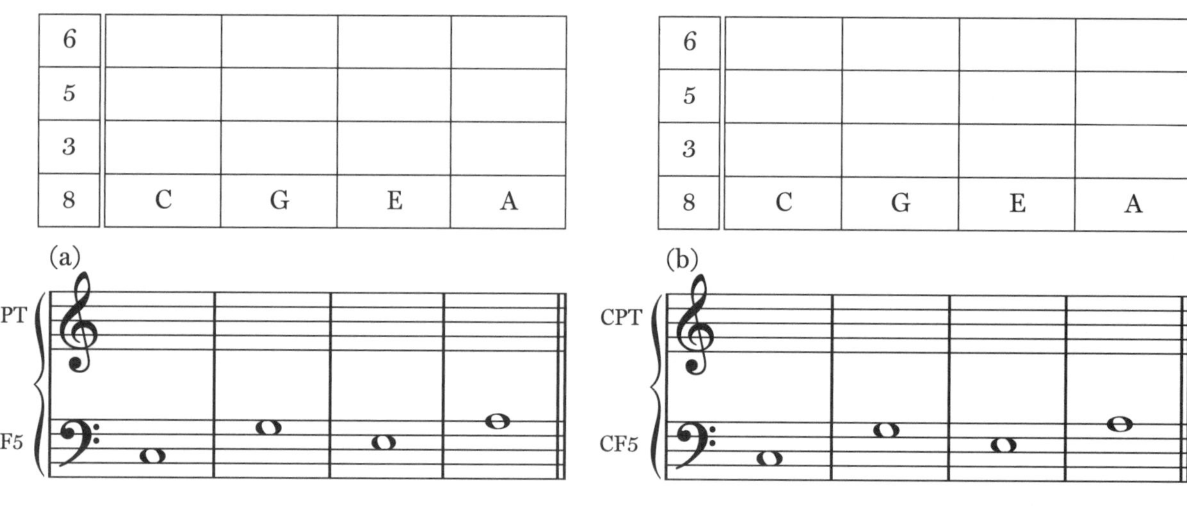

(2) CF6

6				
5				
3				
8	C	B	C	A

6				
5				
3				
8	C	B	C	A

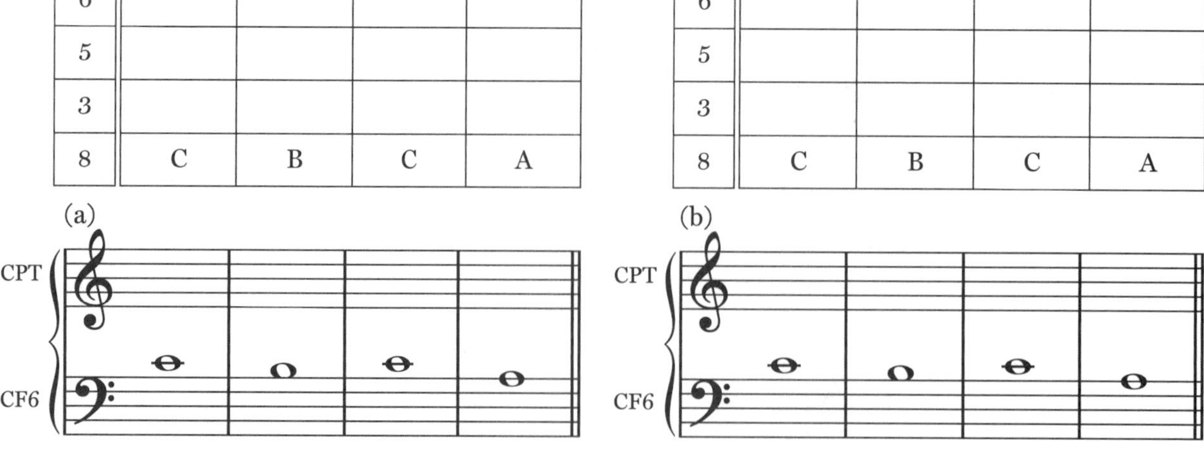

ASSIGNMENT 9.3

I. Closing a counterpoint

Set each of the following *cantus firmus* closings (last four notes) in two different ways. Write in the harmonic interval numbers, and label any skips or leaps in the *cantus firmus*.

A. *Cantus* as upper part

(1) CF1

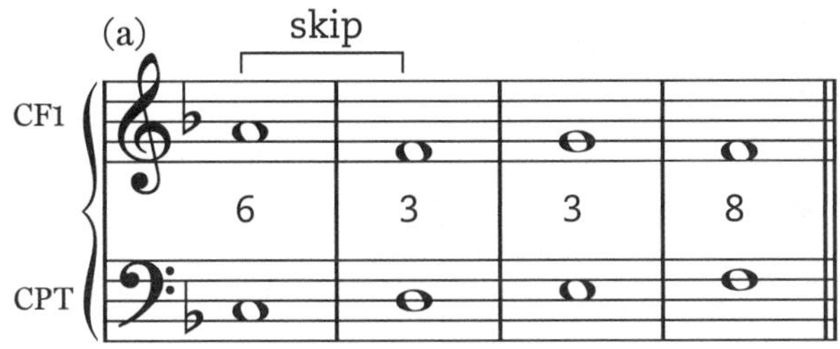

(b)

CF1

CPT

8	A	F	G	F
3	F			
5	D			
6	C			

8	A	F	G	F
3				
5				
6				

(2) CF3

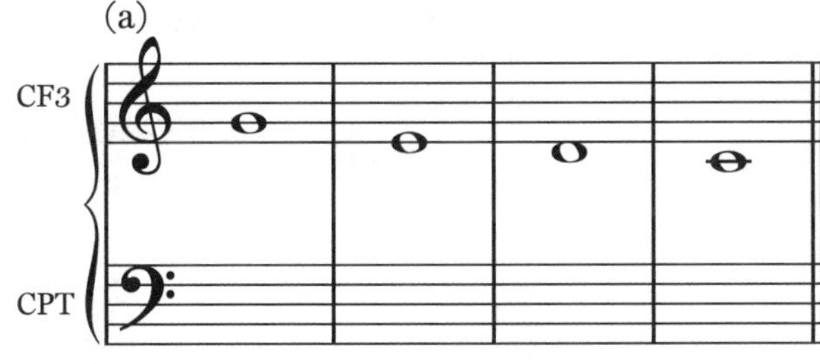

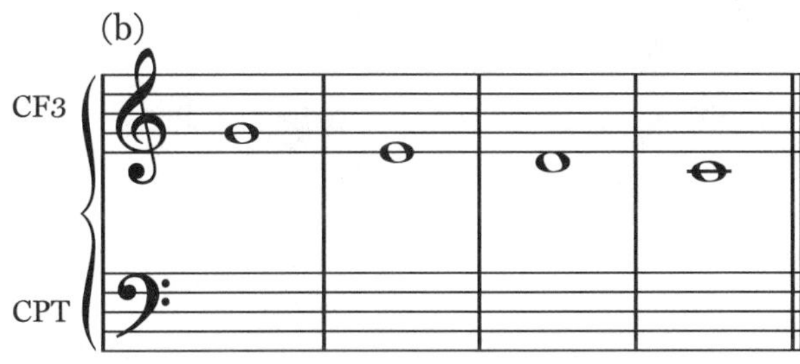

8	G	E	D	C
3				
5				
6				

8	G	E	D	C
3				
5				
6				

(3) CF2 (Remember to use the leading tone in the approach to the cadence in minor counterpoint.)

(a)

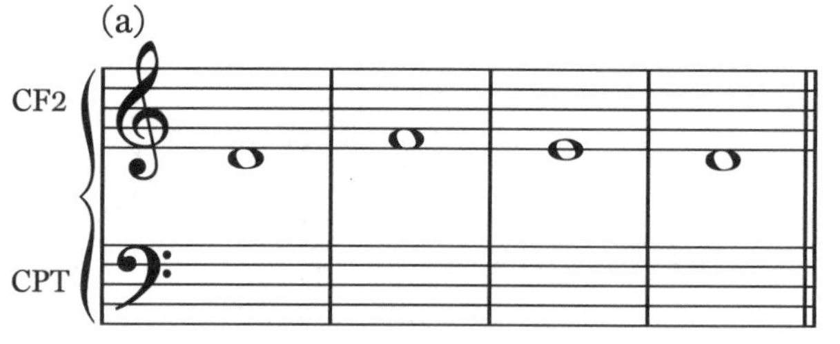

(b)

CF2

CPT

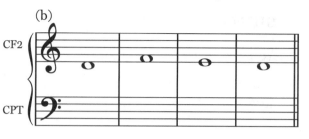

8	D	F	E	D
3				
5				
6				

8	D	F	E	D
3				
5				
6				

B. *Cantus* as lower part

(1) CF1

6				
5				
3				
8	A	F	G	F

6				
5				
3				
8	A	F	G	F

(a)

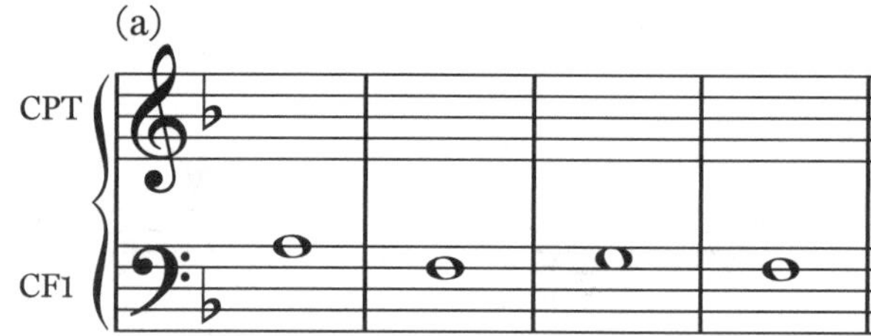

(b)

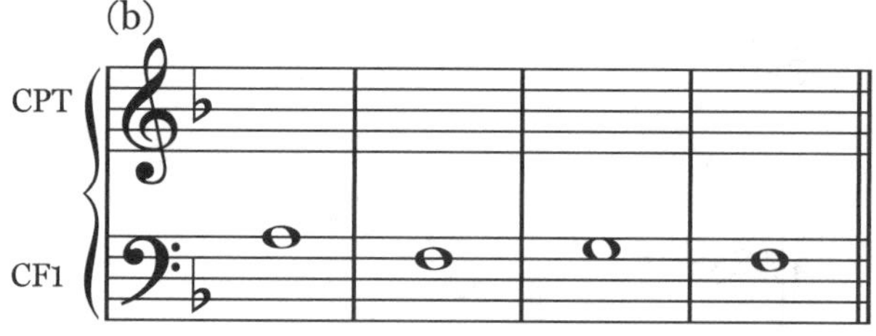

(2) CF3

6				
5				
3				
8	G	E	D	C

6				
5				
3				
8	G	E	D	C

(a)

(b)

CPT

CF3

NAME ____________________

ASSIGNMENT 9.4

I. Evaluating strict counterpoint

Identify the errors in the following settings. First write the harmonic intervals between the staves, then examine the counterpoint. Circle each mistake, list the measures and voice part where the mistake occurs, then label it in the blank boxes with a letter code from the Errors Checklist on page 95. There may be more than one mistake in a location.

A. Find seven errors in six locations.

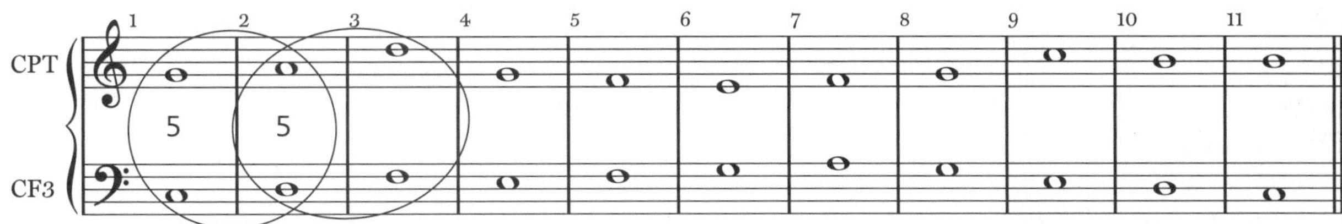

	MEASURE(S)	ERROR CODE(S)	PART (CPT, CF, BOTH)
1	1–2	G	both
2	2–3	L, M	both
3			
4			
5			
6			

B. Find three errors in specific locations and one overall.

1 2 3 4 5 6 7 8 9

CPT

8

CF2

(transposed)

	MEASURE(S)	ERROR CODE(S)	PART (CPT, CF, BOTH)
1			
2			
3			

Error overall: ________

C. Find eight errors in six locations and one overall.

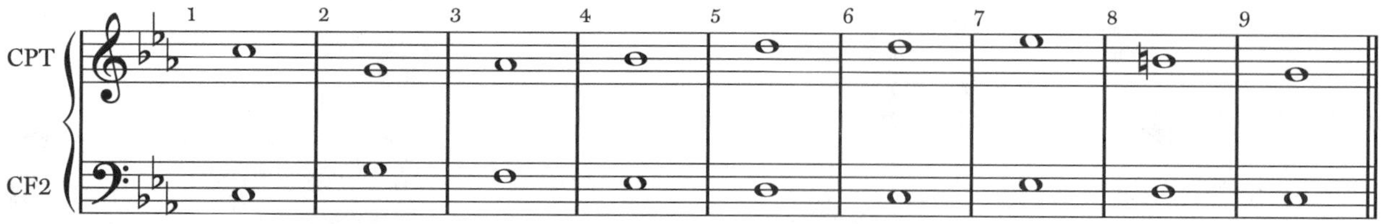

CPT

CF2 (transposed)

	MEASURE(S)	ERROR CODE(S)	PART (CPT, CF, BOTH)
1			
2			
3			

	MEASURE(S)	ERROR CODE(S)	PART (CPT, CF, BOTH)
4			
5			
6			

Error overall: ________

D. Find three errors in two locations and two overall.

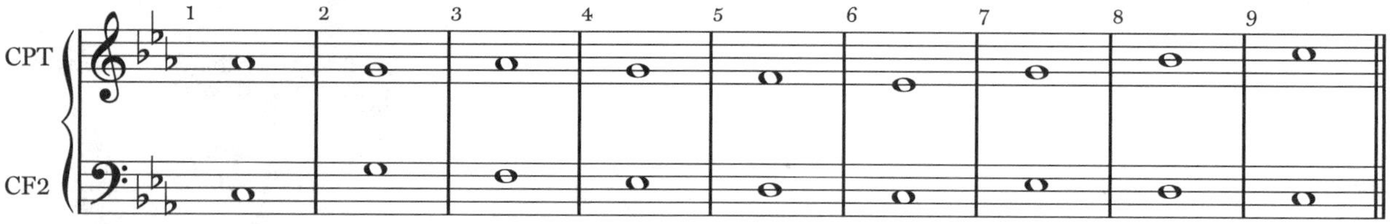

CPT

CF2 (transposed)

	MEASURE(S)	ERROR CODE(S)	PART (CPT, CF, BOTH)
1			
2			

Errors overall: ________

E. Find three errors in the opening (three locations), four in the closing (three locations), and one overall. Both voices are free counterpoint (no *cantus*); indicate upper or lower part or both.

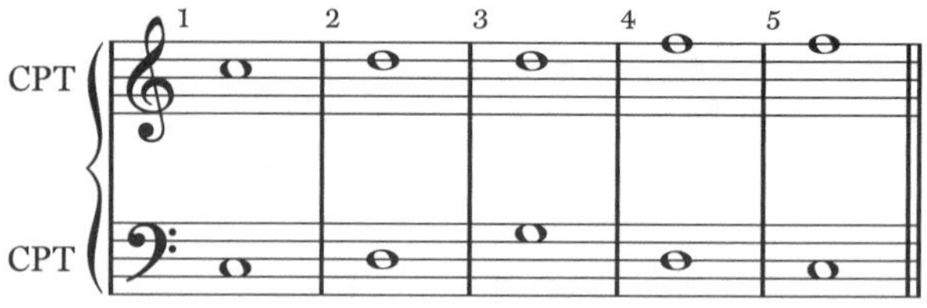

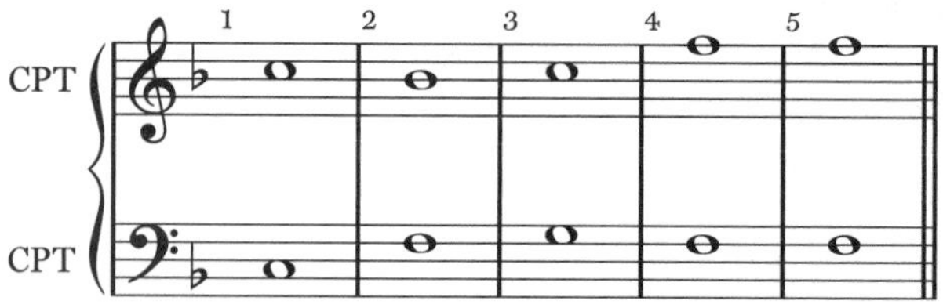

CPT

CPT

CPT

CPT

Opening:

	MEASURE(S)	ERROR CODE(S)	PART (CPT, CF, BOTH)
1			
2			
3			

Closing:

	MEASURE(S)	ERROR CODE(S)	PART (CPT, CF, BOTH)
1			
2			
3			

Error overall: ________

ASSIGNMENT 9.5

I. Writing a note-to-note counterpoint

Write a note-to-note counterpoint for each given *cantus firmus* in strict style, in whole notes. Write the harmonic interval numbers between the staves, and indicate above the CPT line if the motion between the parts is contrary (C), similar (S), oblique (O), or parallel (P). If it helps, fill in the optional table with letter names of the possible consonant pitches.

A. Above a given line

(1)

6	A♭								
5	G								
3	E♭								
8	C								

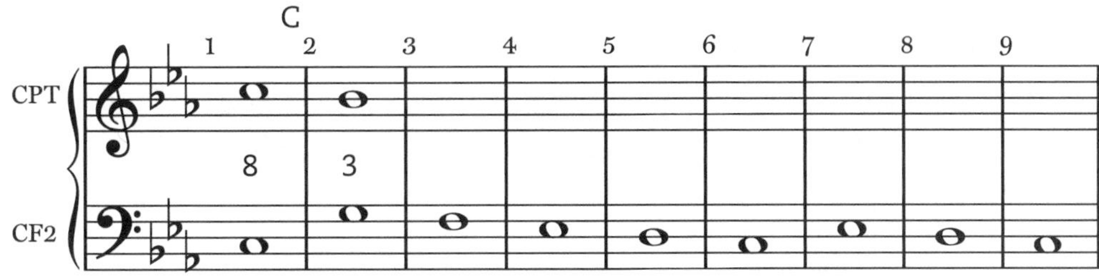

(transposed)

(2)

6											
5											
3											
8											

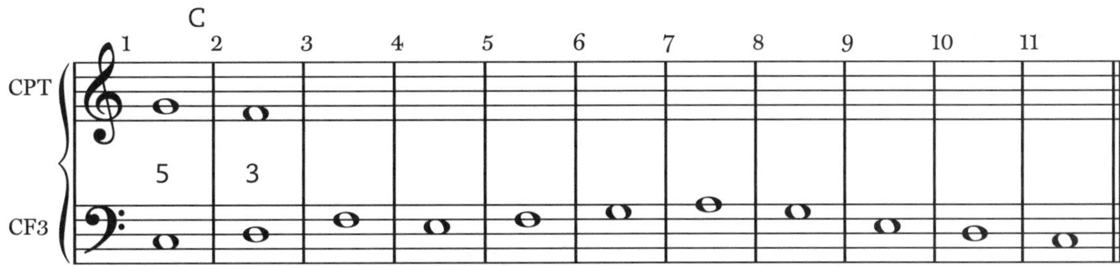

B. Below a given line

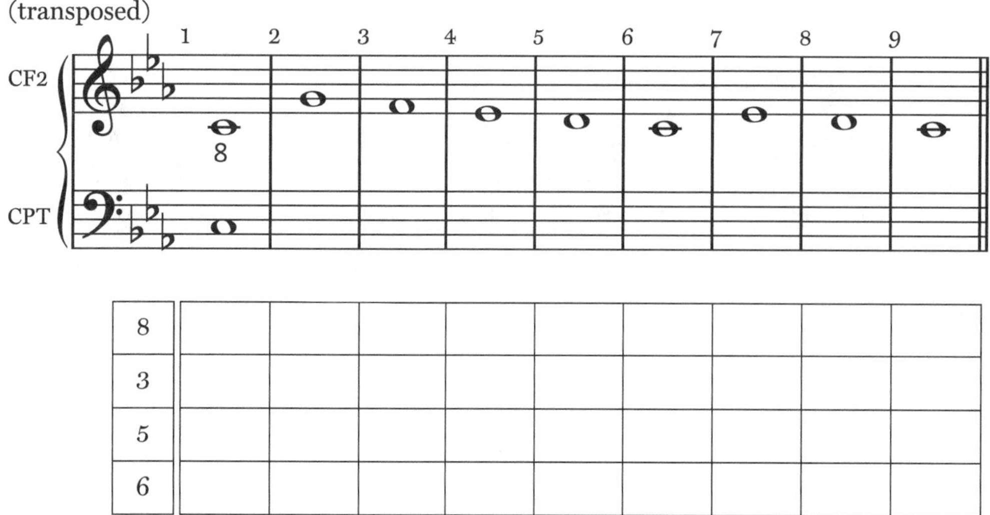

II. Analysis

William Byrd, "Ave verum corpus," mm. 9–15 (soprano and bass)

In the excerpt below, Byrd writes note-to-note counterpoint, though he uses a variety of rhythmic durations (not uniform whole notes, as in first species).

A. Analyze the intervals between the staves.

Translation: Who truly suffered, sacrificed on the cross for mankind:

B. In a few sentences, describe ways in which this passage differs from strict species (other than by its rhythm).

ASSIGNMENT 9.6

I. Writing a note-to-note counterpoint

Write a note-to-note counterpoint for each of the given *cantus firmus* lines in strict style, with whole notes. Write the harmonic interval numbers between the staves, and indicate above the CPT line if the motion between the parts is contrary (C), similar (S), oblique (O), or parallel (P). If it helps, fill in the optional table with letter names of consonant pitches.

A. Above a given line

6												
5												
3												
8												

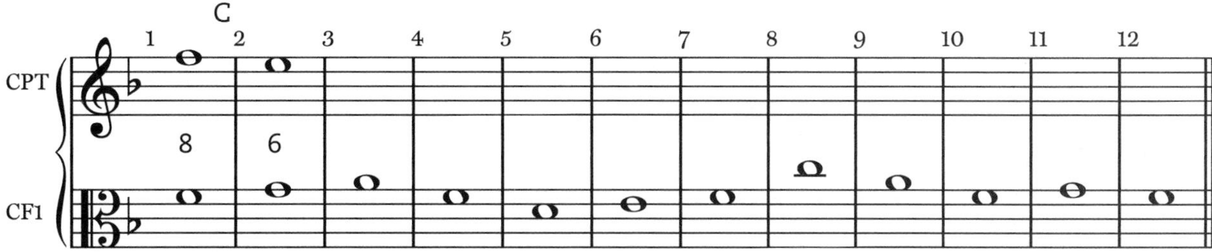

B. Below a given line

(1)

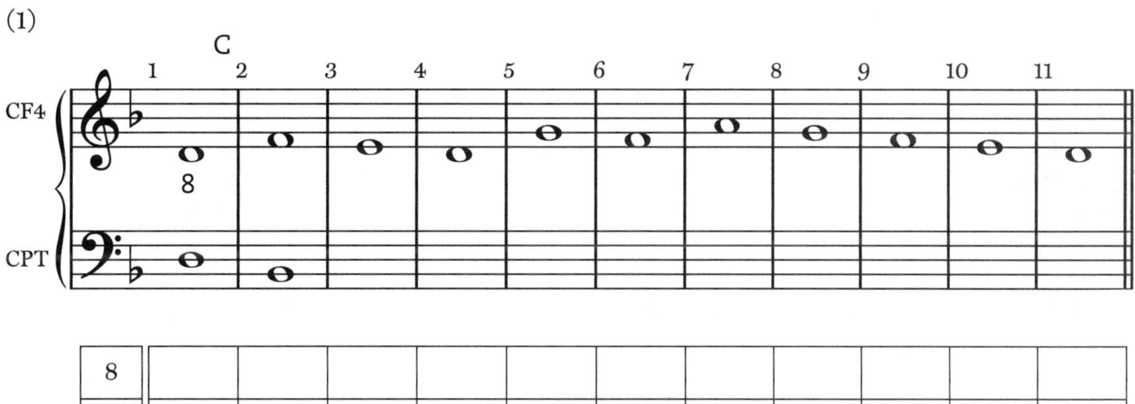

8											
3											
5											
6											

(2)

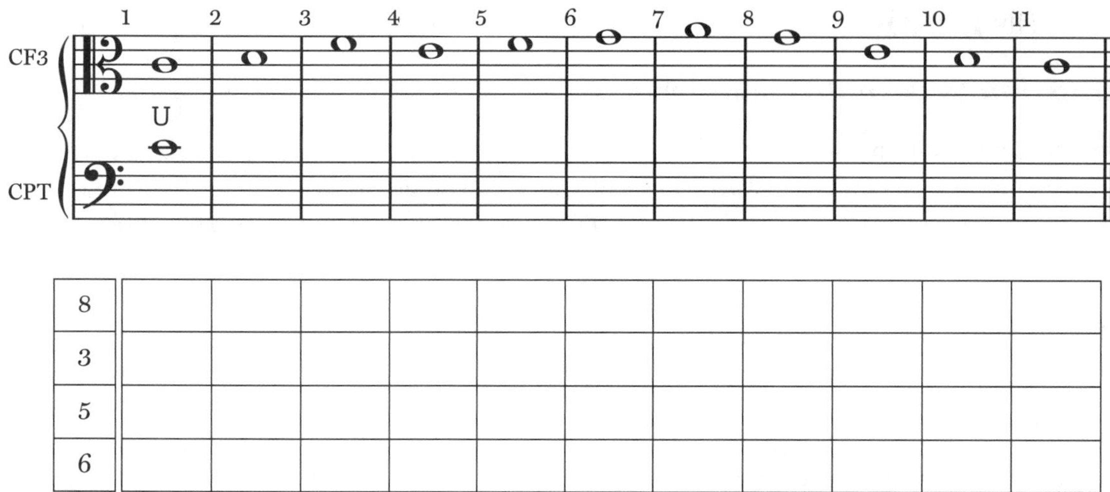

II. Analysis

Orlando di Lasso, "Beatus vir qui in sapientia morabitur," mm. 29–32

The excerpt below is largely note-to-note counterpoint. In the blanks provided, analyze the harmonic intervals between the staves for the 1:1 quarter-note portion of the phrase (beginning with the anacrusis to m. 30).

Translation: "Dei" is "God"

Briefly describe ways in which this interval sequence differs from strict species (other than by its rhythm).

NAME ____________________

10 Melodic and Rhythmic Embellishment in Two-Voice Composition

Checkpoints for Students and Teachers

When writing second-species (2:1) counterpoint, we suggest two passes to check your work:

1. Check the harmonic intervals first.
   - The first and last intervals should be either 8 or U. The first can be 5 only if the counterpoint is above the *cantus*.
   - Each *cantus* note should be paired with a consonance (the first half note in the measure, falling "on the beat"). A dissonance written on this beat is an error.
   - If there is an 8 or 5 on the beat, check the first half note in the next measure for parallel octaves or fifths; also look back at the approach to the 8 or 5, which should be by step in the upper part (check for hidden fifths or octaves) and not from another interval of the same size.
   - The second half note ("offbeat") of each measure may include a dissonant passing or neighbor tone. Make sure any 2, 4, 7, or 9 is prepared and resolved as a passing or neighbor tone, and mark it P or N. An A4 or d5 must be treated as a passing or neighbor tone, and must resolve to the correct interval.
   - The offbeat may be another consonance, approached by step, skip, or leap, in oblique motion with the *cantus* note. You can leap or skip into octaves or fifths on the offbeats; octaves or fifths on consecutive offbeats are also acceptable, unless they draw attention to themselves. If the offbeat note is an 8 or 5, check the connection to the next beat for parallels.
   - The unison (U) should only appear at the beginning or end of the counterpoint (some teachers allow it on the second half of the measure if the voices are close together).
   - The close in strict style should be 3-U (10-8) or 6-8, with the parts approaching the final note in contrary motion by step over the bar line. The next-to-last *cantus* note may be set 2:1 or 1:1; the final note is 1:1. Raise ♭$\hat{7}$ in minor to make a leading tone, and ♭$\hat{6}$ if necessary, but only approaching at the close.
2. Examine the contour and melodic intervals of the counterpoint line.
   - There should be one high or low point, with perhaps a subsidiary high or low point.
   - If the *cantus* includes a skip or leap, the counterpoint should balance it, ideally with steps in the opposite direction.
   - Any leaps in the counterpoint line should be prepared by an approach contrary to the direction of the leap, and followed by steps contrary to the direction of the leap.

- Dissonant melodic intervals (7, d5, A4, A2) are not allowed.
- There should be a mix of perfect consonances, imperfect consonances, and dissonances (treated correctly as passing or neighbor tones). A second-species exercise must include some dissonant passing or neighbor tones; complete lack of them is an error!

When writing third-species counterpoint (4:1), check for the following elements:

1. Check the harmonic intervals first.
    - The first and last intervals should be either 8 or U. The first can be 5 only if the counterpoint is above the *cantus*.
    - Each *cantus* note should be paired with a consonance (the first quarter note in the measure, falling "on the beat"). A dissonance written on the downbeat is an error.
    - There should be some diversity of intervals on the downbeats—ideally no more than three 3 or three 6 in a row, and at least one 8 or 5 in the middle of the exercise (two if it is a long *cantus*) in addition to the opening and closing intervals—to mix the "sweetness" of the imperfect consonances with the "hollowness" of the perfect consonances.
    - If there is an 8 or 5 on the downbeat, check the first quarter note in the next measure for parallel octaves or fifths; also look back at the approach to the 8 or 5, which should be by step in the upper part (check for hidden fifths or octaves) and not from another interval of the same size.
    - If the third quarter note in a measure is an 8 or 5, check the next downbeat, which should not be the same interval (creating parallel octaves or fifths).
    - The intervals 8 or 5 on consecutive offbeats are acceptable unless they draw attention to themselves, through contour or repetition. The intervals 8 and 5 from the second quarter note to the following downbeat, or from the second, third, or fourth quarter to any beat other than the downbeat of the next measure, are acceptable.
    - The unison should only appear at the beginning or end of the counterpoint (some teachers, including Fux, allow it on the second, third, or fourth quarter note if the voices are close together).
    - The second, third, and fourth notes of each measure may include a dissonant passing or neighbor tone or may be a consonance. A consonance may be approached by step, skip, or leap. Make sure any 2, 4, 7, or 9 is prepared and resolved as a passing or neighbor tone, and mark it P or N.
    - An A4 or d5 must be treated as a passing or neighbor tone, and must resolve to the correct interval. In third species, these intervals normally appear on the final quarter note of the measure so as to resolve immediately. To identify places to include them, look for scale degrees $\hat{4}$–$\hat{3}$ or $\hat{7}$–$\hat{1}$ in the *cantus* (without both together the resolution is not possible).
    - The closing intervals should be 3–U (10–8) or 6–8, with the parts approaching the final note in contrary motion by step over the bar line. Raise $\flat\hat{6}$ and $\flat\hat{7}$ in minor only when approaching $\hat{1}$ at the close.
2. Examine the contour and melodic intervals of the counterpoint line.
    - Examine the melody in units of five quarter notes (downbeat to the downbeat of the following measure) for local continuity. Each five-note unit should make a pleasing contour, with a melodic step crossing the bar line. Avoid repeating the same melodic shape in consecutive measures.

- Avoid a static line—circling around a few pitches or repeating a pitch more than three times in a span of two measures—by using a wider range than in second species. Do not immediately repeat any notes, whether within the bar or across the bar line.
- The counterpoint may span up to an octave and a fifth in overall range, but do not move more than an octave in one direction without a change of direction.
- Leaps and skips in the counterpoint line should be placed within the measure (not over the bar line). Leaps are prepared by an approach contrary to the direction of the leap and followed by steps contrary to the direction of the leap. Skips normally involve a change of direction as well and should not follow a series of steps in the same direction.
- Dissonant melodic intervals (7, d5, A4, A2) are not allowed.
- There should be one high or low point, with a subsidiary high or low point. The contour of an upper counterpoint should be like mountains in the distance. A lower counterpoint should be like the mountains reflected in a lake.
- A well-crafted third-species counterpoint creates the feeling of soaring—like a raptor floating on the thermals, swooping downward, then soaring upward. This effect is made from primarily stepwise motion enlivened by judiciously placed skips and employment of a properly placed and prepared leap. Counterpoint melodies that are too conservative—occupying a narrow range or exclusively stepwise—will not soar.

When writing fourth-species counterpoint, check for the following elements:

- The first and last intervals should be either 8 or U. The counterpoint can begin with 5 if it is above the *cantus*.
- The counterpoint begins with a half rest, followed by a half note (preferably tied over the bar line), and ends with a whole note. The second half note in the penultimate measure is not tied over.
- If the counterpoint is below the *cantus*, the last two measures will end with a 2–3 suspension to an 8 or U; if the counterpoint is above the *cantus*, it will close with a 7-6 suspension to 8. Because the closing suspension must be prepared, the last two and a half measures will be $\hat{1}$ tied over and then resolved to $\hat{7}$, followed by $\hat{1}$.
- The second half note in each measure (on the offbeat) should be tied over to the same note on the downbeat of the following measure wherever possible.
- Where possible, the tied-over note should create a dissonant suspension, prepared by a consonance on the offbeat of the previous measure, and resolving down by step on the offbeat.
- When you break species, the second half note is not tied over to the following downbeat. The resulting half notes follow the guidelines for second-species counterpoint.
- Acceptable dissonant suspensions are 4–3, 7–6, and 9–8 when the counterpoint is in the upper voice, and 2–3 when the counterpoint is in the lower part. The consonant suspensions 5–6 and 6–5 may be used when the counterpoint is in either voice.
- The only suspensions that may be used in a chain are 7–6 and 4–3 in the upper part, and 2–3 in the lower. Chains should be broken, either by a change in the

suspension type or by breaking species, to avoid more than three repetitions of the same intervallic pattern.

- The suspensions 9–8 and 6–5 may not be used in chains, as this creates the sound of parallel octaves or fifths.
- If it is not possible to create a dissonant suspension, a consonant note on the offbeat may be tied across the bar to form a consonant interval with the following *cantus* note. When consonance is tied across to consonance, there is no need for resolution on the offbeat downward or by step; instead the counterpoint may step, skip, or leap upward or downward to prepare the next suspension.
- Contour is less of a concern in fourth species (counterpoints tend to move downward), but be careful to avoid excessive use of any one note and to keep the counterpoint and *cantus* lines from crossing or overlapping. It will occasionally be necessary to leap or skip upward within a bar (from one consonant interval to another) to allow the counterpoint room to continue to descend.
- Breaking species should be reserved for the following situations:
  (a) when dissonant suspensions are not available and there is no consonance that can be tied over;
  (b) to reestablish the proper distance between the parts when they are about to cross or to make a more interesting line;
  (c) to break off a chain of suspensions;
  (d) to prevent counterpoint errors and to solve difficult places in the *cantus*.

ASSIGNMENT 10.1

I. Writing 2:1 counterpoint openings

Write a 2:1 counterpoint opening for each given *cantus firmus* line in strict style. Start with either a half rest and a half note or two half notes in measure 1, then continue with two half notes for each remaining measure. Include passing tones, neighbor tones, and consonant skips, and write the harmonic interval numbers between the staves. Circle the interval number for any harmonic dissonance, and check that it forms a correct P or N.

II. Writing 2:1 counterpoint closings

Write a 2:1 counterpoint closing for each given *cantus firmus* in strict style, two half notes per each whole note except for the last (and possibly penultimate) measure. Use passing tones, neighbor tones, and consonant skips, and write the harmonic interval numbers between the staves. Circle the number for any harmonic dissonance, and check that it forms a correct P or N.

ASSIGNMENT 10.2

I. Writing a 2:1 counterpoint

Write a 2:1 counterpoint for each given *cantus firmus* in strict style, using two half notes for each *cantus* whole note. Include passing tones, neighbor tones, and consonant skips, and write the harmonic interval numbers between the staves. Circle the number for each harmonic dissonance.

A. Above a given line

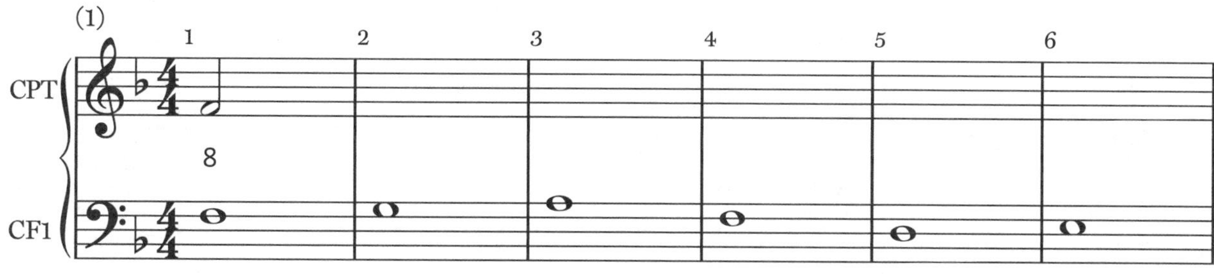

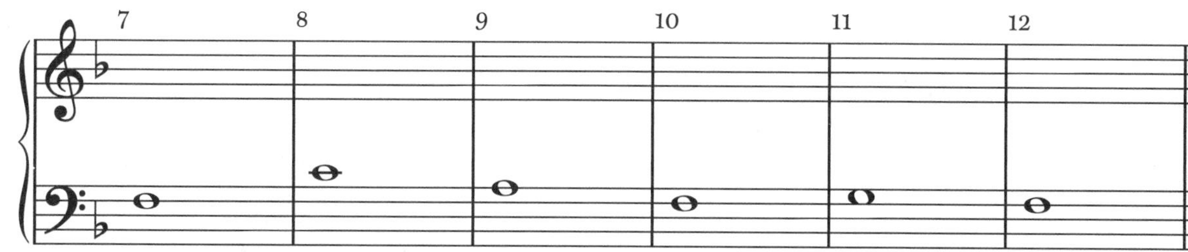

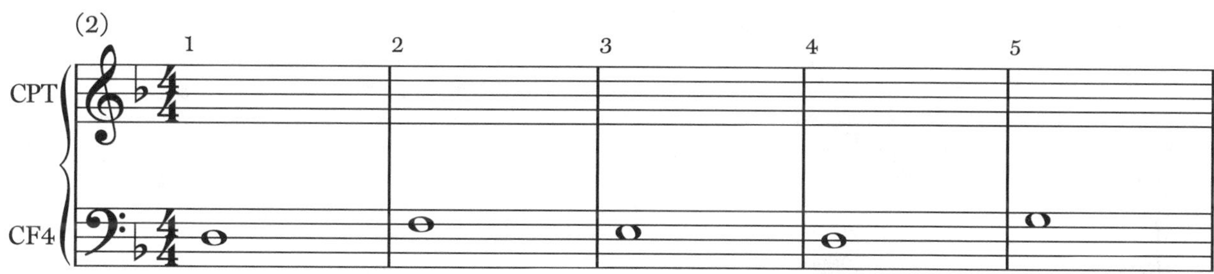

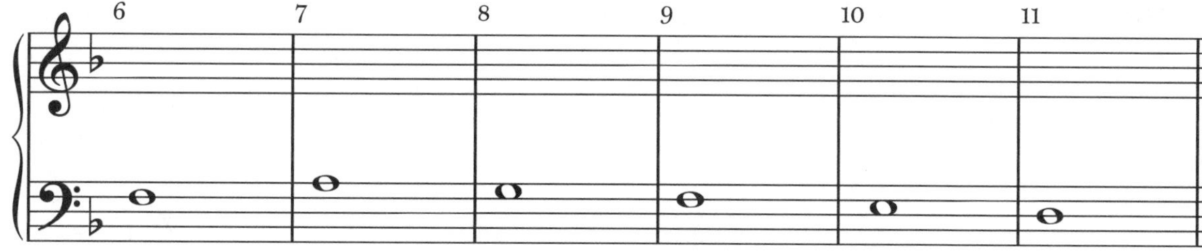

B. Below a given line

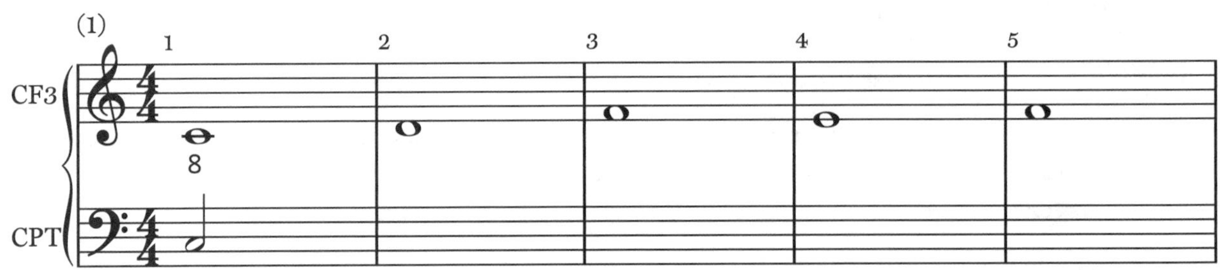

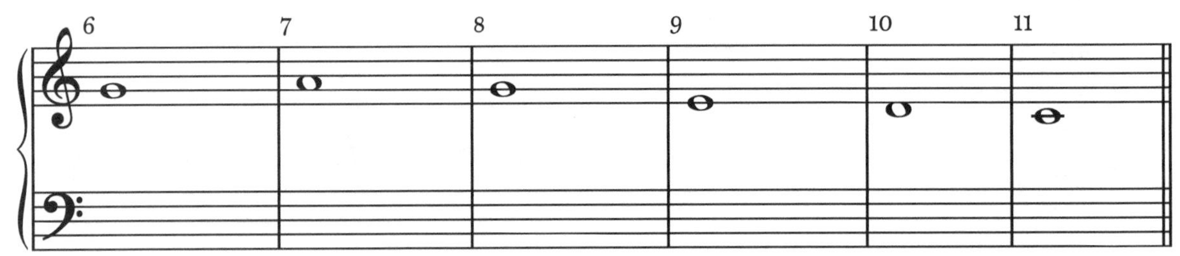

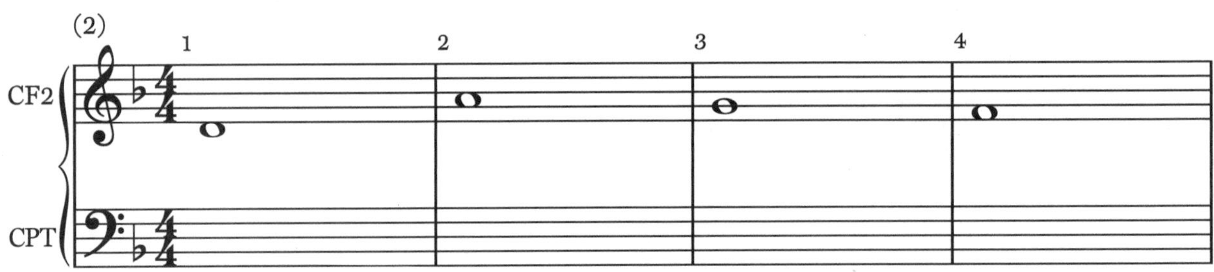

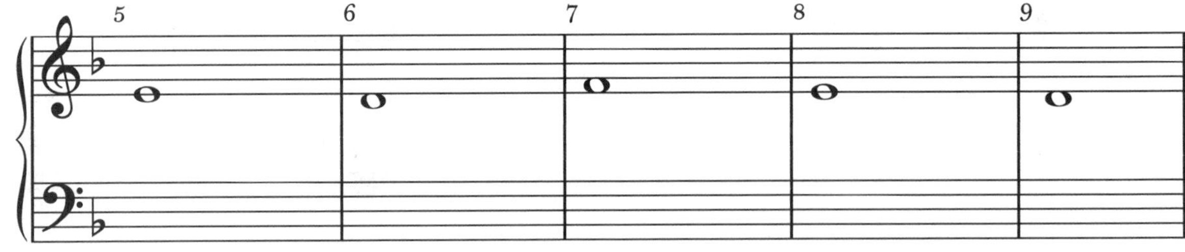

ASSIGNMENT 10.3

I. Writing a 2:1 counterpoint

Write a 2:1 counterpoint in strict style for each given *cantus firmus*, as for Assignment 10.2.

A. Below a given line

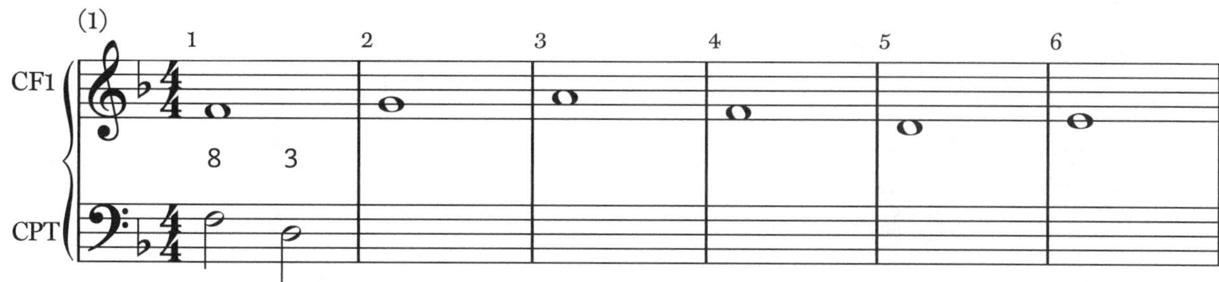

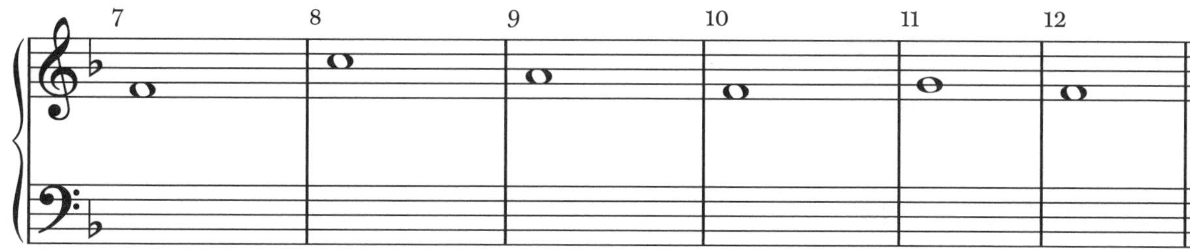

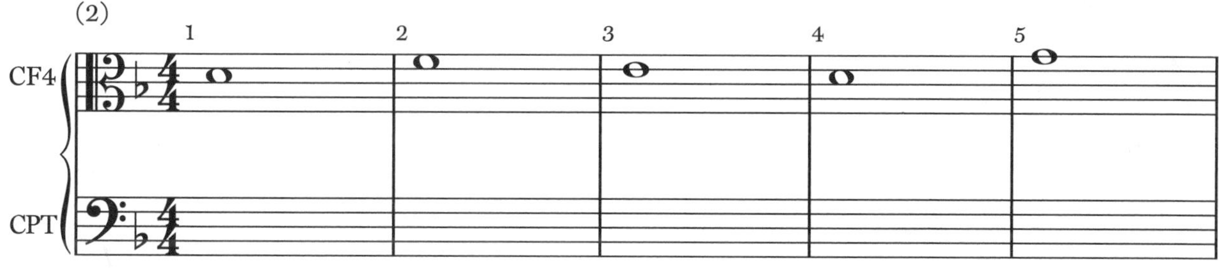

6 7 8 9 10 11

B. Above a given line

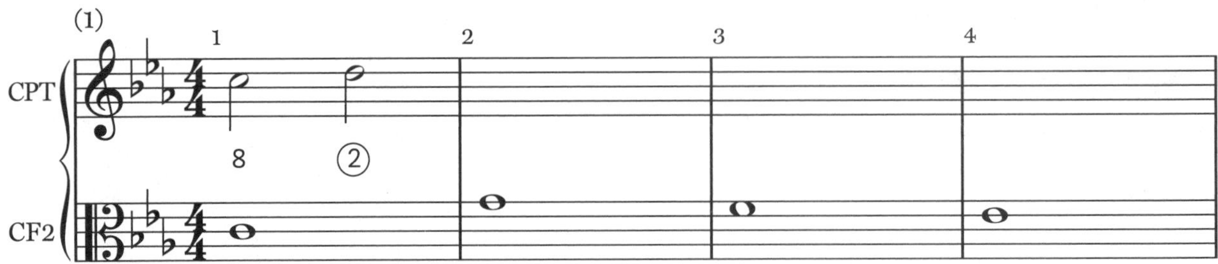

(transposed)

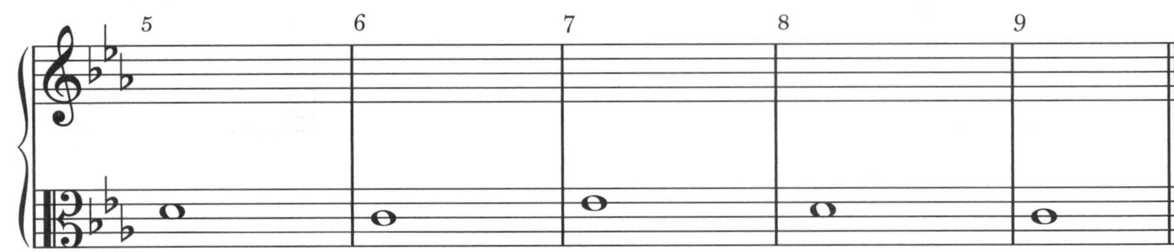

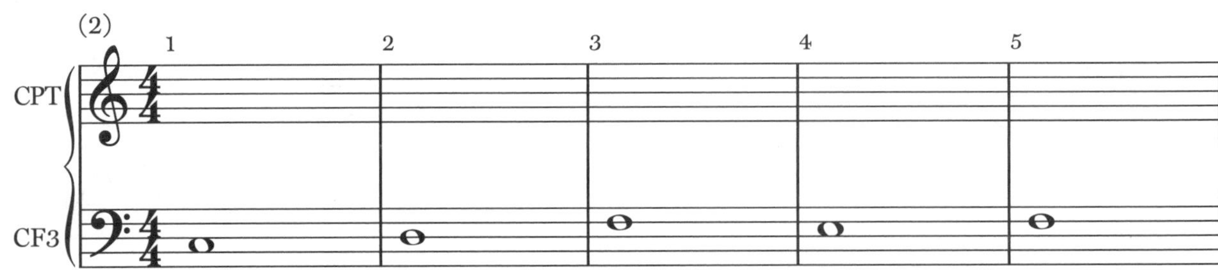

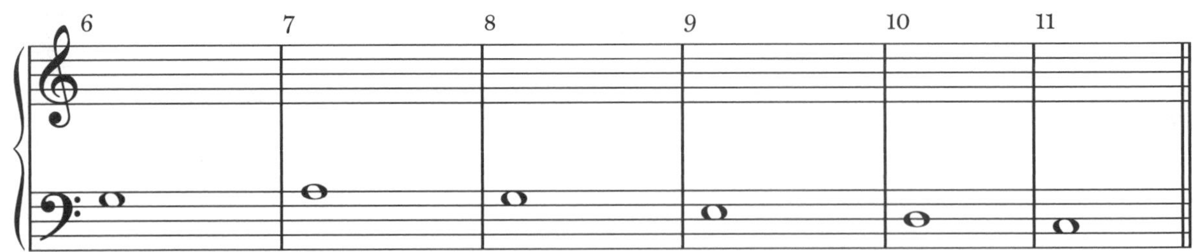

NAME ______________________________

ASSIGNMENT 10.4

I. Writing a 4:1 counterpoint

Write a 4:1 counterpoint for each given *cantus firmus* in strict style, using four quarter notes for each *cantus* whole note, starting either with a quarter rest followed by three quarter notes or a full measure of quarter notes in the counterpoint. Include passing tones, neighbor tones, and consonant skips, and write the harmonic interval numbers between the staves. You may include a cambiata or double neighbor pattern; if so, bracket and label it (both patterns extend a whole measure plus the next downbeat). Circle the number for each harmonic dissonance, and label it as passing (P) or neighboring (N).

A. Below a given line

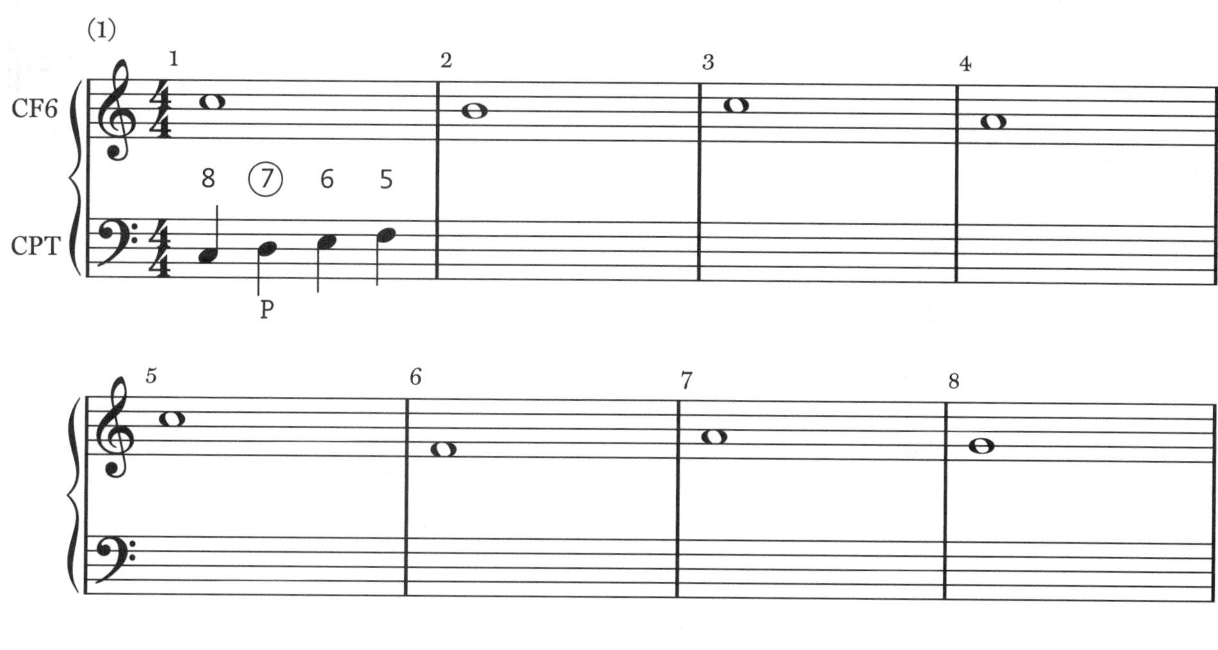

(2)

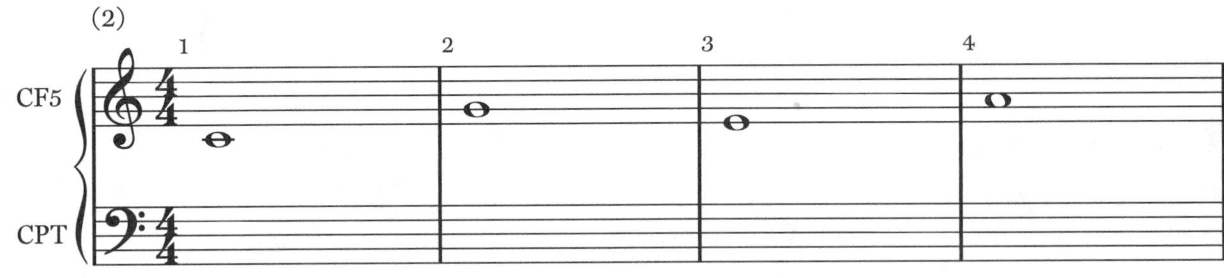

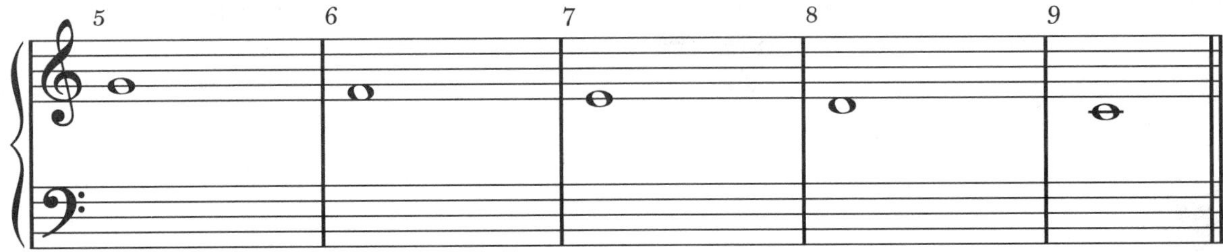

B. Above a given line

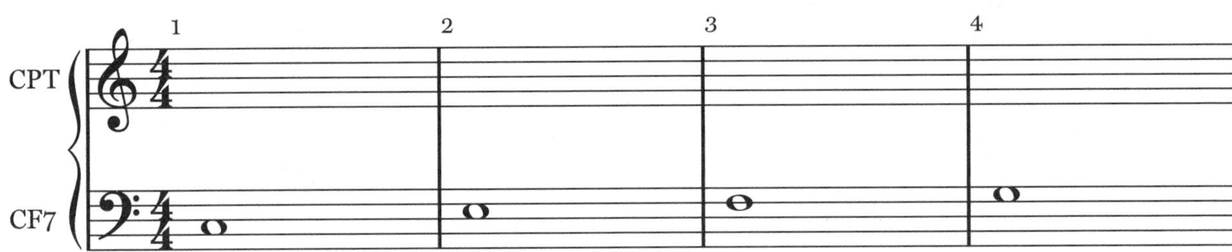

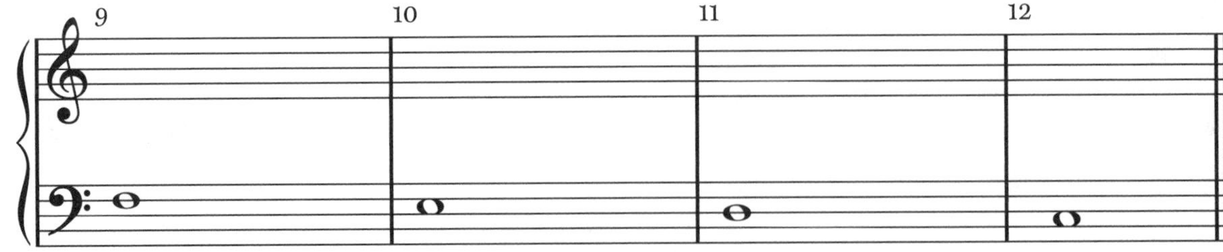

ASSIGNMENT 10.5

I. Suspensions in note-to-note counterpoint

For each note-to-note framework, make a dissonant suspension as shown. Between the staves, write the interval numbers for both the framework and your suspension. Above the staff, label the three parts of the suspension: preparation (prep), dissonant suspension (sus), and resolution (res). Include at least one bass suspension.

(a) (b)

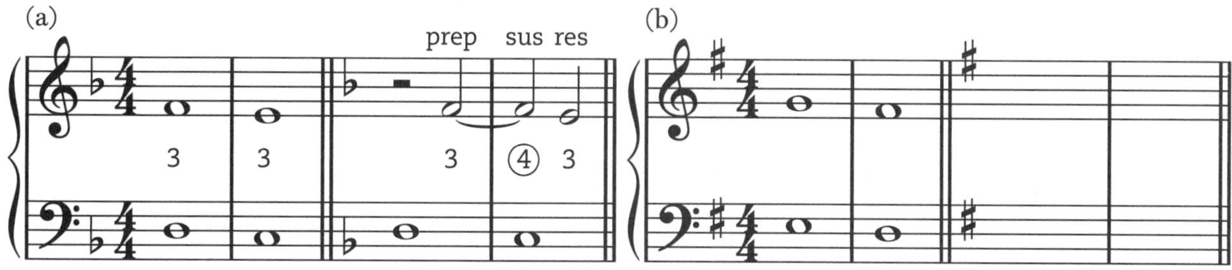

(c) (d)

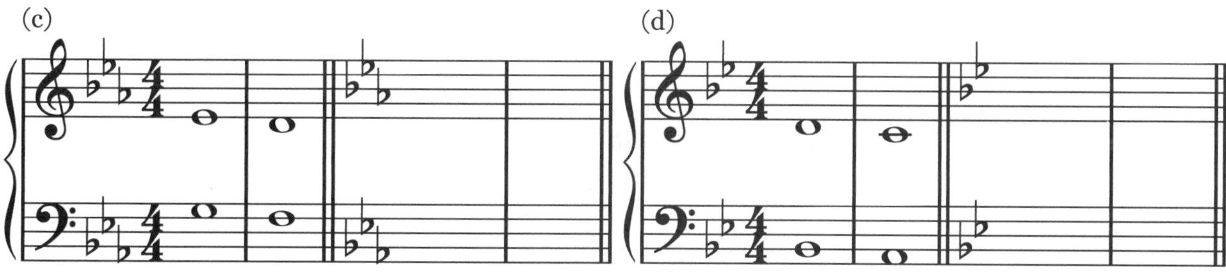

(e) (f)

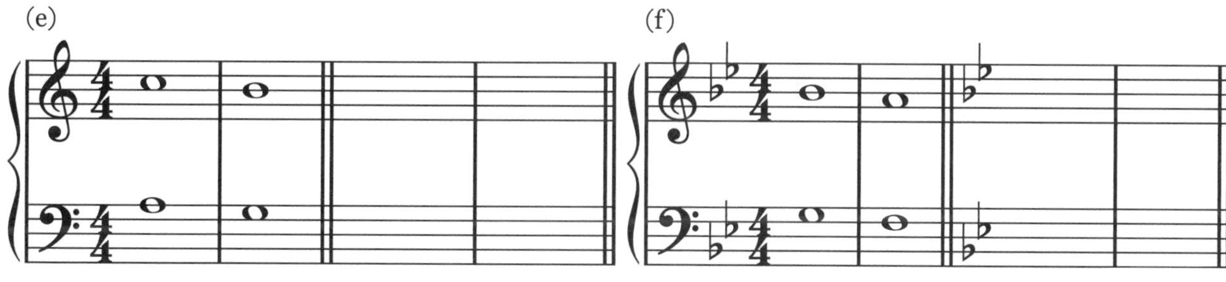

(g) (h)

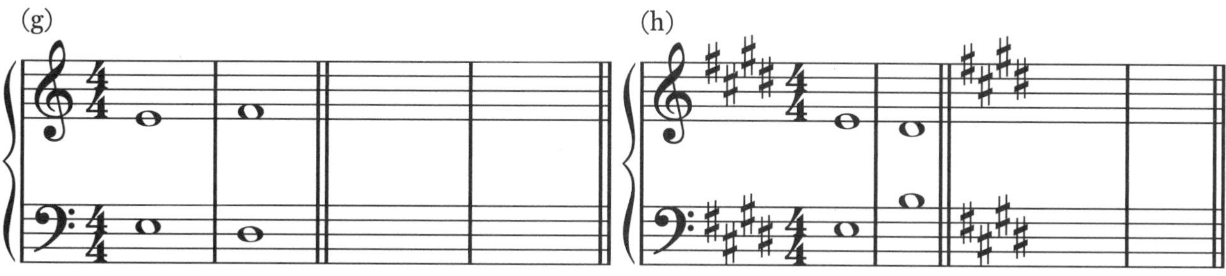

II. Writing chains of suspensions

Use rhythmic displacement to make chains of suspensions from the given parallel thirds or sixths. In (d) and (e), write your own suspension chains, using a different type of suspension in each. Play your chains at a keyboard, or sing or play them as a duet with a partner.

(a) Write suspensions in the upper part.

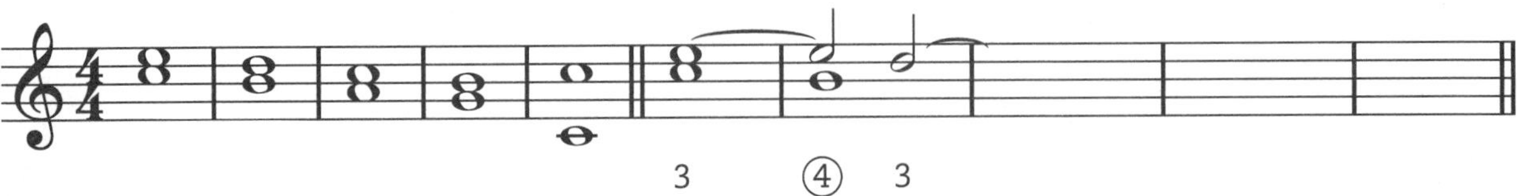

(b) Write suspensions in the lower part.

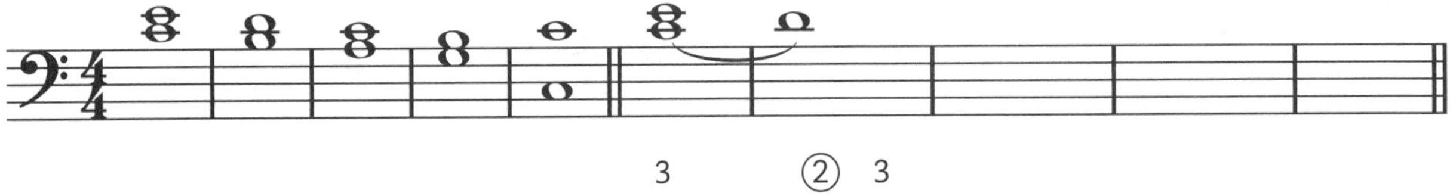

(c) Write suspensions in the upper part.

(d) Write a chain of suspensions.

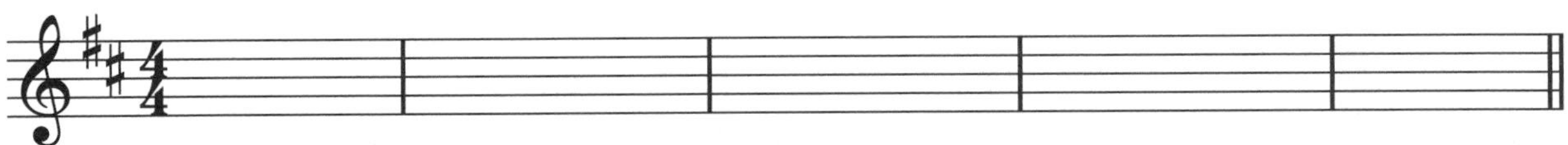

(e) Write another chain, using a suspension type other than the one in (d).

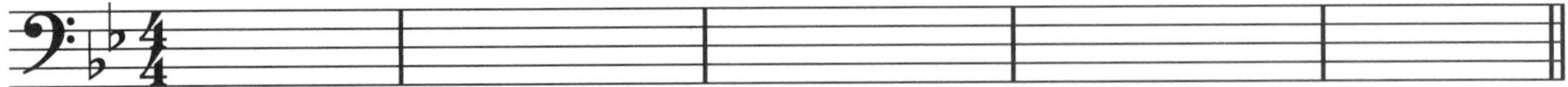

ASSIGNMENT 10.6

I. Writing fourth-species counterpoint

Write a fourth-species counterpoint in strict style for each given *cantus firmus* with two half notes tied over the bar line for each whole note. Write the harmonic interval numbers between the staves, and circle the number for any harmonic dissonance.

A. Above a given line

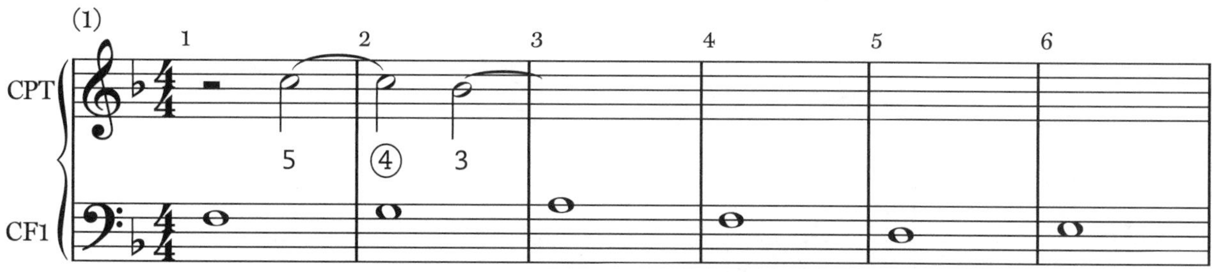

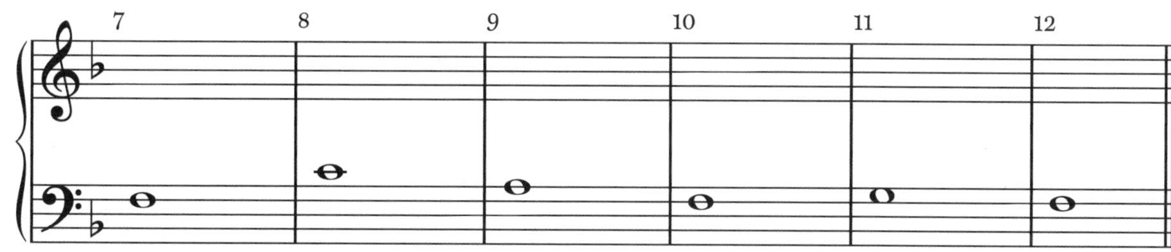

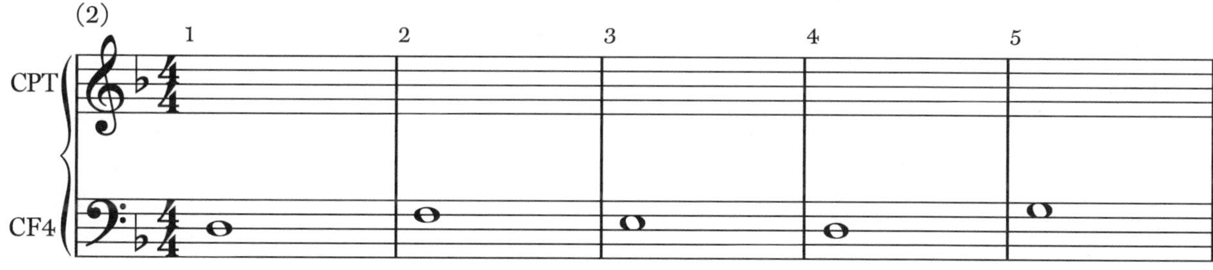

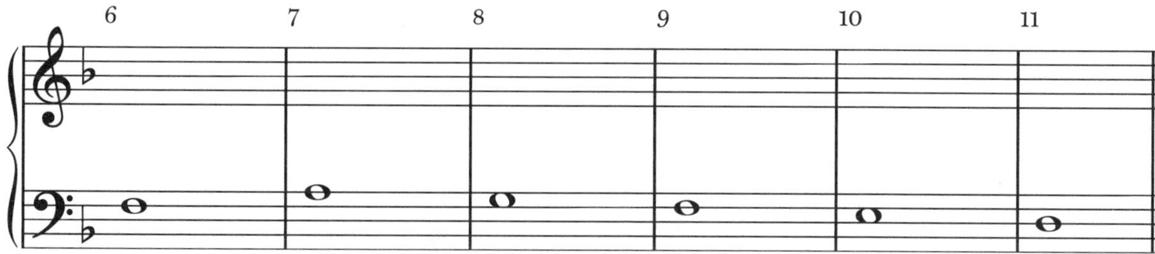

B. Below a given line

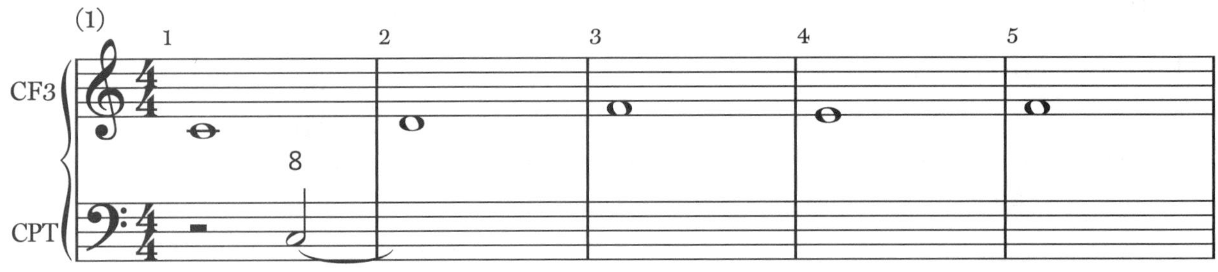

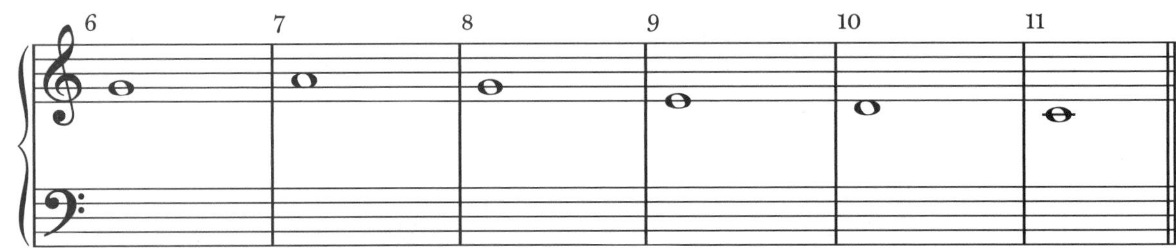

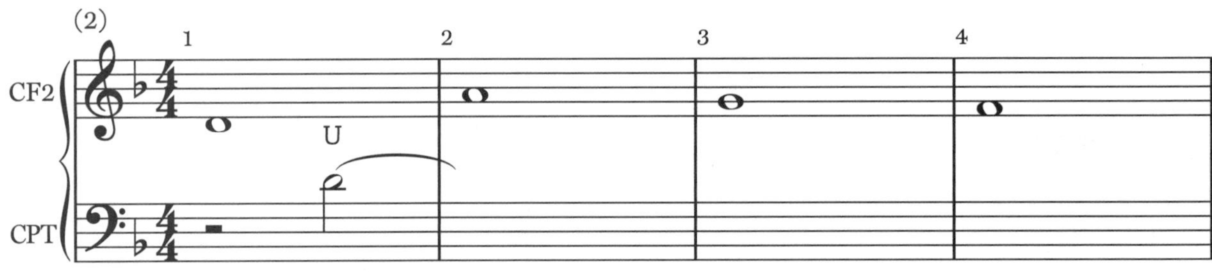

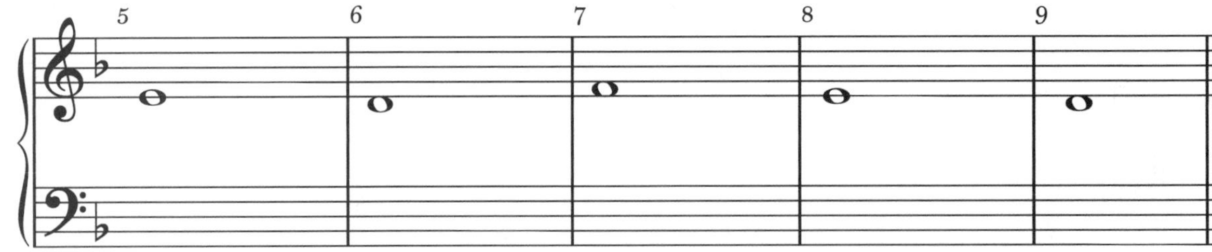

Assignment 10.7

I. Writing fourth-species counterpoint

Write a fourth-species counterpoint in strict style for each given *cantus firmus*, as in Assignment 10.6.

A. Below a given line

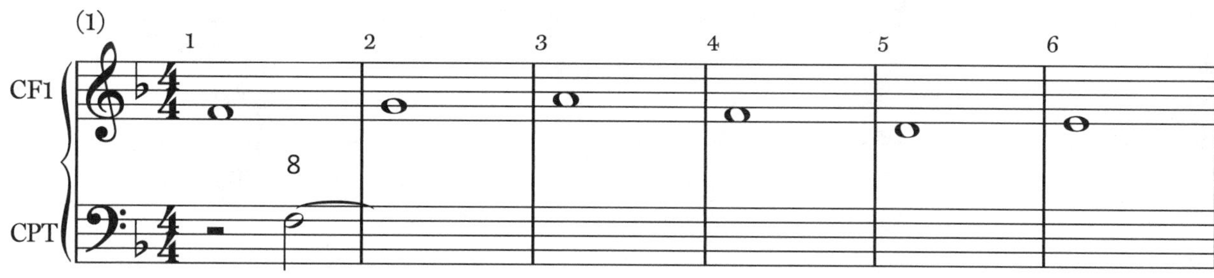

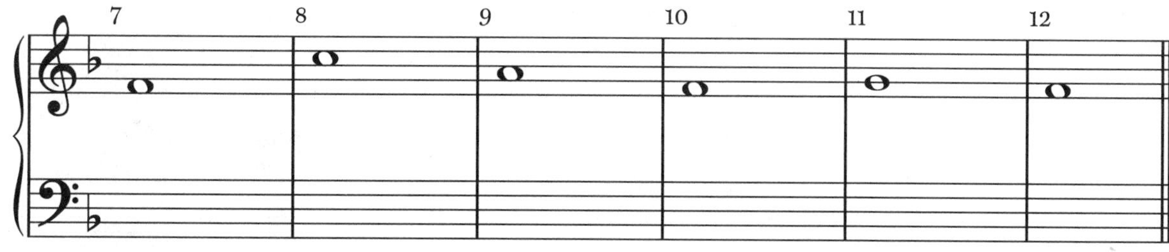

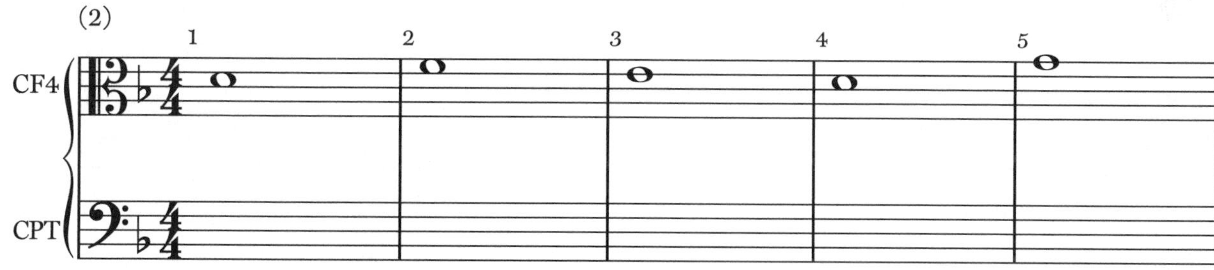

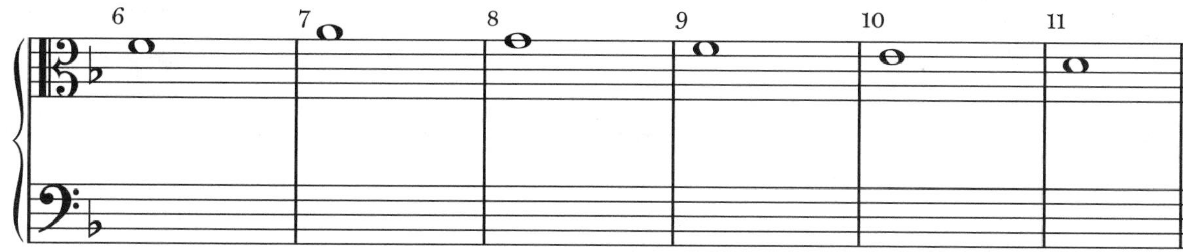

B. Above a given line

(1)

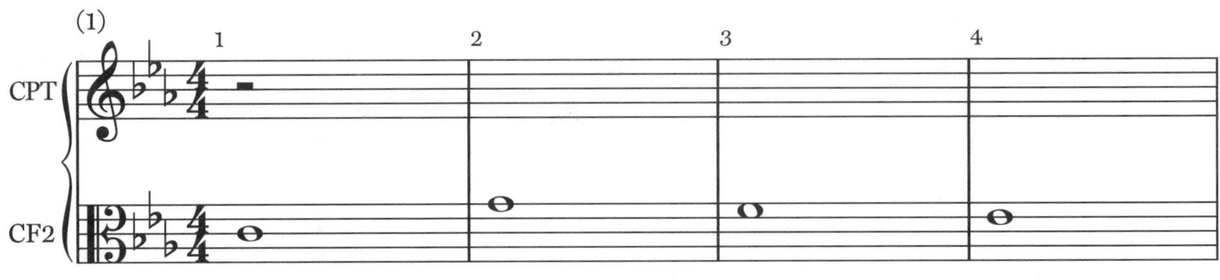

(transposed)

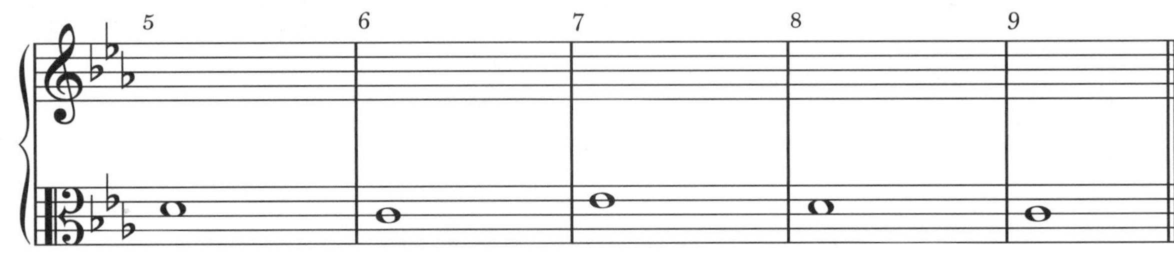

(2)

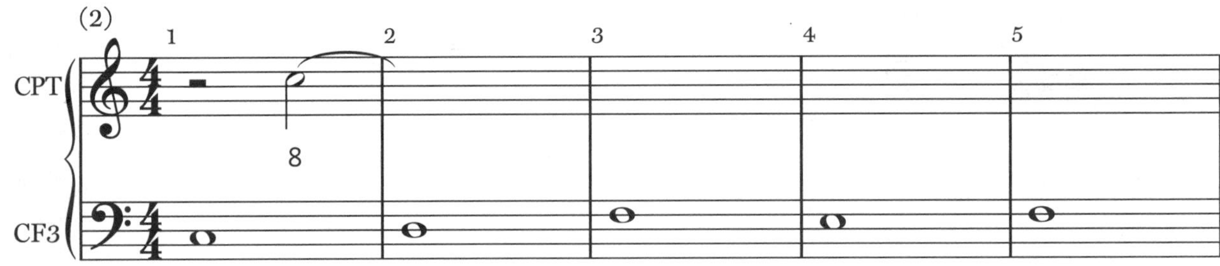

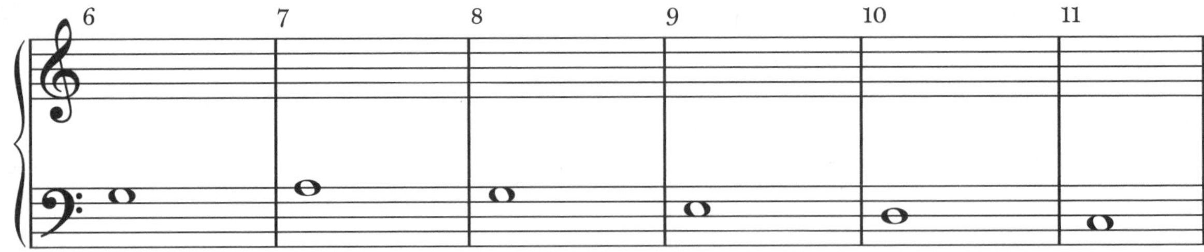

Assignment 10.8

Evaluating second, third, and fifth species

A. Shown are two examples of second-species counterpoint by Jeppesen. Write the harmonic interval numbers between the staves. Circle each dissonance, and identify as a passing tone (P) or neighbor tone (N).

(1)

(2)

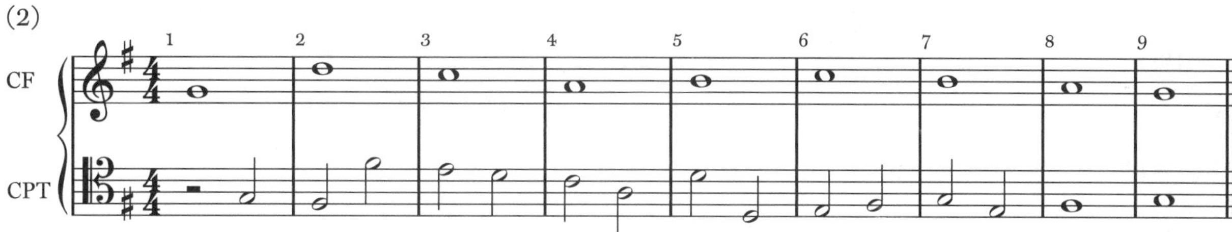

B. In this example of third-species counterpoint by Fux, write the harmonic interval numbers between the staves. Circle each dissonance, and identify as P or N.

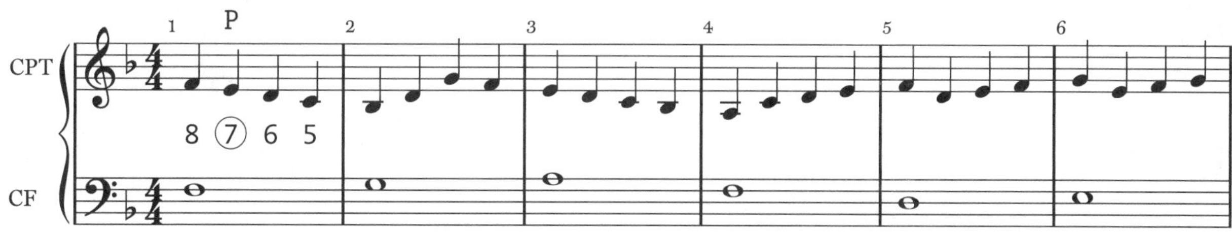

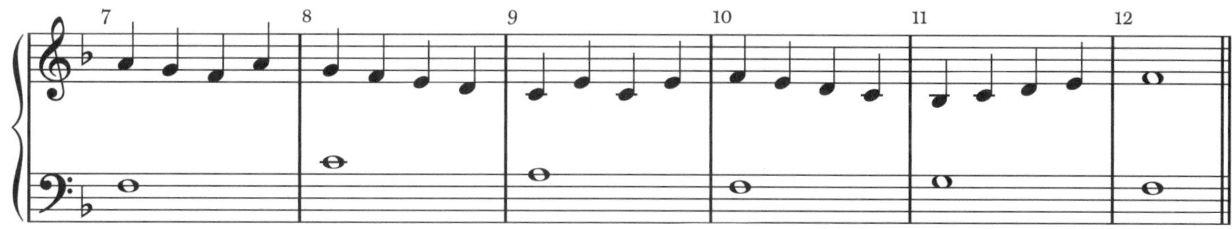

C. In these examples of fifth-species and free counterpoint, write the harmonic intervals between the staves. Circle each dissonance, and identify as a passing tone (P), neighbor tone (N), suspension (sus), or combination.

(1) Johann Joseph Fux

(2) Orlando di Lasso, "Oculus non vidit," mm. 10–20

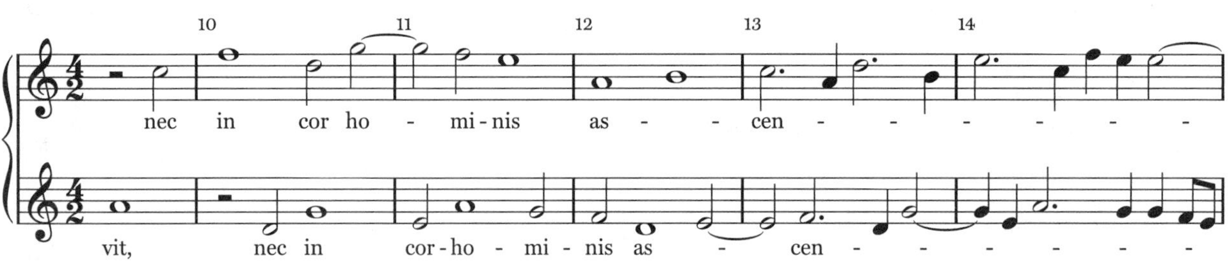

Translation: Nor has it arisen into man's heart what God has prepared

(a) How does Lasso portray the idea of "rising" ("ascendit") musically?

(b) What is the relationship between the two voices at measures 16–18?

Diatonic Harmony and Tonicization

NAME ______________________________

From Species to Chorale Style: Soprano and Bass Lines

ASSIGNMENT 11.1

I. Chorale melody settings

Here are the soprano and bass parts for four settings by J. S. Bach of the first phrase of an anonymous chorale melody, set to different texts and transposed to the same key. Write the scale degrees for the melody above the first setting (A), then sing or play each of these. Label the harmonic intervals between the staves, circling any that are dissonant, then examine the counterpoint. In the blanks above the staff, mark the type of motion from beat to beat: contrary (C), parallel (P), similar (S), or oblique (O). Circle and label any dissonant passing (P) or neighbor (N) tones.

As your teacher assigns: Write a paragraph summarizing the similarities and differences in these settings, or be prepared to compare them in class discussion.

A. "O Welt, sieh hier dein Leben"

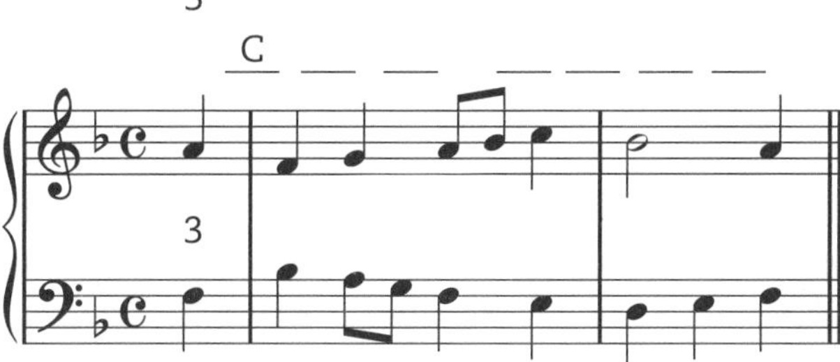

B. "O Welt, ich muss dich lassen"

C. "Nun ruhen alle Wälder"

D. "In allen meinen Taten"

II. Resolving chordal dissonances

For each pair of intervals:

1. Write scale-degree numbers for each note in the specified key.
2. Identify each dissonant interval (d5, A4, or 7).
3. Add notes to resolve the dissonance correctly:

   d5 → 3: both voices move in by step.

   A4 → 6: both voices move out by step.

   7 → 3: the lower voice skips up a P4 or down a P5; the upper voice moves down by step.
4. Identify the scale degree of the notes you added in step 3.
5. Write Roman numerals and figures underneath (V^7, V^6_5, V^4_2; I, I^6, i, or i^6) for each implied chord.

ASSIGNMENT 11.2

I. Opening patterns with note-to-note counterpoint in eighteenth-century style

For each pattern:

1. Write scale-degree numbers for each given note in the specified key.
2. Add a note to complete the pair of intervals. In minor, add an accidental for the leading tone.
3. Label both intervals, circling dissonant intervals, and write the new note's scale-degree number.
4. Label each chord with Roman numerals and figures, selecting from I, i, I^6, i^6, V, V^6, V^7, V$^6_5$, and V$^4_3$.

A. Without an anacrusis

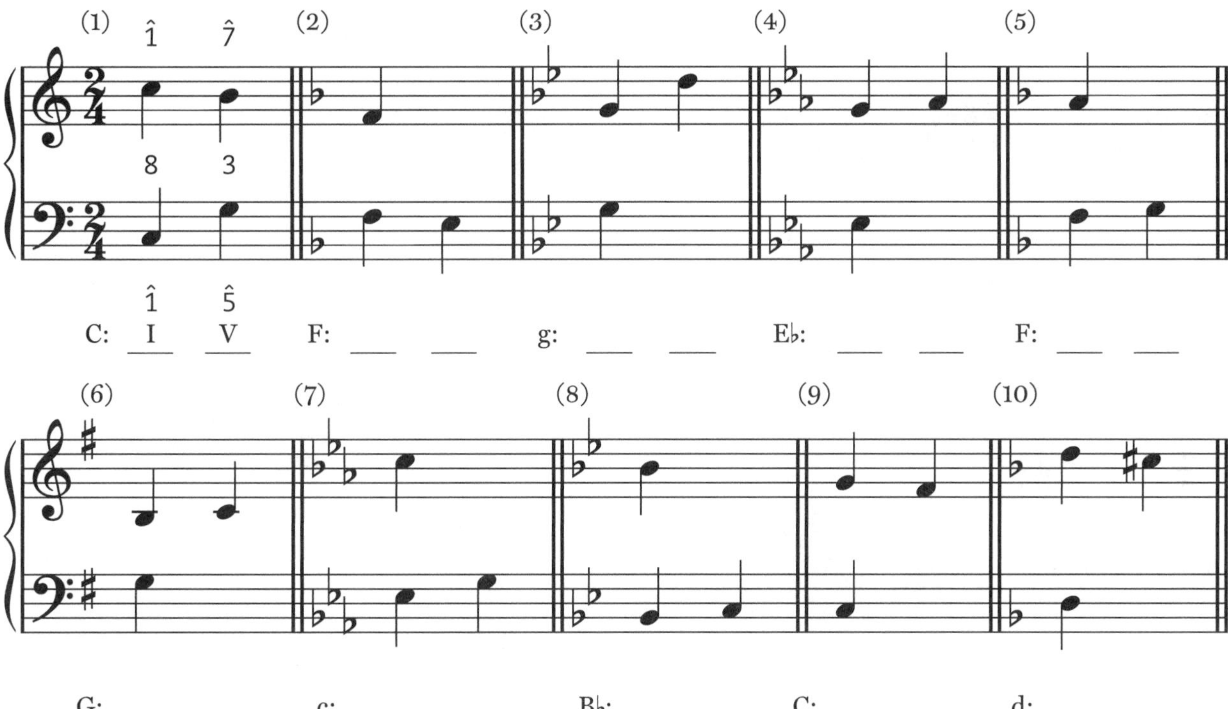

B. With an anacrusis

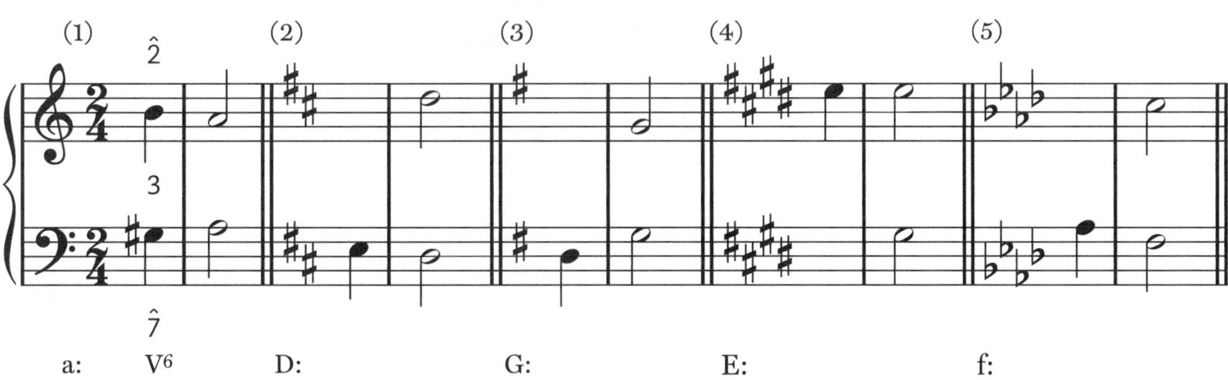

II. *Closing patterns with note-to-note counterpoint in eighteenth-century style*

Follow the instructions for part I.

A. Conclusive closes

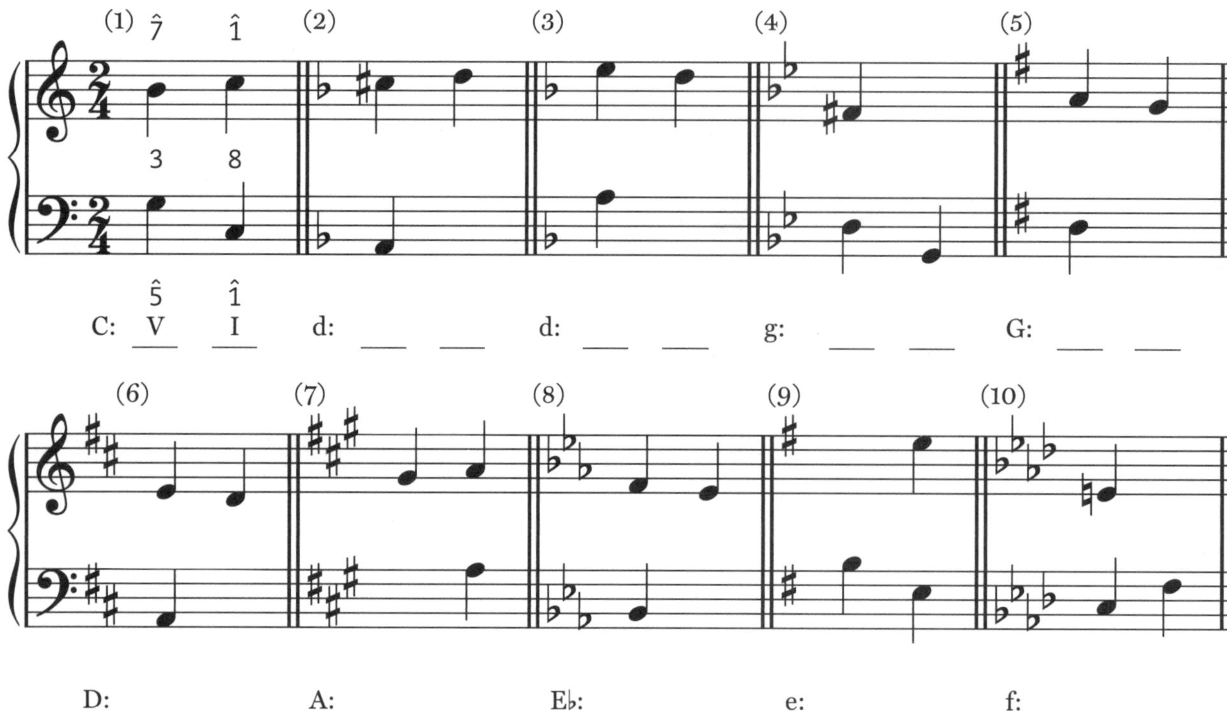

B. Less conclusive closes

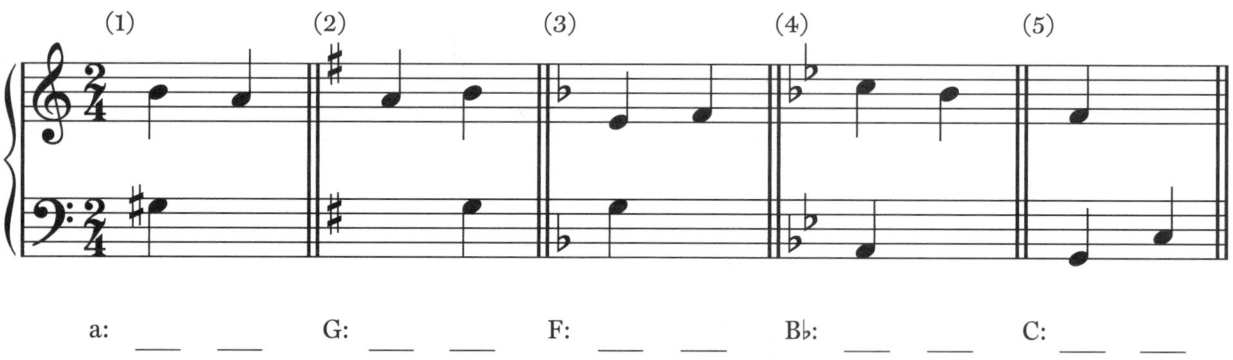

ASSIGNMENT 11.3

Writing a note-to-note counterpoint in eighteenth-century style

A. Above a given bass line

1. Examine the bass line to identify the key and mode, then determine which chords (selecting from I, i, I^6, i^6, V, V^6, V^7, V^6_5, and V^4_3) are implied at the beginning and end, and write those Roman numerals in the blanks.
2. Write the opening and closing counterpoint, then provide one soprano note for each of the other bass notes.
3. You may use chordal dissonances (d5, A4, m7) if they can be resolved correctly; approach these intervals by common tone or step.
4. Label the harmonic intervals between the staves, and circle chordal dissonances.

(a)

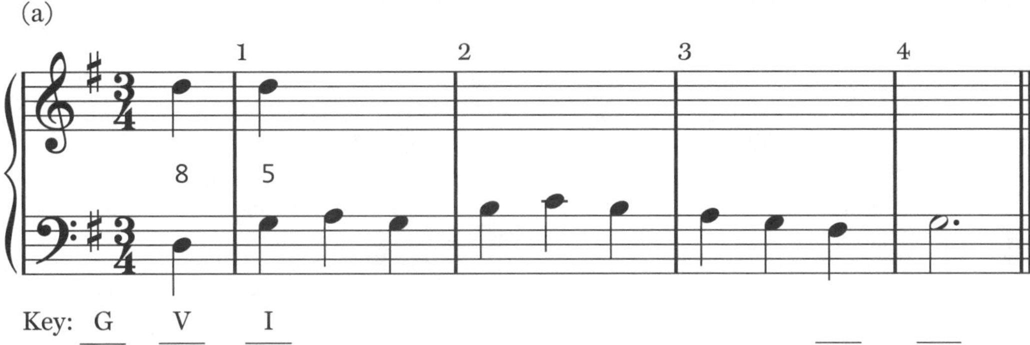

(b)

(c)

B. Below a given chorale melody

1. Identify the key, and determine which chords (selecting from I, i, I^6, i^6, V, V^6, V^7, V^6_5, and V^4_3) are implied at the beginning and end, as for part A.
2. Write the opening and closing counterpoint, then provide one bass note per quarter-note beat.
3. You may use chordal dissonances (d5, A4, m7) if they can be resolved correctly; approach these intervals by common tone or step.
4. Label the harmonic intervals between the staves, and circle chordal dissonances.

(a) "Ich muss meine Abendswerk tun"

(b) "Heut' ist, o Mensch, ein grosser Trauertag"

(c) "In allen meinen Taten"

ASSIGNMENT 11.4

I. Analysis of 2:1 counterpoint in eighteenth-century style

Circle each embellishing tone in each measure, and label as P (passing), N (neighbor), or CS (consonant or chordal skip). Indicate the key and mode for each example, and label the implied harmonies (dominant or tonic only) with Roman numerals and figures.

II. Analysis of suspensions

Circle and label each suspension (sus) and indicate its type (e.g., 4–3). Also label the preparation (prep) and resolution (res). Indicate the key and mode for each example, and label the implied harmonies (dominant or tonic only) with Roman numerals and figures.

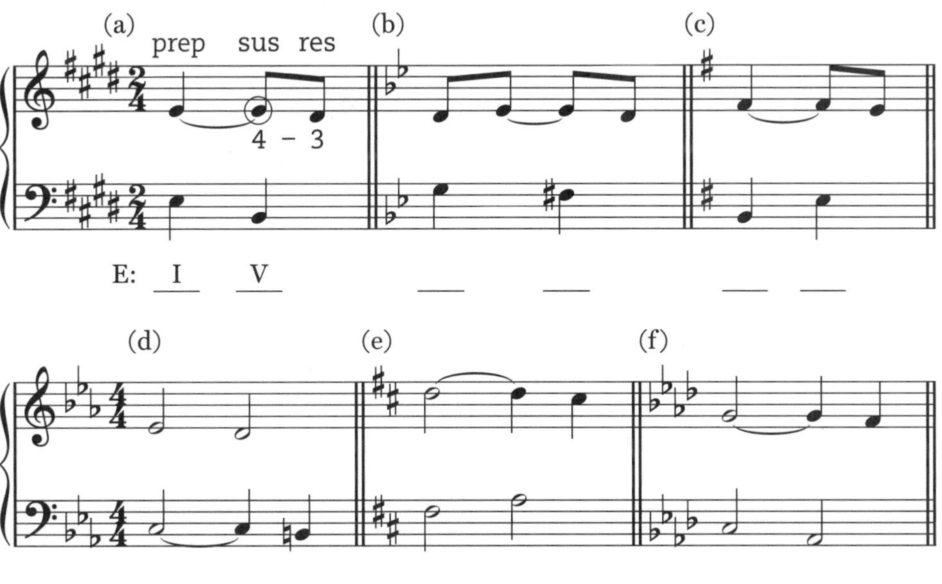

III. *Analyzing suspensions in Handel's "Rejoice greatly," from* Messiah

Listen to the opening of this aria (Anthology 41a), then label the intervals between the soprano and bass lines of the organ part. For each suspension, write 4–3, 2–3, or 7–6 between the staves and "sus" above the staff. At the cadence, write the scale degrees for the soprano and bass and the Roman numerals implied for the final two chords.

A. Mm. 7–9

B♭:

B. Mm. 20–23

B♭:

C. Mm. 34–36

F:

D. Mm. 42–43

F:

NAME ________________________________

ASSIGNMENT 11.5

I. Analysis of chorale-style counterpoint

Given are four settings of the opening phrase of the tune "Nun danket alle Gott" ("Now Thank We All Our God"), a chorale melody composed by Johann Crüger (1648): two settings are by J. S. Bach, one is by Felix Mendelssohn (1840), and one is by the authors.

Write the scale degrees for the melody above the first setting, then sing or play each one. Label the harmonic intervals between the staves, and examine the counterpoint. In the blanks below the staff, identify any implied I or V chords, and indicate inversions. Circle and label any dissonant passing or neighbor tones.

As your teacher assigns: Write a paragraph summarizing the similarities and differences in these settings, or be prepared to compare them in class discussion.

A. J. S. Bach, Chorale No. 32

B. J. S. Bach, Chorale No. 330

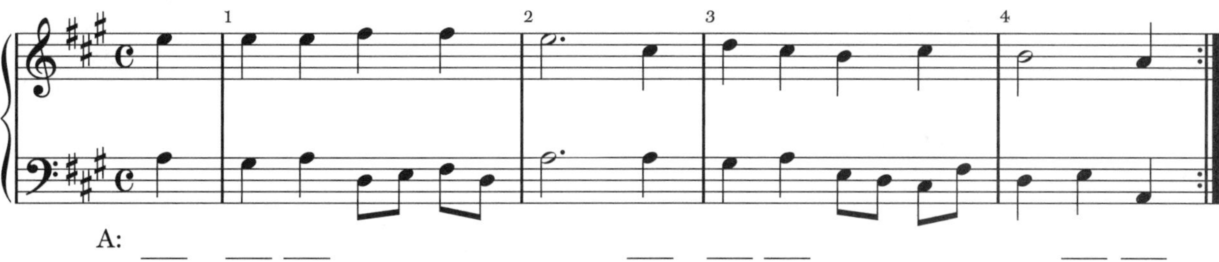

C. Felix Mendelssohn, from Episcopal Hymnal 1940

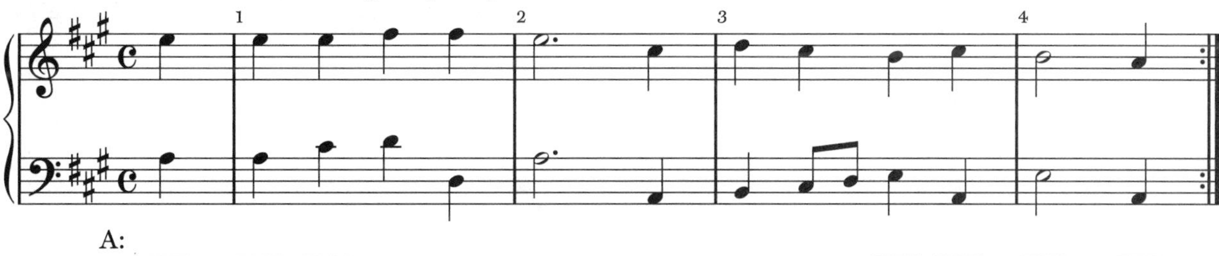

D. Jane Piper Clendinning and Elizabeth West Marvin

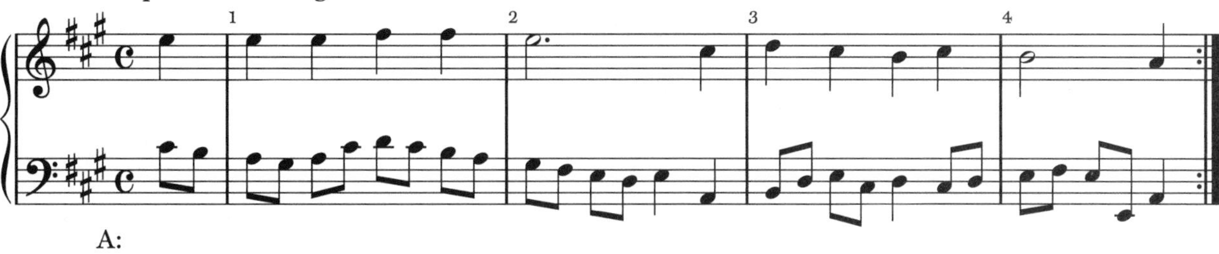

II. Writing chorale-style counterpoint from a given bass line

Write a chorale-style counterpoint for each given line. Combine note-to-note and 2:1 patterns, using 2:1 where possible; you may include suspensions, but don't change the given line. Write the harmonic interval numbers between the staves, circle any dissonant intervals, and label any passing tones, neighbor tones, or suspensions. Identify the key and mode, and write Roman numerals and figures for the opening and closing chords in the blanks, using only I, V(7), and their inversions.

NAME ____________________

ASSIGNMENT 11.6

I. Writing chorale-style counterpoint from a chorale melody

Write a chorale-style counterpoint for each given line. Combine note-to-note and 2:1 patterns, using 2:1 where possible; you may include suspensions, but don't change the given line. Write the harmonic interval numbers between the staves, circle any dissonant intervals, and label any passing tones, neighbor tones, or suspensions. Identify the key and mode, and write Roman numerals and figures for the opening and closing chords in the blanks, using only I and V(7) and their inversions. Write scale-degree numbers above each melody.

A. "In allen meinen Taten," mm. 1-2

Key: F I I6 ___ ___

B. "Heut' ist, o Mensch, ein grosser Trauertag," mm. 4–6

Key: ___ ___ ___ ___

C. "Aus meines Herzens Grunde" (abridged), mm. 16-21

Key: ___ ___ ___ ___ ___ ___ ___ ___ ___

II. J. S. Bach, Chorale No. 168, mm. 4–6 (adapted)

This chorale melody by Matthäus Apelles von Löwenstern (1633) is known as "Heut' ist, o Mensch, ein grosser Trauertag." From Bach's four-part setting, pairs of voices have been isolated in A–C. Consider each pair a two-part counterpoint: write the harmonic interval numbers below the staff (A) or between the staves (B and C), circle any dissonant intervals, and label any passing tones, neighbor tones, or suspensions. (Hint: Watch out for rearticulated suspensions.) For B and C, provide Roman numerals in the blanks. When there is a chordal skip in the bass, calculate the inversion from the lowest bass note. Then compare these two-part counterpoints to the four-voice setting in D, and circle and label any dissonance not found in A–C.

A. Soprano and alto

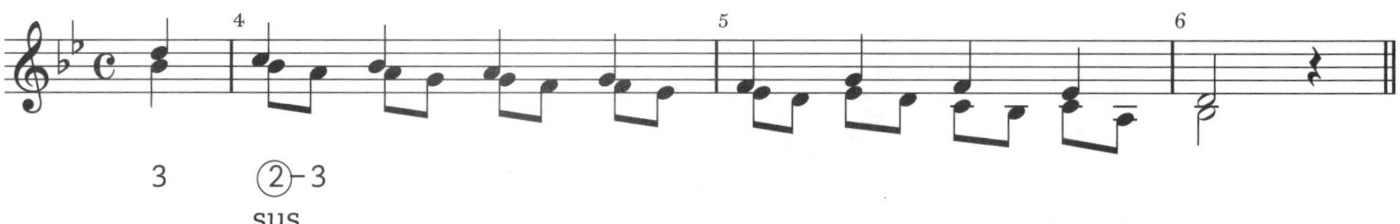

B. Soprano and bass

C. Alto and bass

D. Full chorale setting

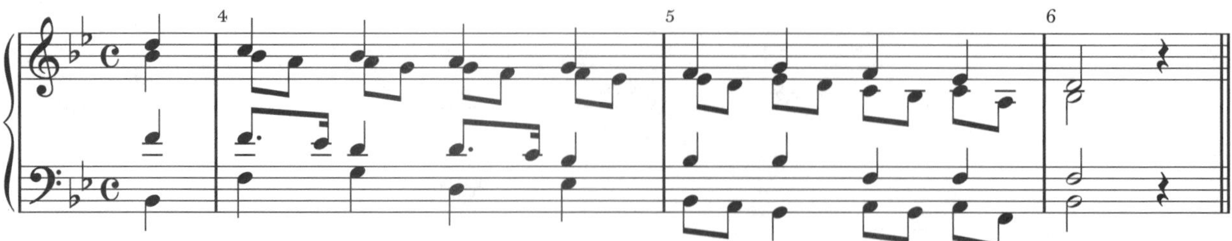

NAME ____________________

12 The Basic Phrase and Four-Part Writing

ASSIGNMENT 12.1

I. Analyzing cadence types

Identify the key of each excerpt, and write Roman numerals for the two chords that end each phrase. Circle the abbreviation that represents the cadence type. If the cadence is an IAC, circle "strong" or "contrapuntal."

A. J. S. Bach, "O Haupt voll Blut und Wunden," mm. 11–12

Key: F

___ ___

HC IAC PAC

If IAC: strong contrapuntal

B. Franz Schubert, "Der Lindenbaum," mm. 29–32

Key: ___

___ ___

HC IAC PAC

If IAC: strong contrapuntal

Translation: I had to travel by it again today in dead of night,

C. J. S. Bach, "Aus meines Herzens Grunde," mm. 1–4

___ ___

HC IAC PAC

If IAC: strong contrapuntal

II. Chorale-style doubling in triads

Write the triads requested in four parts (SATB), using half notes and adding any accidentals needed to make the correct chord quality. Carefully check the stem direction, voice range, doubling, and spacing.

A. Root position

(1) (2) (3) (4) (5) (6) (7) (8)

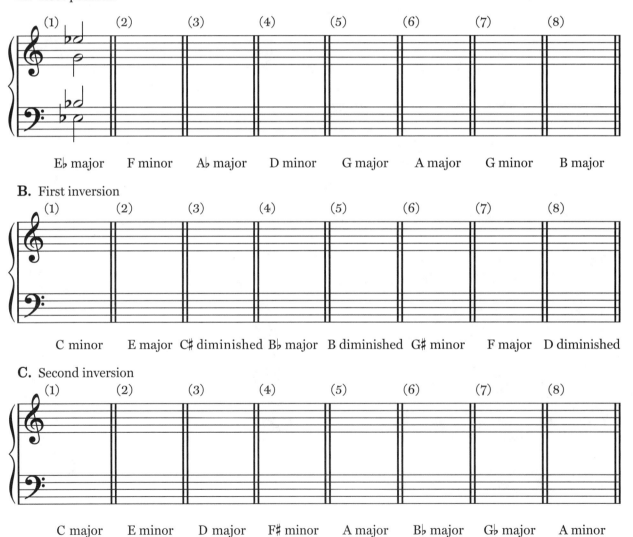

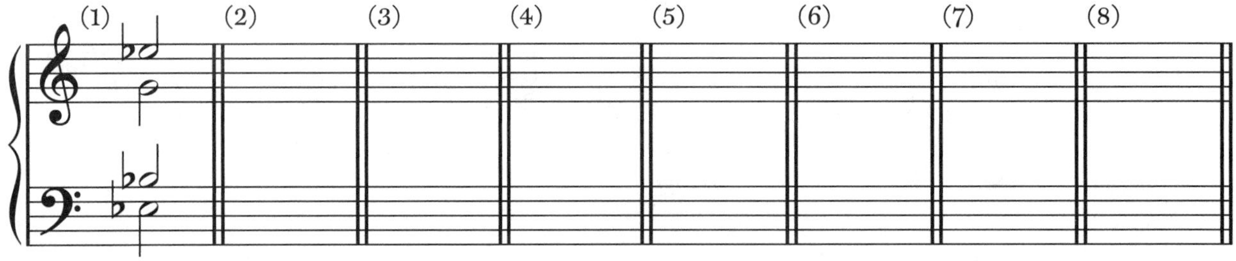

E♭ major F minor A♭ major D minor G major A major G minor B major

B. First inversion

(1) (2) (3) (4) (5) (6) (7) (8)

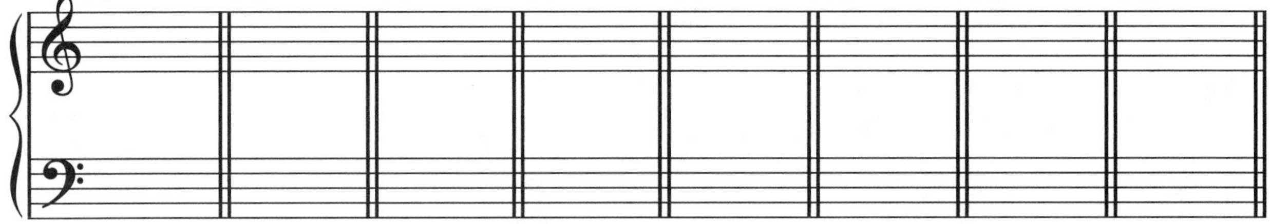

C minor E major C♯ diminished B♭ major B diminished G♯ minor F major D diminished

C. Second inversion

(1) (2) (3) (4) (5) (6) (7) (8)

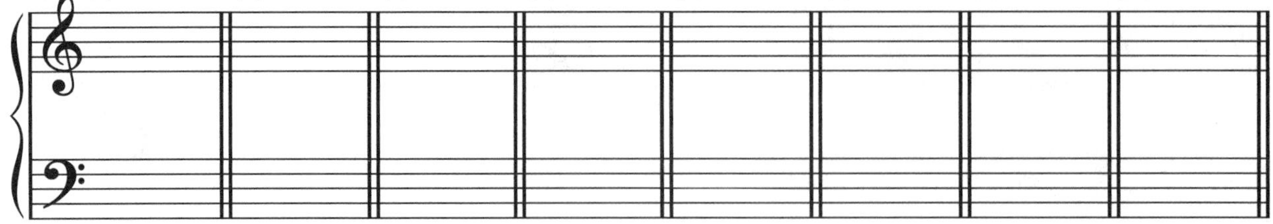

C major E minor D major F♯ minor A major B♭ major G♭ major A minor

NAME ______________________________

ASSIGNMENT 12.2

I. Error detection in chord spacing

Write the root, quality, and inversion ($^5_3$, $^6_3$, or $^6_4$) for each chord in chorale style. Then choose (from the following list) the type of error that applies to the chord, and write the letter in the blank. Rewrite the chord in the measure to the right, with the error corrected.

A. Incorrect doubling

B. Spacing more than an octave between soprano and alto

C. Spacing more than an octave between alto and tenor

D. Voice part out of suggested range

E. Crossed voices

F. Incorrect chord spelling

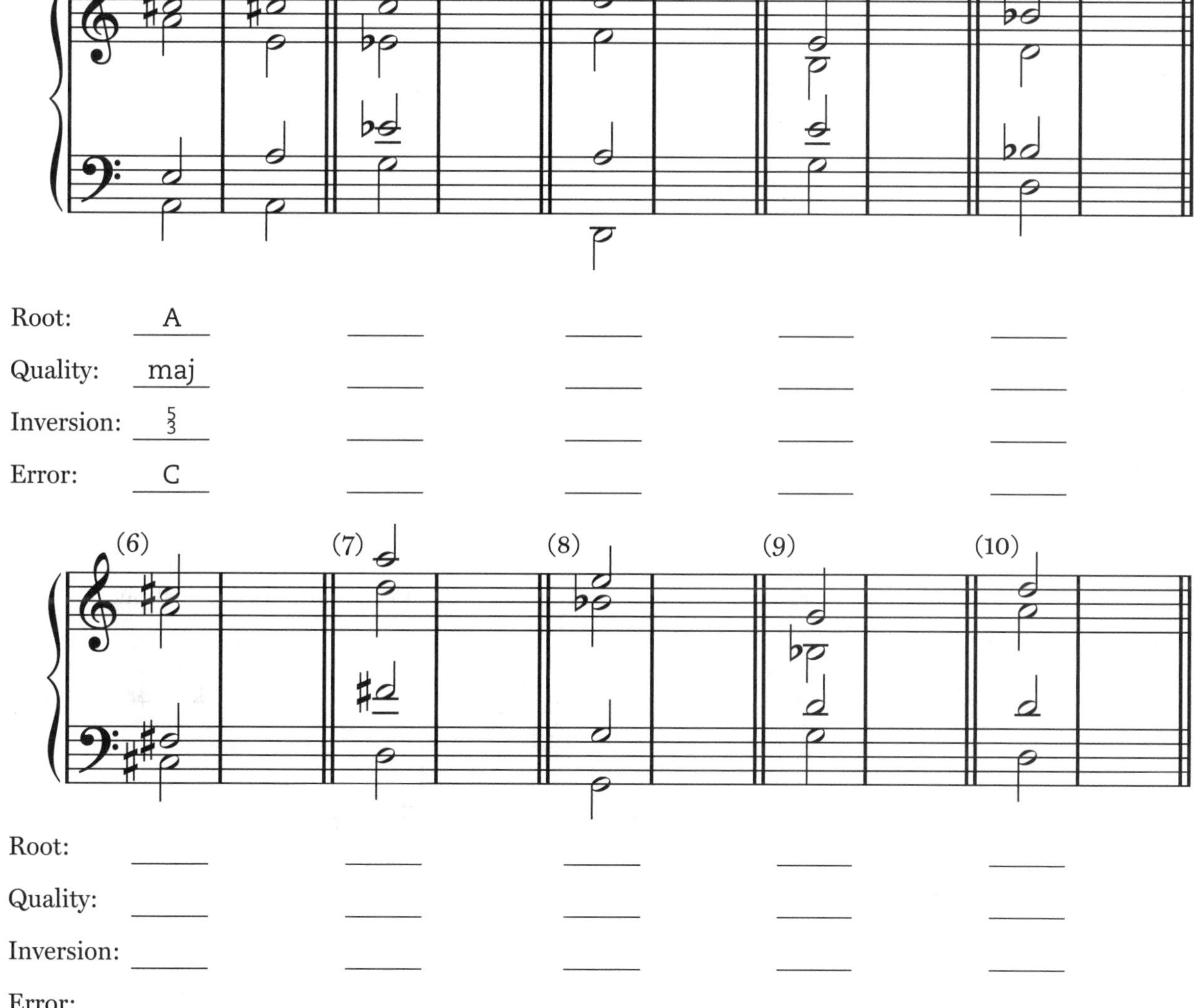

II. Analyzing basic phrases

For each basic phrase given, label the key and provide a Roman numeral analysis. Circle the correct label for each cadence. Finally, complete a contextual analysis (T-D-T) that shows the positions of the tonic and dominant areas in each phrase. If a phrase includes more than one V chord, remember the distinction between contrapuntal and strong dominants: a dominant between the two tonic harmonies early in the phrase prolongs the tonic area (T); the V at the cadence is the strong dominant (D).

A. Friedrich Kuhlau, Sonatina in C Major, Op. 55, No. 1, mvt. 1, mm. 1-4

HC IAC PAC

B. Jeremiah Clarke, *Trumpet Voluntary*, mm. 49-52

HC IAC PAC

C. Johann Kuhnau, Biblical Sonata No. 1, "The Fight between David and Goliath," closing section, mm. 1-8

HC IAC PAC HC IAC PAC

ASSIGNMENT 12.3

I. Scale-degree triads in inversion

For each of the Roman numerals in the keys indicated, notate the triads in quarter notes on the grand staff, in the specified inversion. Use proper chorale-style voicing, stem direction, doubling, and spacing. In minor keys, use the leading tone to spell the chords built on $\hat{5}$ and $\hat{7}$.

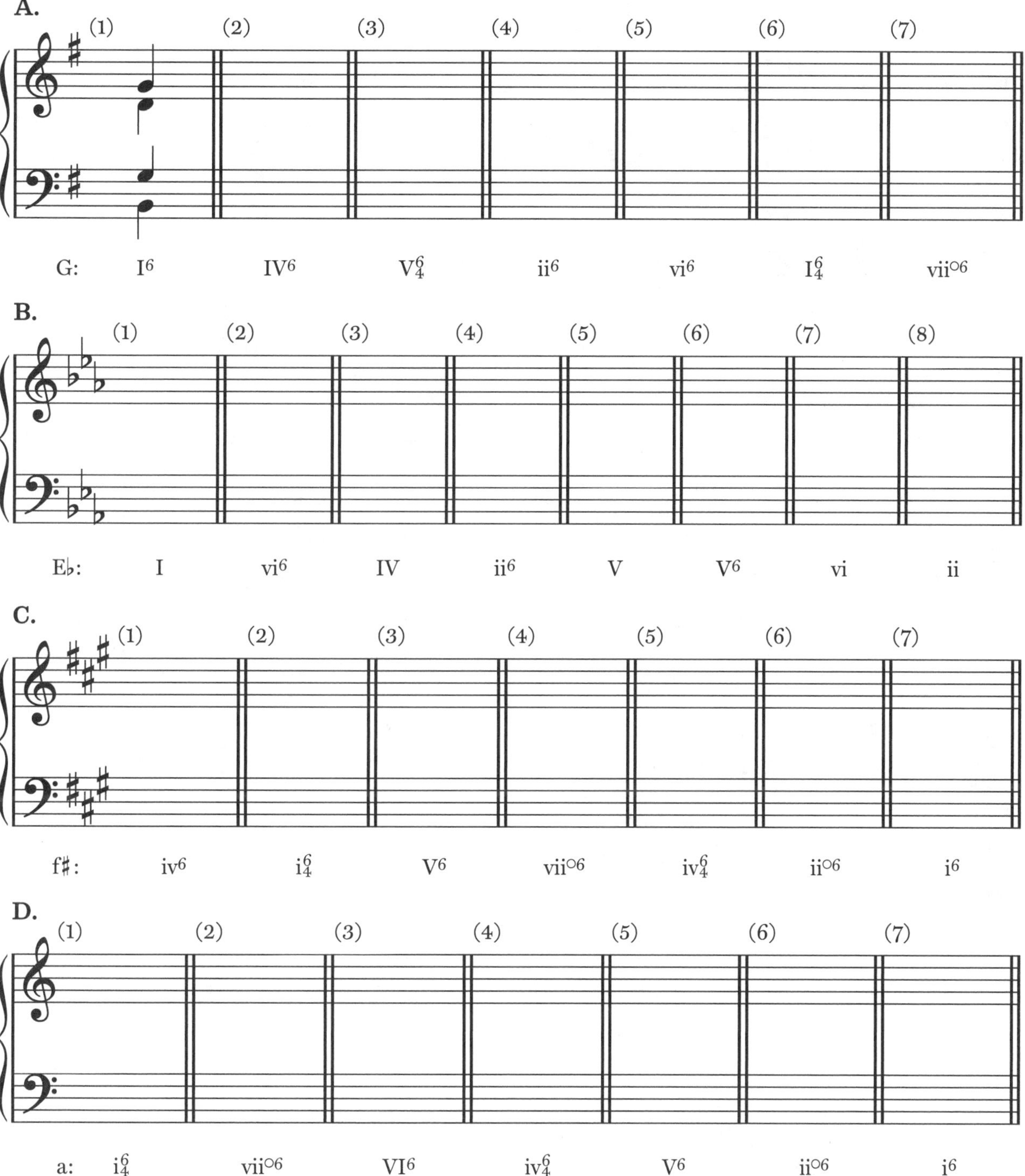

II. Analyzing chorale-style voicing and spacing

(1) Listen to the following piece, or sing it with your class. (2) Write the chords in root position on the staff below the example, and label each chord and quality in the blanks (maj, min, Mm7, etc.). Disregard the circled pitches. (3) Evaluate the spacing; write an asterisk (*) above any chord that diverges from the doubling guidelines, and be prepared to discuss in class. (4) Circle any spots where voices cross.

William Billings, "Chester," mm. 1–12

ASSIGNMENT 12.4

I. Writing triads from figured bass

Write the triad indicated above each given bass note. Use half notes, in four parts, making sure the stem direction is correct. In the blank, write the Roman numeral and inversion symbol for each chord in the key indicated.

A. Chorale-style spacing and voicing

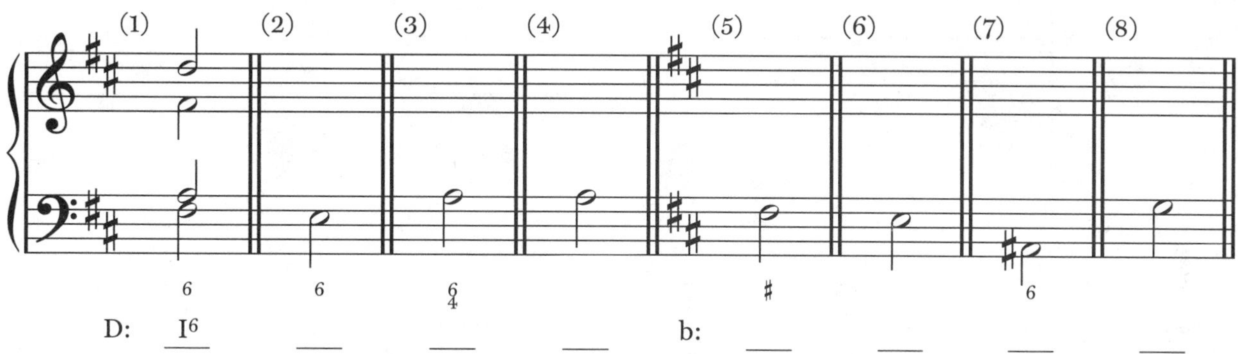

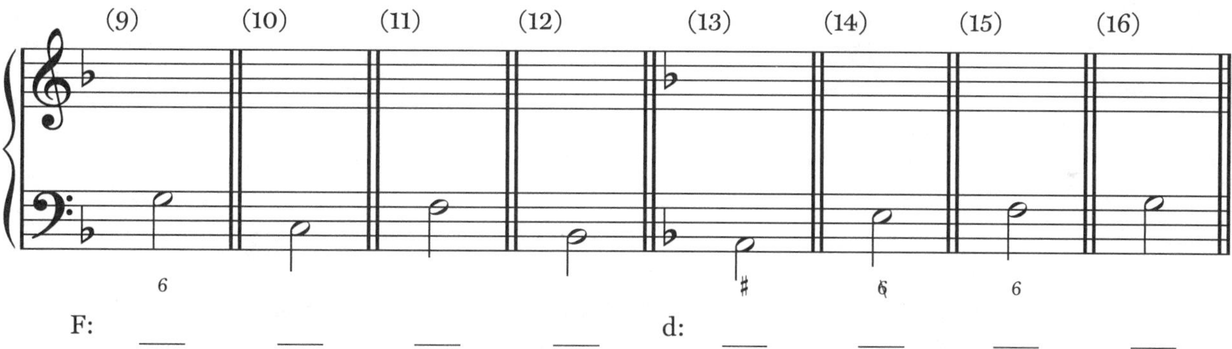

B. Keyboard spacing and voicing (three notes in the right hand and one in the left)

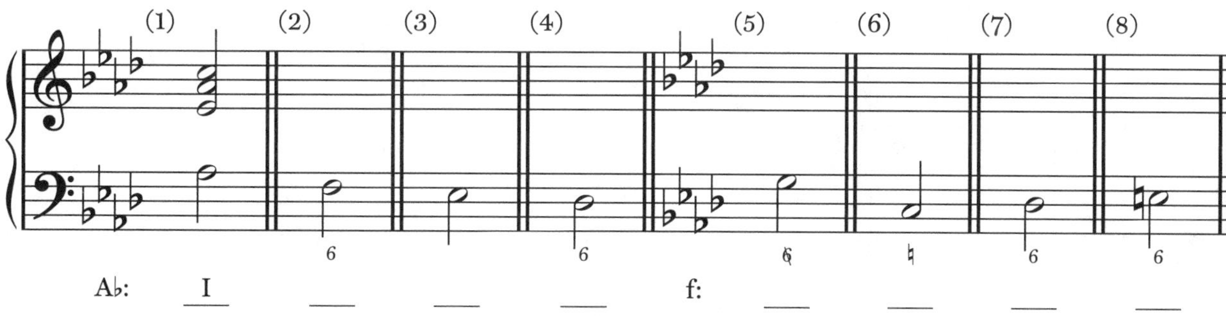

II. Writing cadences with I and V

Write the following cadences in chorale style, with half notes. Provide the appropriate key signatures, and add accidentals as needed in minor keys. Keep a common tone between chords. Draw arrows to show the upward resolution of leading tones.

A. Write a PAC.

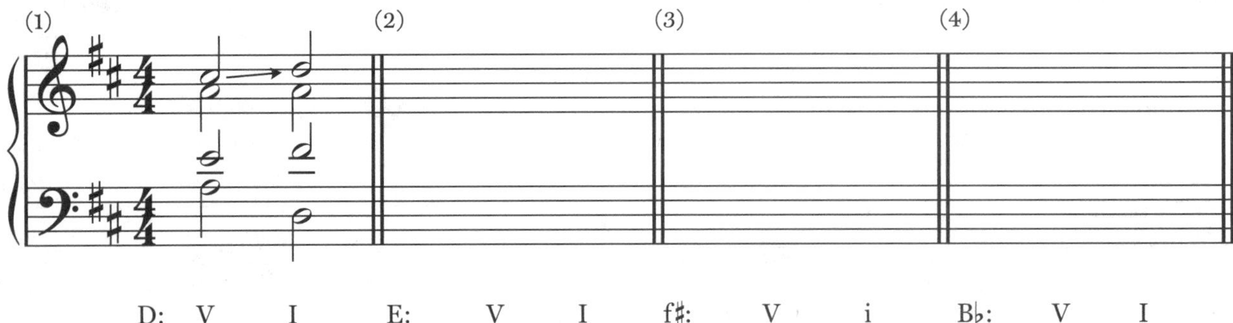

B. Write a strong IAC (root-position triads).

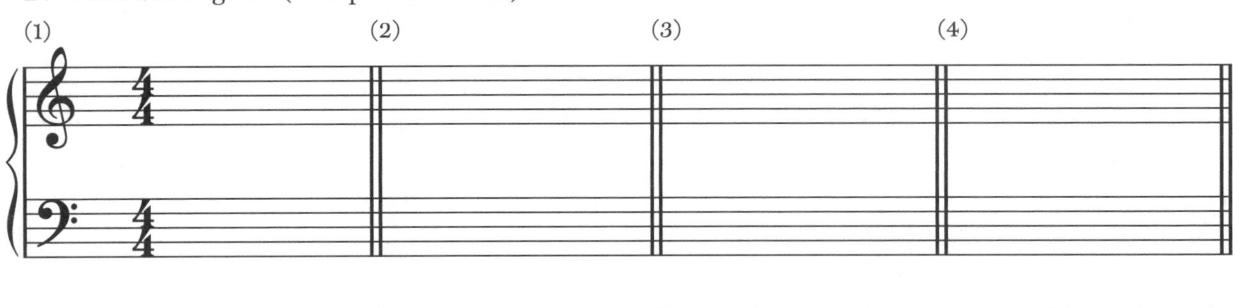

C. Write a HC.

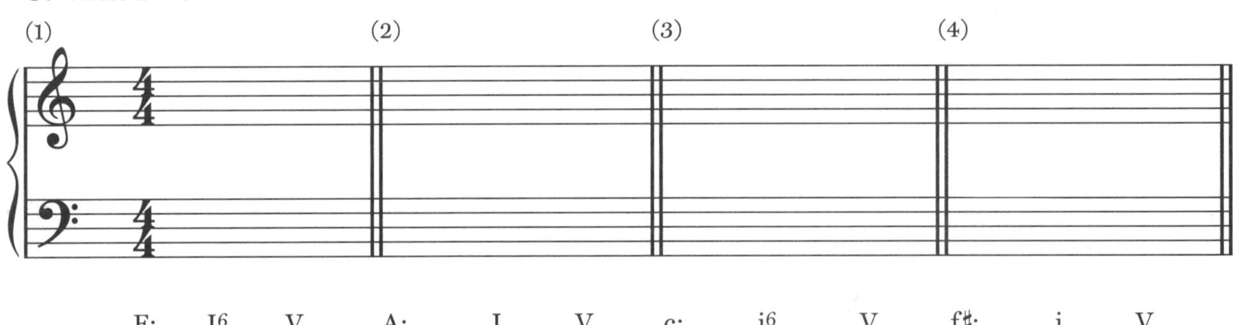

D. Write an authentic cadence (PAC or IAC) of your choice. Circle the appropriate label.

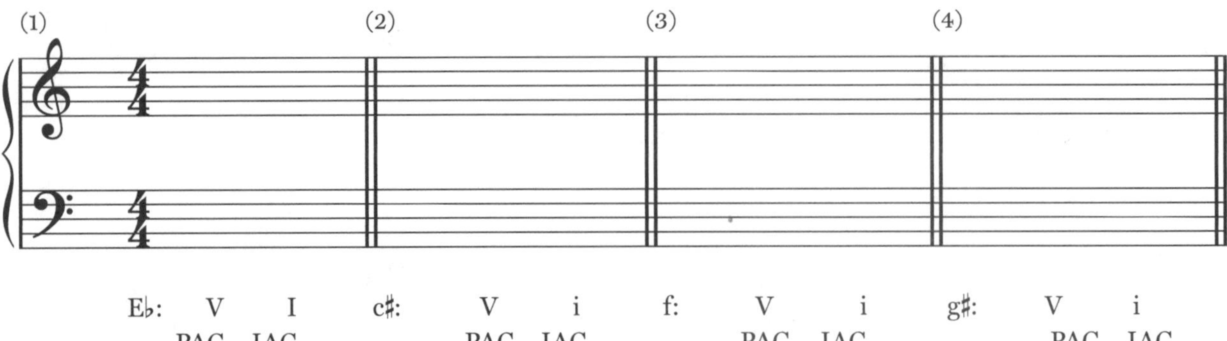

ASSIGNMENT 12.5

I. Writing basic phrases

Write the following progressions in chorale style in the meter indicated, one chord per measure. Provide the appropriate key signatures, and add a contextual analysis beneath the Roman numerals. Where a chord is repeated, change the spacing. Finally, label the cadence type.

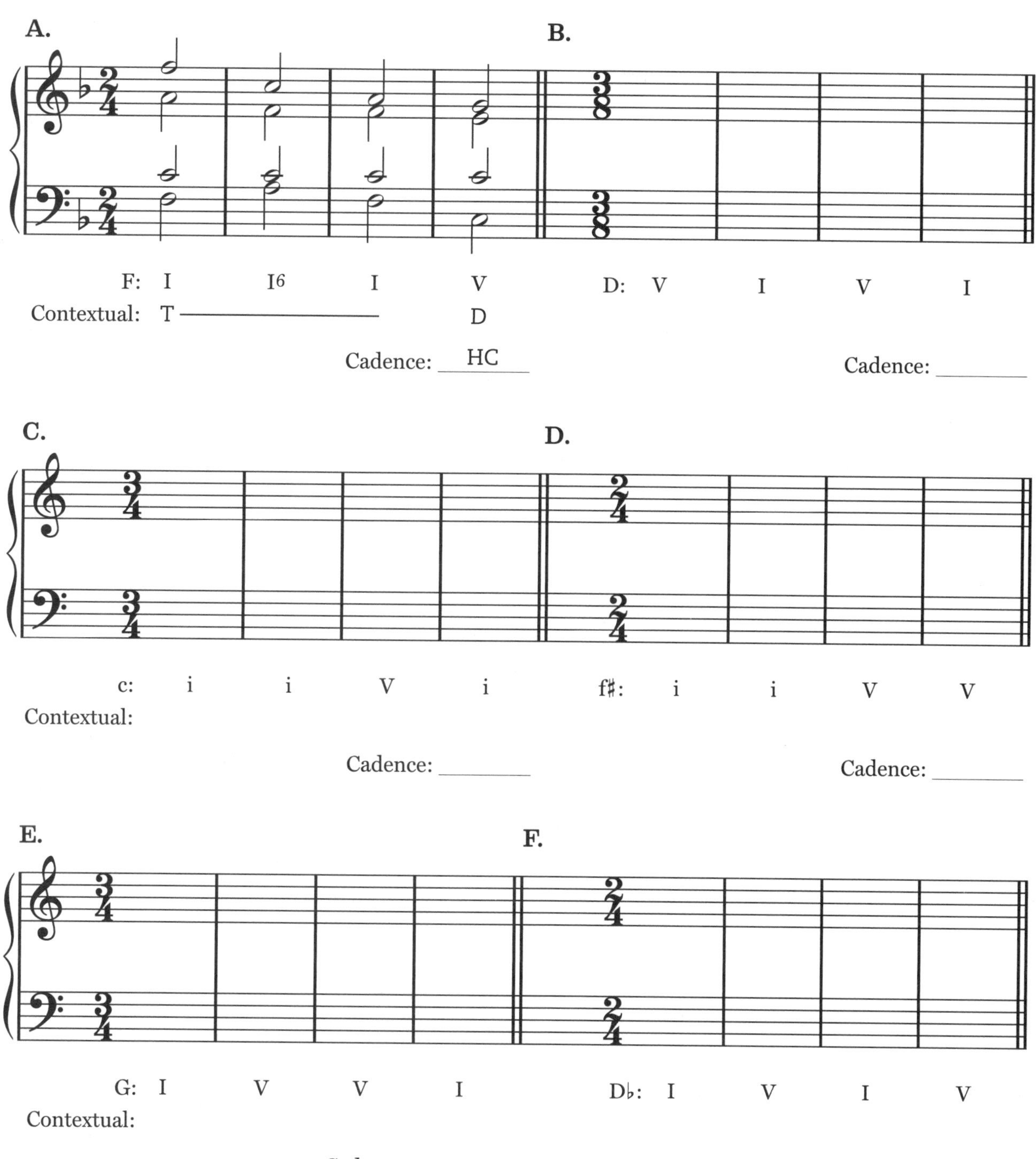

II. Keyboard settings

Below the empty staves are Roman numerals for the progressions you wrote in part I, exercises B and E. On the first staff, write a keyboard setting with arpeggiation, Alberti bass, or another figuration shown in the chapter; follow the voice leading from your chorale-style part writing. On the second staff, convert the major setting into the parallel minor by changing the key signature and adding appropriate accidentals (without changing the part writing or figuration).

A.

(1) Keyboard setting of I B

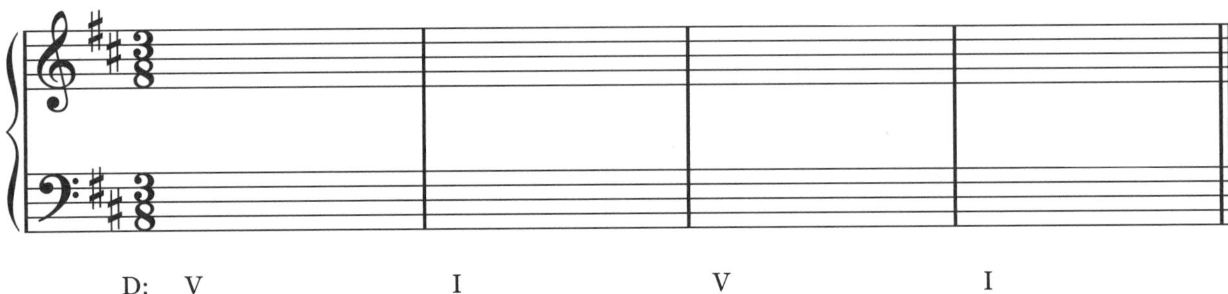

(2) Minor setting of I B

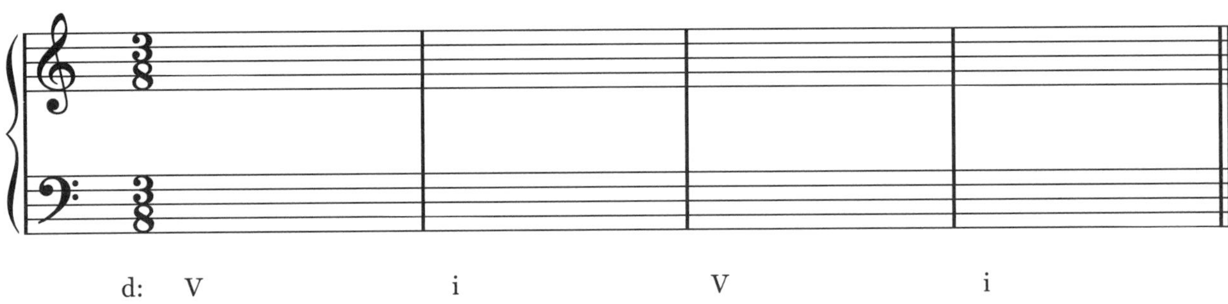

B.

(1) Keyboard setting of I E

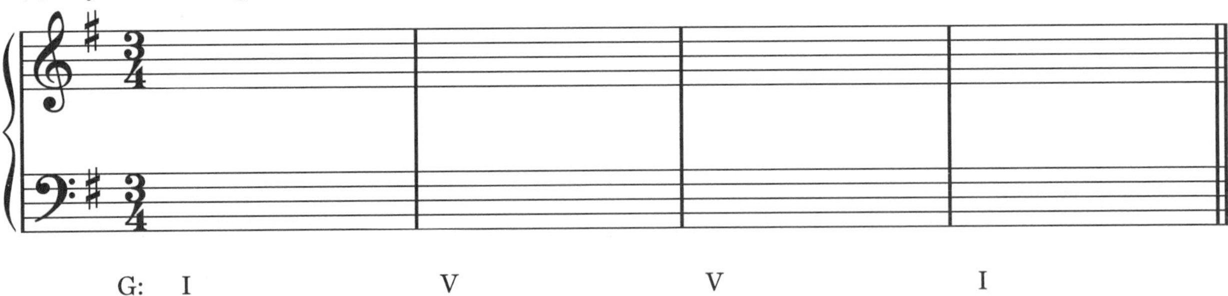

(2) Minor setting of I E

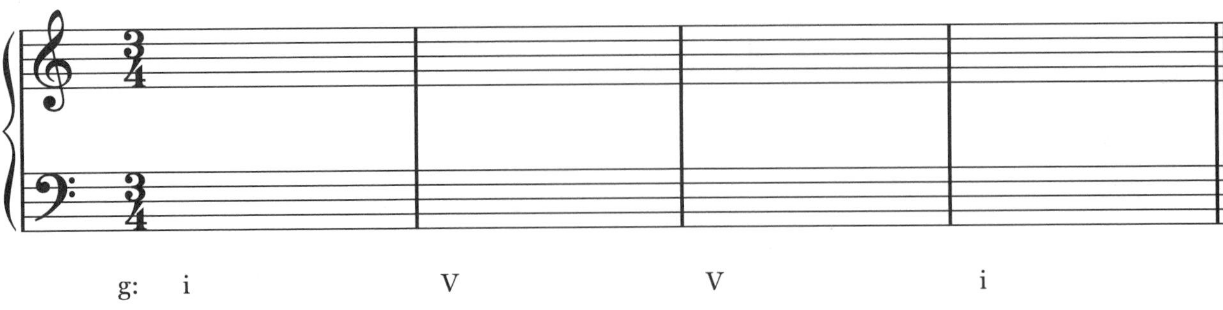

ASSIGNMENT 12.6

I. Folk-melody harmonization

Sing each melody on scale degrees or solfège, or play it on an instrument. Use the scale degrees (and your ears) to harmonize each measure: pick either I or V. You may wish to play the bass and melody at the keyboard. For melody B, use the leading tone for a major V chord, and harmonize measure 6 with i (instead of minor v). Circled notes are embellishing tones, which may be ignored in choosing harmonies.

A. "Hush, Little Baby," mm. 1–8

B. "Peter Gray," mm. 1–8

C. "The More We Get Together," mm. 1–8

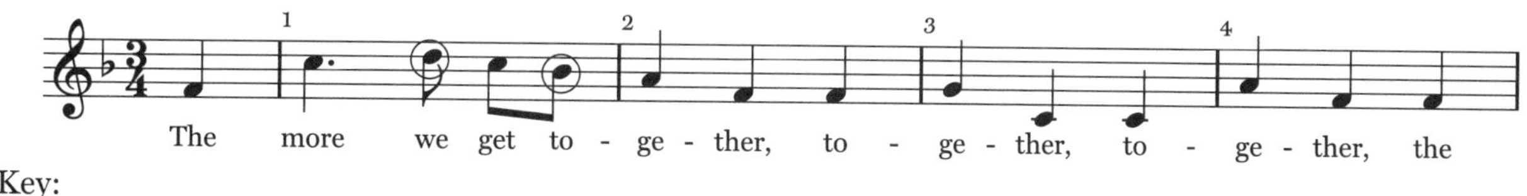

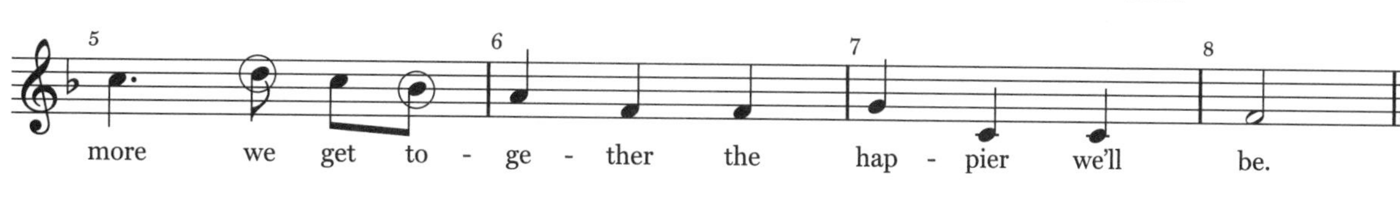

D. Waltz tune, mm. 1-8

II. Writing in freer textures

Write a keyboard accompaniment to one of the melodies in part I. Write the melody on the top staff, and align the accompaniment on the grand staff below it.

Dominant Sevenths, the Predominant Area, and Realizing Figured Bass

ASSIGNMENT 13.1

I. Writing root-position V7–I and V7–i from soprano-bass pairs in chorale style

For each two-chord progression, provide a key signature and write the inner voices in quarter notes. If a harmony is marked with an asterisk, write an incomplete chord. Use the leading tone in minor. Label the leading tone (LT) and chordal seventh (7), and draw arrows to show the resolution of the leading tone up and the chordal seventh down. In the blanks below each example, write "I" or "C" to designate which chords are incomplete and complete.

II. Analysis

Write the key and provide Roman numerals below the staff, disregarding any circled embellishing tones; assume a harmonic rhythm of one chord every one or two measures. Write a contextual analysis below the Roman numerals, assuming two four-bar phrases in each example; label all cadences.

A. W. A. Mozart, "In quegli anni," from *The Marriage of Figaro*, Act 4, No. 2, mm. 42–49

Translation: While I silently gaze at that gift,

B. Franz Schubert, Dance, Op. 9, No. 23, mm. 1–8

ASSIGNMENT 13.2

I. Error detection

In each cadence pattern, locate three voice-leading errors, and mark them on the score. In the blank underneath, write the number of each error type found in that measure.

1. missing/incorrect chord tone
2. parallel fifths or octaves
3. unresolved chordal 7th
4. doubled leading tone
5. unresolved leading tone
6. incorrect Roman numeral or figure

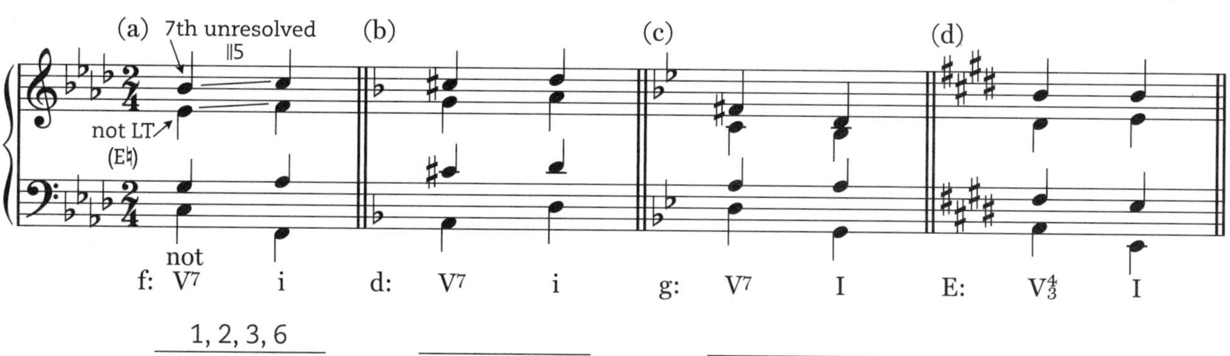

II. Resolving V⁷ and its inversions

Write the following progressions in chorale style, with half notes. Provide the appropriate key signatures, and add accidentals as needed. Draw arrows to show the resolution of leading tones up and chordal sevenths down. For root-position V7–I, make one chord incomplete.

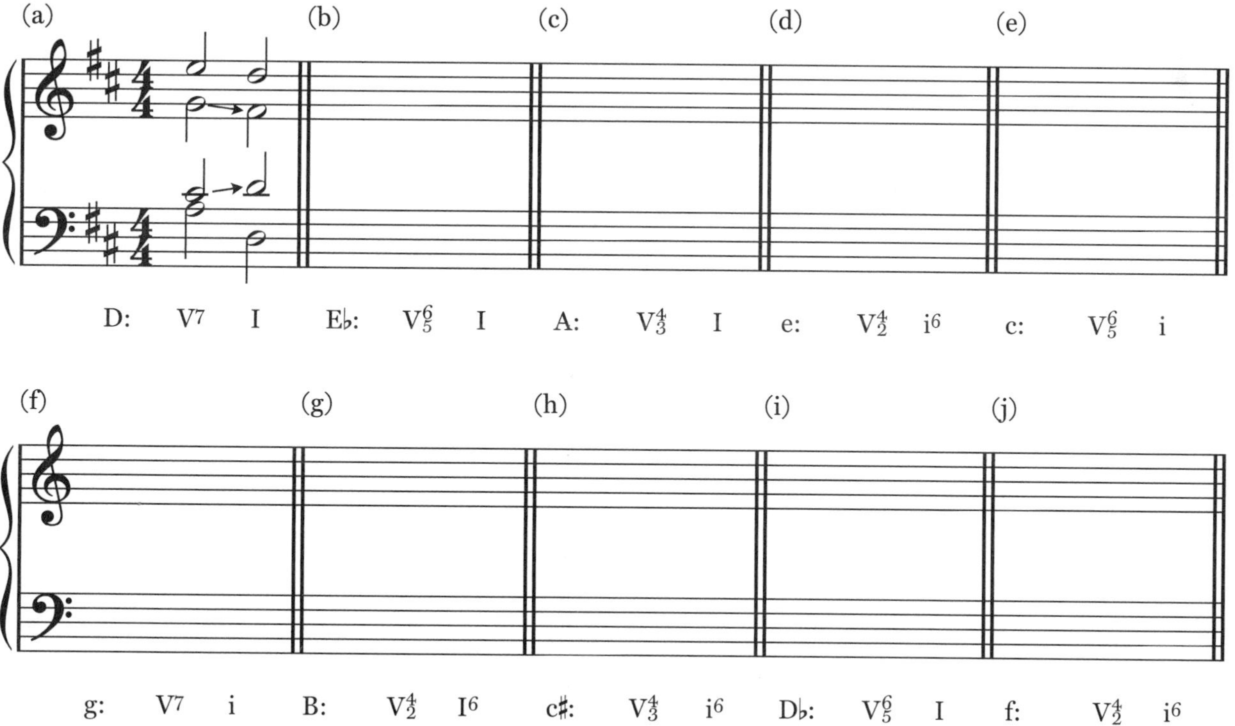

III. *Three-chord progressions in chorale style*

For each progression, provide a key signature and part-write in quarter notes. Use the leading tone in minor. Where V^4_3 appears between two tonic chords, write parallel tenths between the soprano and bass.

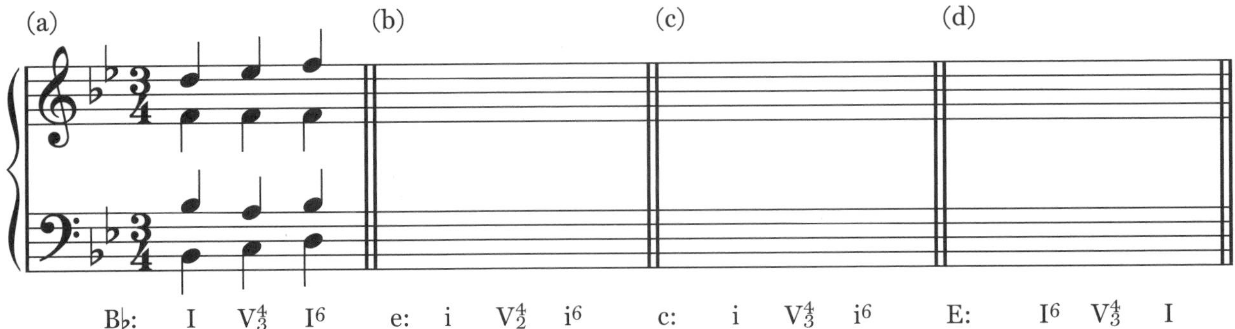

IV. *Writing basic phrases with V^7 and inversions*

Write the following progressions in chorale style in the meter indicated. (Bar lines are indicated with the Roman numerals.) Provide the appropriate key signatures, and add accidentals as needed. Write a contextual analysis beneath the Roman numerals.

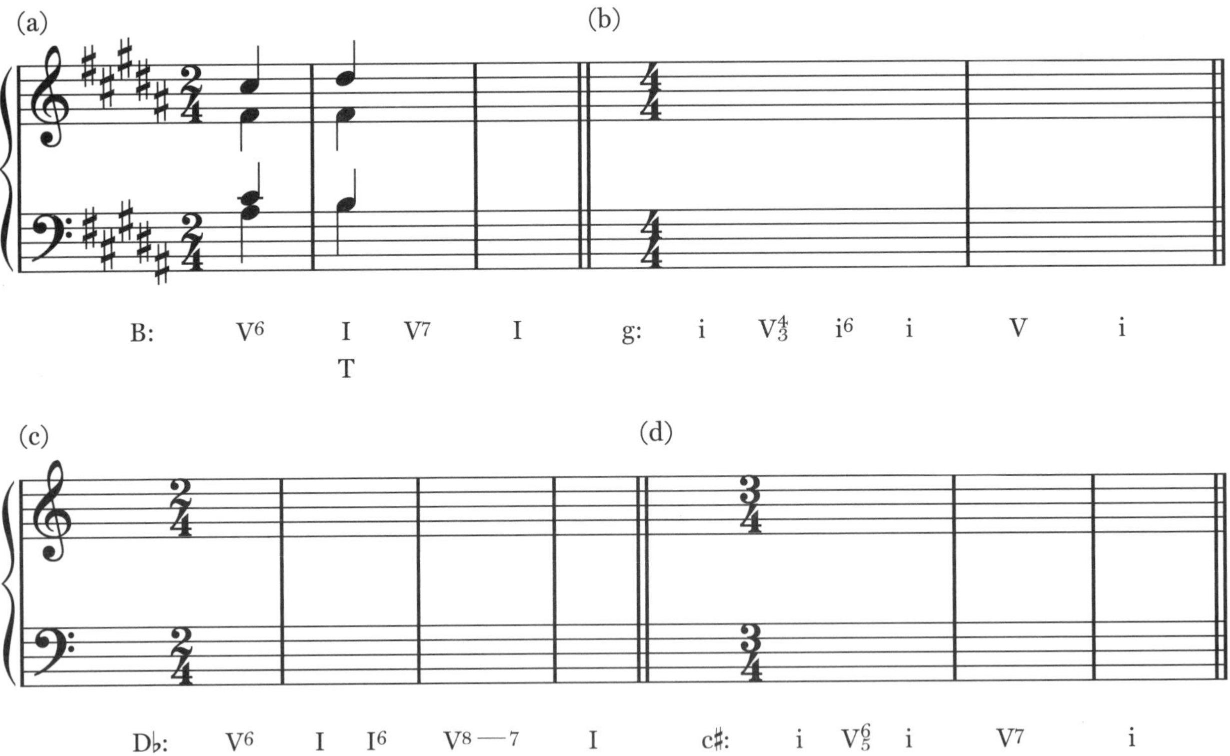

NAME ______________________________

ASSIGNMENT 13.3

I. Connecting predominant and dominant harmonies

Write the following progressions in chorale style with half notes. Provide the appropriate key signatures, and add accidentals as needed.

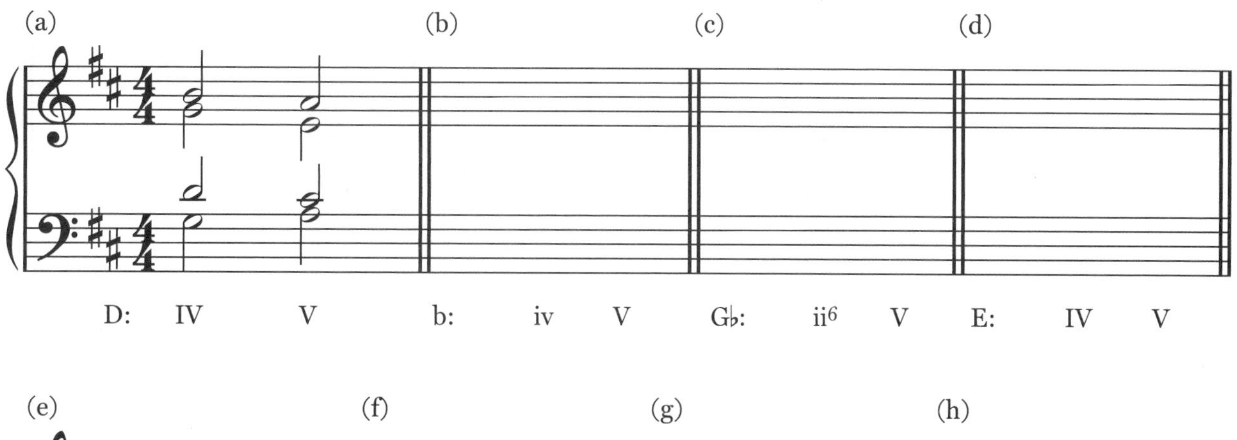

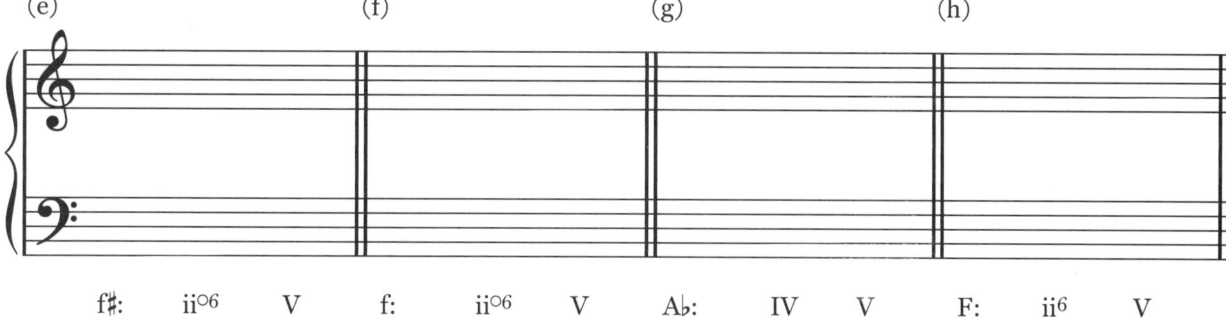

II. Writing predominant and dominant harmonies in short phrases

Write the following phrases in chorale style, using the provided Roman numerals and melody. In the blank under each measure, label the cadence type (HC, PAC, IAC).

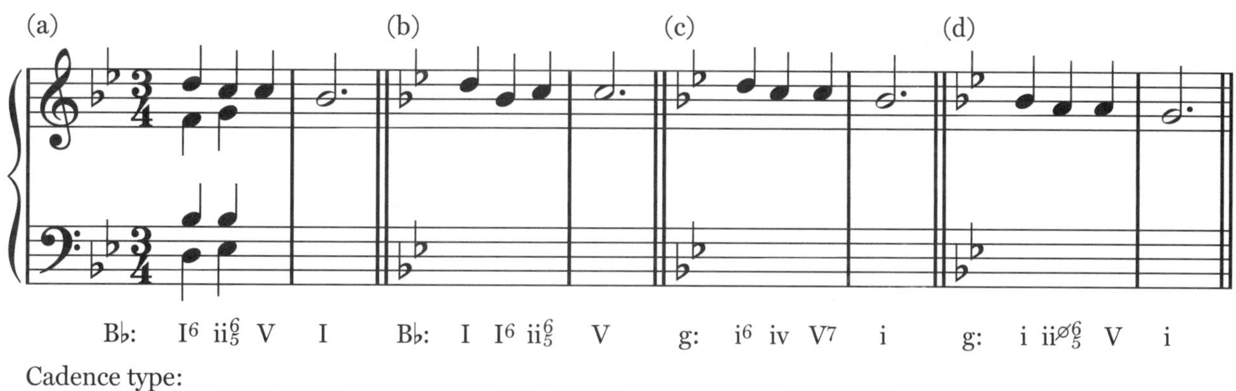

Cadence type: ________ ________ ________ ________

III. Analysis

Write the key, and provide Roman numerals in the blanks below the staff; these should indicate a harmonic rhythm of one or two chords per measure. When a single harmony spans more than one bass note, choose the lowest note to calculate the position/inversion. Write a contextual analysis below the Roman numerals, and label any cadence types.

A. Beethoven, Piano Sonata, Op. 2, No. 3, mvt. 1, mm. 1-8

B. Haydn, String Quartet, Op. 20, No. 5, mvt. 1, mm. 1-5

ASSIGNMENT 13.4

I. Writing basic phrases with predominants

Write the following progressions in chorale style in the meter indicated. In minor, raise ♭$\hat{7}$ to create a leading tone. Provide a contextual analysis below the Roman numerals.

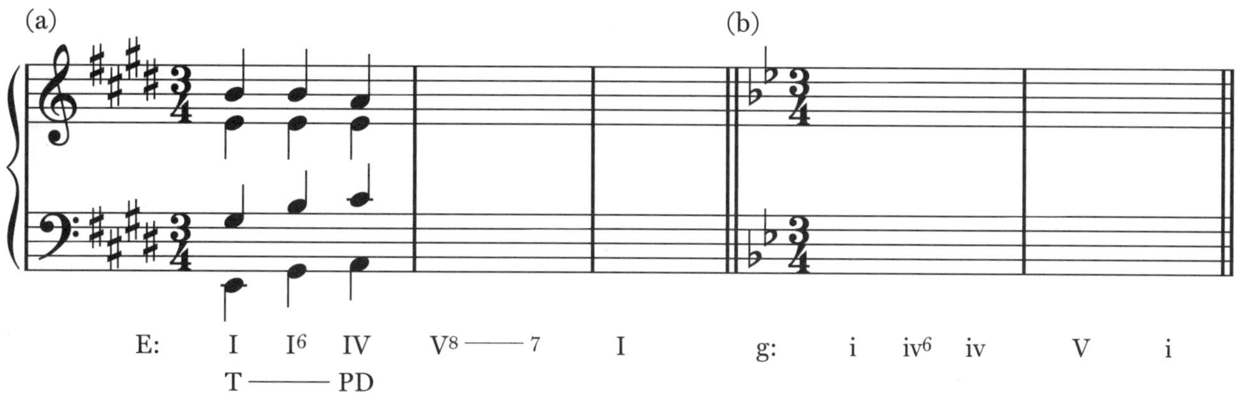

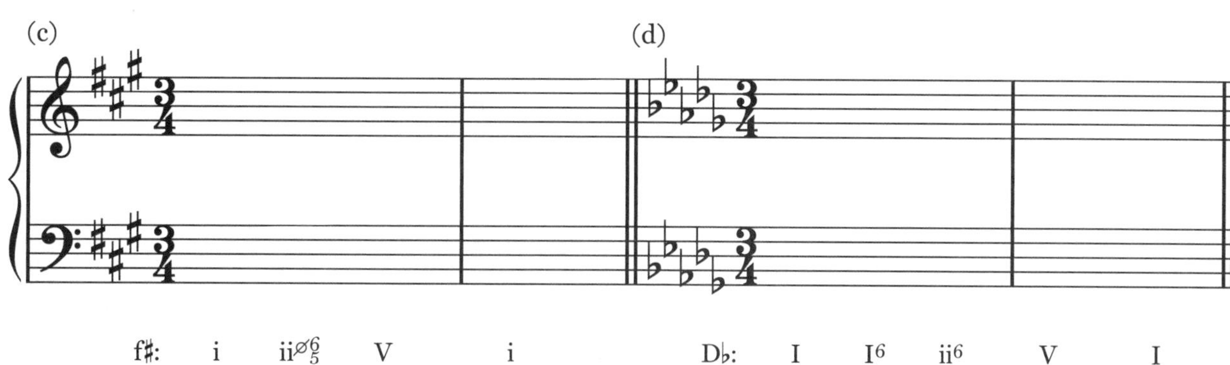

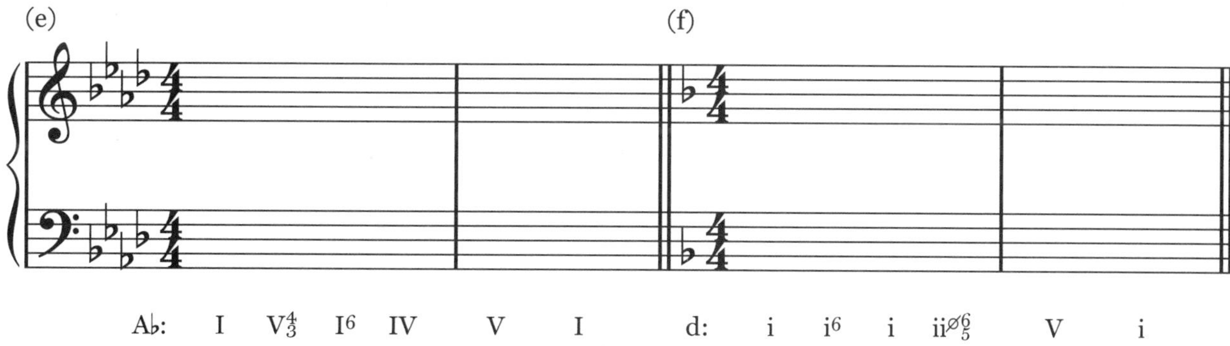

II. Analysis: Frédéric Chopin, Mazurka, Op. 33, No. 2, mm. 1–16

Provide Roman numerals in the blanks below the staff, disregarding any passing or neighbor tones. Indicate the entrance of a chordal seventh off the beat by the figures 8–7 where appropriate. Write a contextual analysis below the Roman numerals, and label each cadence.

This excerpt could be analyzed as four four-measure phrases or two eight-measure phrases; what would be the cadence labels for each analysis? What factors support each interpretation? How might a performer make the phrases clear?

ASSIGNMENT 13.5

I. Figured bass in keyboard style

A. Write the following figured-bass progressions in quarter notes, using keyboard style (three pitches in the right hand and the bass line in the left). In the blanks, write the key and a Roman numeral analysis.

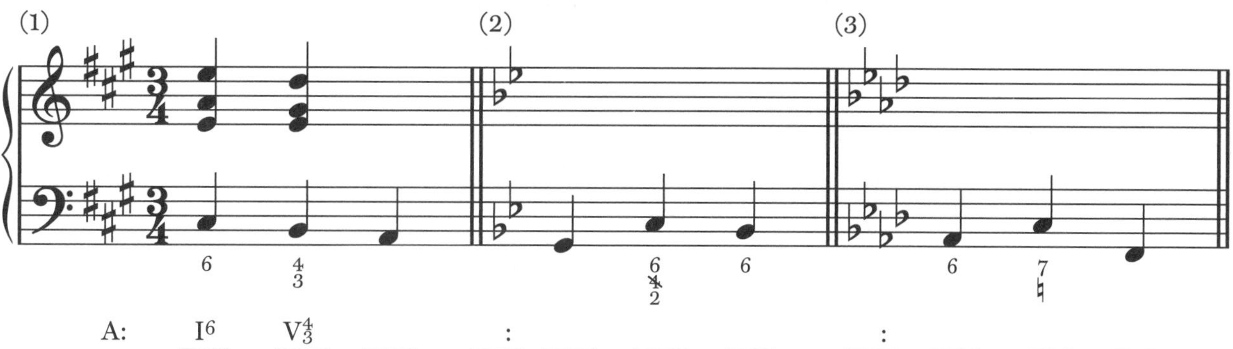

B. Analysis: Antonio Vivaldi, *Gloria*, mvt. 6, mm. 7–11

Realize the given figured bass to accompany the soprano solo. Use keyboard spacing and dotted-quarter rhythms as shown. Write the key, Roman numerals, and cadence type below the staff. Then provide a contextual analysis for the phrase beginning in measure 9.

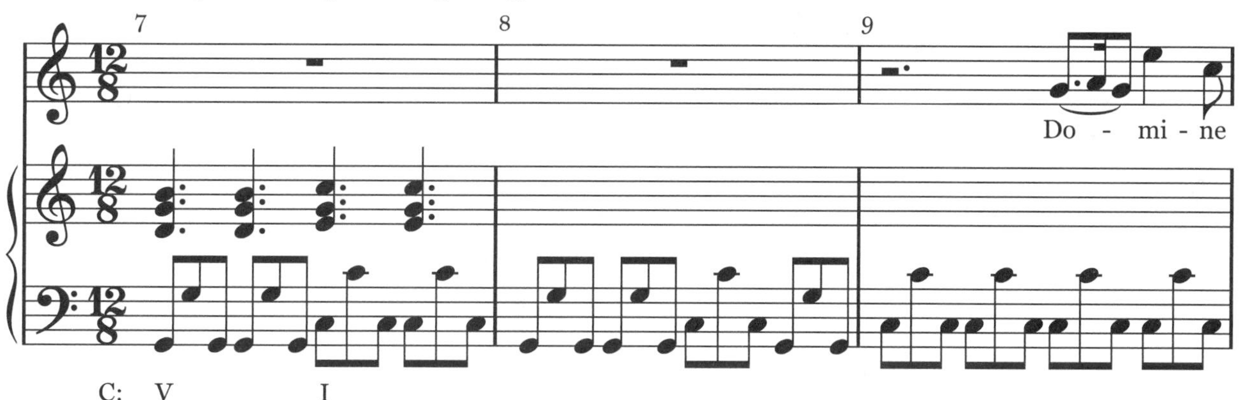

Translation: Lord God, heavenly king

C. Analysis: Arcangelo Corelli, Allemanda, from Trio Sonata in A Minor, Op. 4, No. 5 (adapted)

Realize the figured bass using keyboard style with quarter-note rhythms. Write the key, Roman numerals, and cadence type below the staff.

(1) Mm. 13–15

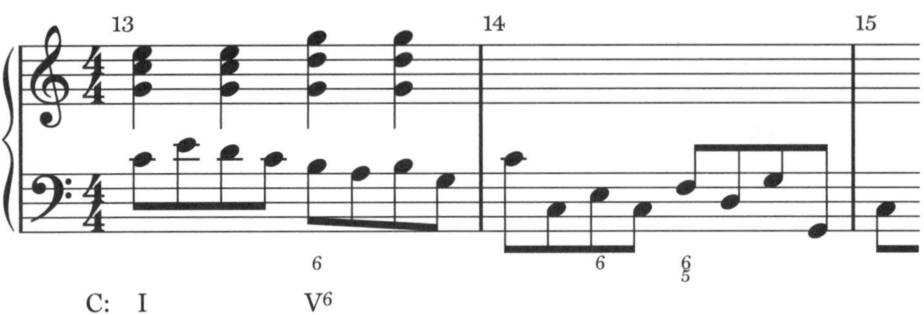

Cadence:

(2) Mm. 15–17

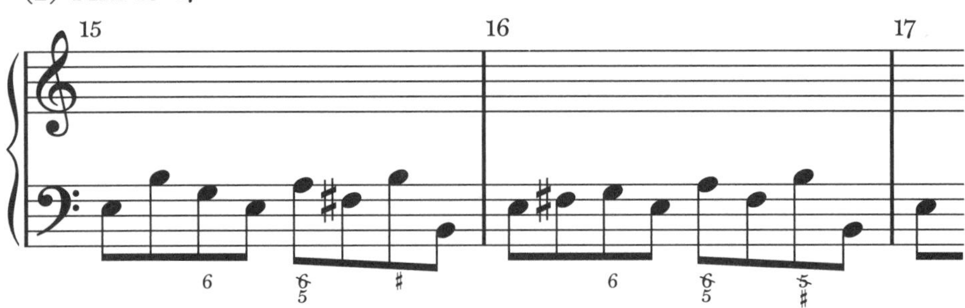

Cadence:

(3) Mm. 17–19

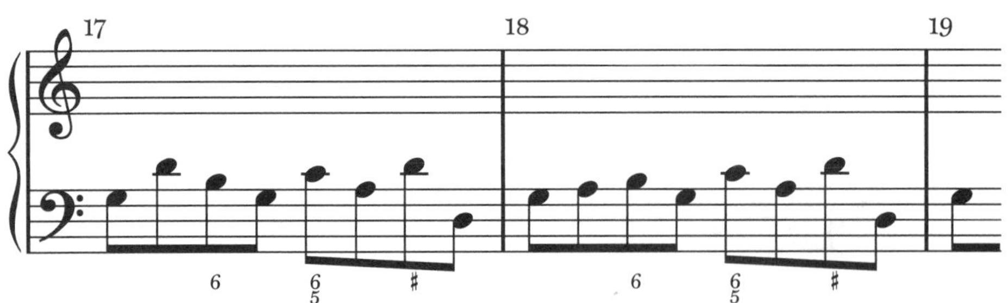

Cadence:

ASSIGNMENT 13.6

I. Analysis of chorales

Write the key, and provide a Roman numeral and contextual analysis for each chorale phrase, ignoring any circled embellishing tones. Indicate the entrance of a chordal seventh off the beat by the figures 8–7 where appropriate. Label each cadence type. For class discussion: How does the placement of the embellishments and the choice of inversions add to the interest of each harmonization?

A. J. S. Bach, "Lass, o Herr, dein Ohr sich neigen," mm. 1–3

B. J. S. Bach, "Lobt Gott, ihr Christen allzugleich," mm. 1–2

II. Figured bass in chorale style

Complete the inner voices for these chorale melodies with figured bass. Write the key, Roman numerals, and cadence type below each staff.

A. J. S. Bach, "O Haupt voll Blut und Wunden," phrase 6, mm. 11–12

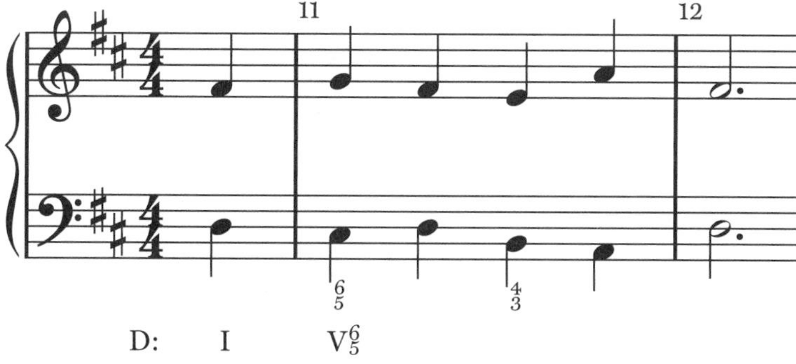

B. J. S. Bach, "Liebster Jesu! wir sind hier," phrases 1 and 2, mm. 1–5

Cadence: Cadence:

C. J. S. Bach, "Herzliebster Jesu, was hast du verbrochen," phrase 1, mm. 1–3

Cadence:

D. J. S. Bach, "Christus, der ist mein Leben," phrase 1, mm. 1–4

Cadence: Cadence:

NAME ______________________________

Expanding the Basic Phrase

ASSIGNMENT 14.1

I. Writing cadential $^6_4$s from Roman numerals

A. Write the following cadence patterns in four parts, with quarter and half notes in the meter indicated. Add accidentals as needed. Circle the cadence type: HC, IAC, or PAC.

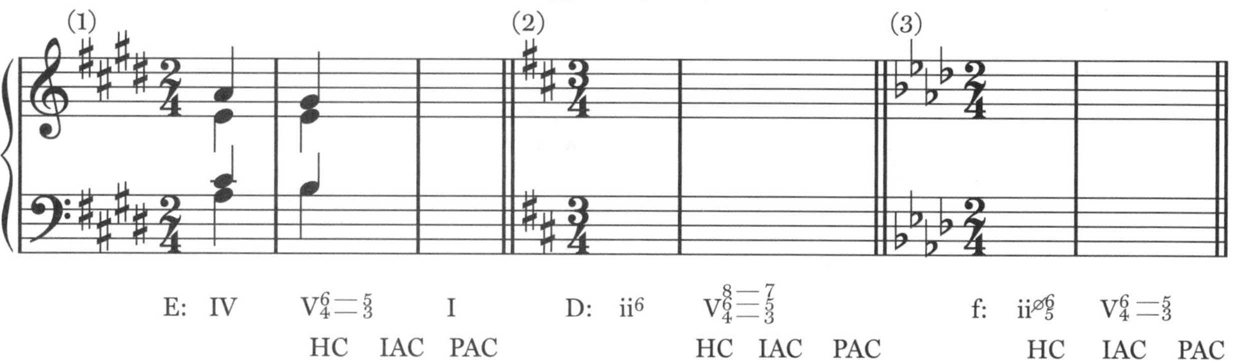

B. Write the following longer progressions in four parts, with rhythms appropriate to the meter indicated. Add accidentals as needed, and a contextual analysis beneath.

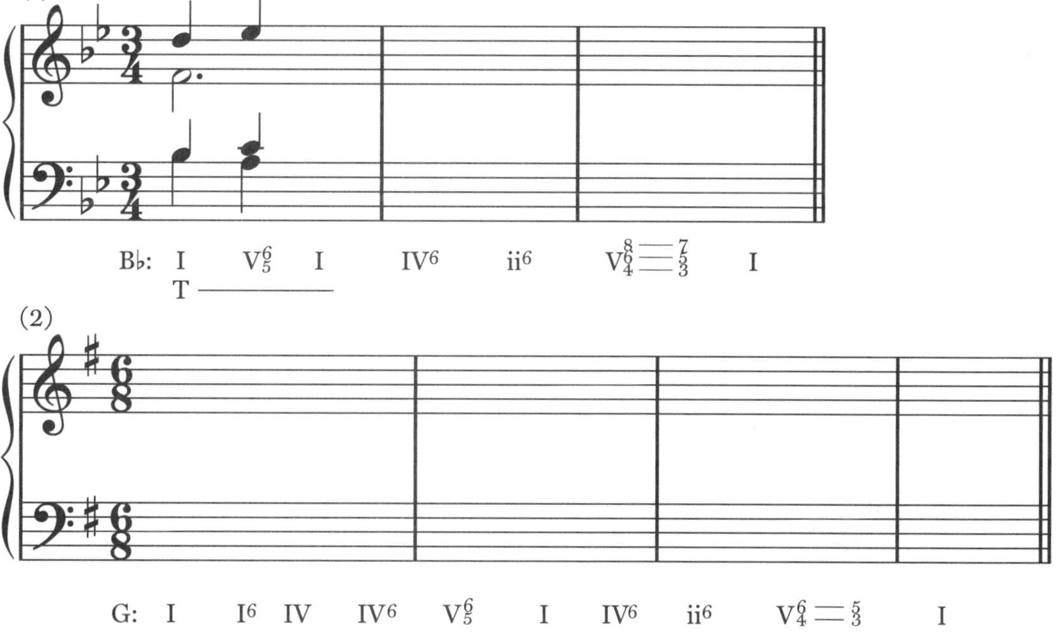

II. Analysis with $^{6}_{4}$ chords

For each musical excerpt below, locate the cadential $^{6}_{4}$. Circle the $^{6}_{4}$ chord and write the key and Roman numerals for the cadence only.

A. Amy Cheney Beach, Gavotte Fantastique, Op. 54, No. 2, mm. 5–8

5
6
7
8

B. J. S. Bach, "Schafe können sicher weiden," mm. 39–40

39
40
und was Län - der glück - lich macht.

Translation: And that which makes countries fortunate.

C. Fernando Sor, Menuetto for Solo Guitar, Op. 5, No. 1, mm. 13–16

13
14
15
16

D. Robert S. Weir and Calixa Lavallée, "O Canada," mm. 25–28

25
rit.
26
27
28
O Can - a - da! We stand on guard for thee.

ASSIGNMENT 14.2

I. Writing cadential $^6_4$s from figured bass

A. Write the following cadence patterns in keyboard style, with quarter and half notes in the meter indicated. Add accidentals as needed, and analyze with Roman numerals. Circle the cadence type.

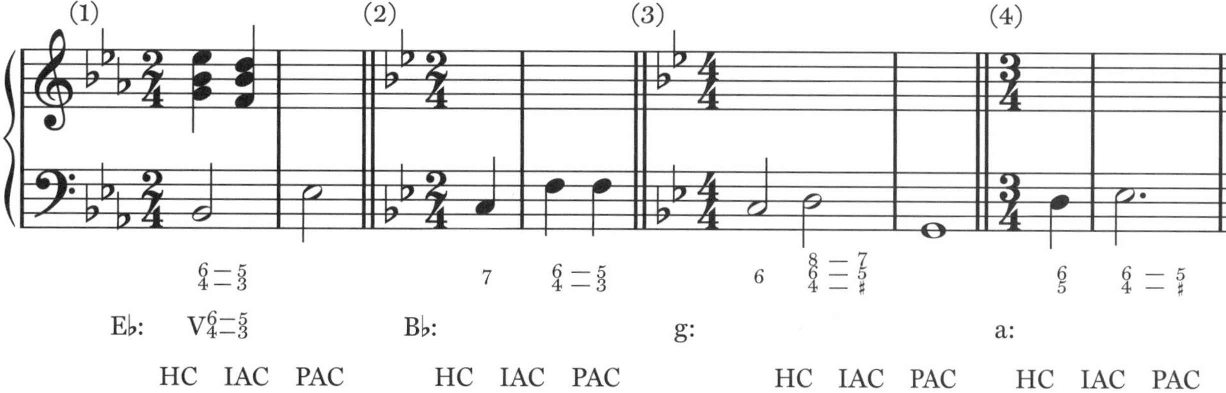

B. Write the following longer progressions in keyboard style, with rhythms appropriate to the meter indicated. Add accidentals as needed, and provide a Roman numeral and contextual analysis. Write the right hand primarily in three parts, but you may occasionally shift to two parts to assist with proper voice leading.

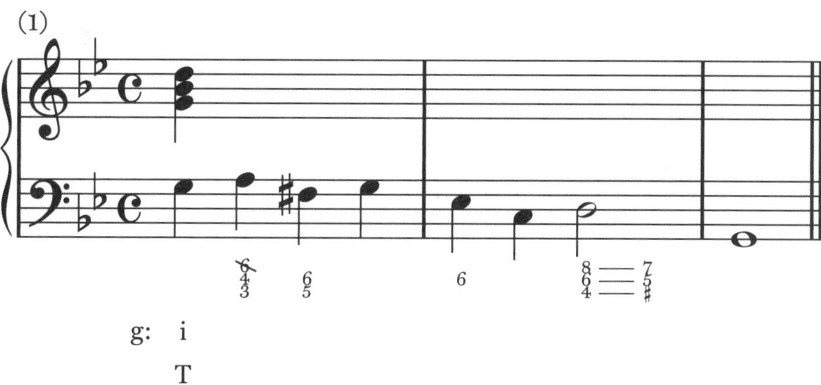

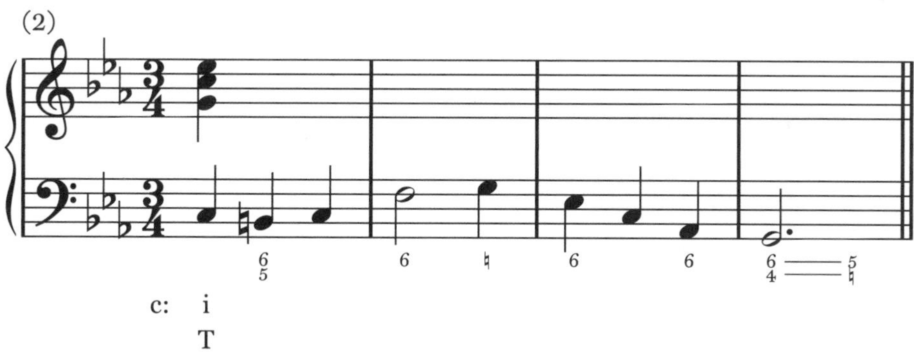

II. Brief analysis

Identify the key of each excerpt, and provide a Roman numeral and contextual analysis. Disregard any circled notes.

- Where a triad is arpeggiated, choose the lowest note to determine its inversion.
- Where the tonic area is expanded by V, draw a horizontal line after the "T."
- Circle the correct cadence type.

A. Fanny Mendelssohn Hensel, "Neue Liebe, neues Leben," mm. 52–56

HC IAC PAC

Translation: [The sweet, mischievous] maiden holds me so tightly against my will

B. W. A. Mozart, Piano Sonata in B♭ Major, K. 570, mvt. 3, mm. 1–4

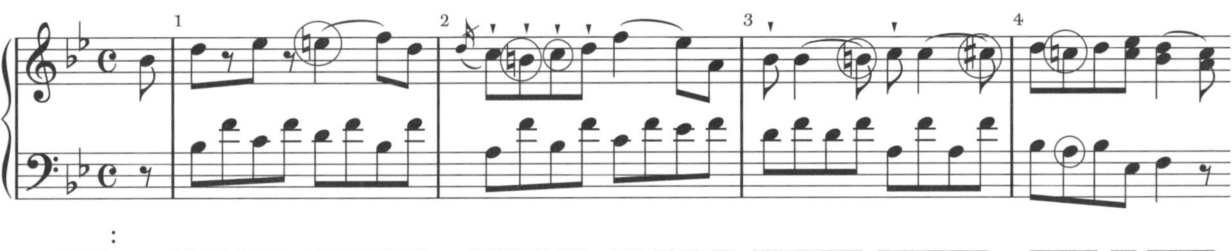

HC IAC PAC

C. Franz Schubert, Sonatina for Violin and Piano, Op. 137, No. 3, mvt. 2, mm. 1–4

HC IAC PAC

ASSIGNMENT 14.3

I. Writing pedal (or neighboring) $^6_4$s

Write the following $^6_4$ patterns in four parts, using primarily quarter notes, in the indicated meter. Add accidentals as needed. Write (ped $^6_4$) or (N$^6_4$) to show the type.

A. From Roman numerals: Write in chorale style and add a contextual analysis.

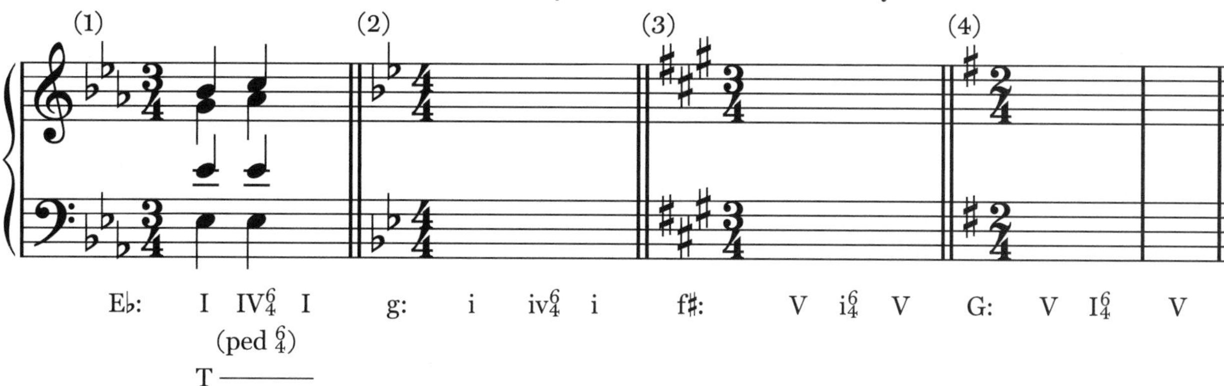

B. From figured bass: Write in keyboard style and provide Roman numeral and contextual analyses.

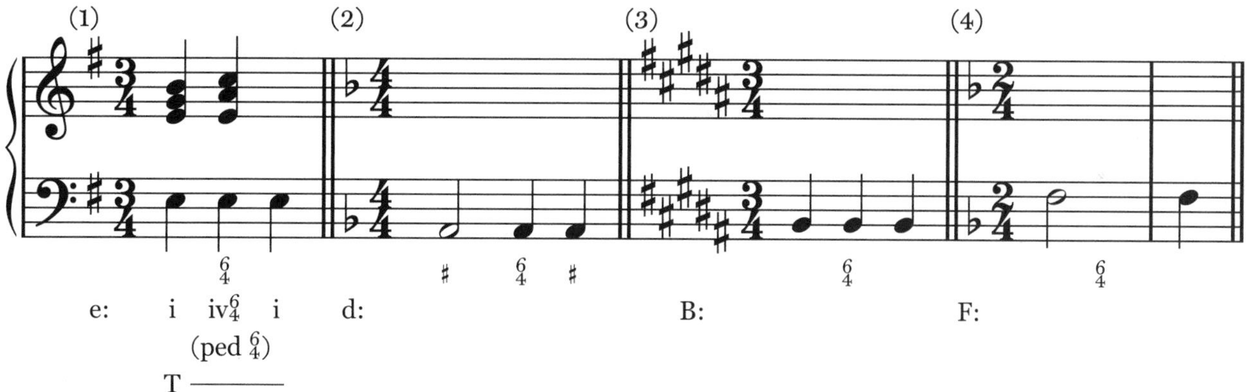

II. Writing arpeggiating $^6_4$s

Write the following $^6_4$ patterns in four parts, using primarily quarter notes, in the indicated meter. Add accidentals as needed, and write (arp $^6_4$) to show the $^6_4$ type.

A. From Roman numerals: Write in chorale style and add a contextual analysis.

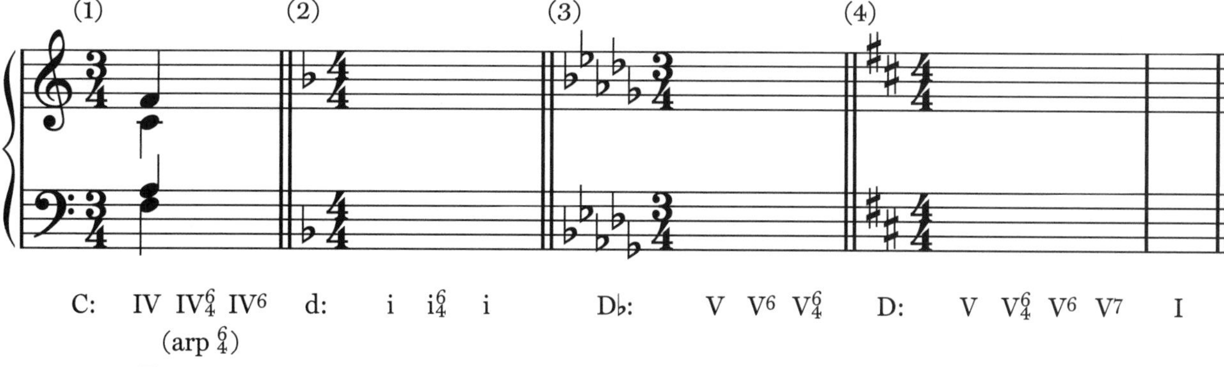

B. From figured bass: Write the progression in keyboard style and provide Roman numeral and contextual analyses.

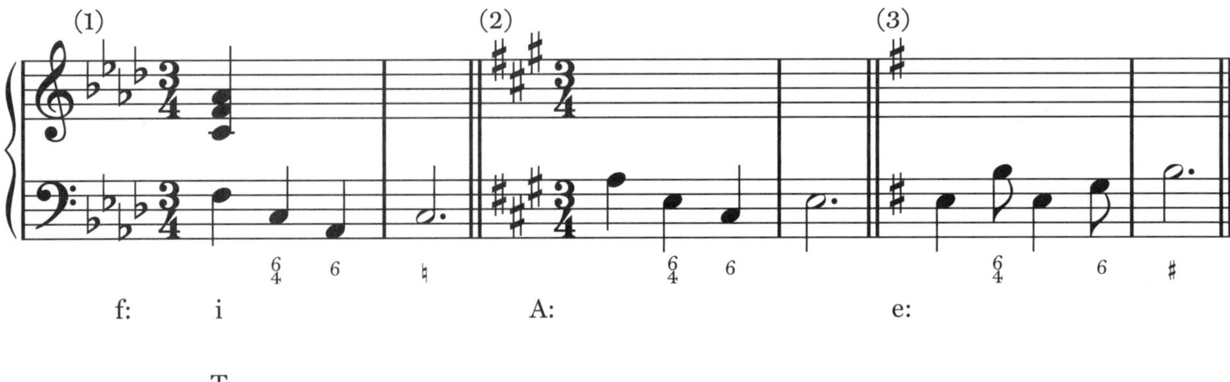

III. Analysis

Label the key, then analyze with Roman numerals and specify the $^6_4$ chord type, if applicable. Provide a contextual analysis under the Roman numerals and identify the cadence type.

A. J. S. Bach, "O Haupt voll Blut und Wunden," mm. 3–4
(Hint: Measure 3 begins with a 9–8 suspension.)

Translation: Full of sorrow and full of scorn,

B. W. A. Mozart, Piano Sonata in C minor, K. 457, mvt. 2, mm. 1–3

ASSIGNMENT 14.4

I. Passing $^6_4$ chords

Write each example, using quarter notes. Provide two levels of Roman numerals to show which harmony is expanded.

A. From Roman numerals in chorale style

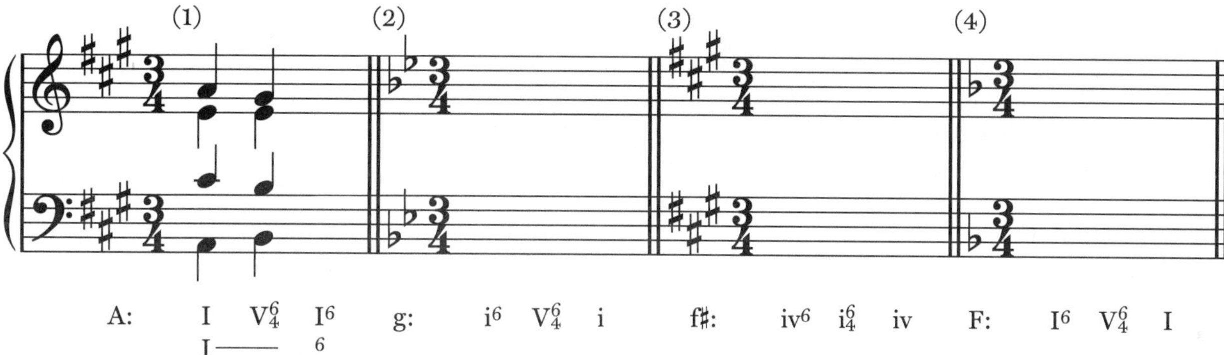

B. From figured bass in keyboard style

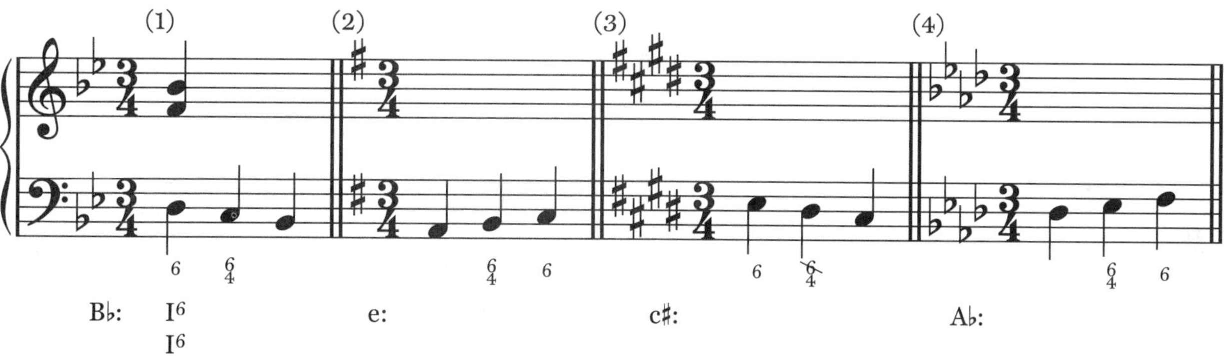

II. Figured Bass

Realize figures for the given melody in chorale style. Analyze with Roman numerals, label each $^6_4$ chord type, and provide a contextual analysis.

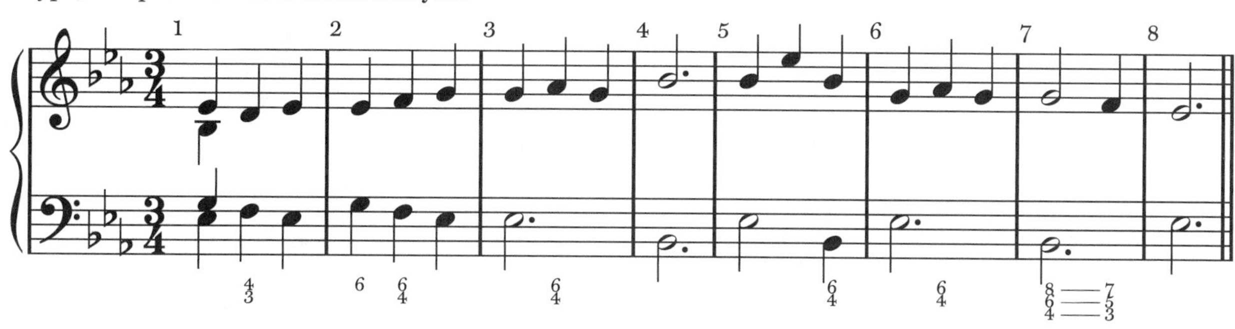

III. Analysis: Recognizing $^6_4$ chords

In these excerpts, circle each of the $^6_4$ chords, then circle the type(s): pedal (neighboring), cadential, arpeggiating, or passing. (Some passages have two $^6_4$ chords.)

A. Beethoven, Piano Sonata in C Minor, Op. 13 ("Pathetique"), mvt. 1, m. 1

pedal (neighboring) $^6_4$ cadential $^6_4$ arpeggiating $^6_4$ passing $^6_4$

B. Handel, Chaconne in G Major, mm. 29–32

pedal (neighboring) $^6_4$ cadential $^6_4$ arpeggiating $^6_4$ passing $^6_4$

C. Robert Schumann, "Wilder Reiter," from *Album for the Young*, mm. 1–4

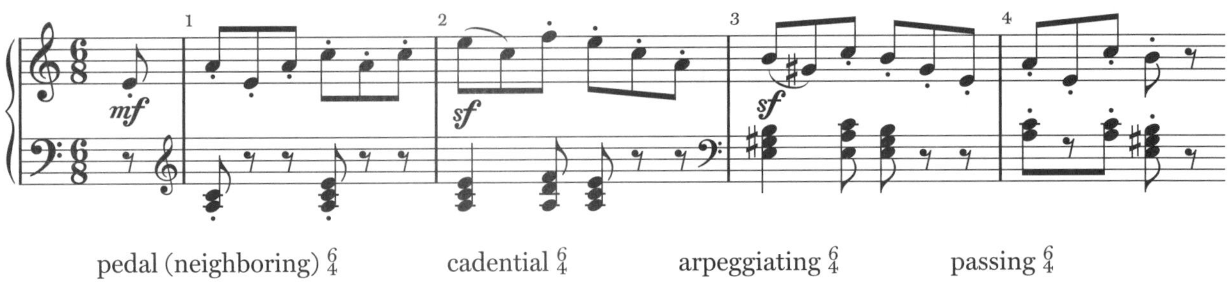

pedal (neighboring) $^6_4$ cadential $^6_4$ arpeggiating $^6_4$ passing $^6_4$

D. Elisabeth-Claude Jacquet de la Guerre, Sonata No. 2 in D Major for Violin and Continuo, mvt. 3, mm. 26–29

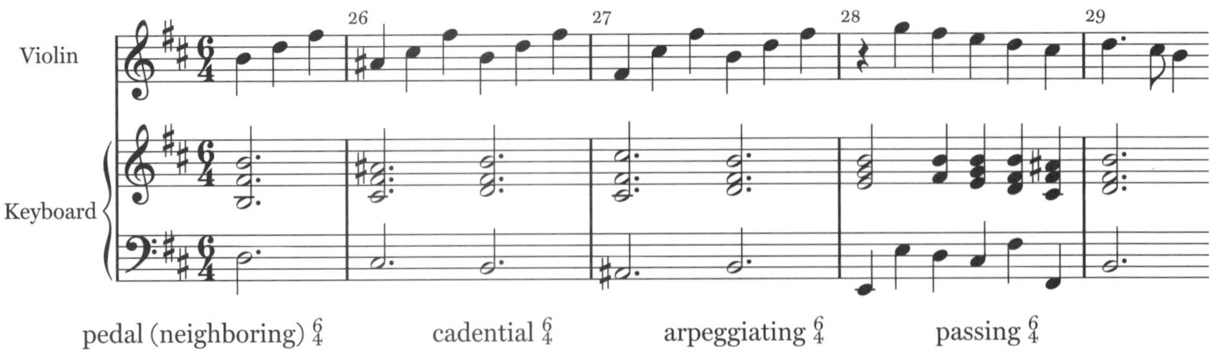

pedal (neighboring) $^6_4$ cadential $^6_4$ arpeggiating $^6_4$ passing $^6_4$

NAME ___

ASSIGNMENT 14.5

I. Writing $^6_4$ chords from figured bass

Write the following phrases in keyboard style, with quarter, half, and dotted-half notes in the meter indicated. Add accidentals as needed and analyze with Roman numerals. Provide a contextual analysis underneath.

II. Figured bass: Rule-of-the-octave harmonization

The "rule of the octave" was a type of eighteenth-century keyboard exercise with a bass line that spanned an octave by step (like the one shown). Musicians memorized and transposed them to every key. Part-write the progression from figured bass, then write the key and a Roman numeral analysis below the staff. Because this is a keyboard exercise, write in keyboard style, with three notes in the right hand. Specify each $^6_4$ type.

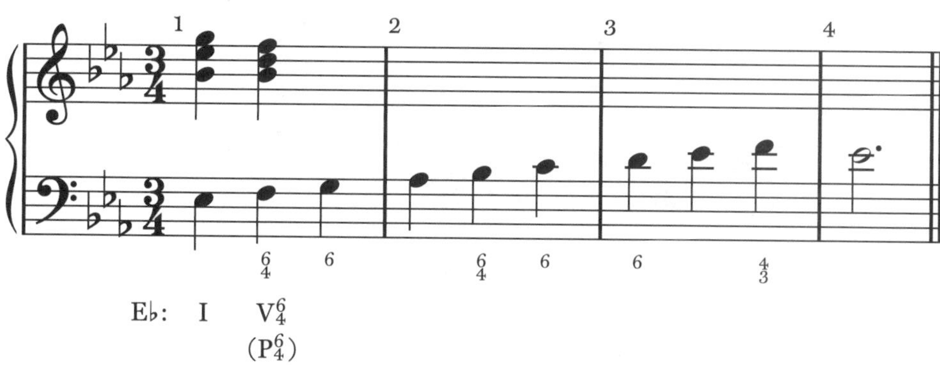

III. Analysis with $\begin{smallmatrix}6\\4\end{smallmatrix}$ chords

For each excerpt, supply Roman numerals in the blanks provided, then add a contextual analysis below. Disregard the circled notes. For each $\begin{smallmatrix}6\\4\end{smallmatrix}$ chord, label its type. For the minuet, base your analysis on the chords implied by the two voices. For an arpeggiating bass, choose the inversion from the lowest pitch in the measure.

A. Anonymous, Minuet in D Minor from the *Anna Magdalena Bach Notebook*

(1) Mm. 1–4

B. W. A. Mozart, Violin Sonata in C Major, K. 296, mvt. 3, mm. 9–16

NAME ______________________________

ASSIGNMENT 14.6

I. Part-writing with the submediant

Write each example in four parts, using primarily quarter notes.

A. From Roman numerals in chorale style

After writing the harmonic progression, add a contextual analysis below the Roman numerals.

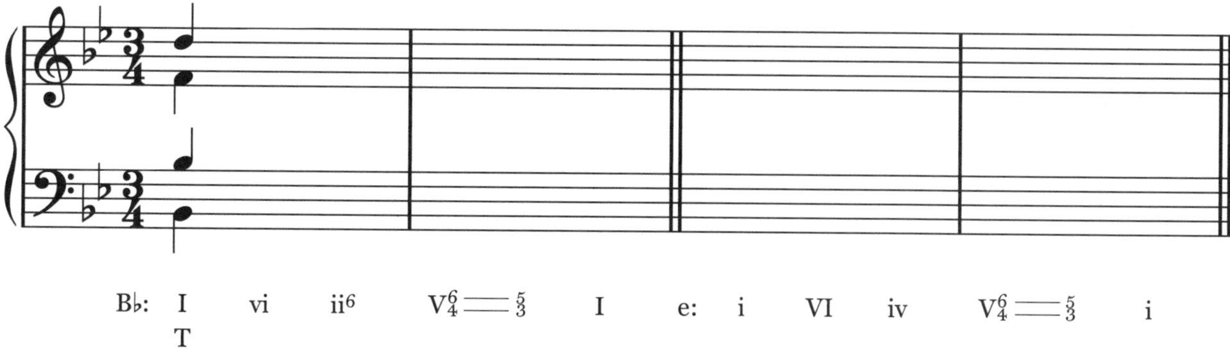

B. From figured bass in keyboard style

Provide a Roman numeral and contextual analysis that shows how the tonic area is expanded.

(1)

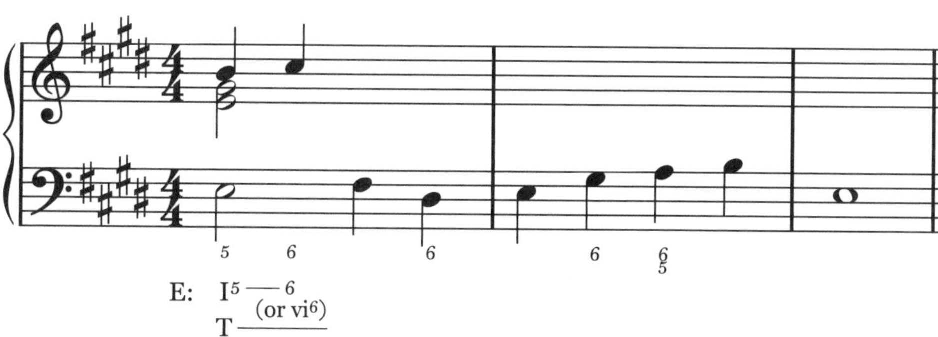

(2)

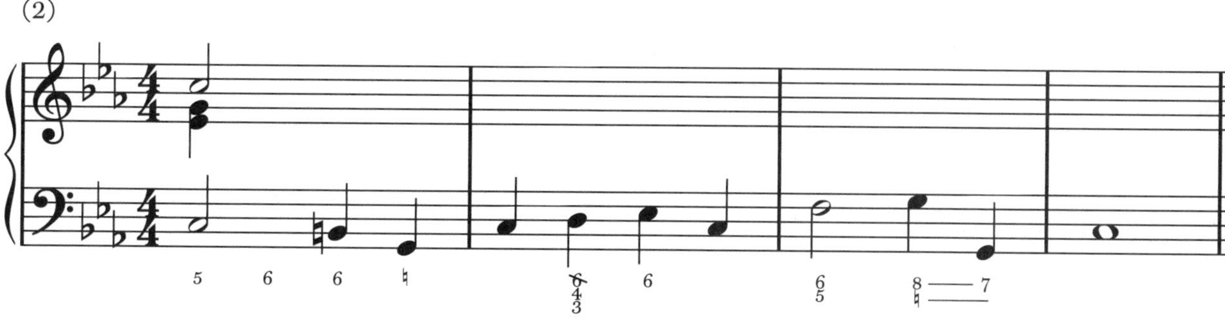

II. Analysis of tonic expansion with vi

Label the key, then analyze with Roman numerals. Provide a contextual analysis under the Roman numerals, and identify the cadence type.

A. "St. Anne," mm. 1–2

1
2
1. O God, our help in a - ges past,
2. Be - fore the hills in or - der stood,
B♭: I
T

B. Franz Schubert, "Du bist die Ruh," mm. 8–11

8
9
10
11
Du bist die Ruh, der Frie - de mild,
pp

Translation: You are rest, the gentle peace,

C. Hy Zaret and Alex North, "Unchained Melody," mm. 13–17

13
14
15
16
17
Time goes by so slow - ly and time can do so much,

NAME ________________

15 New Cadence Types and Diatonic Root Progressions

ASSIGNMENT 15.1

I. Writing deceptive, plagal, and Phrygian cadences

Write the following cadence patterns in chorale style, with half notes. Identify each cadence pattern as deceptive, plagal, or Phrygian.

A. From Roman numerals: Provide the appropriate key signature, and add accidentals as needed.

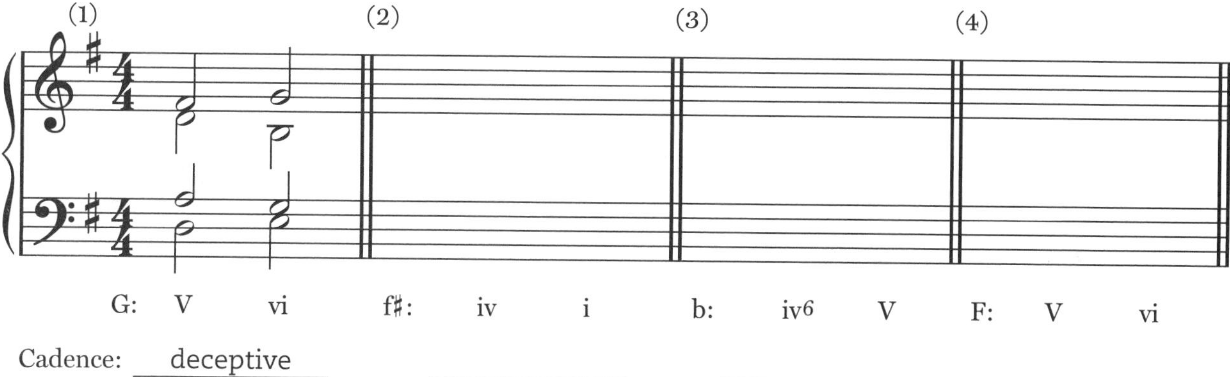

B. From figured bass: Provide a Roman numeral analysis under the figures.

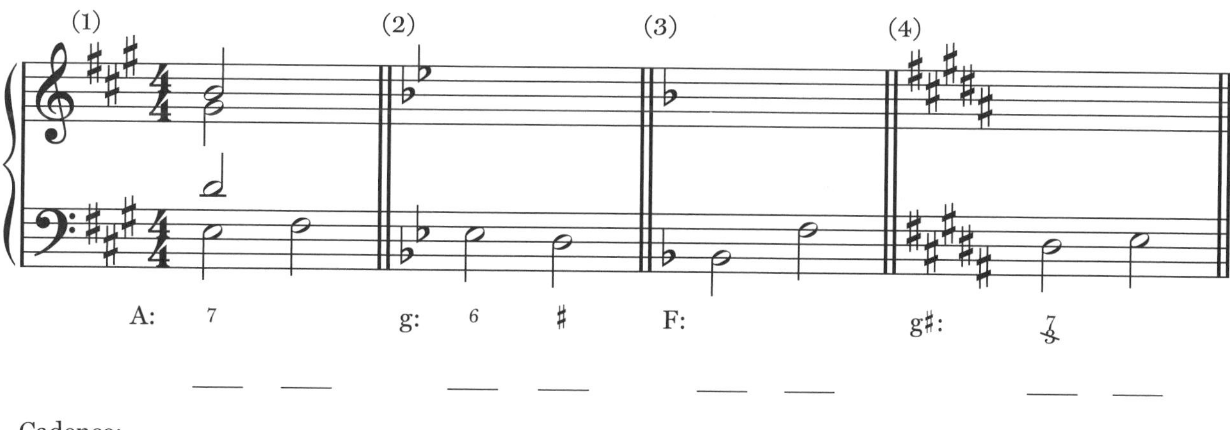

II. Cadences in chorale settings

Identify each cadence by circling the correct label. In each example, circle one spacing or voice-leading irregularity, and write its type in the blank.

A. Michael Praetorius, "Rosa Mystica," mm. 1-5

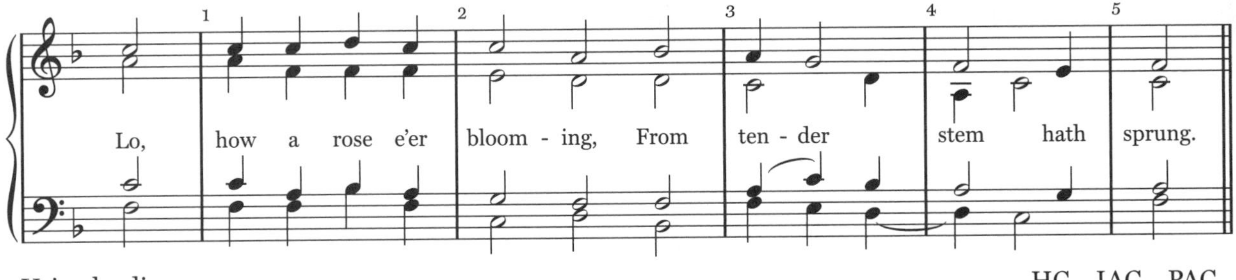

Voice-leading: ____________________

HC IAC PAC

B. J. S. Bach, "O Mensch, schau Jesum Christum an," mm. 8–11

This example uses a Baroque key signature: one flat in the signature and E♭s written in as needed. Analyze this passage in G minor.

Voice-leading: ____________________

deceptive plagal Phrygian

C. John Henry Hopkins Jr., "We Three Kings," mm. 26–33

Voice-leading: ____________________

deceptive plagal Phrygian

ASSIGNMENT 15.2

I. Writing deceptive, plagal, and Phrygian cadences

Write the following cadence patterns from Roman numerals in chorale style and identify them as deceptive, plagal, or Phrygian.

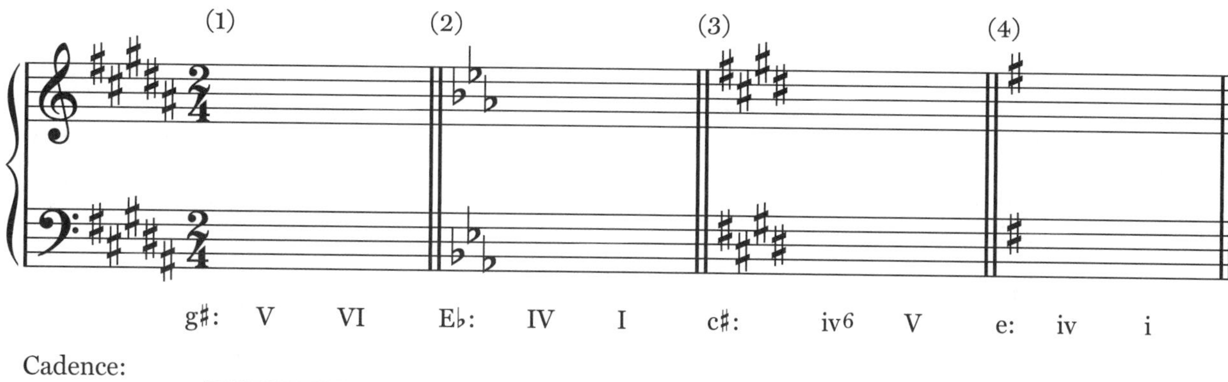

Cadence: ______________ ______________ ______________ ______________

II. Realizing figured bass: Arcangelo Corelli, Allemanda, from Trio Sonata in A Minor, Op. 4, No. 5

Realize the figured bass in keyboard style (add two or three pitches in the right hand, treble clef). Write a Roman numeral and contextual analysis beneath the staff, and label the cadence type.

A. Mm. 10–12: The figures $\substack{5\\4}$ and 6 in measures 10–11 indicate the 4–3 suspension in violin 1, with a change of bass (to a first-inversion triad) as the suspension resolves.

Cadence: ______________

This progression features (circle any that apply):

deceptive resolution minor v plagal extension parallel $\substack{6\\3}$ chords

B. Mm. 27-28: The figures 9 and 6 in measure 27 indicate the 9-8 suspension in the violin 2 that resolves with a change of bass.

A deceptive resolution appears in measure ________. Cadence: ______________

III. Analysis

Provide a Roman numeral and contextual analysis for the excerpt, and identify the cadence type.

Arcangelo Corelli, Sarabanda, from Violin Sonata in E Minor, Op. 5, No. 8, mm. 5-8

Cadence: ______________

This progression features (circle any that apply):

ascending seconds descending thirds parallel $^6_3$ chords minor v

ASSIGNMENT 15.3

I. Analysis

In the space below each excerpt, circle the name of the root progression that governs the passage. In these popular-music pieces, some chords are enriched with additional tones. Look for the underlying triads or seventh chords—usually one per measure—to find the root progression.

A. Frederick J. Perren and Dino Fekaris, "I Will Survive," mm. 2–5

Root progression: descending thirds descending fifths ascending seconds

B. Edwards, Dixon, and Williams, "Duke of Earl," mm. 1–4

Root progression: descending thirds descending fifths ascending seconds

C. Richard Rodgers and Oscar Hammerstein, "My Favorite Things," from *The Sound of Music*, mm. 27–30

Root progression: descending thirds descending fifths ascending seconds

II. Writing chords from Roman numerals

In each key specified, write the harmonies indicated by the Roman numerals in chorale style.

A. Descending fifths

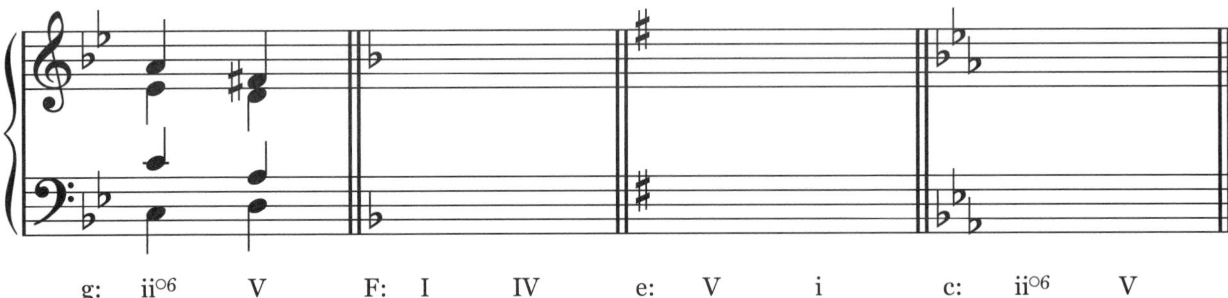

B. Descending thirds

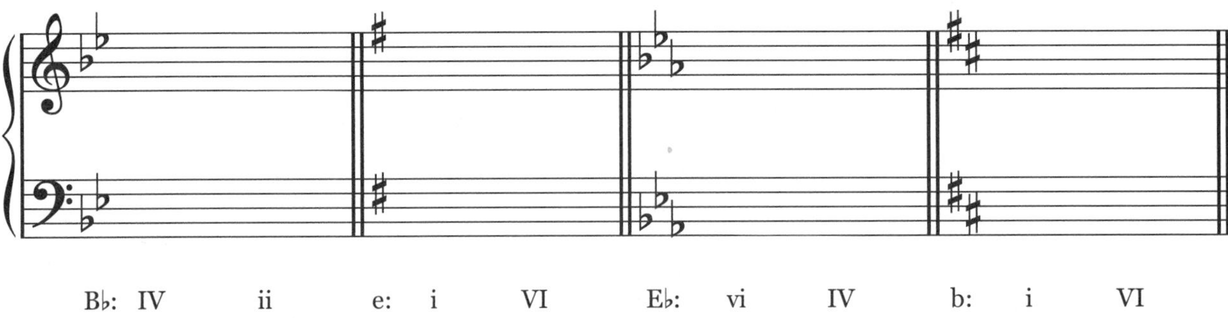

C. Ascending seconds

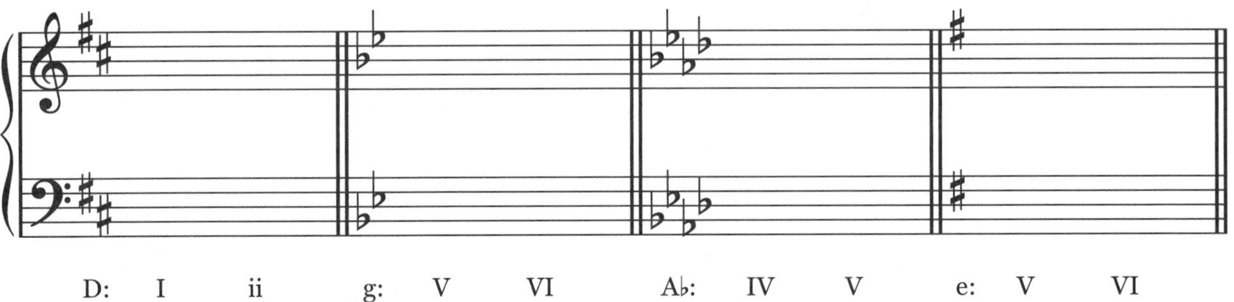

D. Longer progressions

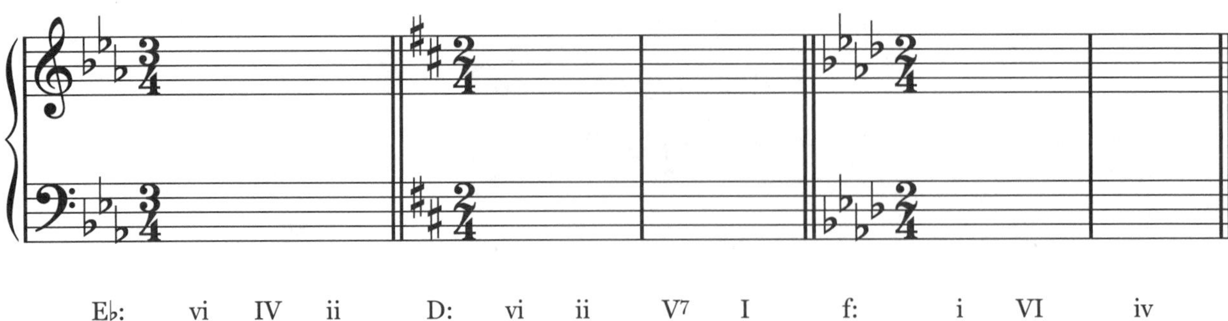

NAME ______________________________

ASSIGNMENT 15.4

I. Writing music with root progressions

Write the following progressions in chorale style, with quarter and half notes, in the meter indicated. Above the staff, bracket and label any chord pair with roots related by ascending second (asc. 2), descending fifth (desc. 5), or descending third (desc. 3). Some brackets will overlap.

A. From Roman numerals

(1)

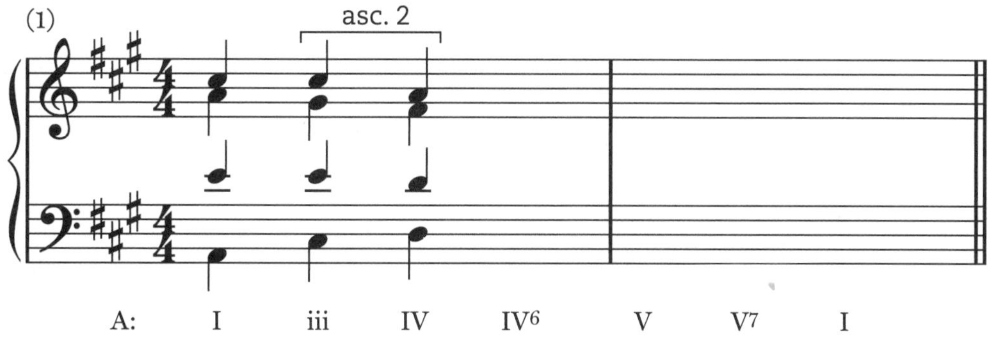

(2)

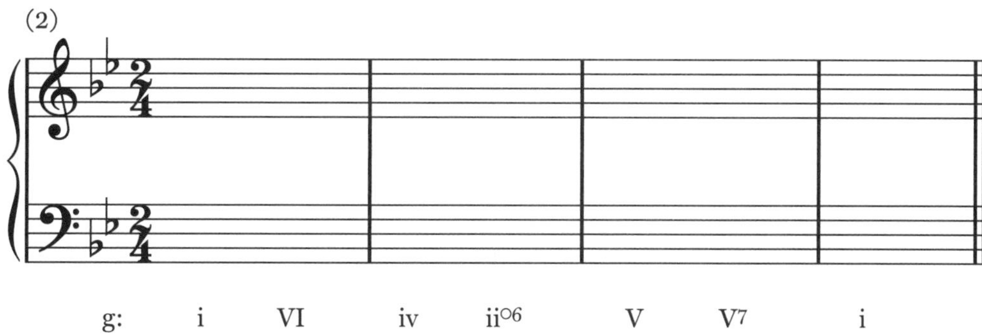

B. From figured bass. Provide a Roman numeral analysis.

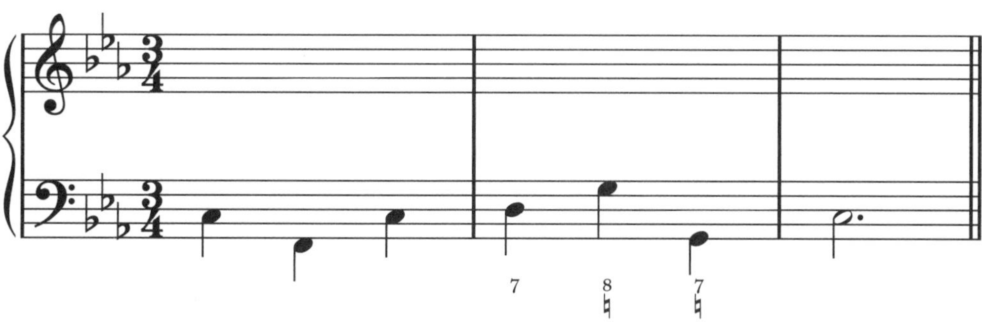

II. Analysis

For each excerpt, identify the key, provide a Roman numeral analysis, and answer the questions that follow.

A. Antonio Vivaldi, *Gloria*, "Et in terra pax," mm. 30–33

(1) The excerpt ends with a (circle one):

plagal extension deceptive resolution Phrygian cadence authentic cadence

(2) The rhythmic device marked with brackets above the soprano part in this performing edition is a (circle one):

polyrhythm tuplet hemiola hypermeasure

B. W. A. Mozart, Piano Sonata in C Major, K. 545, mvt. 3, mm. 1–4

(1) Measures 1–2 feature (circle one):

descending fifths descending thirds parallel $^6_3$ chords

(2) Measure 3 features (circle one):

descending fifths descending thirds parallel $^6_3$ chords

ASSIGNMENT 15.5

I. Figured bass: Rule-of-the-octave harmonization

Part-write the progression from the figured bass given, then write the key and a Roman numeral analysis below the staff. Because this is a keyboard exercise, write in keyboard style, with three notes in the right hand. Begin with $\hat{1}$ in the highest voice.

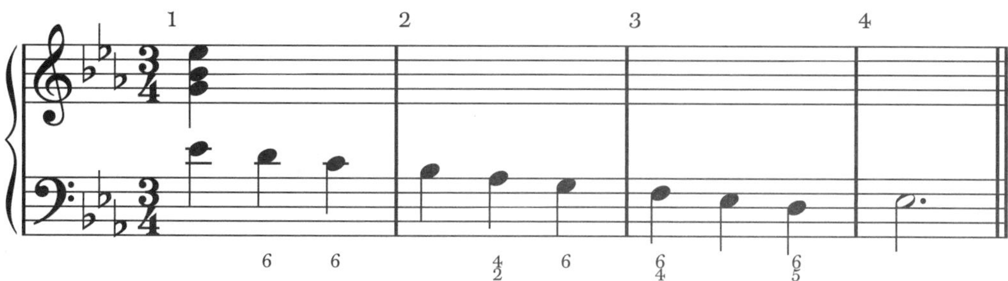

This progression features (circle any that apply):

cadential $^{6}_{4}$ passing $^{6}_{4}$ ascending seconds descending thirds parallel $^{6}_{3}$ chords

II. Analysis

Provide Roman numerals and figures for the following excerpts, and answer the questions below each. Write a contextual analysis underneath the Roman numerals.

A. W. A. Mozart, Piano Sonata in G Major, K. 283, mvt. 1, mm. 112–114

Hint: In writing the Roman numeral analysis, consider each rhythmically displaced note as part of the chord that began on the beat. Circled pitches are embellishing, and not part of the chord.

(1) This progression is embellished with suspensions in the top part.
What type are they? (circle one): 7–6 4–3 9–8 2–3

(2) This progression features (circle any that apply):
cadential $^{6}_{4}$ passing $^{6}_{4}$ descending fifths descending thirds parallel $^{6}_{3}$ chords

(3) With which type of cadence does this example end? (circle one)
PAC IAC HC Phrygian DC plagal

B. W. A. Mozart, Piano Sonata in C Major, K. 545, mvt. 1, mm. 63–73 (Anthology 62a)

Hint: Measure 68 includes chromaticism that we will study in Chapter 19. Ignore that measure for now.

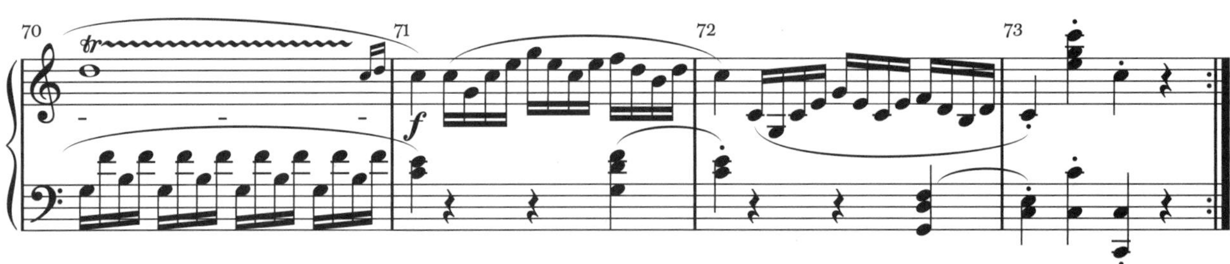

(1) The harmonic rhythm in this example is primarily (choose one)

one chord per measure   two chords per measure   three or more chords per measure

(2) What is the cadence type in measures 69–71? (circle one)

PAC   IAC   HC   Phrygian   DC   plagal

(3) What is the cadence type in measures 72–73? (circle one)

PAC   IAC   HC   Phrygian   DC   plagal

(4) Measures 71–73 are called a ______________________________

(5) This passage features (circle any that apply):

cadential $^6_4$ passing $^6_4$ descending fifths   descending thirds   parallel $^6_3$ chords

NAME ____________________

Embellishing Tones

ASSIGNMENT 16.1

I. Writing embellishments

Add passing or neighbor tones as specified, using eighth notes on the offbeat between the given chords.

- Don't change the voicing or spacing.
- There are multiple correct answers; play the progressions with the passing or neighbor tones you have added to check that they sound good and do not create voice-leading problems.
- Provide a Roman numeral analysis.

A. Add passing tones.

B. Add neighbor tones.

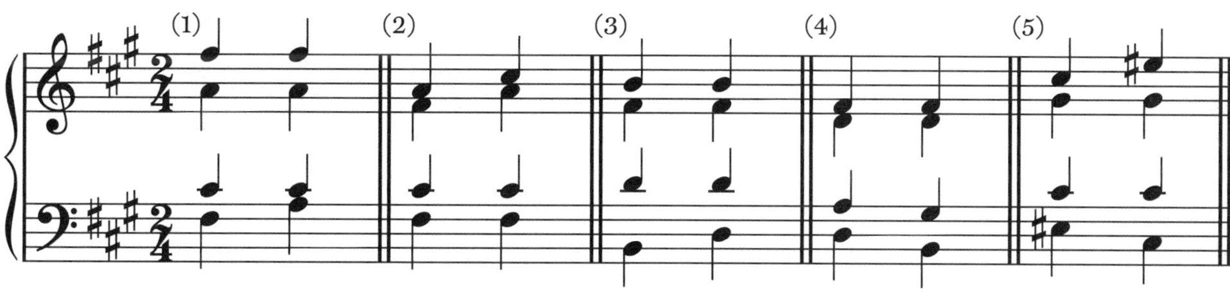

C. Add simultaneous passing tones.

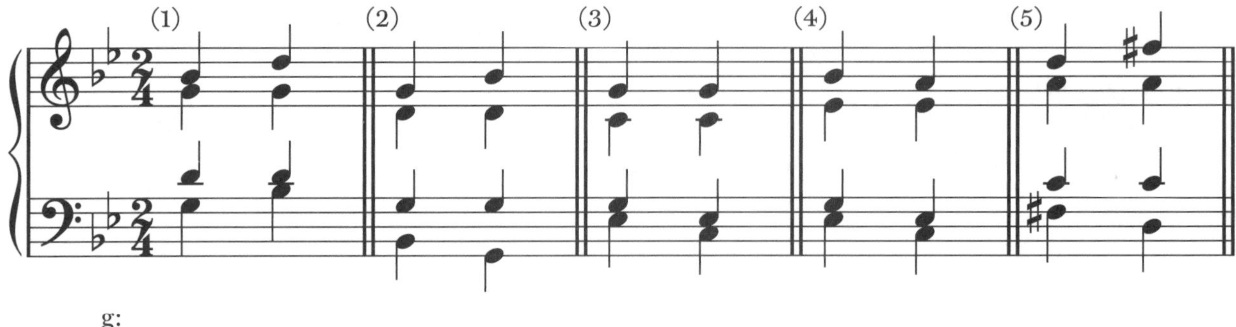

D. Add simultaneous passing and neighbor tones.

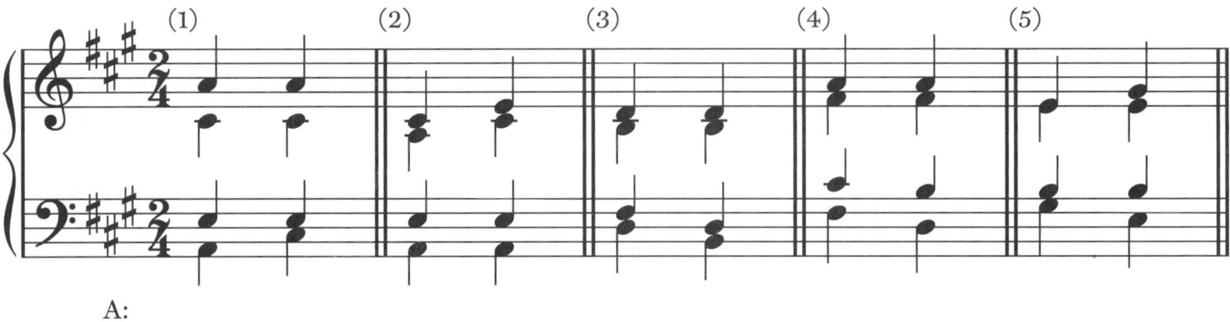

II. Part-writing

Write the following progressions in four parts (chorale style), including the specified embellishing tones. Write a soprano line that makes an interesting melody and correct counterpoint with the bass. Include passing tones, neighbor tones, and at least one pair of simultaneous passing or neighbor tones, and use eighth-note motion in at least one part on each beat except the last measure. When a chord is repeated, you may change the voicing of the upper three parts to incorporate passing tones. Circle and label each embellishing tone in your setting.

A.

B.

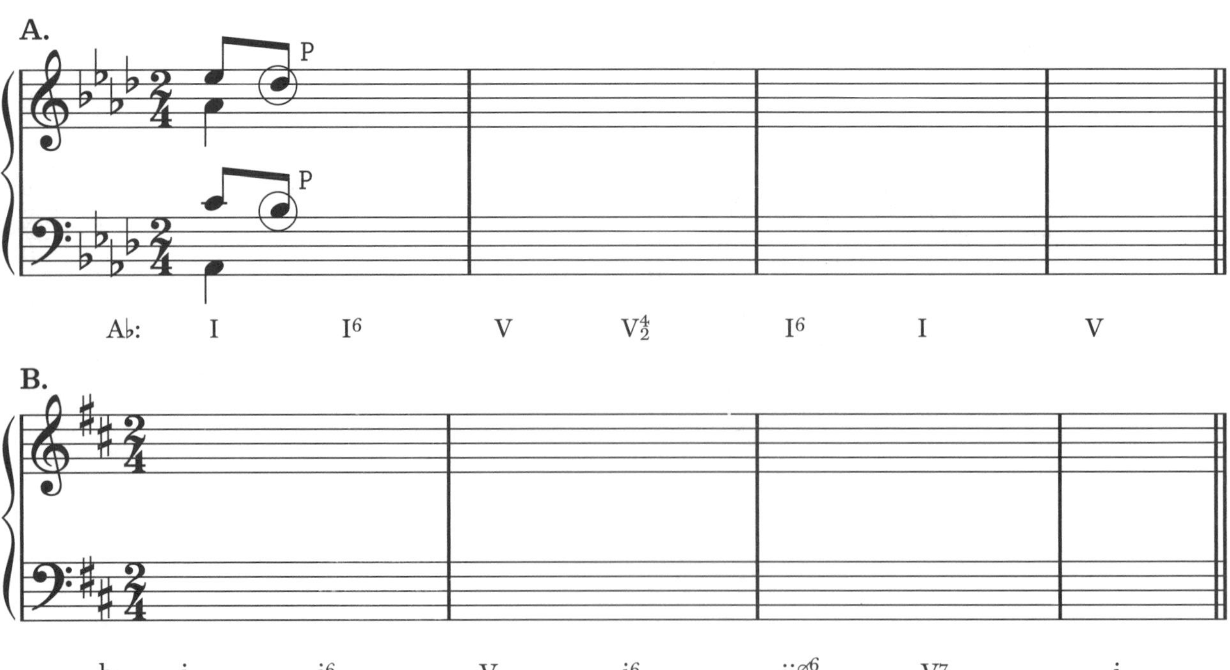

ASSIGNMENT 16.2

I. Writing suspensions and retardations in four parts from Roman numerals

Write the following progressions in four parts (chorale style) with durations appropriate for the given meter. Include suspensions or retardations where specified, with the proper preparation and resolution. Provide a contextual analysis below the Roman numerals, and label the cadence type.

II. Part-writing

Write the following progressions in four parts (chorale style), including the specified embellishing tones. Write a soprano line that makes an interesting melody and good counterpoint with the bass. Circle and label each embellishing tone in your setting.

A. Include passing tones, neighbor tones, and a suspension.

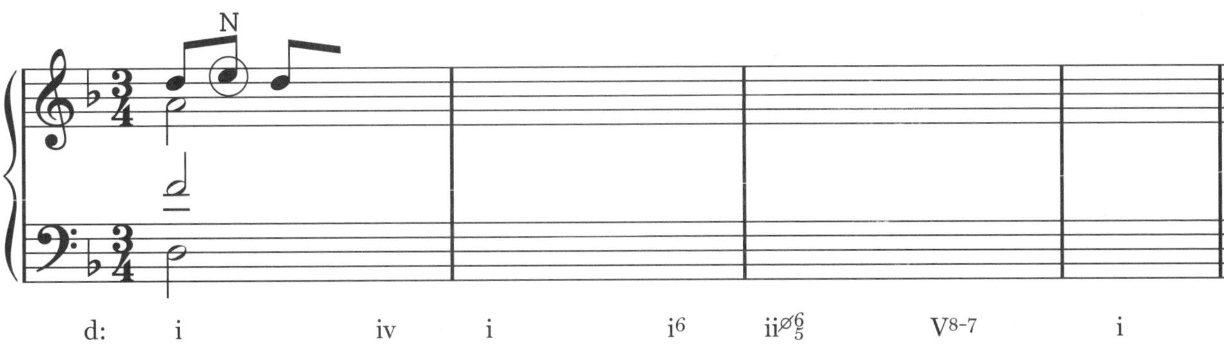

B. Include one set of simultaneous passing or neighbor tones and two suspensions.

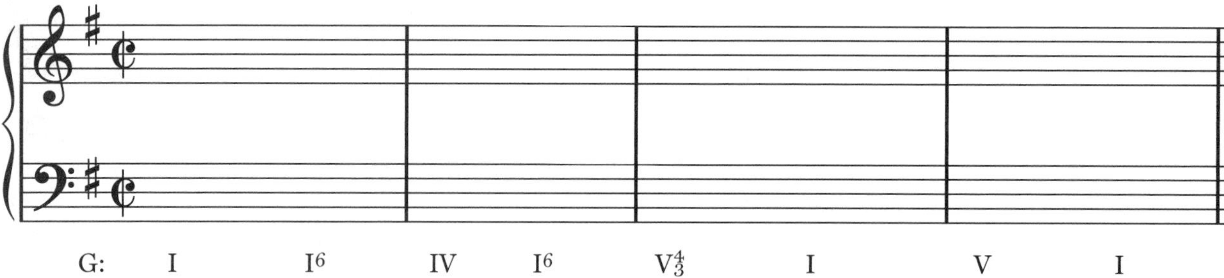

G: I I6 IV I6 V4/3 I V I

III. Analysis

Write a Roman numeral under each chord. Circle and label each embellishing tone. Provide a contextual analysis.

W. A. Mozart, String Quartet in D Minor, K. 421, mvt. 4, mm. 1–4

A blank staff has been included in case you want to make a reduction to help you identify the chords.

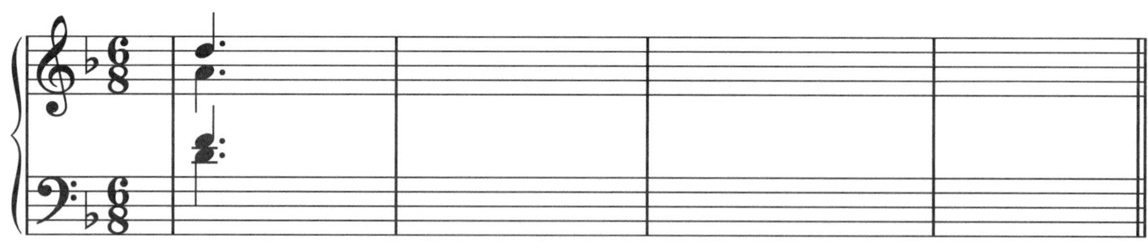

d: i
T

ASSIGNMENT 16.3

I. Writing anticipations

Add an anticipation in the soprano part to each short progression, using a ♩. ♪ or ♩ ♪ rhythm. Provide a Roman numeral analysis.

II. Analysis: Henry Purcell, "Dido's Lament," from Dido and Aeneas, mm. 38–44

Provide a Roman numeral analysis, and circle and label each embellishing tone in the vocal melody. In measure 39, label a new chord on beat 2, with a tonic pedal point. In measure 41, analyze with a downbeat 7-6 suspension, as shown. In measure 42, consider beat 2 to be a passing chord.

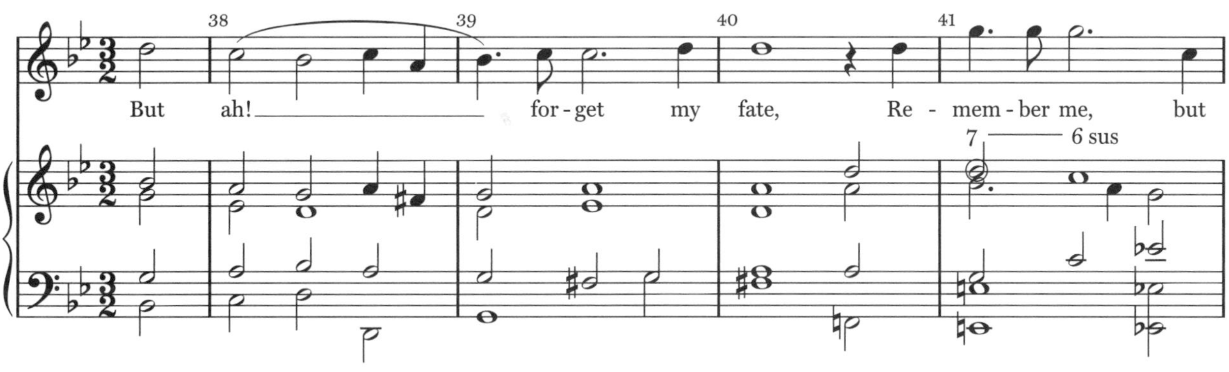

III. Analysis

Circle and label the embellishing tones in the following excerpts. Provide a Roman numeral analysis in the blanks. Bracket and label any passages with pedal points as "tonic pedal" or "dominant pedal." Provide a contextual analysis.

A. Beethoven, Sonatina in F Major, Op. Posth., mvt. 2, mm. 1–8

B. Beethoven, Sonatina in F Major, Op. Posth., mvt. 2, mm. 17–29 (analyze this passage in C major)

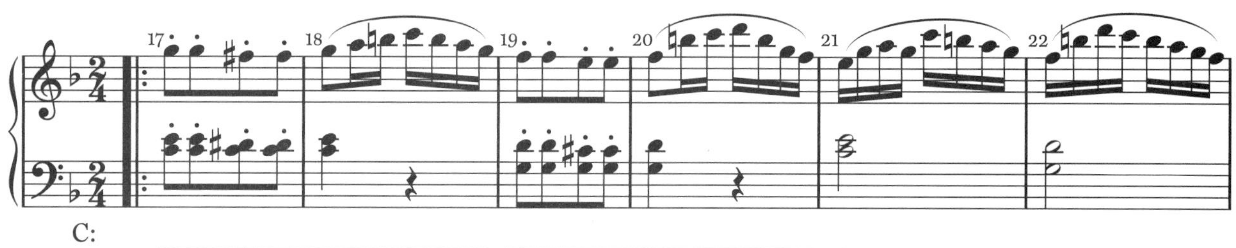

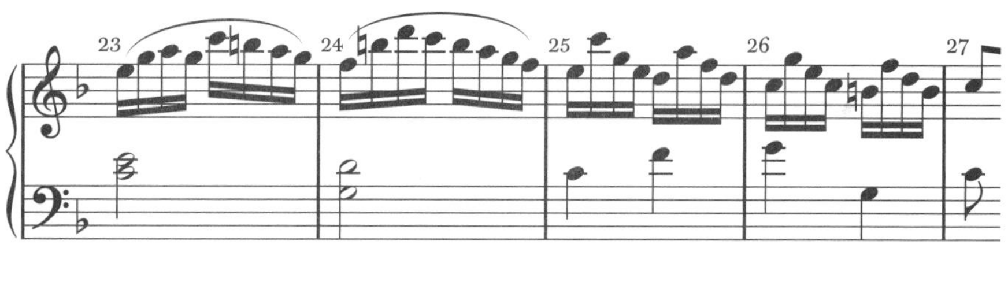

C. Robert Schumann, "Ich grolle nicht," from *Dichterliebe*, mm. 32–36

ASSIGNMENT 16.4

I. Analyzing mixed embellishing tones

A composer's choices of embellishments are a marker of style. Examine the circled embellishing tones in the following excerpts.

- Consider the immediate harmonic context and label each with the abbreviation P, N, IN, ANT, ret., or sus in the score. As your teacher directs, complete the table beneath the passage.
- If instructed to do so, circle the abbreviation for the embellishing tones in each measure on the chart below.
- In the blanks to the right, specify the type of suspension if present, and write "chromatic" if the P, N, or IN embellishment is chromatic (do not consider the leading tone in minor to be chromatic).

A. Scott Joplin, "Pine Apple Rag," mm. 5–12 (Anthology 52)

Measure 5:	P	N	IN	ANT	RET	SUS	____________
Measure 6:	P	N	IN	ANT	RET	SUS	____________
Measure 7:	P	N	IN	ANT	RET	SUS	____________
Measure 9:	P	N	IN	ANT	RET	SUS	____________
Measure 10:	P	N	IN	ANT	RET	SUS	____________
Measure 11:	P	N	IN	ANT	RET	SUS	____________
Measure 12:	P	N	IN	ANT	RET	SUS	____________

B. J. S. Bach, "Jesu, meine Freude," mm. 1–8

Measure 1:	P	N	IN	ANT	RET	SUS	__________
Measure 2:	P	N	IN	ANT	RET	SUS	__________
Measure 3:	P	N	IN	ANT	RET	SUS	__________
Measure 5:	P	N	IN	ANT	RET	SUS	__________
Measure 7:	P	N	IN	ANT	RET	SUS	__________
Measure 8:	P	N	IN	ANT	RET	SUS	__________

II. Harmonic analysis with pedal point

Provide a Roman numeral analysis and bracket measures that include a pedal point. Circle and label all embellishing tones

Clara Schumann, Romanze, Op. 21, No. 1, mm. 105–112 (Anthology 82)

ASSIGNMENT 16.5

I. Embellishing tones in popular music

Examine the embellishing tones in the passages that follow and answer the questions.

A. Taylor Swift, "Back to December," mm. 33-37

(1) Measures 33-35 feature repeated P N IN ANT RET SUS

(2) The cadence in measure 37 includes P N IN ANT RET SUS

B. Bono, The Edge, and U2, "Stuck in a Moment You Can't Get Out Of," mm. 5-7

(1) Measure 6, beats 1-2 feature P N IN ANT RET SUS

(2) The dissonance over the bar line between measures 6-7 is

P N IN ANT RET SUS

C. John Deacon, "You're My Best Friend," mm. 5-8

(1) The accompaniment features IN ANT PED RET SUS

(2) The end of each vocal subphrase ("make me live" and "give to me") features

P N IN ANT RET SUS

II. Analysis of a March

John Philip Sousa, "The Thunderer March" (condensed band score), mm. 21-28

Despite its complicated sound, the opening of this march has a simple harmonic plan, enlivened by a variety of melodic embellishments. Listen to the entire first strain (section) of the march online. There is a four-measure introduction, followed by a passage similar to the one shown here but without the countermelody (middle staff). After another eight-measure phrase completes a parallel period, the entire period is repeated with the countermelody in measure 21-28. Consider the harmonic progression first, then answer the questions that follow.

(1) The harmony prolonged in measures 21-24 is T PD D

It is embellished in the bass line by a leap of a P4 (from F to C) that creates this type of $^6_4$ chord:

cadential passing neighboring arpeggiating

(2) In measures 25-26, the harmony prolonged is T PD D

Here, the bass line leap of a P5 (from G to C) reflects which of the following?

change of harmony change of inversion

(3) The cadence type at the end of the eight-measure phrase is ____________________.

(4) The *tr* indication in the cornet melody in measures 21, 25, and 27 is for a trill—a rapid alternation of the note indicated and the pitch a diatonic scale step above it. The end of the trill is embellished by a note below, as shown. These embellishments are all

passing tones neighbor tones suspensions

(5) The countermelody in the trombones, saxophones, and baritones features chord tones along with this type of embellishment:

passing tones neighbor tones suspensions

NAME ______________________________

ASSIGNMENT 16.6

Embellishing tones in variation sets

In parts A and B, first listen to the theme while following the Anthology score. Then examine the variations shown here. Circle and label all embellishing tones (e.g., P, N, IN, DN [double neighbor]); for suspensions and retardations, include the type (e.g., 4–3 sus). In the blank provided, indicate what types of embellishments are employed in each variation.

A. W. A. Mozart, Piano Sonata in D Major, K. 284, mvt. 3 (Anthology 60)

(1) Variation 4, mm. 69–72

Embellishment type(s): ________________

(2) Variation 11, mm. 188–191

Embellishment type(s): ________________

B. W. A. Mozart, *Variations on "Ah, vous dirai-je Maman"* (Anthology 64)

(1) Variation 3, mm. 73-80 (in mm. 76-79, align the notes in the right hand as a chord to identify the embellishments)

Embellishment type(s): ___________________

(2) Variation 6, mm. 145-152 (in mm. 147-150, there are embellishing tones in both hands)

Embellishment type(s): ___________________

(3) Variation 9, mm. 217-224

Embellishment type(s): ___________________

NAME ____________________

Voice-Leading Chords: vii°6, vii°7, viiø7, and Others

ASSIGNMENT 17.1

I. Writing and resolving vii°6

Write the following chorale-style progressions, in quarter notes, from the given Roman numerals. Provide the key signature and any needed accidentals. Draw an arrow to show the correct resolution of the leading tone.

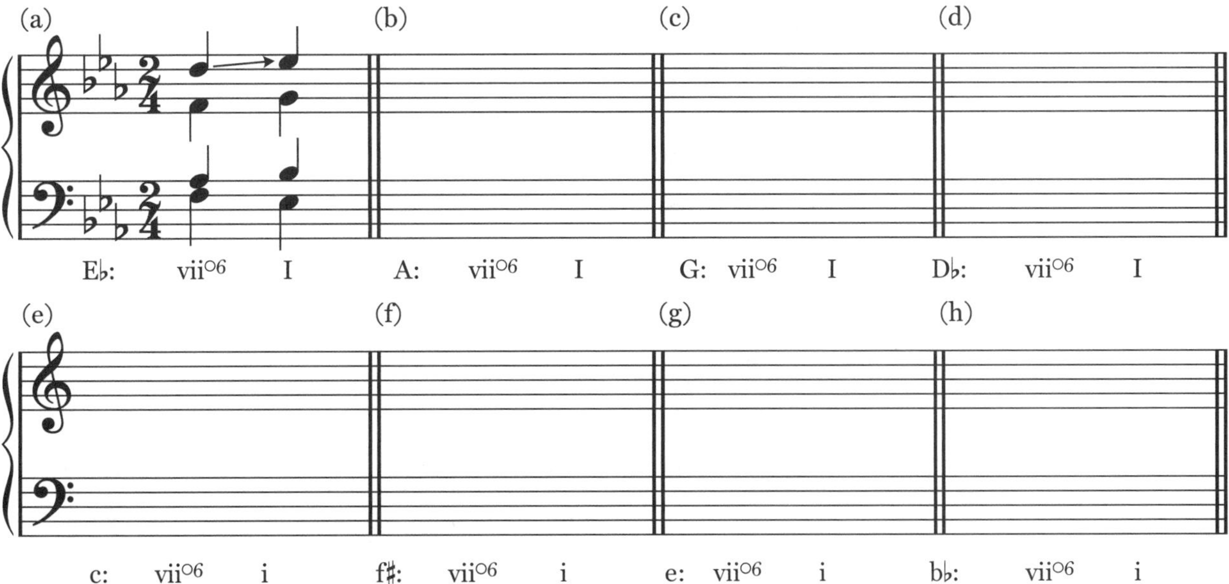

II. Expanding the tonic area with passing vii°6 or V^6_4 chords

Write the following chorale-style progressions from the Roman numerals or figured bass. In part A, provide the key signature. In both A and B, write a second level of Roman numerals to show the tonic expansion. Use a voice exchange [as shown by the crossed lines in example A(1)] in each progression, and mark it as shown.

A. From Roman numerals

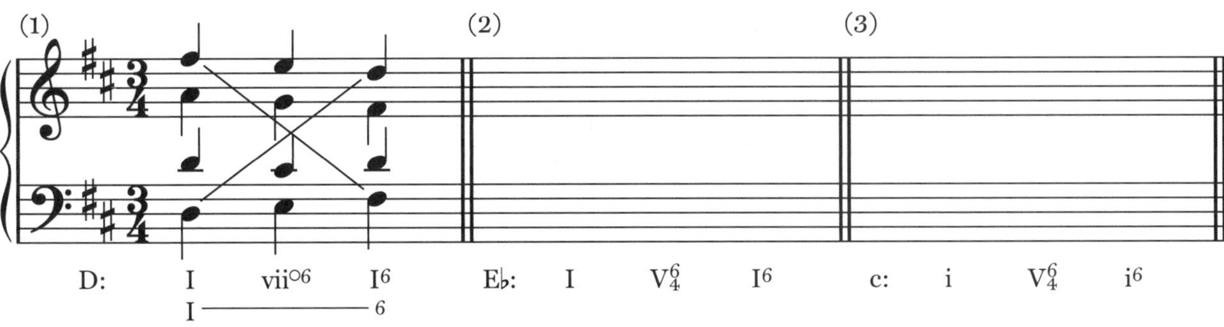

B. From figured bass

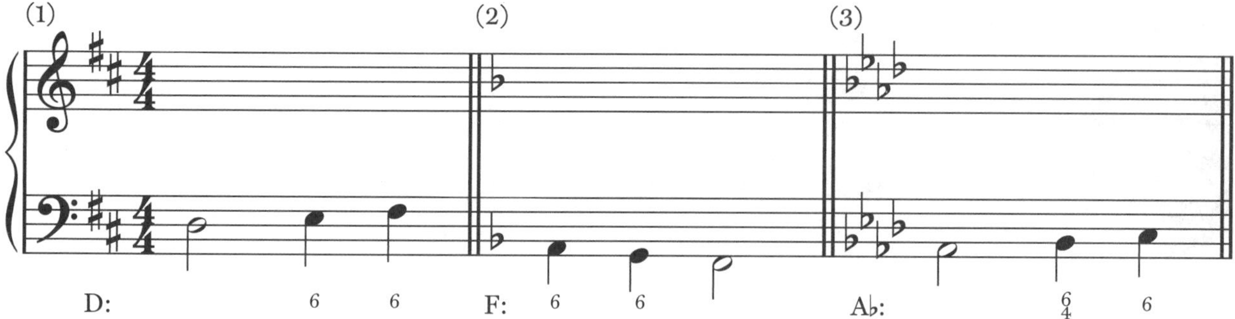

III. Analysis with vii°6

For each passage, identify the key then write a Roman numeral analysis in the blanks provided. Add a contextual analysis beneath, beginning with the first tonic triad.

A. J. S. Bach, "Wachet auf," mm. 25–27

B. Handel, Chaconne in G Major, mm. 13–16

C. J. S. Bach, "O Haupt voll Blut und Wunden," mm. 1–2

ASSIGNMENT 17.2

I. Resolving vii∅7 and vii°7

Part-write the following chorale-style progressions, in quarter notes, from the Roman numerals. Provide the key signatures and needed accidentals, and draw arrows to show the resolution of leading tones and chordal sevenths.

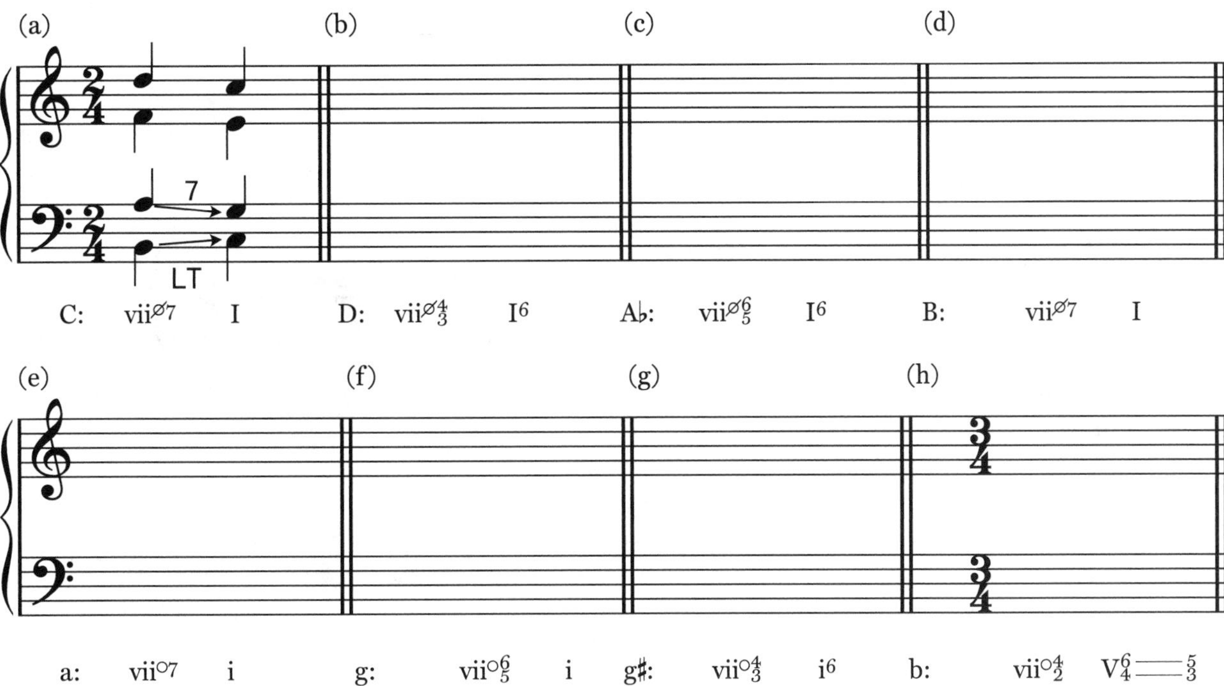

II. Harmonizing melody fragments with leading-tone seventh chords

For each melody fragment, expand the tonic area using vii°6 or vii°6/5. Provide Roman numerals on two levels to show the tonic expansion.

A. In a minor key

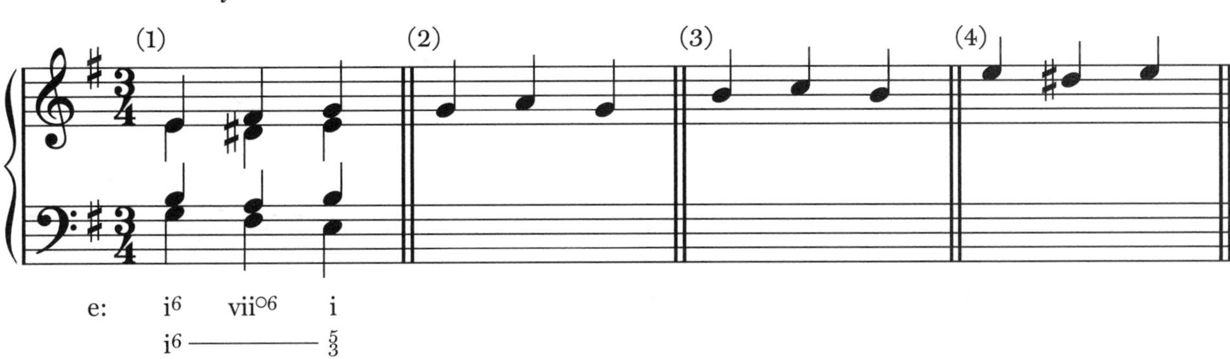

B. In a major key

Write a vii$^{\circ 6}_{5}$; add an accidental to lower the chordal seventh.

III. Expanding the tonic with passing chords

Part-write the following four-part progressions, in quarter notes, from the Roman numerals or figured bass. In part A, provide the key signatures and accidentals needed. In both A and B, write a second level of Roman numerals to show the tonic expansion.

A. From Roman numerals, in chorale style

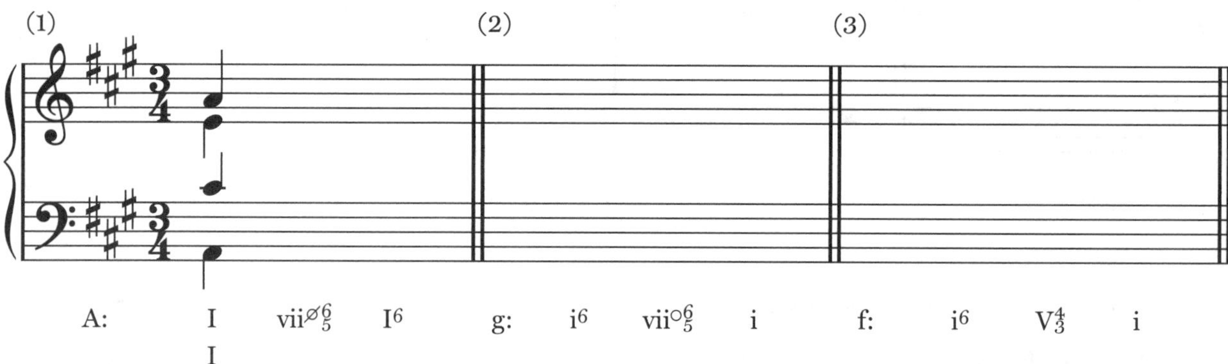

B. From figured bass, in keyboard style

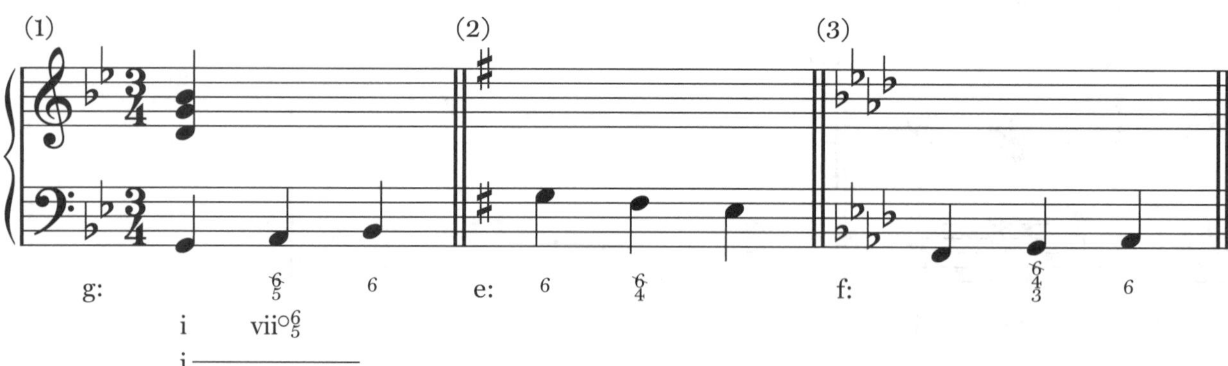

ASSIGNMENT 17.3

I. Chorale analysis with vii°6: J. S. Bach, "Aus meines Herzens Grunde"

Listen to this chorale (Anthology 7a), then provide a Roman numeral analysis for these chorale phrases. Circle and label all embellishing tones, and label the cadences. For suspensions, label the type (e.g., 7-6 sus). Each phrase begins with a substantial tonic prolongation prior to the cadence. Below the Roman numerals, add a two-level contextual analysis that shows how the tonic area is expanded with embedded PD-D-T in the first level, and the overall basic phrase T-PD-D-T progression in the second level.

A. Mm. 1-7

B. Mm. 15-21

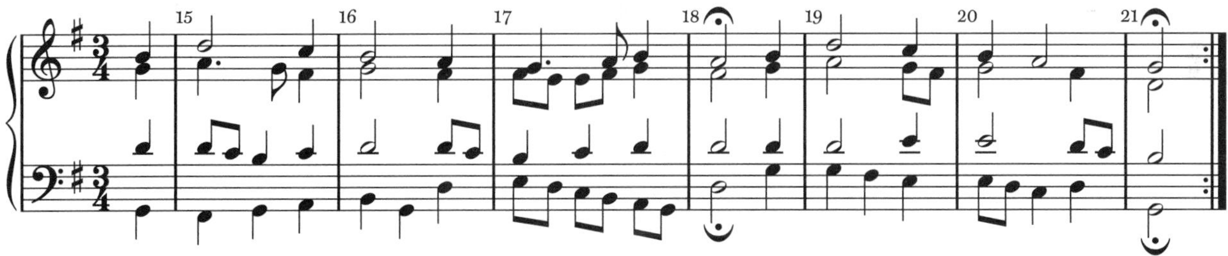

II. Analysis: Muzio Clementi, Sonatina in G Major, Op. 36, No. 5, mvt. 3, mm. 1–16

Write Roman numerals under the staff, circle and label all embellishing tones, and label the cadences.

Write a few sentences explaining the function of the vii^ø7 chords.

ASSIGNMENT 17.4

I. Writing passing and neighboring $^4_2$ chords

Write the following progressions from Roman numerals in chorale style.

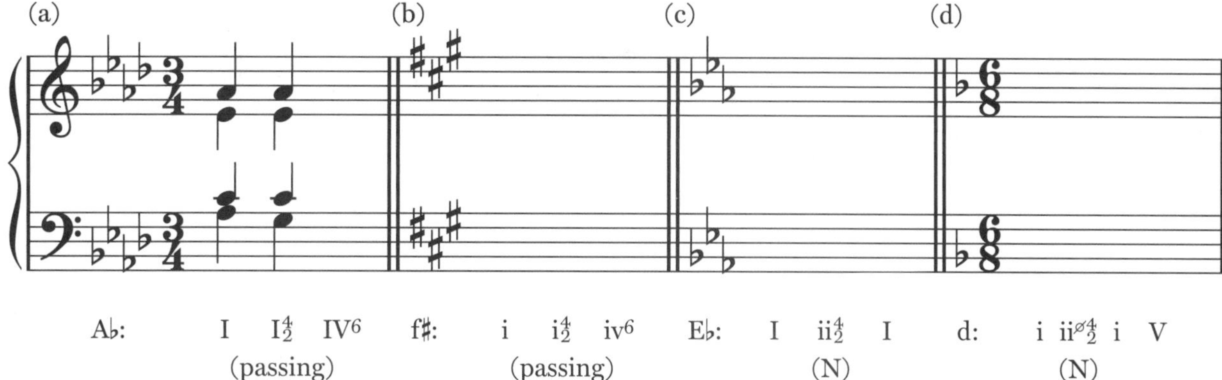

II. Figured-bass realization

Realize this figured bass excerpt in keyboard style. Provide a Roman numeral analysis; write "passing" for each passing $^4_2$ chord.

J. S. Bach, Cantata No. 140, mvt. 1, mm. 1-5

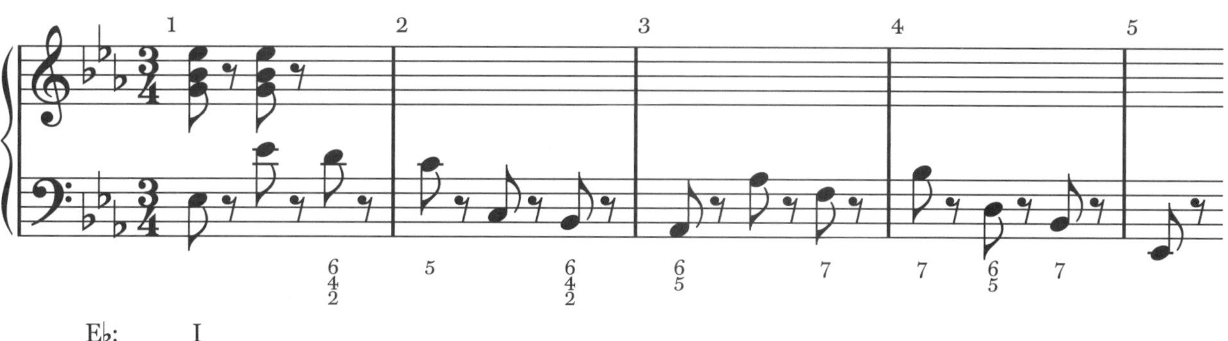

III. Analysis

Write a Roman numeral analysis.

A. Handel, "Rejoice greatly," from *Messiah*, mm. 3-7

Circle and label all embellishing tones. This excerpt contains parallel $^6_3$ chords; provide a Roman numeral for each sonority and then bracket and label the parallel $^6_3$ passage.

B. Antonio Vivaldi, "Cum Sancto Spiritu," from *Gloria*, mm. 69–78

This is a reduction of the choral and orchestra parts of this work, which is scored for SATB choir, orchestra, and continuo. Complete the Roman numeral and contextual analysis. Label suspensions above the staff.

Note: This example includes two chords we have not studied yet for which Roman numerals are provided; we will learn about these in Chapter 19.

In addition to $\frac{4}{2}$ chords, this example includes two rarely employed triads: iii and vii° in root position. Explain how each of these chords are used.

NAME ______________________________

ASSIGNMENT 17.5

I. Setting scalar bass lines (rule-of-the-octave harmonization)

The rule of the octave was an eighteenth-century musician's keyboard exercise, memorized and transposed to every key. In A (1) and B (1), realize the figured bass in keyboard style, then write a Roman numeral analysis below the staff. In A (2) and B (2), revise these harmonizations using substitute chords vii°6 and vii°7 or their inversions for V^6_4 and V^4_3. You may also substitute other harmonies, such as vi for I, I^4_2 for V6 with a descending $\hat{7}$, or ii^4_3 for IV6. Play both solutions to hear the difference.

A. Ascending

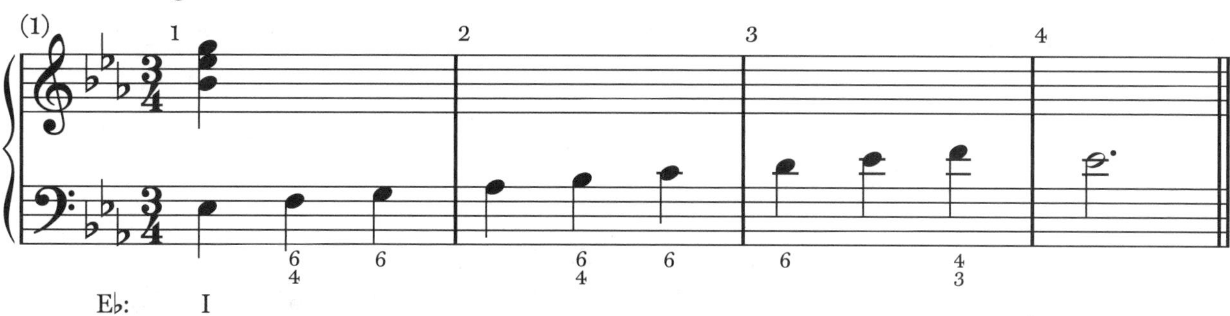

(2) Substitute leading-tone chords

B. Descending

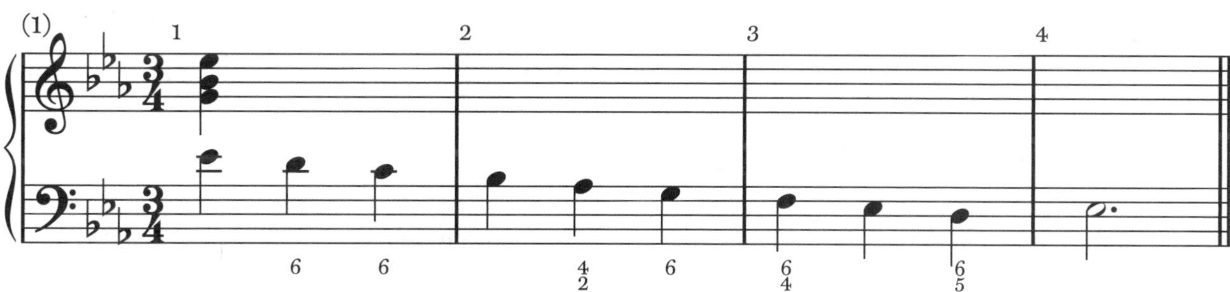

(2) Substitute leading-tone chords

E♭: I

II. Harmonizing scalar melodies

Choose a harmonization for these melodies, incorporating passing chords and phrase-model progressions. Include at least one leading-tone triad or seventh chord. Where possible, aim for a bass line in stepwise contrary motion to the soprano. Write in chorale style, and provide a Roman numeral analysis below the staff.

A. Ascending, major key

D: I6

B. Descending, major key

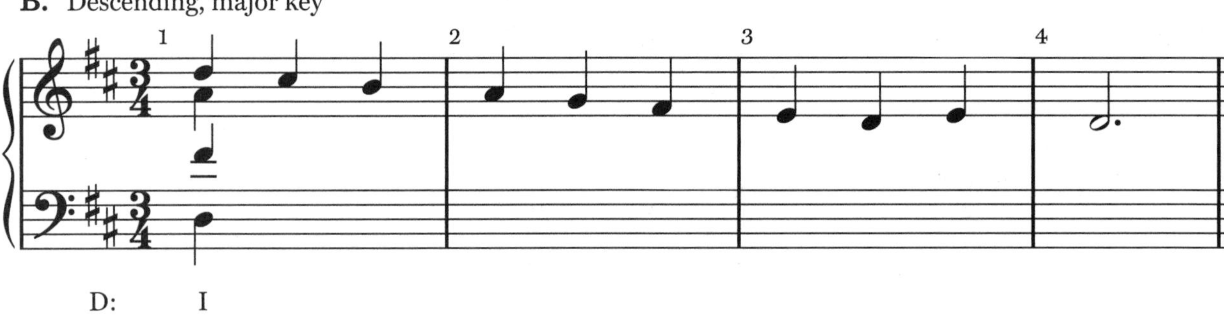

D: I

C. Ascending, minor key

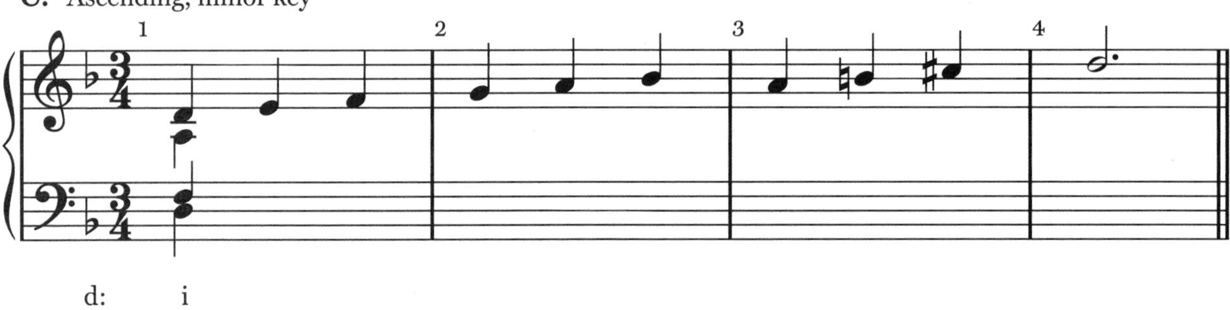

d: i

D. Descending, minor key (Hint: Use minor v to set the subtonic scale degree.)

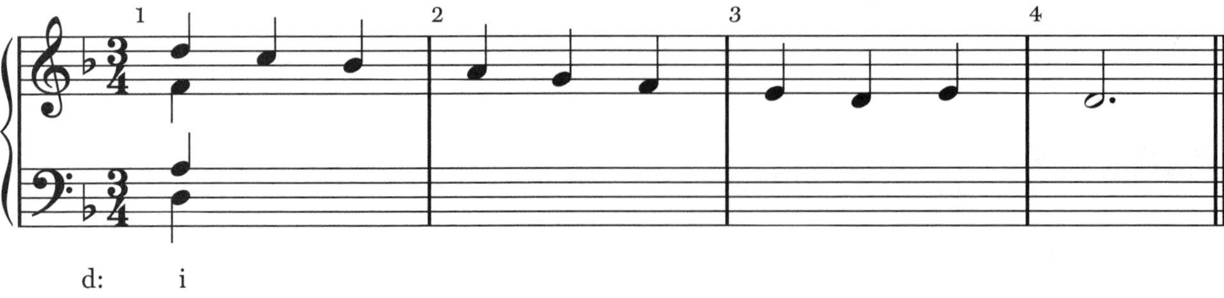

d: i

Phrase Structure and Motivic Analysis

ASSIGNMENT 18.1

I. Analysis

These musical excerpts are examples of sentences; bracket and label the basic idea, its repetition, and the continuation-cadence units. Also indicate the number of measures in each. Write the cadence types below the staff.

A. Beethoven, Piano Sonata, Op. 49, No. 1, mvt. 1, mm. 1–8

B. W. A. Mozart, Minuet, from Violin Sonata in C Major, K. 6, mm. 1–8 (mark the keyboard part)

II. Composing a sentence from a given motive

Given the two-measure idea in G minor from Beethoven's Bagatelle Op. 119, No. 1, compose a sentence with the following guidelines:

- Use 2 + 2 + 4 measure groupings.
- Answer the harmonic motion of the basic idea (i to V) with a variant of the basic idea that moves from V to i.
- Develop the motive further in the final four measures with accelerated motion toward a PAC.

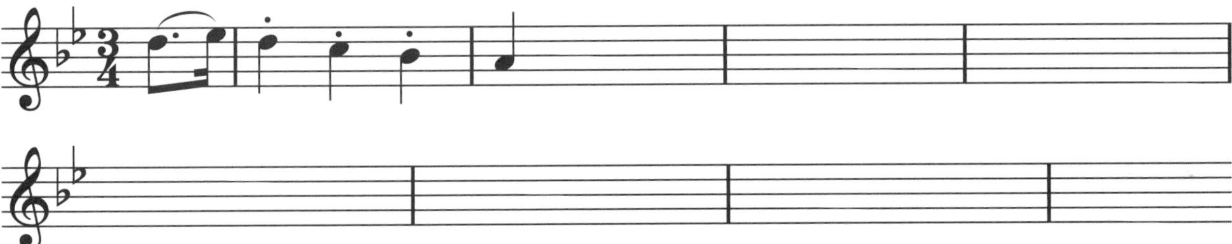

III. Motivic transformations

These motives are from the first movement of Clementi's Sonatina in F Major, Op. 36, No. 4. Listen to each one, then write its inversion. For the inversion, invert the contour and retain the interval size (don't attempt to match the interval quality). Play your solutions and alter them if necessary to "make sense" in the key and meter (there may be more than one possible solution). A first note is suggested.

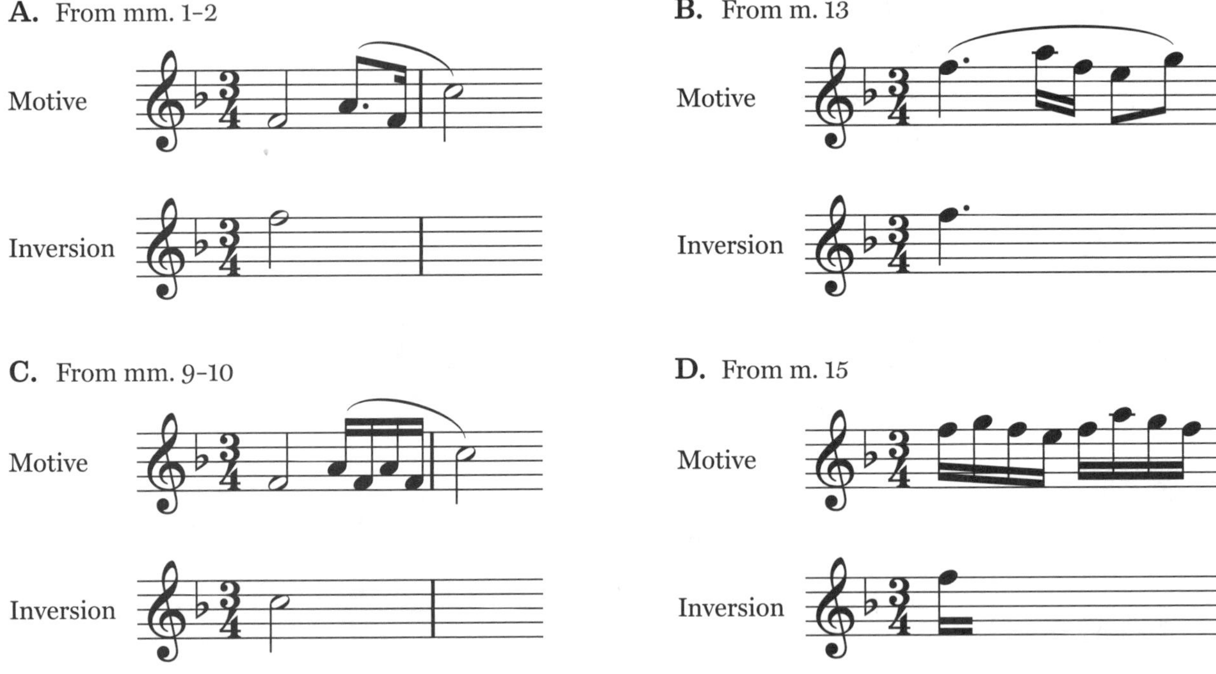

ASSIGNMENT 18.2

Analyzing phrase structure and motives

A. W. A. Mozart, Piano Sonata in C Major, K. 545, mvt. 3 (Anthology 62c)

(1) Listen to this excerpt (mm. 1–8) to determine its phrase structure. Write a Roman numeral analysis below the staff, and label each cadence type.

C: (I) vi

(2) Circle the term that best describes measures 1–4:

(a) parallel period (b) contrasting period (c) sentence (d) subphrase

(3) Circle the term that best describes measures 1–8:

(a) parallel period (b) contrasting period (c) sentence (d) subphrase

(4) Now listen to the entire movement (Anthology 62c). On the score provided in part (1), bracket two motives in the first eight measures that appear later in the piece. In the following table, list measure numbers where they reappear, and indicate how they are transformed.

Motive 1 (from mm. 1–8): mm. ______________________

Motive 2: mm. ______________________

MOTIVE 1 RETURNS	HOW TRANSFORMED?	MOTIVE 2 RETURNS	HOW TRANSFORMED?

B. W. A. Mozart, Piano Sonata in B♭ Major, K. 333, mvt. 3, mm. 1–16

Listen to this excerpt, then draw a phrase diagram of all sixteen measures.

- Include the number of measures in each phrase, letters to show whether the phrases are parallel or contrasting, and cadence types.
- Indicate how many phrases and periods are in this excerpt, and of what type.
- Circle on the score two different motives and their repetition in an altered form.
- Draw an arrow from each motive to its transformation.

Phrase diagram:

NAME ____________________

ASSIGNMENT 18.3

I. Analysis

A. Beethoven, *Für Elise*, mm. 1-8 (Anthology 17)

Listen to the opening of this piano piece while following your anthology score.

(1) Draw a diagram that represents the phrase structure of measures 1-8. Include the number of measures in each phrase, cadence types, and letters (**a**, **a′**, **b**, **b′**) to show melodic relationships.

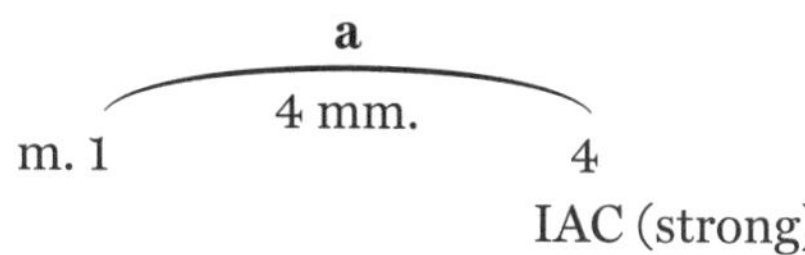

(2) Circle the term that best describes this passage:

(a) parallel period (b) contrasting period (c) repeated phrase (d) two independent phrases

B. Franz Schubert, "Der Lindenbaum," from *Winterreise*, mm. 9-24 (Anthology 80)

Start by listening to the introduction and first stanza of this song (to m. 24), while following your Anthology score.

(1) Draw a diagram that represents the phrase structure of measures 9-24. Include the number of measures in each phrase, cadence types, and letters (**a**, **a′**, **b**, **b′**) to show melodic relationships.

(2) Circle the term that best describes measures 9-16:

(a) parallel period (b) contrasting period (c) repeated phrase (d) two independent phrases

(3) Circle the term that best describes measures 17-24:

(a) parallel period (b) contrasting period (c) repeated phrase (d) two independent phrases

C. W. A. Mozart, String Quartet in D Minor, K. 421, mvt. 3, Trio, mm. 40-47 (Anthology 63b)

(1) Draw a diagram that represents the phrase structure of measures 40-47. Include the number of measures in each phrase, cadence types, and letters (**a**, **a′**, **b**, **b′**) to show melodic relationships.

II. Composing complete parallel periods

In this exercise, you will write a harmonic progression and two melodies that fit with it. Each melody should be an eight-measure parallel period, with each parallel period consisting of two phrases. Work on your own staff paper, or use notation software to prepare your score. We strongly recommend that you work at a keyboard, so you can hear the progression you have written while composing your melodies.

- Start by preparing your score. Use three staves—one for your melody, and two below it connected with a grand staff for your keyboard harmonization.
- Write a four-part harmonic progression of your choice, in keyboard style, that follows an antecedent-consequent model (T–PD–D, T–PD–D–T). Use a slow harmonic rhythm, with one or two chords per measure. The tonic harmony may last for one or more measures at the beginning of each phrase, with an acceleration at the cadence.
- Play your progression at a keyboard, or listen to it using notation software, and sing improvised melodies to go with the progression. Use parallel structure: the first part of each phrase should have the same melody.
- When you have composed a melody you like, write it out on the top staff above the harmonization.
- Prepare three additional staves: on the lower two, write out your harmonization again; on the upper staff, write a second (different) melody following the same procedure.

Extra challenge: Make a piano setting from your harmonization to accompany one of your melodies.

You may sketch your ideas here, but prepare a clean score on your own paper to submit.

ASSIGNMENT 18.4

I. Writing consequent phrases

Here, you will write antecedent-consequent phrases in Classical style, based on major-key melodies from Mozart piano sonatas. Sing through the antecedent phrases (ending on a HC), then write two possible consequent phrases, each ending on a PAC. For your first solution, write a parallel period; for your second, write a contrasting period. The slurs are Mozart's markings; slurs are optional in your answer. (If you like, find a score and compare your consequent phrase with Mozart's!)

A. Piano Sonata in B♭ Major, K. 281, mvt. 3, mm. 1–4

Antecedent:

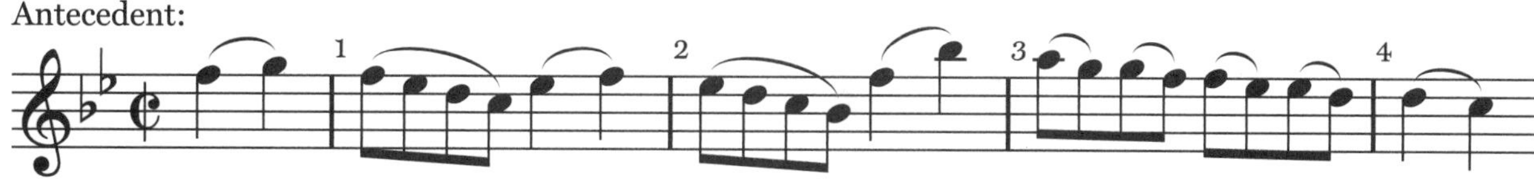

Consequent 1 (parallel):

Consequent 2 (contrasting):

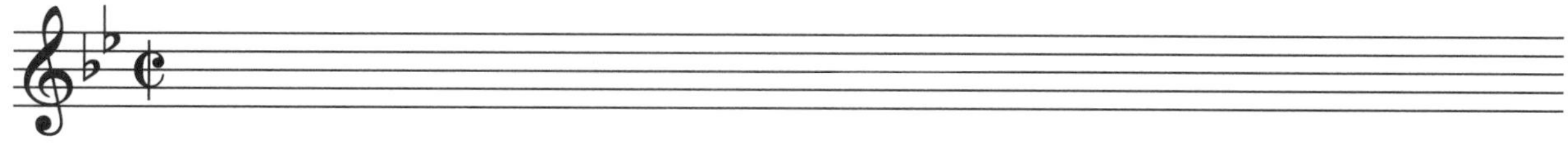

B. Piano Sonata in D Major, K. 284, mvt. 3, mm. 1–4

Antecedent:

Consequent 1 (parallel):

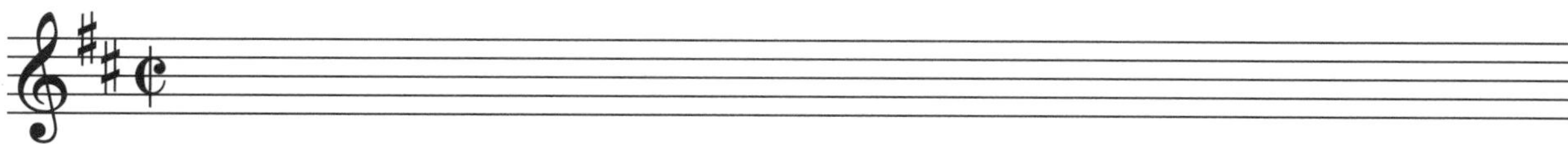

Consequent 2 (contrasting):

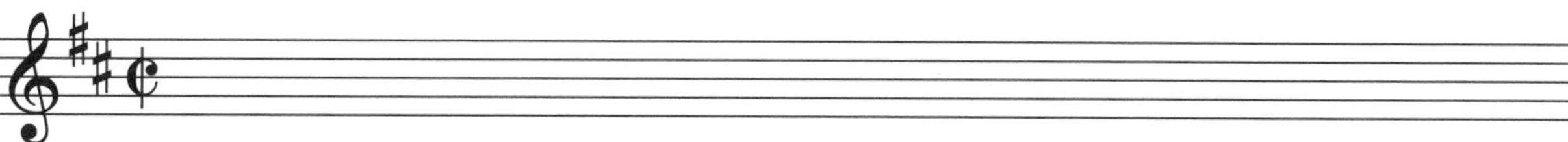

C. Piano Sonata in D Major, K. 311, mvt. 3, mm. 1–4

II. Analysis, Beethoven, Sonata in C Minor, Op. 10, No. 1, mm. 1–22

The following score provides the opening of the movement through the first PAC. Draw a phrase diagram below the score that divides the music into its component parts, giving the number of measures in each. Label your diagram with appropriate terms (including possible phrase extensions).

NAME ______________________________

ASSIGNMENT 18.5

I. Analysis: Joseph Haydn, Piano Sonata No. 13 in E Major, mvt. 2

Listen to or play through this movement. Write a Roman numeral analysis for measures 1–8 and label the cadences.

(1) Measures 1–4 are best described as a subphrase because:

(a) its motives are not developed. (b) it has no cadence. (c) it is short.

(2) Circle the term that best describes measures 1–8:

(a) parallel period (b) contrasting period (c) single phrase (d) sentence

(3) Measures 9–14 comprise a six-bar phrase. The phrase expansion occurs at the (circle one)

beginning middle end

(4) Cite two places in measures 9–14 (right-hand melody) that relate motivically to measures 1–8. Give measure numbers and the relationship to the original motive.

MEASURE NUMBER	RELATIONSHIP TO ORIGINAL	LOCATION OF ORIGINAL MOTIVE

(5) Measures 15–24 comprise a ten-bar phrase. Compare with measures 1–8. The phrase expansion occurs at the (circle one)

beginning middle end

(6) Name two ways that this final phrase differs from measures 1–8.

(a)

(b)

(7) How are the motives in the phrase expansion related to what has been heard previously?

ASSIGNMENT 18.6

Phrase analysis: Beethoven, Violin Sonata in C Minor, Op. 30, No. 2, mvt. 1, mm. 1–24

Listen to the first twenty-four measures of this sonata movement.

(1) The opening of this movement is characterized by short motives and subphrases separated by rests Remember to look for cadences as you determine the phrase structure.

Provide a phrase diagram for the first sixteen measures. Include the number of measures in each phrase, letters to show whether the phrases are parallel or contrasting, and cadence types.

(2) Circle the term that best describes measures 1-16:

(a) parallel period (b) contrasting period (c) two independent phrases (d) sentence

(3) Circle the term that best describes measures 9-16:

(a) parallel period (b) contrasting period (c) two independent phrases (d) sentence

(4) Find two lead-ins, and give their measure numbers: m. _________ ; m. _________

(5) For class discussion or a short essay (on your own paper): (a) Describe the relationship between the violin and piano in terms of texture and shared melodic content. (b) What musical factors indicate that the first eight measures are introductory? (c) What is the source of the thematic material in measures 17–24?

NAME ______________________________

Secondary Dominant and Leading-Tone Chords to V

ASSIGNMENT 19.1

I. Spelling root-position secondary dominants to V

Write the triad or seventh chord in each key requested, in whole notes. Provide the key signature, and then add any necessary accidentals to adjust the chord quality.

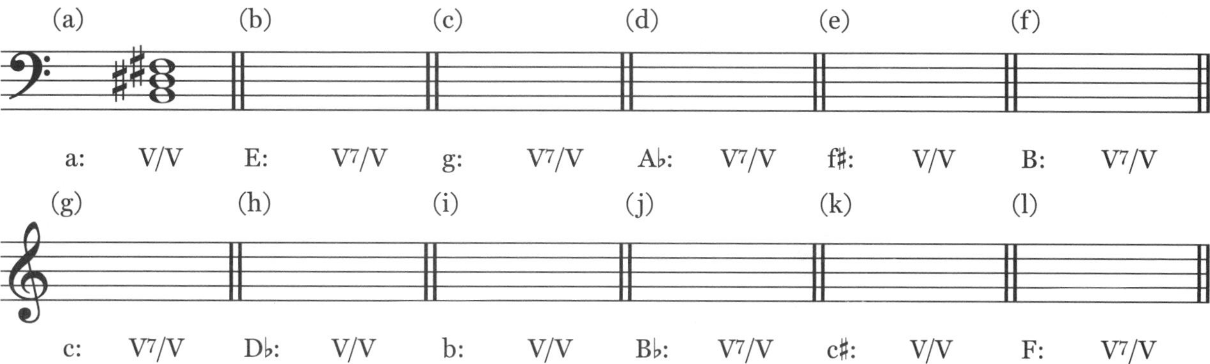

II. Resolving root-position secondary dominants to V

Write the two- and three-chord patterns in chorale style in the keys specified using quarter notes.

- Draw arrows to show temporary leading tones resolving up and chordal sevenths down.
- For V7/V to V, make one chord complete and the other incomplete.
- For V7/V to V7, move the temporary leading tone down to the chordal seventh of V7.
- In minor keys, add an accidental to the V chord to make it major.

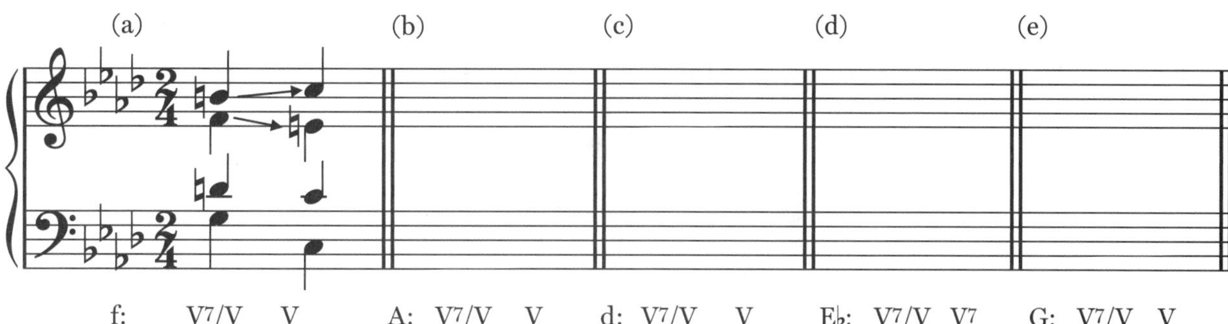

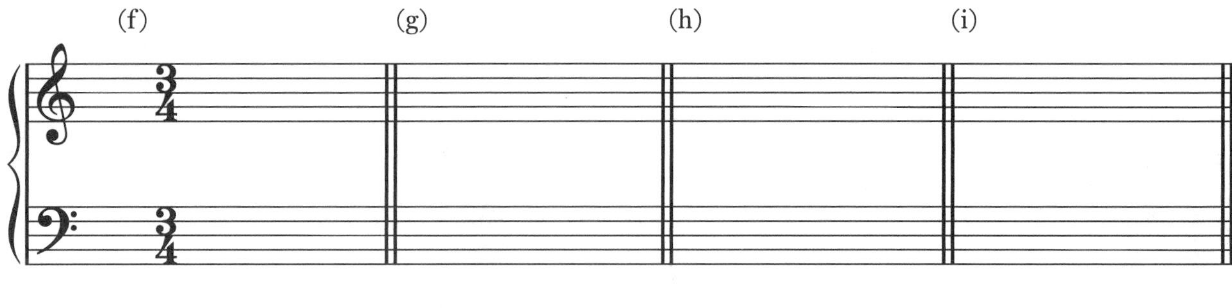

A♭: V7/V V7 I   e: V7/V V^{6}_{4}—$^{5}_{3}$ B: V7/V V^{6}_{4}—$^{5}_{3}$ c: V7/V V7 i

III. Analysis

Provide a Roman numeral analysis.

A. Love, Melcher, Phillips, and McKenzie, "Kokomo," mm. 11–14

B. Billy Joel, "Piano Man," mm. 18–25

Hint: This excerpt features a stepwise descending bass. Consider the B in the bass in measure 19 (doubled in the tenor) as a passing tone against the opening tonic harmony.

NAME ______________________________

ASSIGNMENT 19.2

I. Spelling secondary dominants to V with inversions

Write the secondary dominant in each key requested, in whole notes. Provide the key signature, and then add any necessary accidentals to adjust the chord quality.

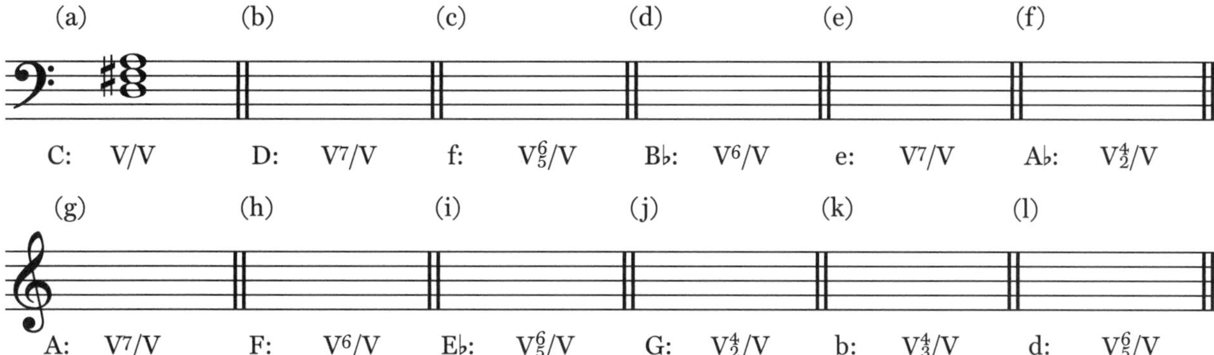

II. Resolving secondary dominants to V

Write the two-chord pairs in chorale style in the specified keys using half notes. Draw arrows to show resolutions of leading tones up and chordal sevenths down. Compare with Assignment 13.2, part II. How are the progressions there related to these?

III. Resolving secondary dominants to V7

Write the two-chord pairs in chorale style in the specified keys using quarter notes. Draw arrows to show resolutions of the chordal seventh down; resolve $\sharp\hat{4}$ to $\natural\hat{4}$, the chordal seventh of the dominant.

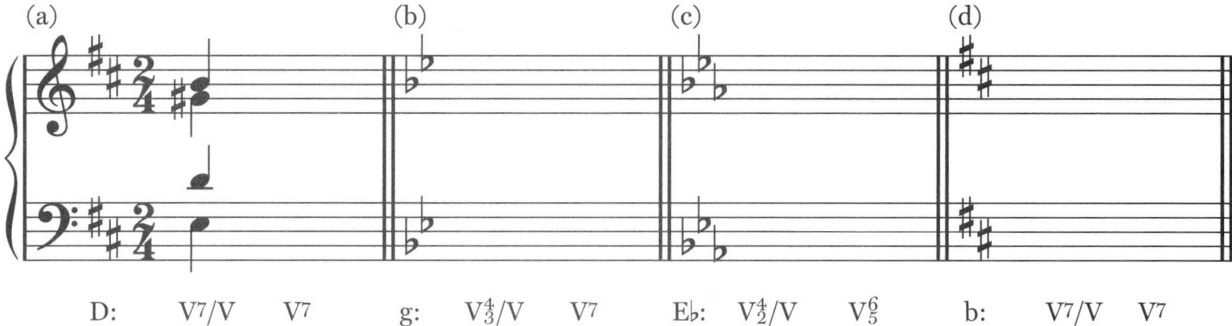

IV. Analysis

A. W. A. Mozart, Piano Sonata in C Major, K. 545, mvt. 3, mm. 10–12 (Anthology 62c)

Provide a Roman numeral and contextual analysis, and label the cadence type (PAC, IAC, HC, THC, or DC).

Cadence: ________

B. W. A. Mozart, Piano Sonata in D Major, K. 284, mvt. 3, mm. 22–25 (Anthology 60)

Provide a Roman numeral analysis and label the cadence type (PAC, IAC, HC, THC, or DC). Label one chord per measure in measures 22-23 with the lowest note determining the inversion.

D: I ————————

Cadence: ________

ASSIGNMENT 19.3

I. Preparing and resolving secondary dominants

Write the chords in chorale style in the keys specified.

- For (a)-(c) approach the chromatic tone by half step to avoid cross relations.
- For (d)-(f) write a chromatic voice exchange and mark it with an X.
- For (e) and (f), add a passing chord (in eighth notes) between the first two chords.

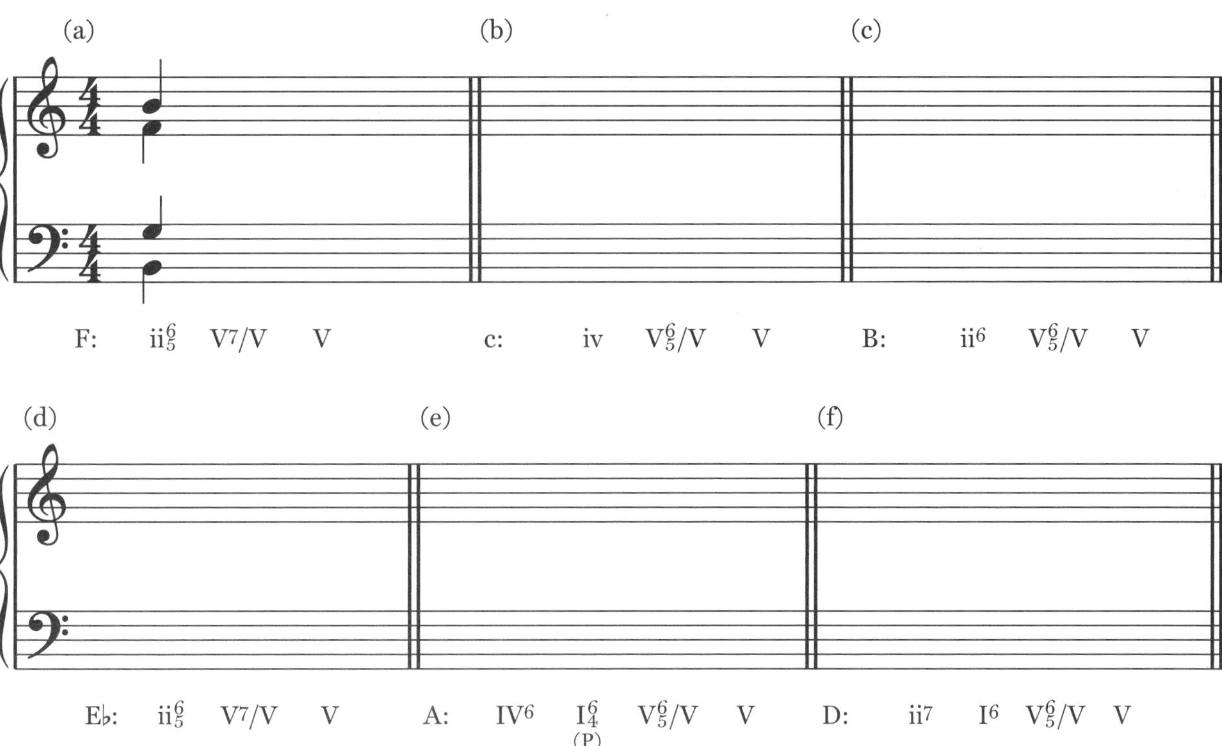

II. Writing secondary dominants in a phrase

A. From Roman numerals: Write the progressions in the keys and meters indicated in chorale style. Remember to approach the chromatic tone in the secondary dominant by half step to avoid cross relations. Add a contextual analysis below the Roman numerals.

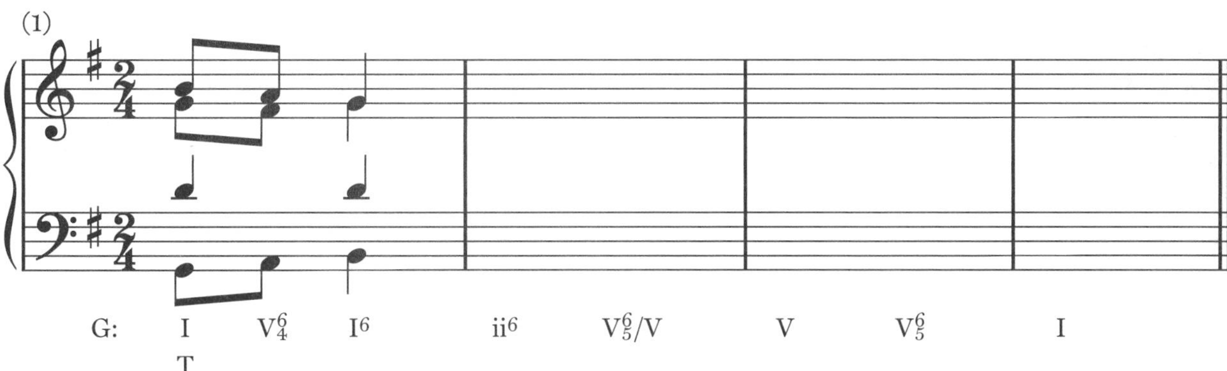

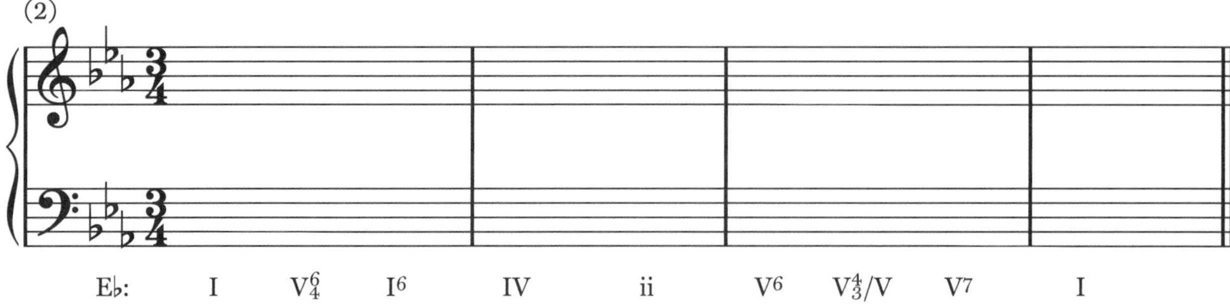

B. From figured bass: Realize the following figured bass in keyboard style. Provide Roman numeral and contextual analyses in D major.

Arcangelo Corelli, Preludio, from Sonata in D Minor, Op. 4, No. 4, mm. 1-5

III. Analysis: W. A. Mozart, String Quartet in D Minor, K. 421, mvt. 3, mm. 48–55

Listen to the example (Anthology 63b), and analyze the measures reproduced here. Provide one Roman numeral per measure; use the downbeat of the measure to determine the inversion. Circle and label embellishing tones.

ASSIGNMENT 19.4

I. Spelling secondary leading-tone chords to V

Write the secondary diminished seventh chord in whole notes, in each key requested. Provide the key signature, and add any necessary accidentals to adjust the chord quality.

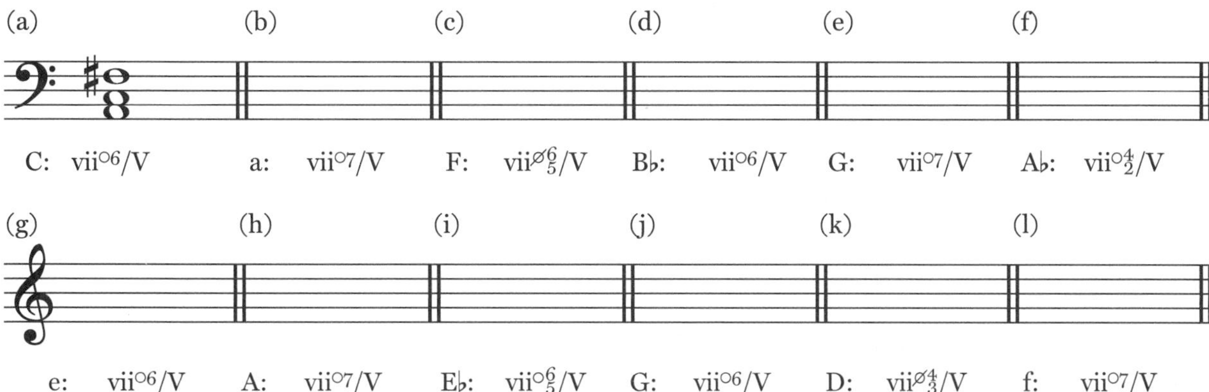

II. Resolving secondary leading-tone chords to V

Write the two-chord pairs in chorale style in the specified keys using half notes. Provide the key signature, and draw arrows to show the resolution of leading tones up and chordal sevenths down.

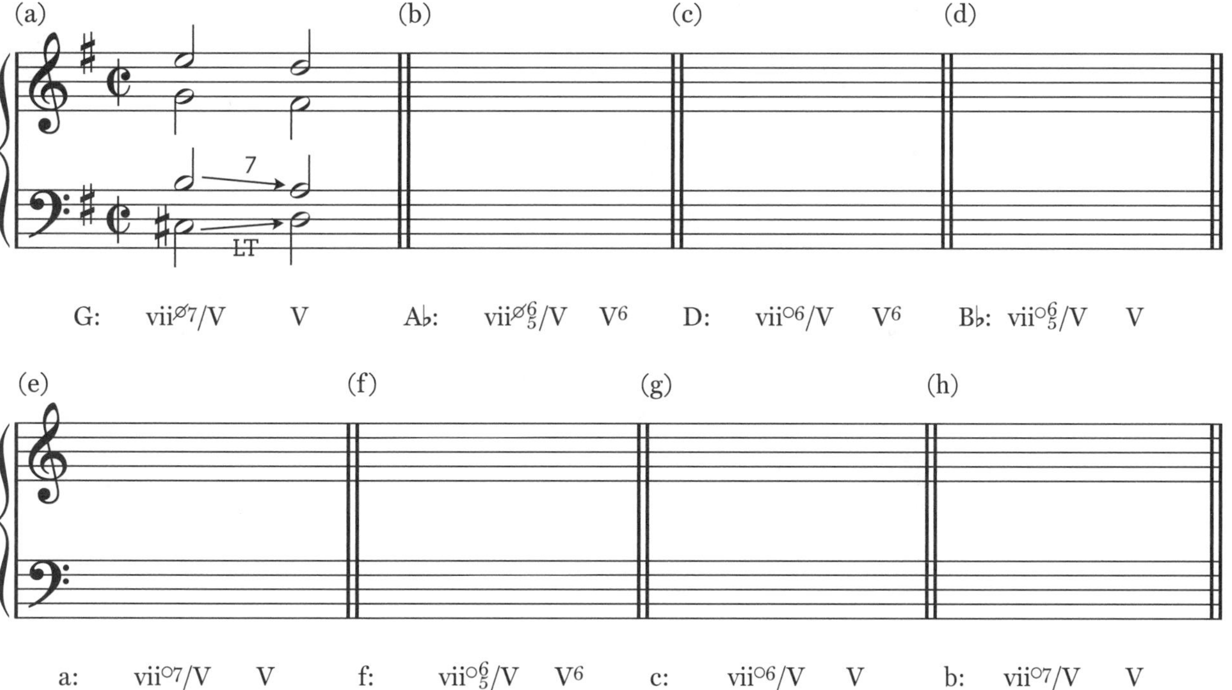

III. Resolving secondary leading-tone chords to V7

Write the two-chord pairs in chorale style in the specified keys using quarter notes. Provide the key signature, and resolve $\sharp\hat{4}$ to $\natural\hat{4}$, the chordal seventh of the dominant.

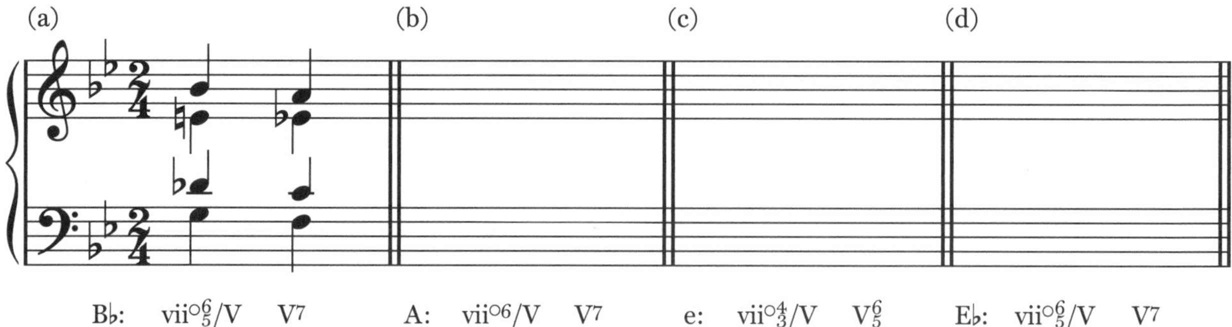

IV. Analysis

For each excerpt, identify the key and provide a Roman numeral analysis in the blanks provided.

A. Robert S. Weir and Calixa Lavallée, "O Canada," mm. 9–12

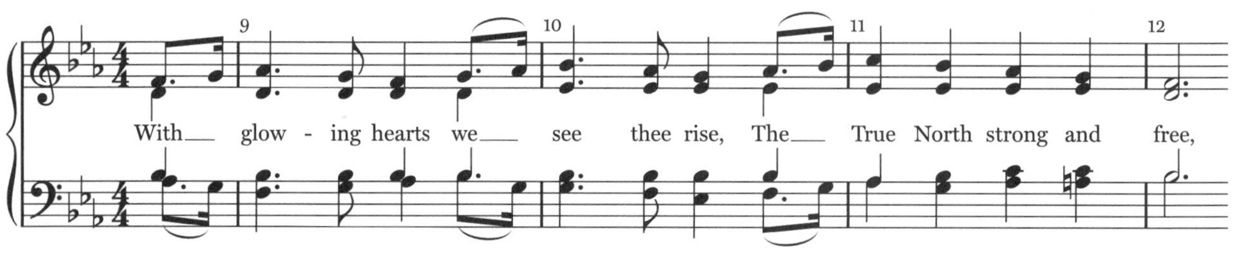

B. Fanny Mendelssohn Hensel, "Die Mainacht," mm. 15–17 (analyze in E♭ major)

ASSIGNMENT 19.5

I. Spelling review

Spell each of the secondary-function chords, in whole notes. Provide the key signature, and then add any necessary accidentals to adjust the chord quality.

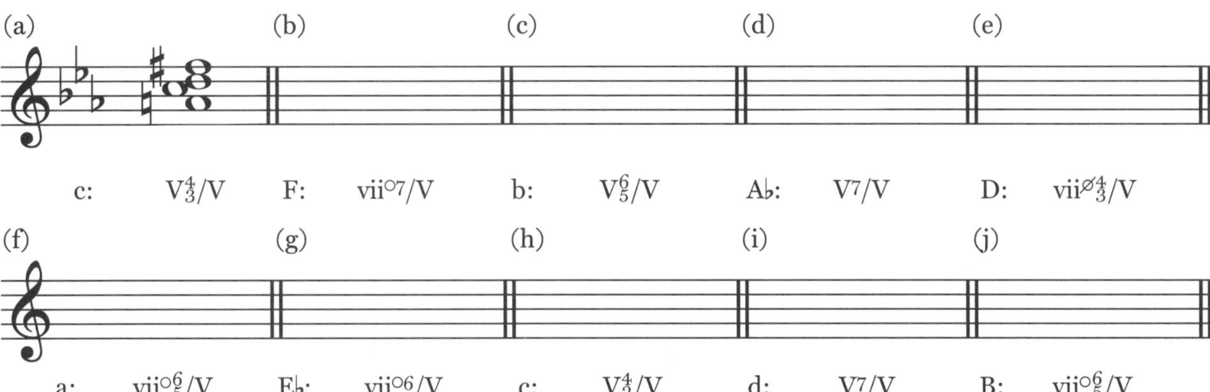

II. Writing dominant expansions

Write the dominant expansion progressions in chorale style in the specified keys using quarter notes. Draw arrows to show the resolution of leading tones up and chordal sevenths down.

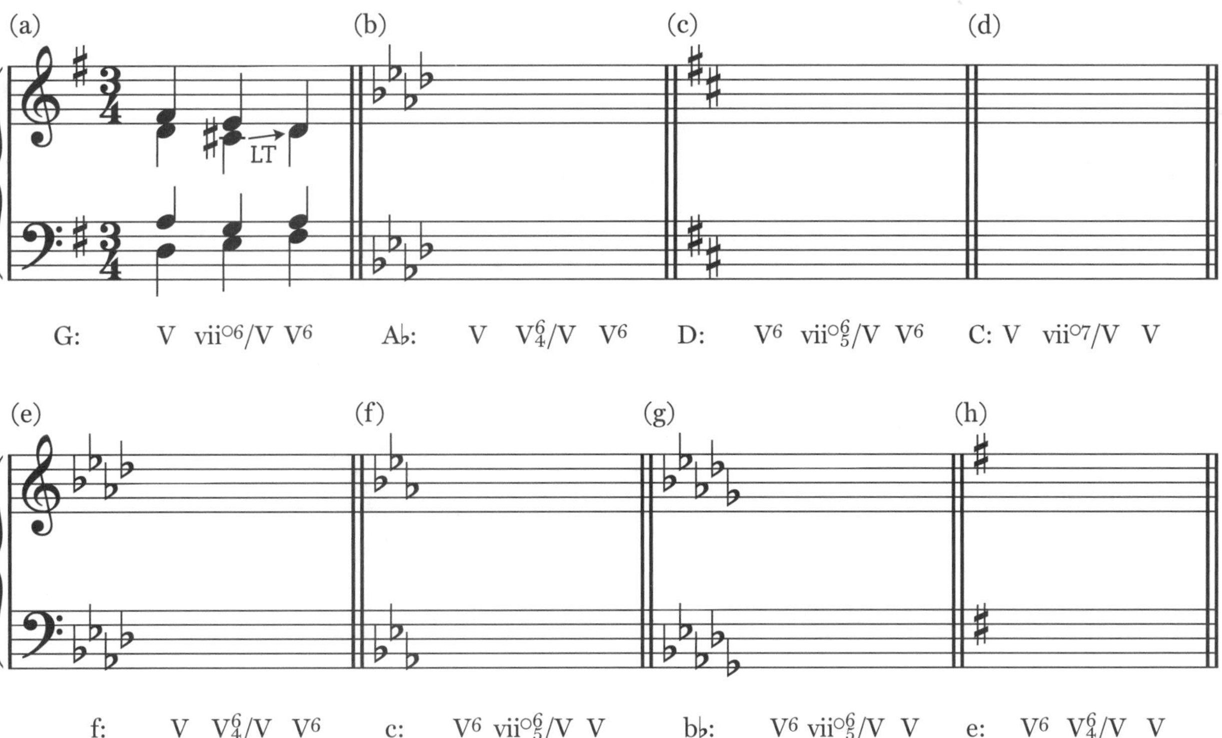

III. Analysis

Identify the key, then provide a Roman numeral and contextual analysis for the following excerpts.

A. Elizabeth-Claude Jacquet de la Guerre, Gigue, from Suite No. 3 in A Minor, mm. 10–12

B. Handel, "Rejoice greatly," mm. 9–11

Re-joice, re - joice, re-joice great - ly,

C. Johannes Brahms, *Variations on a Theme by Haydn*, mm. 11–18

Piano 1
Piano 2

NAME ______________________________

Tonicizing Scale Degrees Other Than V

ASSIGNMENT 20.1

I. Spelling secondary dominant chords

Write the chords requested, in whole notes. Provide the key signature, then add any necessary accidentals to adjust the chord quality. It might also be helpful to provide the chord of resolution as a block chord, as shown in (a); space is provided for you to do this. Don't worry about voice leading for now.

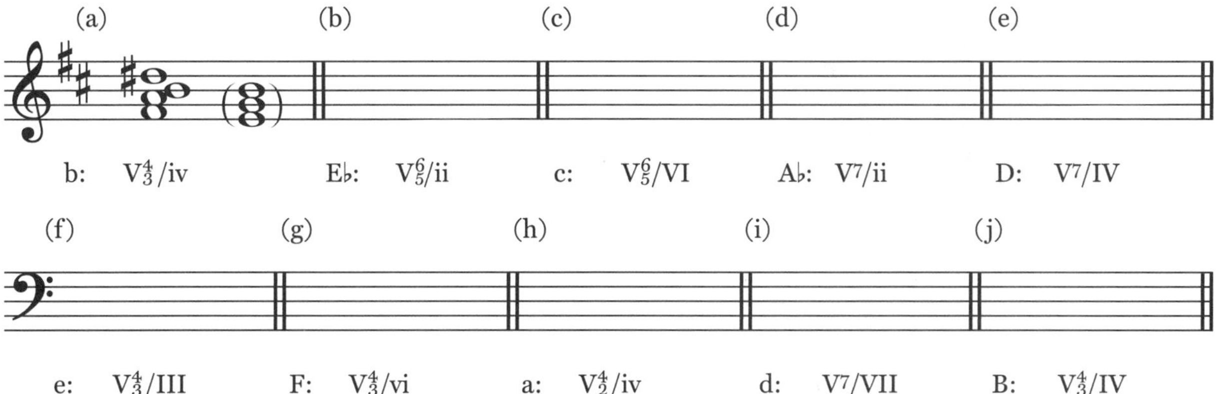

II. Resolving secondary dominants

Write the two-chord pairs in chorale style in the specified keys using quarter notes. Provide the key signature, and draw arrows to show the resolution of leading tones up and chordal sevenths down. For root-position chords, remember to make one complete and one incomplete.

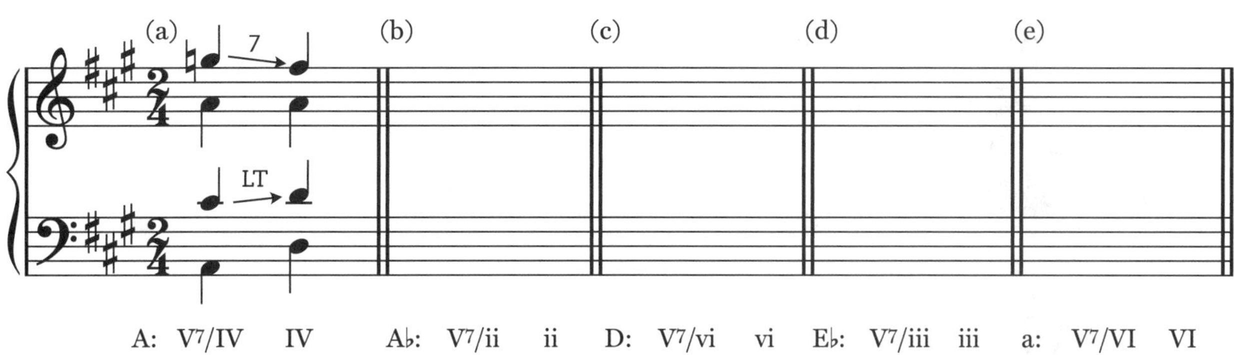

III. Analysis: Franz Schubert, "Erlkönig"

This song (Anthology 77) tells the story of a sick boy and his father, who are riding through a storm at night on horseback. The son hears the calls of the Elf King (a mythic creature associated with darkness and doom), who eventually woos the boy to his death. The passages below are sung by the Elf King.

A. Provide a Roman numeral and contextual analysis for measures 66 to 72. Begin the basic phrase with T in measure 67.

B. Now look at the passage from measures 86 to 96. Provide Roman numerals and measure numbers for two different secondary dominants that are found in this passage. Do they resolve as you would expect?

	ROMAN NUMERAL	MEASURES	REGULAR RESOLUTION?
(1)	__________	__________	__________
(2)	__________	__________	__________

C. Optional: Listen to the entire song with the score to put this verse (mm. 86–96) into perspective. Then either (1) prepare for a class discussion, or (2) write a short essay, to answer the following questions: What is the mood of this verse? How do the accompaniment pattern, melodic embellishment, and harmonic choices correspond to the text? What interpretive choices by the performers would help bring out the mood?

ASSIGNMENT 20.2

I. Resolving secondary dominants

Write the two-chord pairs in chorale style in the specified keys using quarter notes. Provide the key signature, and draw arrows to show the resolution of leading tones up and chordal sevenths down.

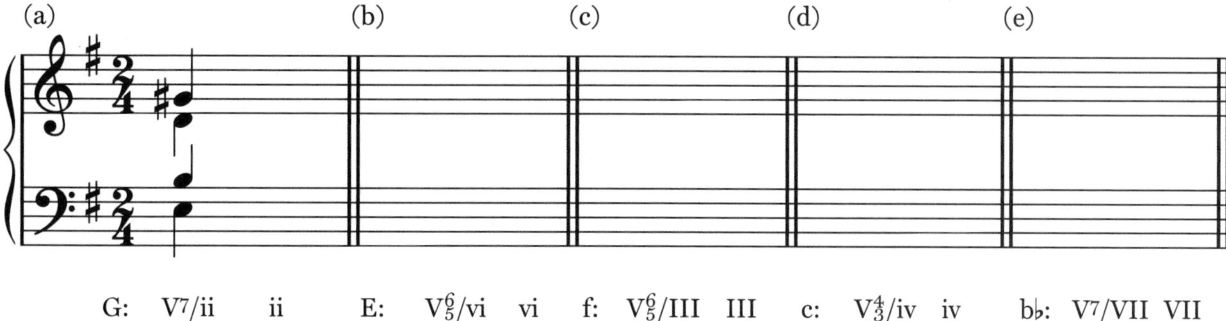

II. Writing secondary dominants

Write the progressions in chorale style in the keys and meters indicated. When the temporary leading tone requires an accidental, prepare and resolve it stepwise in a single voice to avoid cross relations. Add a contextual analysis below each.

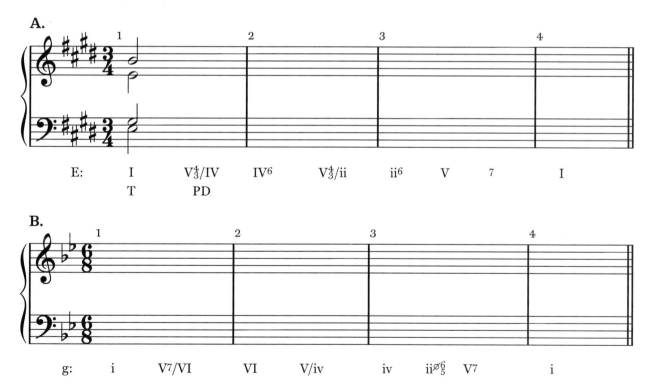

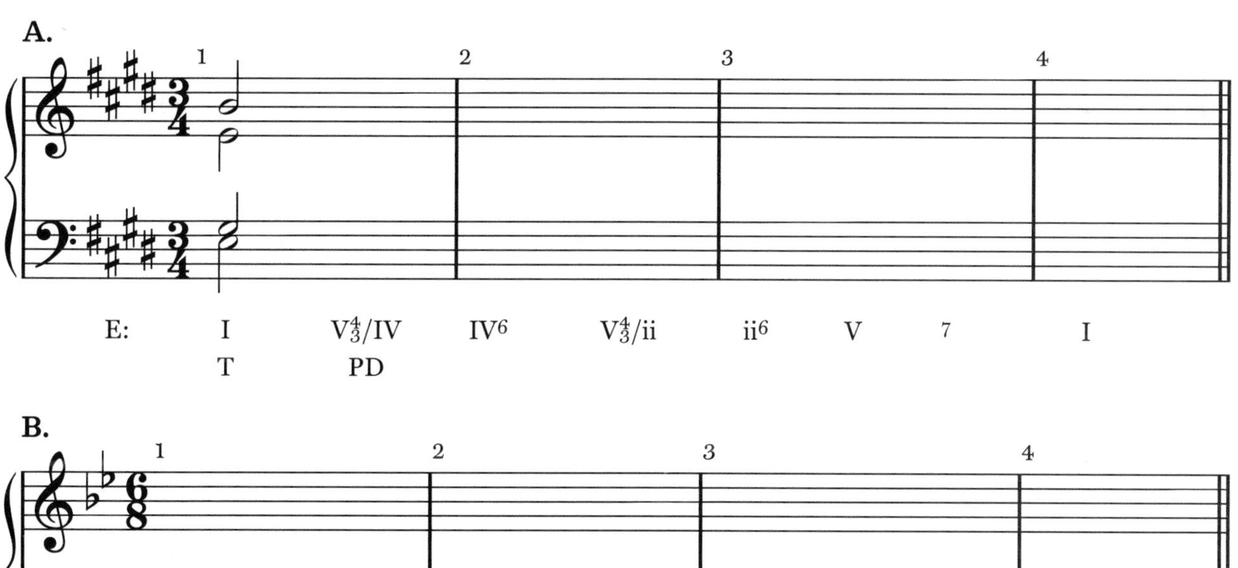

B.

1 2 3 4

g: i V7/VI VI V/iv iv ii$^{ø6}_5$ V7 i

III. Analysis: Arcangelo Corelli, Preludio, from Sonata in D Minor, Op. 4, No. 8, mm. 25-38 (Anthology 32)

Provide a Roman numeral analysis for the passage, then answer the questions that follow. (The Roman numerals need not include the many suspensions indicated by the figures.)

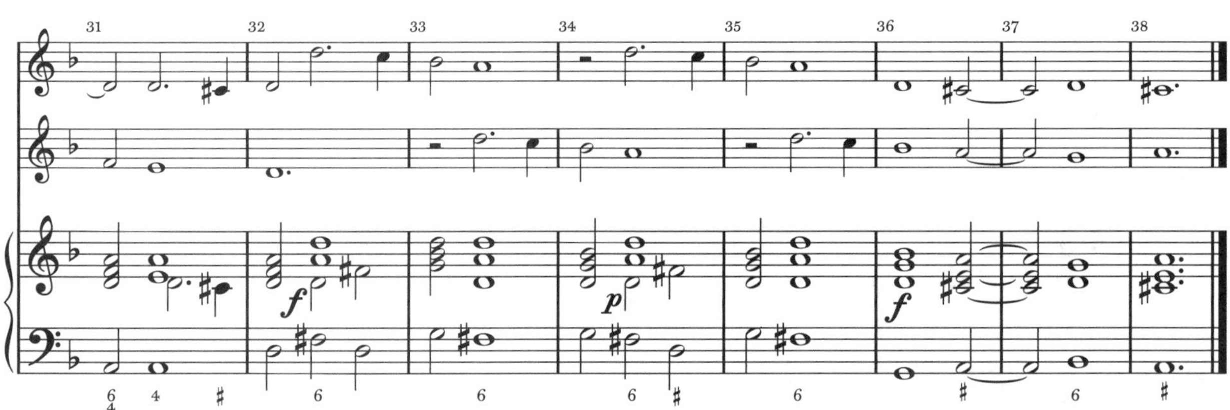

(a) This passage tonicizes just one triad repeatedly. What is it? ________________

(b) This tonicization prolongs what function within the basic phrase? ________________

(c) What type of cadence does it prepare? ________________

(d) What rhythmic device marks the cadence? ________________

ASSIGNMENT 20.3

I. Spelling secondary dominants and leading-tone chords

Write the requested chords using whole notes. Provide the key signature, then add any necessary accidentals to adjust the chord quality. It might also be helpful to provide the chord of resolution as a block chord, as shown in (a); space is provided to do this. Don't worry about voice leading for now.

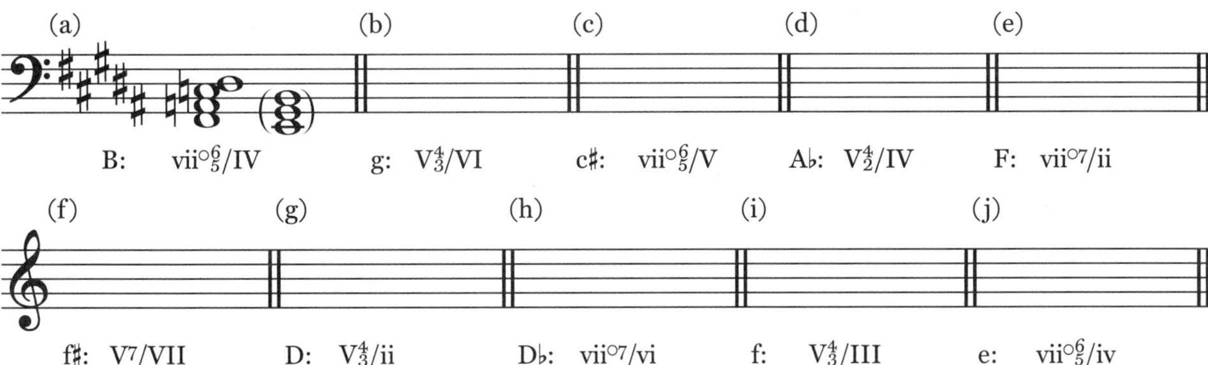

II. Resolving secondary leading-tone chords

Write the two-chord pairs in chorale style in the specified keys using quarter notes. Provide the key signature, and draw arrows to show the resolution of leading tones up and chordal sevenths down.

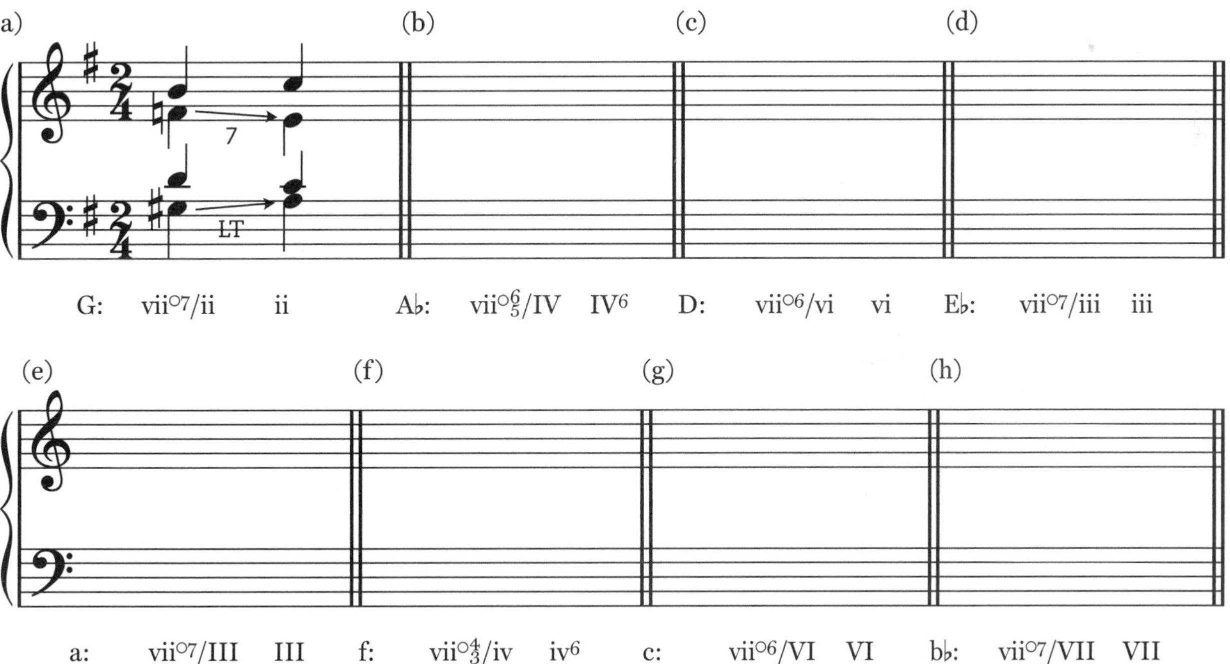

III. Analysis

Provide a Roman numeral analysis for each passage.

A. J. S. Bach, Prelude in C Major, mm. 18–24 (Anthology 11a)

18
19
20
C: V7
21
22
23
24

In which measures does a secondary dominant resolve irregularly? What is irregular about it?

B. Queen, "Killer Queen," mm. 12–14

Hint: This excerpt ends on a minor dominant.

12
13
14
Cav - i - ar and cig - a - rettes, well versed in et - i - quette, ex - tr'or - di - nar - i - ly nice.

ASSIGNMENT 20.4

I. Analysis: W. A. Mozart, "Voi, che sapete," from The Marriage of Figaro, *mm. 21–28 (Anthology 58b)*

Provide a Roman numeral analysis.

F: I

II. Preparing and resolving secondary chords

Write the three-chord progressions in chorale style in the specified keys using quarter notes. Provide the key signature, then prepare the temporary leading tone with stepwise motion and resolve the tendency tones properly.

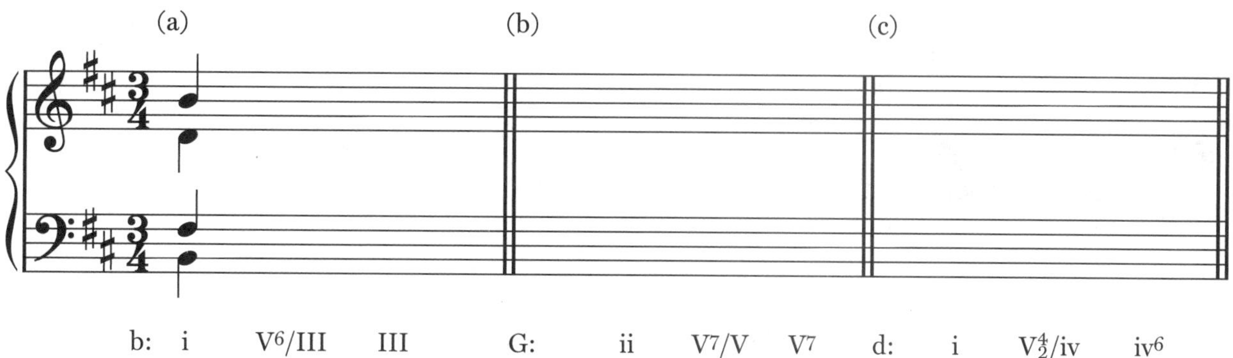

(d) (e) (f)

E♭: I vii°7/ii ii f: i vii°7/VII VII A: IV6 vii°$^6_5$/V V

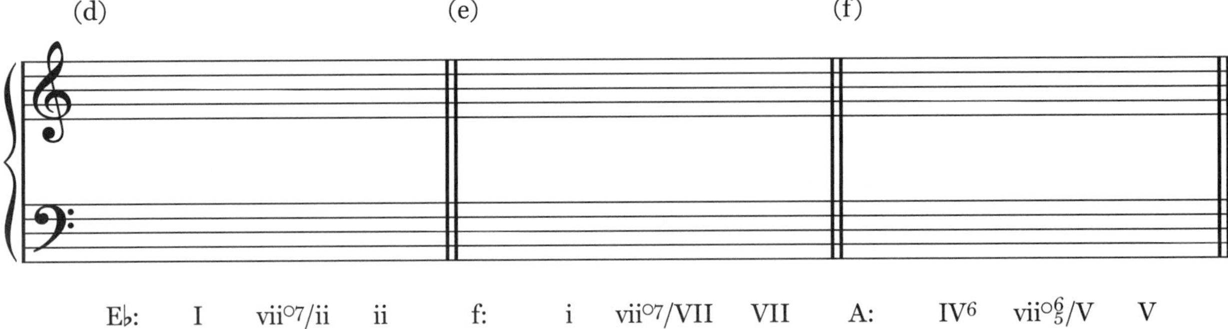

III. Figured bass

Realize the figured-bass continuo part on the grand staff. Use keyboard style (three voices in the right hand, the bass line provided in the left) and a whole-note harmonic rhythm (half notes in m. 57). If necessary for proper voice leading, you may temporarily reduce the texture to two voices in the right hand. Write a Roman numeral analysis beneath the bass line.

Antonio Vivaldi, *Gloria*, mvt. 1, mm. 50–61

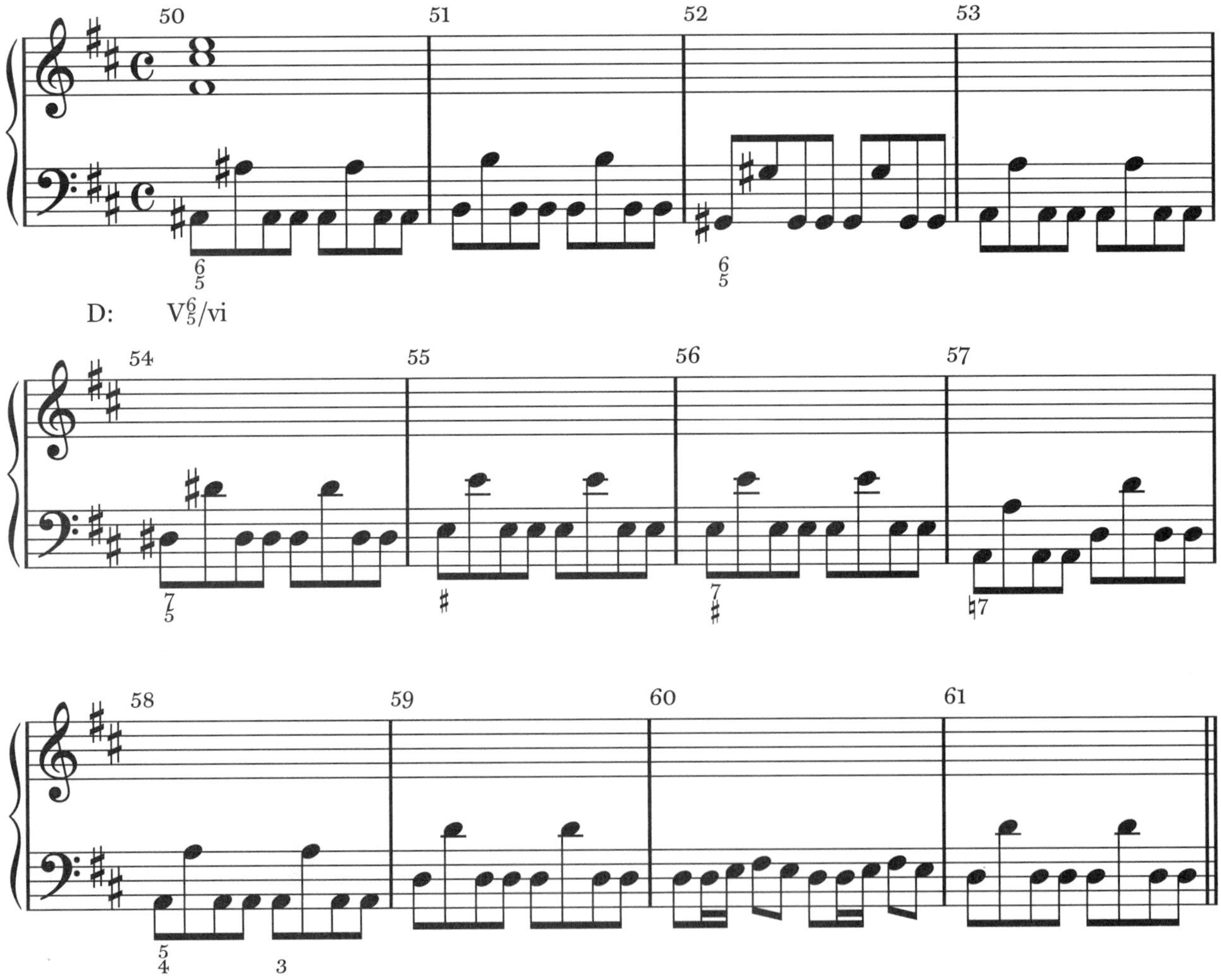

50
51
52
53
6 5
6 5
D: V6 5/vi
54
55
56
57
7 5
♯
7 ♯
♮7
58
59
60
61
5 4
3

What is unusual about the resolution of the harmony in measures 54–55?

ASSIGNMENT 20.5

I. Figured bass: Antonio Vivaldi, "Qui tollis," from Gloria, mm. 8-15

Realize the following figured bass in keyboard style. The soprano line of the choral part is shown; don't worry about doubling keyboard voices with the soprano. This excerpt is in E minor; provide a Roman numeral analysis underneath.

Translation: Hear us now, as we make our prayers to thee

II. Analysis

Write the key and Roman numerals for each excerpt, then answer the questions that follow.

A. J. S. Bach, Chaconne, from Violin Partita No. 2 in D minor, mm. 92-96

(1) Which diatonic triad is tonicized in this phrase? ____________________

(2) Is this a common choice for a phrase ending in a minor key? ____________________

B. Scott Joplin, "Solace," mm. 57–60

(1) Which diatonic triad is tonicized in this phrase? ______________________

(2) Is this a common choice for a phrase ending in a major key? ______________________

C. Johannes Brahms, *Variations on a Theme by Haydn*, mm. 1–5

Add a contextual analysis below the Roman numerals.

(1) What is the cadence type? ______________________

(2) Which chords are tonicized in this passage? ______________________

(3) Are these commonly tonicized chords in a major-key piece? ______________________

NAME ______________________

ASSIGNMENT 20.6

I. Figured bass: J. S. Bach, "Jesu, meine Freude"

Realize this chorale tune, without modulating from E minor (although you may include tonicized half cadences). After completing and checking your harmonization for part-writing errors, add embellishing tones to make a typical chorale texture. Provide a Roman numeral analysis.

Bach set this melody many times. Compare your setting with one of his (for example, Chorale Nos. 96, 263, 283, 324, or 356), as well as with those of your classmates.

II. Analysis

For each excerpt, determine the key and provide Roman numerals with inversions. Circle the Roman numerals for any secondary dominant or leading-tone chord with an irregular resolution. Ignore any circled pitches.

A. J. S. Bach, "Er kommt," from Cantata 140 (*Wachet auf*), mm. 11-13

Translation: To welcome the Bridegroom. There! Behold, he comes this way!

B. Beethoven, Piano Sonata in C Minor, Op. 13 (*Pathétique*), mvt. 3, mm. 48-51

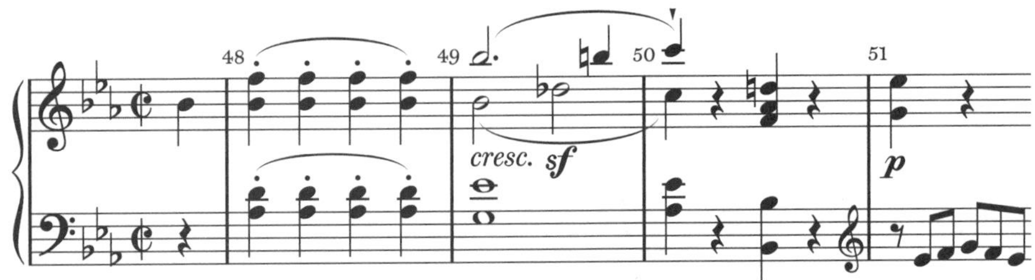

C. Johannes Brahms, "Die Mainacht," mm. 15-19 (Note that both hands of the piano are notated in treble clef.)

Translation: Veiled by leaves a pair of doves coo their delight in front of me,

NAME ____________________

21 Sequences

ASSIGNMENT 21.1

I. Completing sequences

Each of the following frameworks shows a two-chord sequence pattern and the first chord of its transposition, written in keyboard style.

- Examine the given pattern, then complete the sequence so that it connects to the harmonic conclusion shown. Remember to maintain the exact voice leading and doubling in the transpositions.
- Bracket the sequence pattern and each of its transpositions, and use arrows with numbers above to show the interval of transposition.
- Write the LIP (linear intervallic pattern) interval numbers between the staves, and fill in the name of the sequence type and LIP in the blanks provided.
- Complete the Roman numeral analysis.

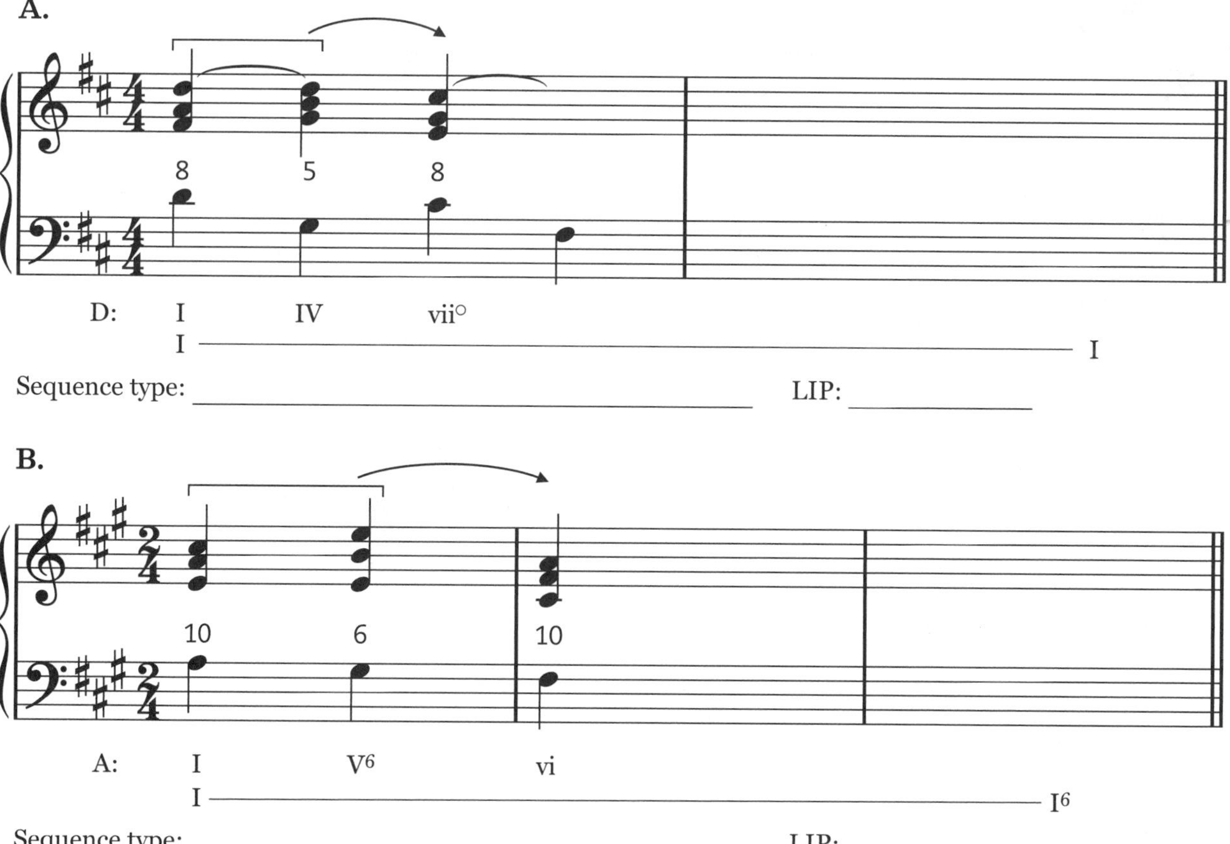

C.

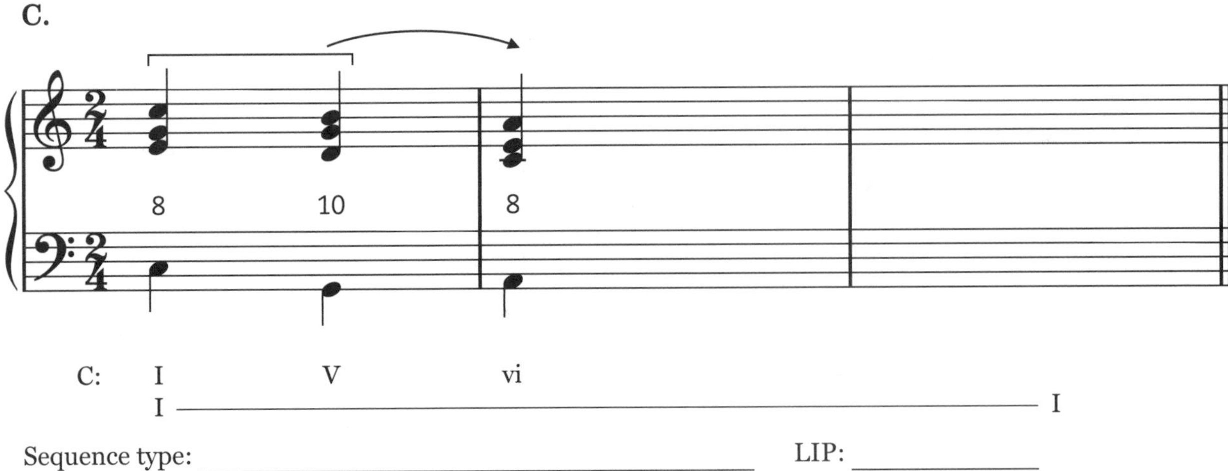

Sequence type: ______________________ LIP: __________

II. Analysis of sequences

Locate the sequence in each short excerpt. Mark the sequence pattern with a bracket above the staff and add an arrow with the interval of transpositions. Then identify the pattern length in beats, interval of transposition, and sequence type.

A. Beethoven, *Für Elise*, mm. 17–20

Pattern length: ______________ Interval of pattern transposition: ______________

Sequence type: ______________

B. J. S. Bach, Chaconne, from Violin Partita No. 2 in D Minor, mm. 56–59

56 57 58 59

Pattern length: ______________ Interval of pattern transposition: ______________

Sequence type: ______________

ASSIGNMENT 21.2

I. Writing three-voice sequences

Each of the frameworks shows an incomplete sequence that typically appears in three parts to avoid the parallels that doubling would create.

- Examine the given pattern, then complete the sequence so that it connects to the harmonic conclusion shown.
- Write the LIP (linear intervallic pattern) interval numbers between the staves, and fill in the name of the sequence type and LIP in the blank.

A.

Sequence type: ____________________ LIP: __________

B.

Sequence type: ____________________ LIP: __________

C.

Sequence type: ____________________ LIP: __________

II. Analysis of sequences from popular music

Locate the sequence in each excerpt. Above the staff write in the chord symbols (e.g., Fm). Below the staff, provide a Roman numeral analysis. Identify the pattern length in measures, interval of transposition, and sequence type in the blanks below.

A. Colleen Fitzpatrick, "Graduation," mm. 9–12

Pattern length: ______________ Interval of transposition: ______________ Sequence type: ______________

B. Moroder, Forsey, and Cara, "Flashdance—What a Feeling," mm. 5–12

Pattern length: ______________ Interval of transposition: ______________ Sequence type: ______________

ASSIGNMENT 21.3

Figured-bass realization

Realize these figured basses. For each:

- Write in keyboard style (two or three voices in the right hand).
- Provide a Roman numeral analysis.
- Mark the sequence pattern with a bracket above the staff, and add an arrow with the interval of transposition.
- Identify the sequence type.
- Identify the LIP with interval numbers (e.g., 10-10-10).
- Follow any specific instructions given with the individual exercises.

A. Antonio Vivaldi, *Gloria*, mvt. 1, mm. 8-15

This type of sequence is usually voiced with two upper parts instead of three; change to three upper voices after the sequence, at the cadence. Write primarily half notes.

Sequence type: ______________________________ LIP: __________

Cadence type (mm. 12-13): __________

B. Antonio Vivaldi, Violin Concerto, Op. 8, No. 4 ("L'inverno"), from *Le quattro stagioni*, mvt. 2 (adapted), mm. 10–13

Use quarter-note chords, with two or three parts in the right hand.

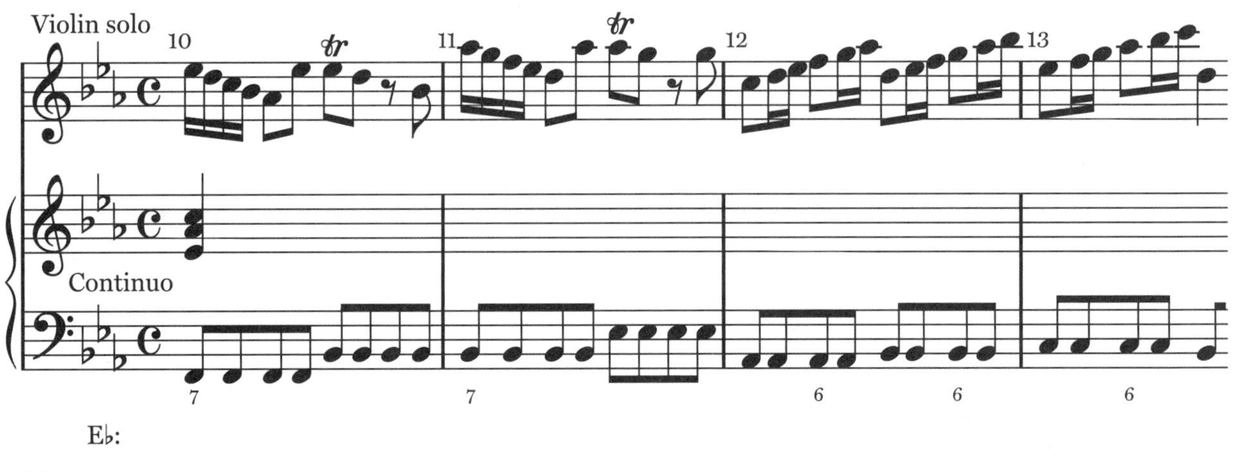

Measures 10–11
Pattern length: ______________ Interval of transposition: ______________

Measures 12–13
Pattern length: ______________ Sequence type: ______________

C. Antonio Vivaldi, *Gloria*, mvt. 7, mm. 18–26

Despite the key signature, this excerpt is in C major. Change to a three-voice texture (two voices in the right-hand part) when the sequence begins in measure 20.

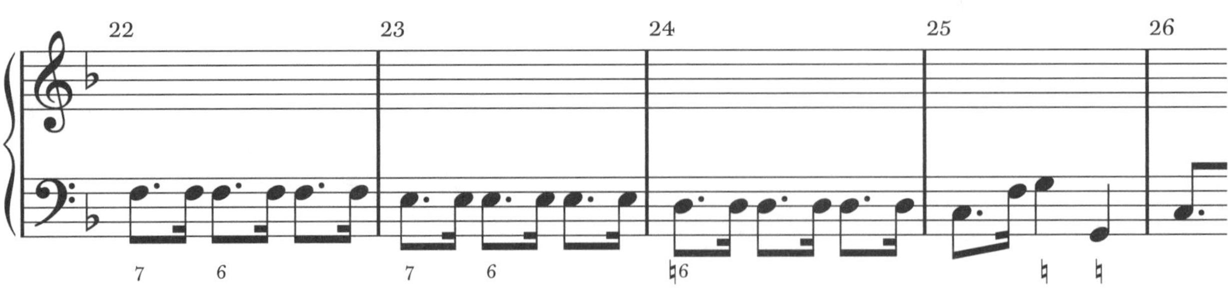

Sequence type: ______________ LIP: ______________

Cadence type (mm. 25–26): ______________

ASSIGNMENT 21.4

Analysis

A. W. A. Mozart, Sonata in C Major, K. 545, mvt. 1

Listen to the opening of this movement, following your score (Anthology 62a).

(1) Bracket the pattern of the sequence above the treble staff and add an arrow with the interval of transposition. Then make a chordal reduction of measures 5–9 on the grand staff, with one whole-note chord per measure. (Although scales are prominent in this excerpt, don't show them in the reduction. They simply decorate the underlying sequence framework; focus on the downbeats.) Identify the sequence type and LIP.

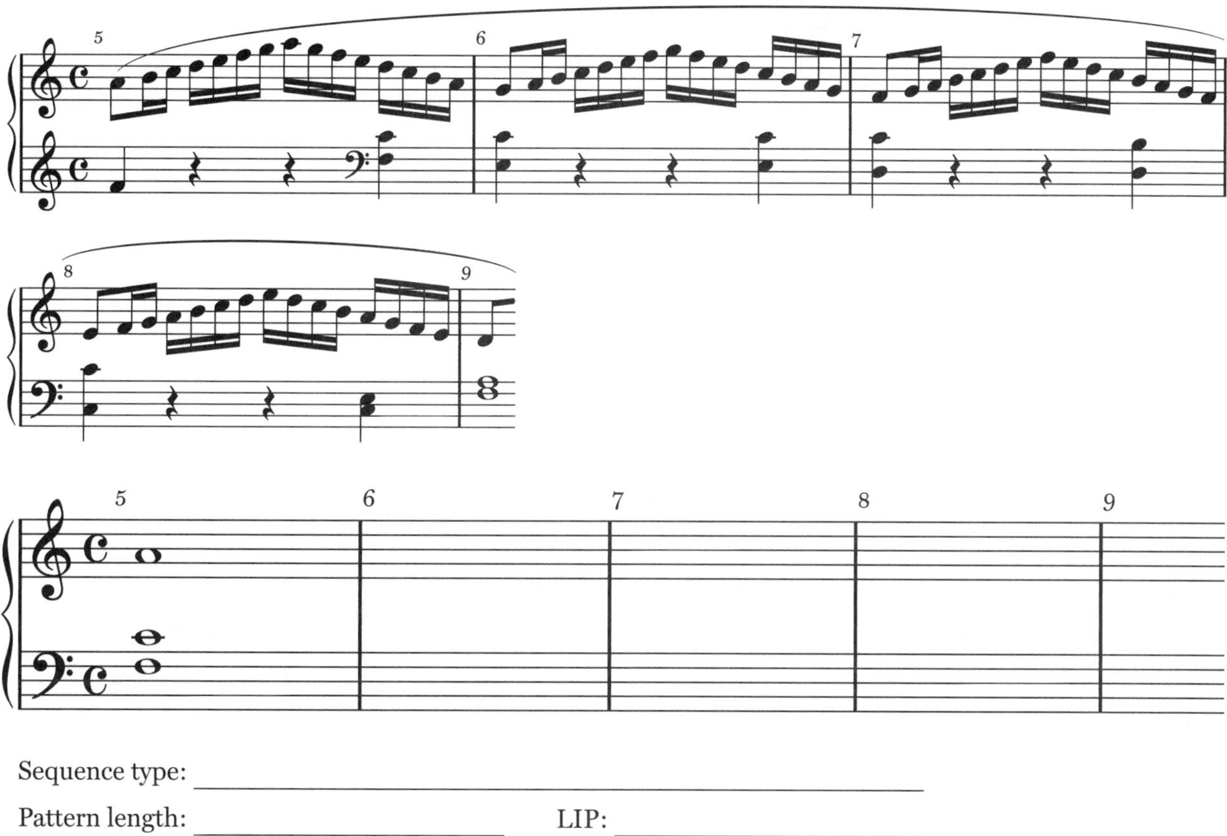

Sequence type: ______________________________

Pattern length: ____________________ LIP: ____________________

(2) Bracket the sequence pattern and add an arrow with the interval of transposition, then make a two-voice reduction of measures 18–21 on the grand staff, with two half notes per measure. (Again, use the strong beat and harmonic rhythm to guide your reduction.) This passage is in G major. Label each chord with Roman numerals that represent the entire harmony. Bracket the pattern and its transpositions in your reduction.

Sequence type: ______________________________

Pattern length: ______________ LIP: ______________

B. J. S. Bach, Invention in B♭ Major, mm. 4–5

Bracket the sequence pattern and label the interval of transposition, then make a two-voice reduction of measures 4–5 (through beat 3) on the grand staff. The harmony changes on each beat. In the reduction, show only the highest and lowest note in each chord, but label each chord with a Roman numeral that represents the entire harmony (the fifth is omitted in most of the chords). Bracket the pattern and its transpositions in your reduction.

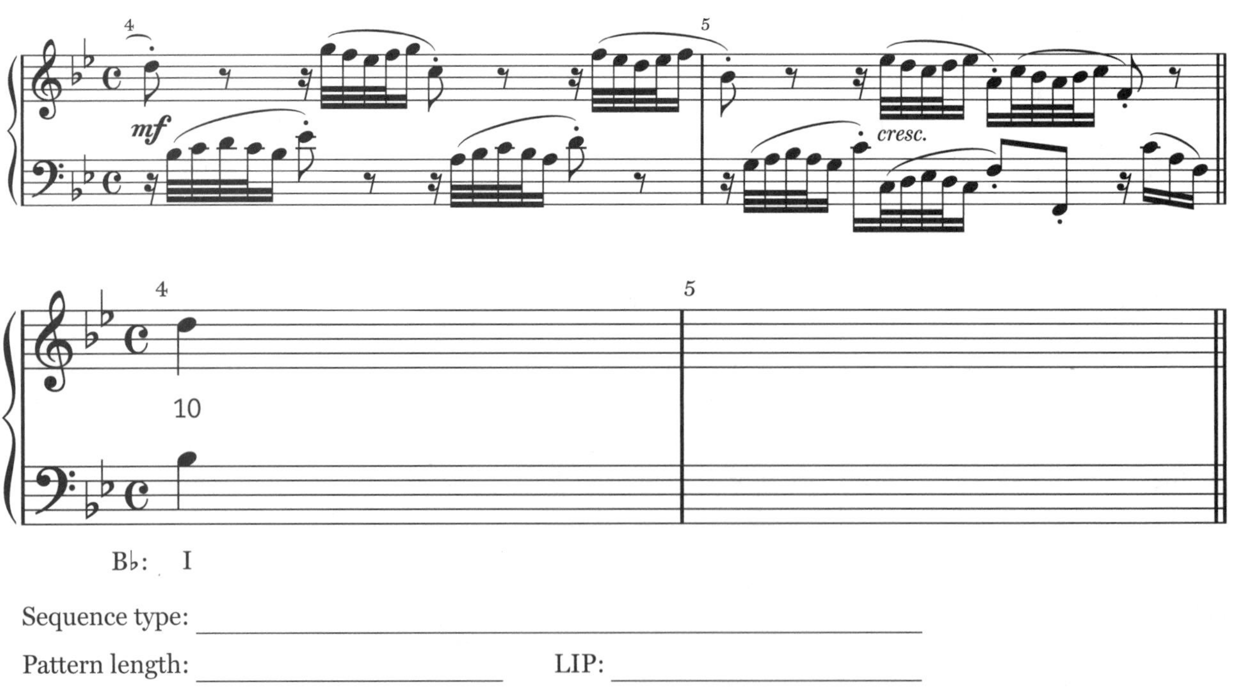

Sequence type: ______________________________

Pattern length: ______________ LIP: ______________

NAME ___________________

ASSIGNMENT 21.5

I. Completing sequences with seventh chords

Continue the two-chord pattern of measure 2 as a descending-fifth sequence with seventh chords.

- Prepare all sevenths by common tone and resolve down by step.
- For sequences with all root-position seventh chords, alternate complete and incomplete chords.
- Bracket the two-chord pattern above the staff and add an arrow with the interval of transposition.

A. Use alternating seventh chords in the sequence.

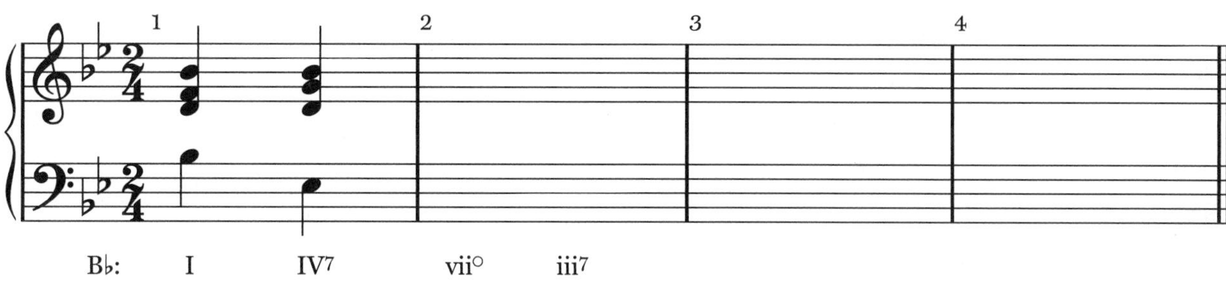

B. Use all seventh chords in the sequence.

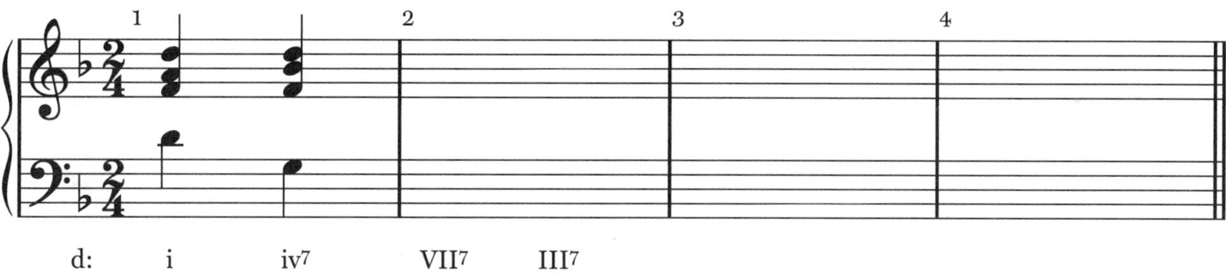

II. Figured bass

Arcangelo Corelli, Allemanda, from Trio Sonata in A Minor, Op. 4, No. 5, mm. 23–24

Realize the figured bass in keyboard style (three notes in the right hand). Provide Roman numerals and a contextual analysis that includes a sequence label. (Reminder: 9 6 in the figures of the final measure denotes a 9-8 suspension with change of bass.)

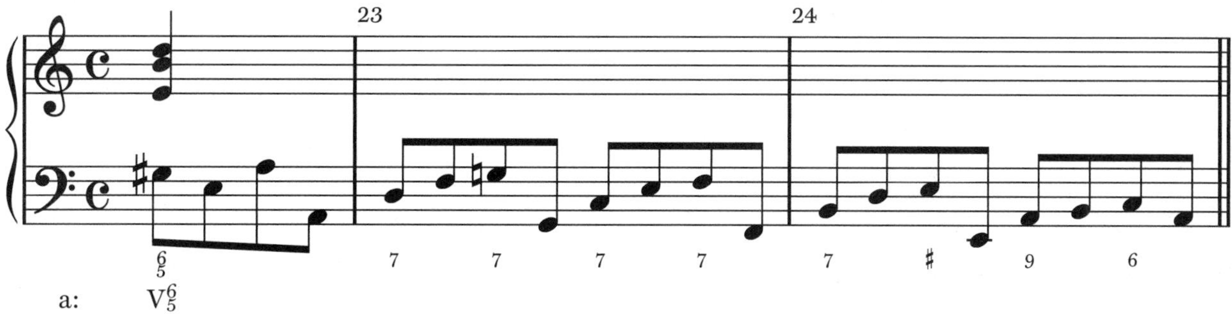

III. Analysis

Bracket the pattern of the sequence above the treble staff and add an arrow with the interval of transposition. Provide Roman numerals for each chord and then identify the sequence type.

A. Handel, Chaconne in G Major, Variation 13, mm. 105–108

Sequence type: ______________________________

B. J. S. Bach, Prelude, from Cello Suite No. 2 in D Minor, mm. 4–8

For this sequence, analyze in D minor with one Roman numeral per measure (watch for seventh chords).

Sequence type: ______________________________

C. W. A. Mozart, *Variation on "Ah, vous dirai-je Maman,"* Variation VII, mm. 169–176

Sequence type: ______________________________

ASSIGNMENT 21.6

I. Chromatic sequences

Complete the diatonic sequence frameworks shown in A. Then write embellished versions with secondary dominants as described for B–D. Provide a Roman numeral analysis for each exercise.

A. Descending-fifth sequence with seventh chords, root position

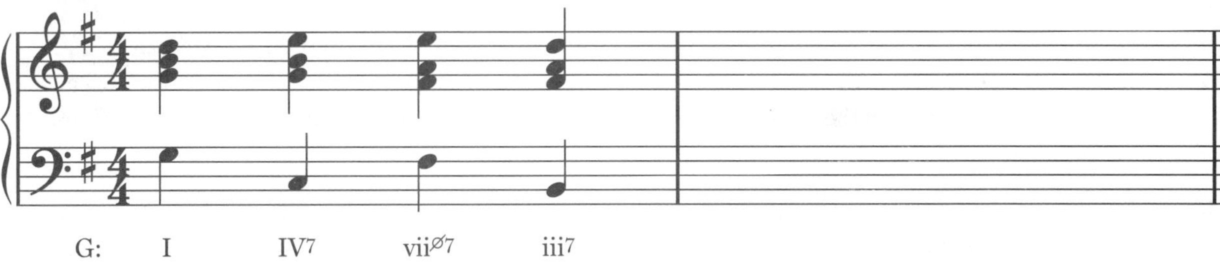

B. With incomplete secondary dominants alternating with triads. Draw arrows to show the resolutions of leading tones up and chordal sevenths down.

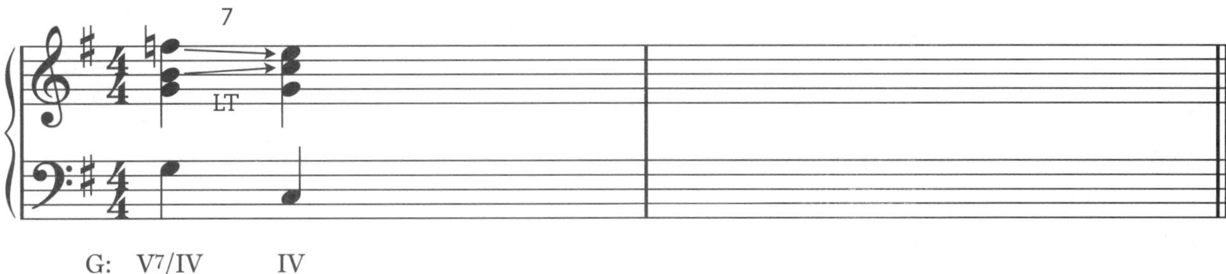

C. With incomplete secondary dominants alternating with triads. Draw arrows to show the resolutions of leading tones up and chordal sevenths down.

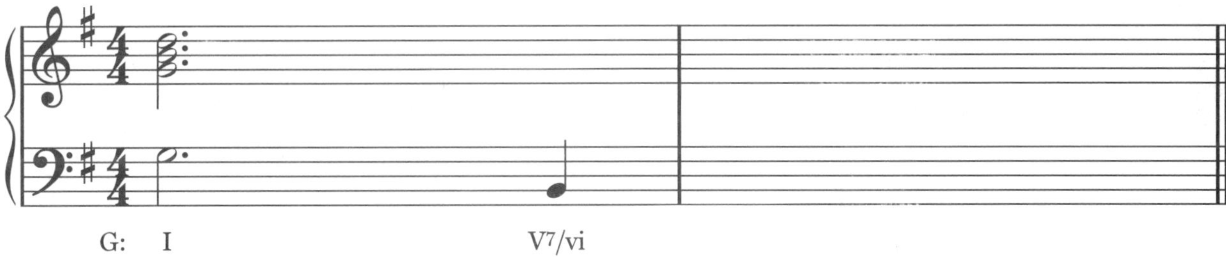

D. With each chord a secondary dominant. Draw arrows to show leading tones and chordal sevenths both resolving down.

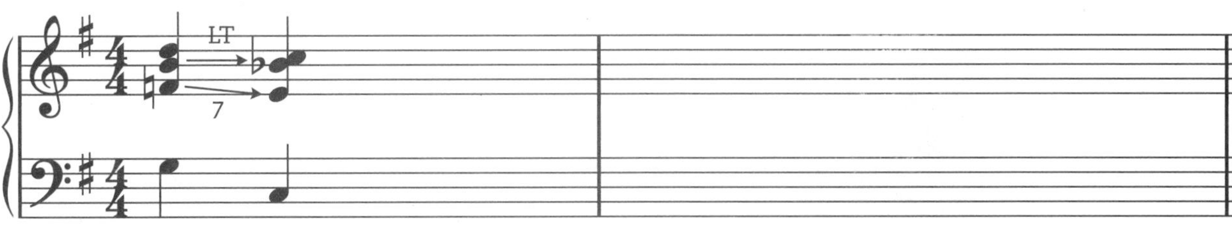

II. Creative writing

Write your own sequence-based composition. First decide what combination of instruments you will use.

A. *Song or solo with keyboard accompaniment*: Set up the score with three staff lines—the top line for the solo part (choose either bass or treble clef), and the lower two for the keyboard part in a grand staff. If you are writing for a vocalist, select a text, and make sure the vocal line falls within an appropriate range for the singer (soprano, alto, tenor, or bass). A good model is Hensel's "Neue Liebe," measures 1–8. If writing for an instrument, make sure your solo falls within the range for that instrument. For transposing instruments, prepare both a score for the accompanist and the transposed part for the soloist.

B. *Unaccompanied solo*: For unaccompanied vocalist or solo instrument, set up the staff with the appropriate clef for the instrument you have chosen. This assignment is more difficult than A or C, because the solo line will need to capture the sense of the sequence framework through arpeggiation or compound melody, while making a playable/singable line.

C. *Keyboard solo*: Use a grand staff, and make sure right- and left-hand parts are playable (not too wide a reach) and are idiomatic for the keyboard. There are many models of keyboard sequences in the chapter.

Choose a sequence framework that you like (from examples or assignments), then follow this procedure:

- Select a key and mode. Write in the key signature.
- Sketch an opening progression that establishes the tonic harmony in measures 1–2; perhaps use one of the tonic-expansion progressions.
- Sketch in the cadences: use a half cadence in measures 7–8 and a PAC in 15–16.
- Transpose the sequence framework you have selected to the key and mode you have chosen. Sketch it in measures 3–6.
- Embellish the sequence framework by adding passing or neighbor tones, or arpeggiate it to create the accompaniment or solo part, or apply a melodic or rhythmic motive to make an interesting sequence. Any of the voice-leading strands of the sequence (S, A, or T) in the chapter or workbook examples can serve as the highest part, as long as the entire strand is in the same part and there is one of each strand. The bass lines of these frameworks need to stay in the bass.
- Copy measures 1–6 in 9–14 to start the second phrase of a parallel period.

Chromatic Harmony and Form

NAME ____________________

22 Modulation

ASSIGNMENT 22.1

I. Triad functions

In the following charts, four triads are given in the top row. For each Roman numeral in the left-hand column, and for each triad given, fill in the appropriate key. For example, in which key would an E major triad function as III?

A.

	C MAJOR TRIAD	E MAJOR TRIAD	G MAJOR TRIAD	A♭ MAJOR TRIAD
I	C major			
III	A minor			
IV	G major			
V				
VI				
VII				

B.

	A MINOR TRIAD	D MINOR TRIAD	F MINOR TRIAD	B MINOR TRIAD
i	A minor			
ii	G major			
iii	F major			
iv				
v				
vi				

II. Identifying pivot chords

On the upper staff, write the diatonic triads for each scale degree of the first key. On the lower staff, copy those same chords, but add the necessary accidentals for the new key. Label all chords with Roman numerals. Draw a box around each of the possible pivot-chord pairs. For minor keys, write the triads on $\hat{5}$ and $\hat{7}$ twice: once in natural minor and once with the leading tone.

A. Modulation from G major to D major (I to V)

B. Modulation from E minor to B minor (i to v)

E minor

B minor

C. Modulation from G minor to B♭ major (i to III)

G minor

B♭ major

ASSIGNMENT 22.2

I. Modulating phrases with pivot chords

Write a six-chord progression that modulates between the keys specified, using chorale style. The first three chords should establish the first key. Choose an appropriate pivot chord (you may refer back to charts you made in Assignment 22.1, II), and write its Roman numeral in both keys; continue the analysis to the end. Remember to include accidentals needed for the cadence in the new key, and resolve all leading tones and sevenths.

A. Modulation from G major to D major (I to V)

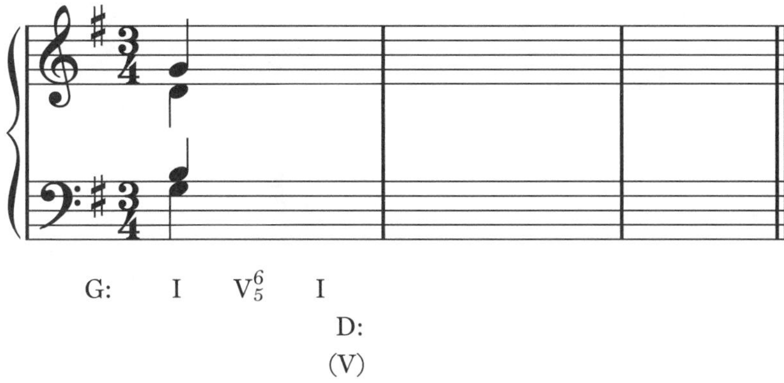

B. Modulation from E minor to B minor (i to v)

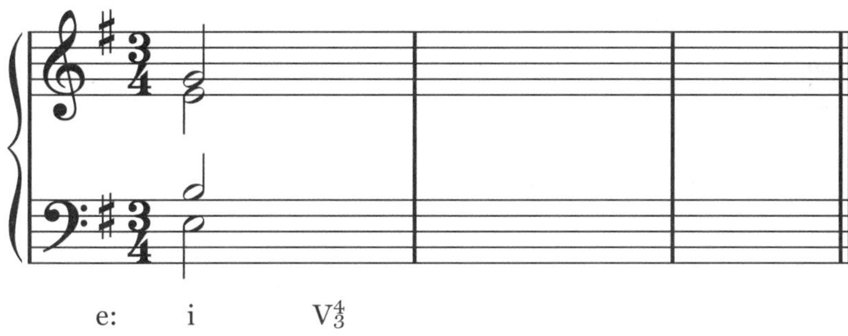

C. Modulation from G minor to B♭ major (i to III)

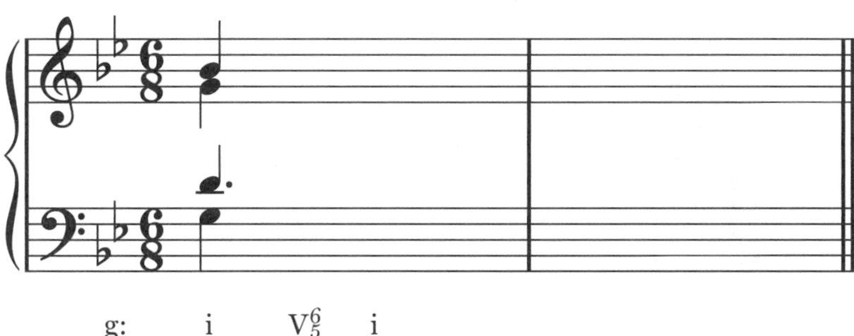

II. Analysis: Scott Joplin, "Pine Apple Rag," mm. 53–60

Provide a Roman numeral analysis for this passage. The harmonic rhythm is one or two chords per measure. Be prepared to answer the questions that follow for class discussion.

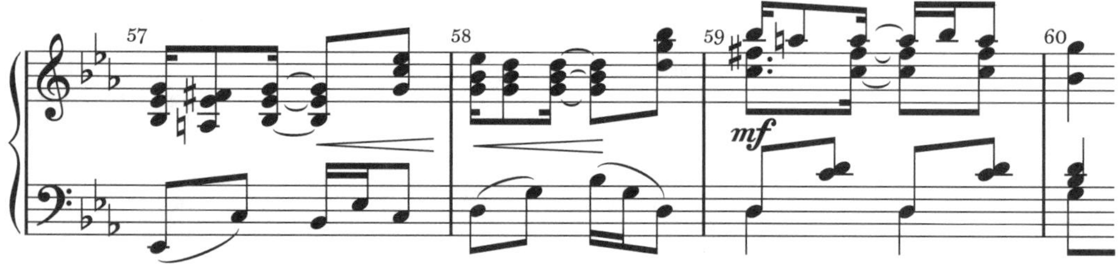

(a) If the harmonic rhythm is one or two chords per measure, how do you label the syncopated eighth-note "chord" in measures 53, 54, and 57? If considered an actual chord, does it resolve as expected?

(b) What type of cadence appears in measures 59–60? Is this modulation to a key you would expect?

(c) Where and what is the pivot chord?

(d) How is the new key established? Does the music continue in that key? (Consult the complete score, Anthology 52.) If so, for how long? If not, what happens next?

NAME ____________________

ASSIGNMENT 22.3

I. Writing modulating phrases from Roman numerals

Write the two-phrase progressions in the keys and meters indicated, using keyboard style (three notes in the right hand within the span of an octave, and one note in the left hand).

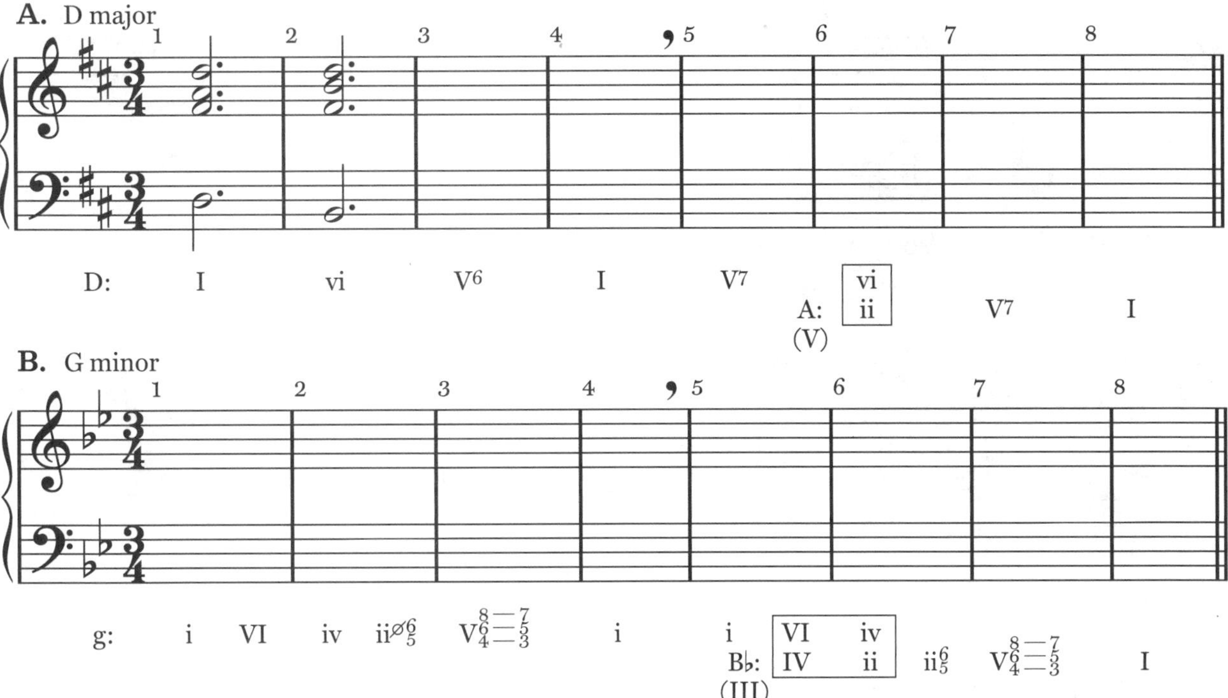

C. Write a keyboard elaboration of the progression in exercise A. (Hint: Use a Classical-style Alberti bass; embellish the melody slightly to add interest.)

II. Analysis: J. S. Bach, Prelude in E♭ Major, from The Well-Tempered Clavier, *Book II, mm. 1–12*

Listen to this prelude, or play through it at the keyboard, and analyze with Roman numerals. This excerpt includes both a tonicization and modulation. Label each. You may wish to circle and label the embellishing tones in the score to help you identify the chords.

How do you distinguish between the tonicization and modulation in this passage?

ASSIGNMENT 22.4

I. Analysis: Johann Phillip Kirnberger, "La Lutine," mm. 1–24

Provide a Roman numeral analysis for this piece, and label the phrases and cadence types. Most measures have a harmonic rhythm of one or two chords per measure, but those approaching a cadence may have three to four harmonies suggested by the counterpoint. This piece includes a modulation to a closely related key and two sequences; locate and label the pattern and level of transposition for each sequence.

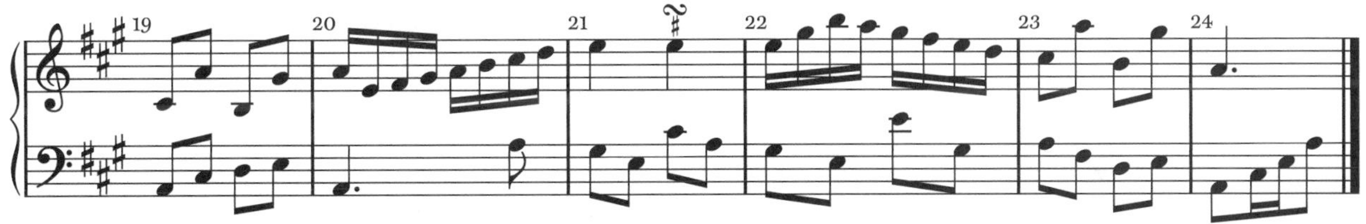

(1) Where does the modulation take place? Is it a pivot-chord modulation or a direct modulation? What evidence supports your answer?

(2) What types of sequences are employed?

(3) The music from the beginning returns in measure 17; how has it been changed?

II. Figured bass: Jean-Baptiste Loeillet, Sonata in B Minor, Op. 3, No. 10, mvt. 3, mm. 1–8

Prepare a keyboard realization of the given figured bass to accompany the flute melody. Write in keyboard style, as shown in measure 1, primarily in half notes (with the exception of m. 7, beat 1). Provide a Roman numeral analysis.

Cadence type: ______________

NAME ____________________

ASSIGNMENT 22.5

I. Figured bass: J. S. Bach, "Erhalt uns, Herr, bei deinem Wort," mm. 1–8

Of this chorale's four phrases (indicated by the fermatas), the first establishes the tonic, the second tonicizes (but does not modulate to) the relative major, the third modulates to the relative major, and the final phrase returns to the tonic key by means of a direct (or phrase) modulation.

Realize the figured bass in chorale style, as shown in measure 1, with one chord on each beat. Provide a Roman numeral analysis, identify each cadence type, and show pivot chords by drawing a box around the pivot Roman numerals in each key. If possible, arrange for a performance in class.

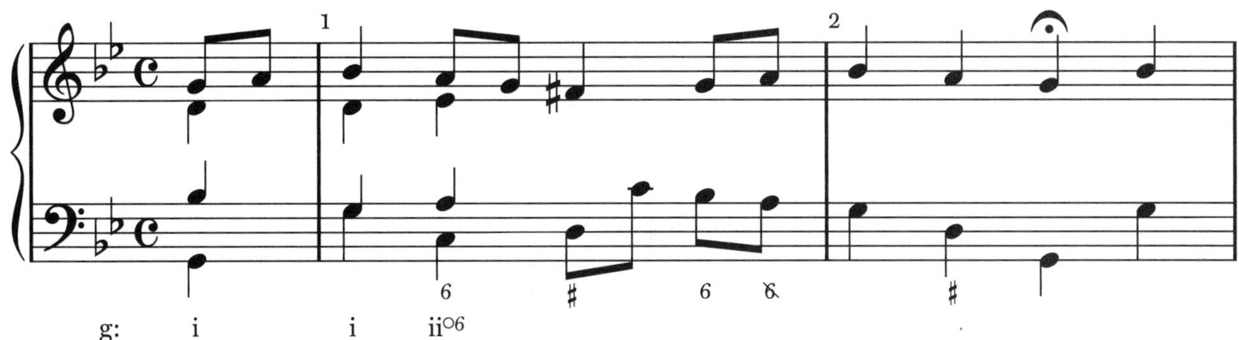

Cadence type: ____________________

Cadence type: ____________________

Cadence type: ____________________

Cadence type: ____________________

II. Listening for Modulations in Popular Music

A. Randy Edelman, "Weekend in New England"

This entire song is in C major except the final section, which is in a different key. First, listen to a performance by Barry Manilow online, then answer the questions. Preparation for the modulation begins around 2′45″, with the modulation itself around 2′52″ (at the text "when will").

(1) The modulation is up a half step, to D♭ major. What is this key's relationship to C major? Is it a closely related key?

(2) Though this modulation sounds abrupt, how is it prepared? Consider the harmonic rhythm, hypermeter, and orchestration.

(3) Listen to the entire song again, paying special attention to the lyrics. Is there something in the text of the song prior to this transition that might motivate the modulation?

B. Dolly Parton, "I Will Always Love You"

For this song, listen to two famous performances online: as sung by Dolly Parton, who wrote the music and lyrics, and as sung by Whitney Houston for the movie *The Bodyguard*. There are many differences in the ways these two performers embellish the vocal melody, and one version includes a modulation that the other does not. (Because modulations like this can be a part of the arrangement and may not necessarily appear in all performances of the song, this is sometimes called an "arranger's modulation.")

(1) Which performance of the song includes a modulation? Where does the modulation occur (using timings from the recording)? Does the song end in the new key?

(2) What effect does the modulation have?

(3) Now listen to at least one other performance of this song, by Sarah Washington (a dance-beat version), Linda Ronstadt, LeAnn Rimes, or John Doe. Which version—Parton's or Houston's—is the performance most like? Is the modulation included?

NAME ______________________________

ASSIGNMENT 22.6

I. Common-tone or pivot-tone modulations

Given a tonic triad in D major, how many keys can be reached by using D, F♯, or A as a pivot tone? Write each chord as indicated. For some, there are two possibilities (e.g., D as the third). Under the chord, indicate (1) the major or minor key for which it would be the tonic and (2) the Roman numeral relationship to D major (e.g., B♭ major would be ♭VI). Remember: an accidental before a Roman numeral applies to the root, and the upper- or lowercase Roman numeral denotes the quality: ♭VI in D major is B♭–D–F♮. For the last chord, in which the common tone represents the seventh of a V^7, indicate to which key the V^7 would resolve.

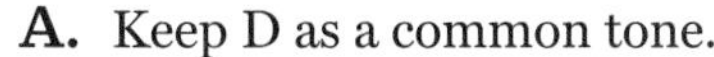

A. Keep D as a common tone.

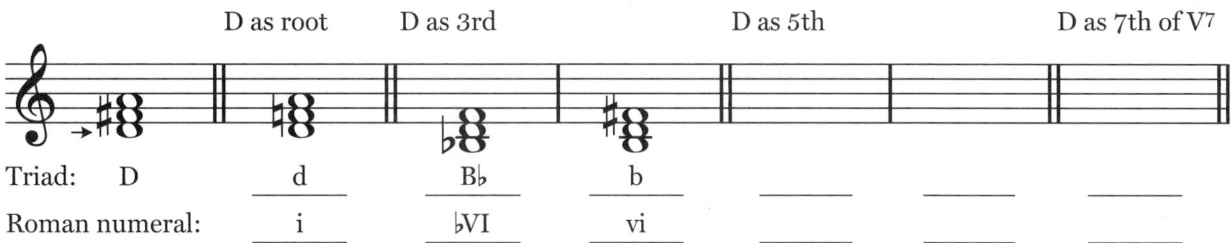

B. Keep F♯ as a common tone.

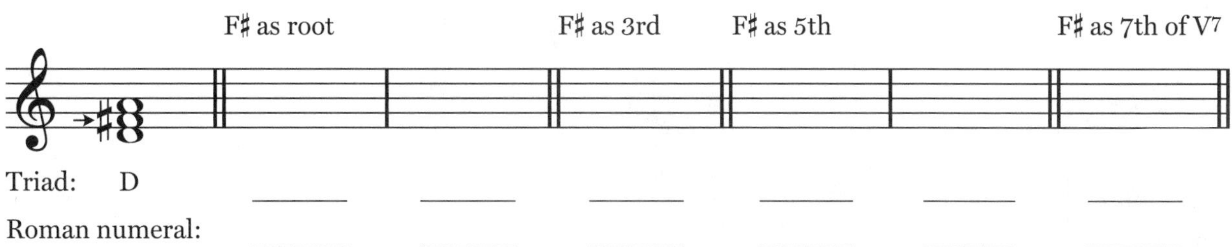

C. Keep A as a common tone.

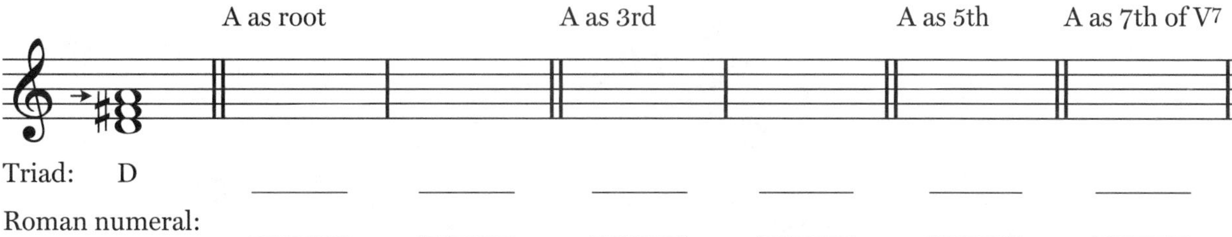

II. Enharmonic respelling of fully diminished seventh chords

Resolve each given diminished seventh chord in (1). Then invert the chord and respell it enharmonically in (2)-(4) so that each note is the root. Resolve each vii°7 chord to its tonic, based on the given Roman numeral (i or I). In the blanks provided, indicate the key of the tonic to which each chord resolves.

(1) given resolution (2) respelled resolution (3) respelled resolution (4) respelled resolution

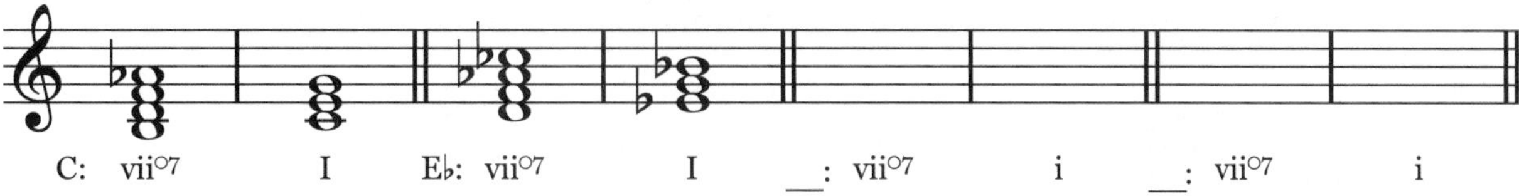

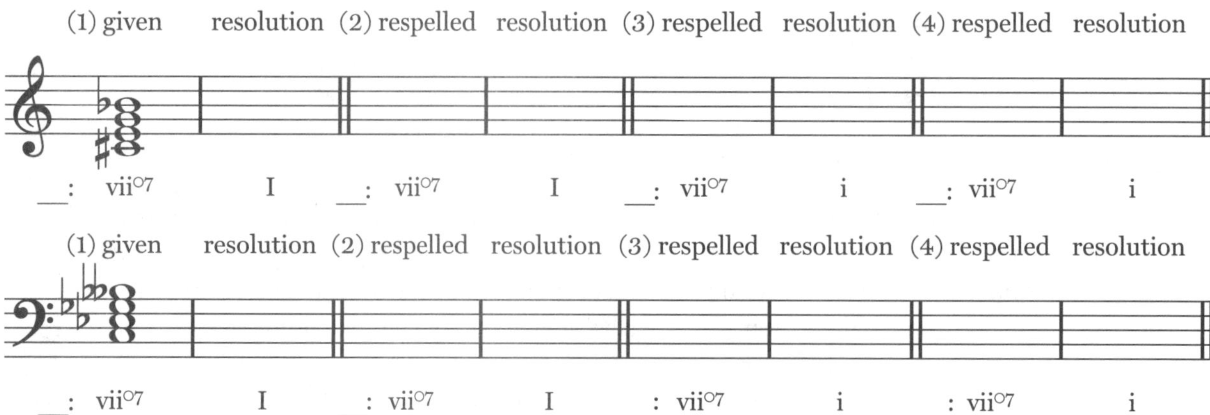

III. Analysis: Robert Schumann, "Widmung," from Myrthen, *mm. 26–30*

Provide a Roman numeral analysis, one chord per measure, through measure 29. The excerpt begins in E major. Mark any cadences and modulations, then answer the questions that follow. The harmony of measure 27 is blurred by a 4–3 suspension and a pedal point; label the whole measure with the harmony that sounds after the suspension resolves, on beat 3.

Translation: You lift me lovingly above myself, my good spirit, my better self!

(1) The bass line in 26–29 is a (circle one) tonic pedal dominant pedal

(2) What type of modulation is used in this passage? ______________________

Binary and Ternary Forms

ASSIGNMENT 23.1

I. Analyzing binary-form types

Listen to each movement. Write uppercase letters above the score to represent the large sections and lowercase to show phrase structure. Label cadences, then circle the appropriate labels.

A. W. A. Mozart, *Variations on "La belle Françoise,"* K. 353, mm. 1–12

Circle any labels that apply to the form:

rounded simple continuous sectional balanced binary

B. Fernando Sor, Menuetto, Op. 5, No. 1, mm. 1–16

Circle any labels that apply to the form:

rounded simple continuous sectional balanced binary

II. Form and Harmonic Analysis: Joseph Haydn, Scherzo, from Sonata No. 9 in F Major, mvt. 3, mm. 1–24

Listen to the movement, then provide a complete Roman numeral analysis. Write uppercase letters above the score to represent large sections and lowercase to show phrase structure. Label cadences.

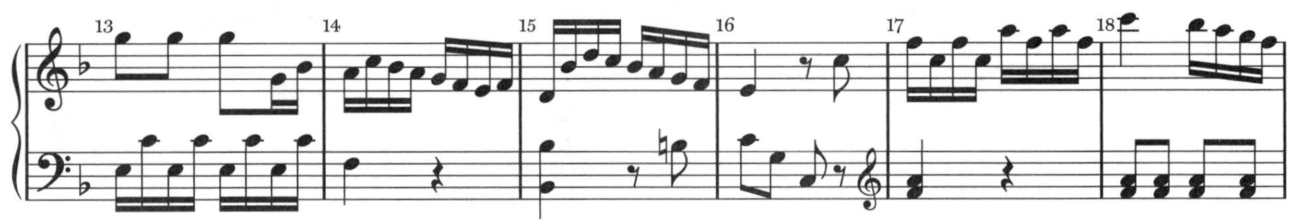

A. Circle any labels that apply:

rounded simple continuous sectional balanced binary

B. Complete a chart of the form. Include form letters, cadences, and number of measures in each phrase, as shown.

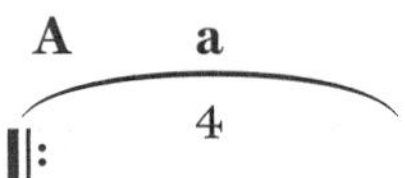

F: IAC

ASSIGNMENT 23.2

I. Analyzing binary forms

Listen to these themes that Mozart selected as the basis for sets of variations. Write uppercase letters above the score to represent the large sections and lowercase to show phrase structure. Label cadences, and be sure to indicate any changes of key. Provide a Roman numeral analysis.

A. W. A. Mozart, *Variations on a Theme by Grétry*, K. 352, mm. 1–16

(1) Circle any labels that apply to the form:

rounded   simple   continuous   sectional   balanced   binary

(2) Indicate the type of harmonic disturbance:

Monte   *Fonte*   *Ponte*   none of these

B. W. A. Mozart, *Variations on "Lison dormait"* (theme by Nicolas Dezède), K. 264, mm. 1–32

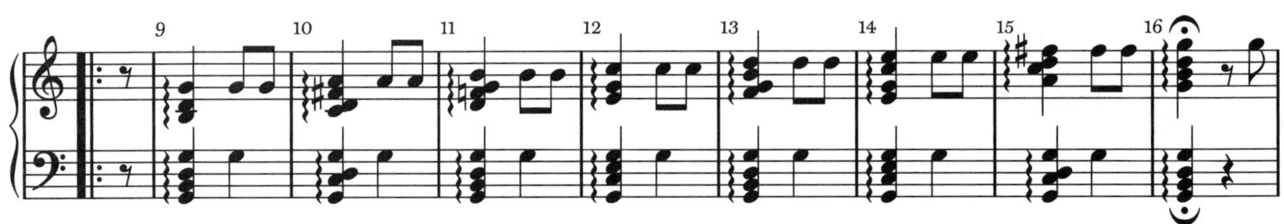

(1) Circle any labels that apply to the form:

rounded simple continuous sectional balanced binary

(2) Indicate the type of harmonic disturbance:

Monte *Fonte* *Ponte* none of these

(3) Complete a chart of the form. Include form letters, cadences, and number of measures in each phrase.

ASSIGNMENT 23.3

Figured bass: Arcangelo Corelli, Sarabanda, from Sonata in E Minor for Violin and Continuo, Op. 5, No. 8

Realize this figured bass to accompany the violin melody. Write in keyboard style, with one chord per beat and three (occasionally two) voices in the right hand. (The $\frac{7}{4}$ in mm. 9, 11, 17, and 19 indicates that the bass note on beat 3 is a passing tone; the note on the "and" of beat 3 is the chord tone.) Provide a Roman numeral analysis, and label any cadences and modulations. Identify any sequences with brackets and arrows above the staff and label the sequence type below the Roman numerals.

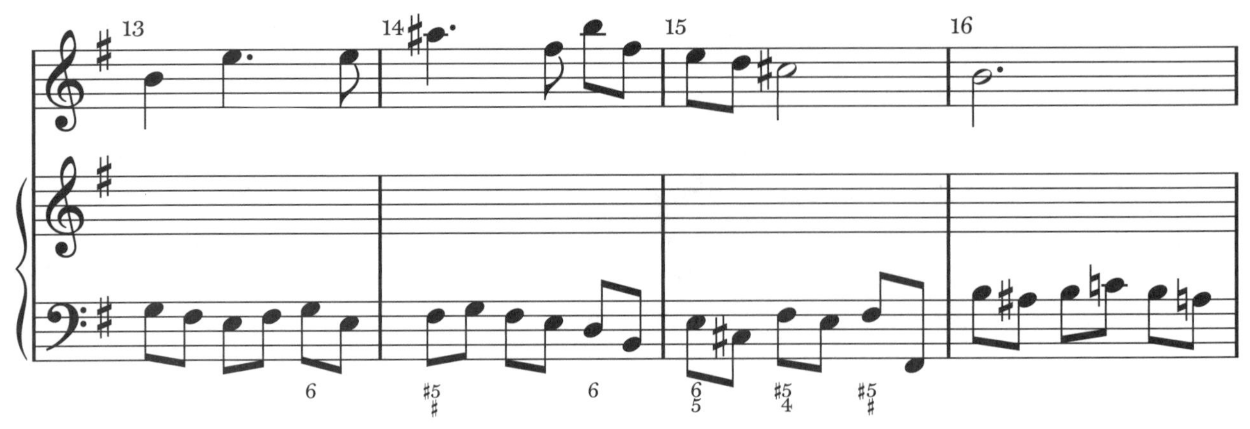

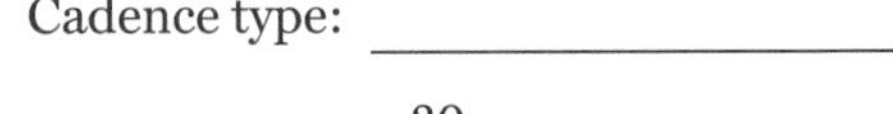

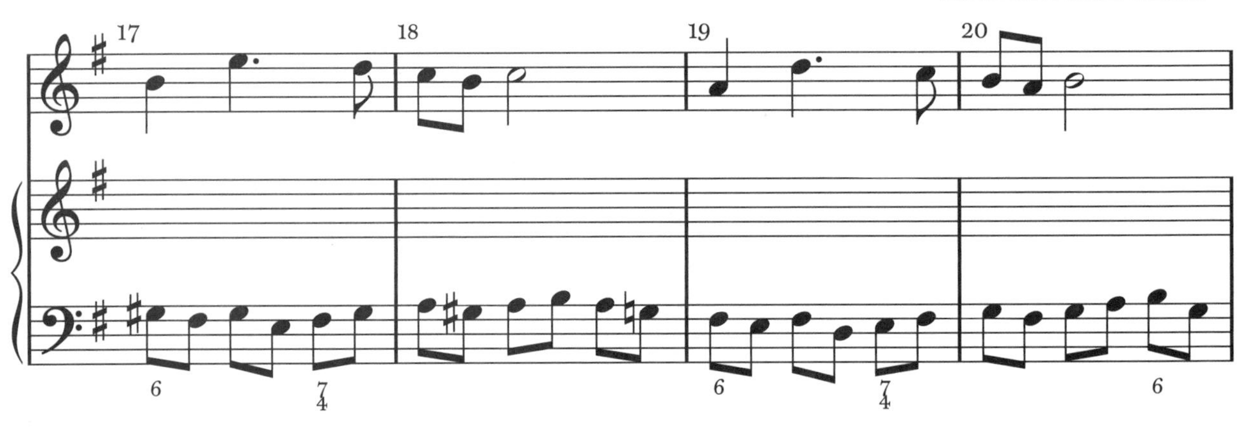

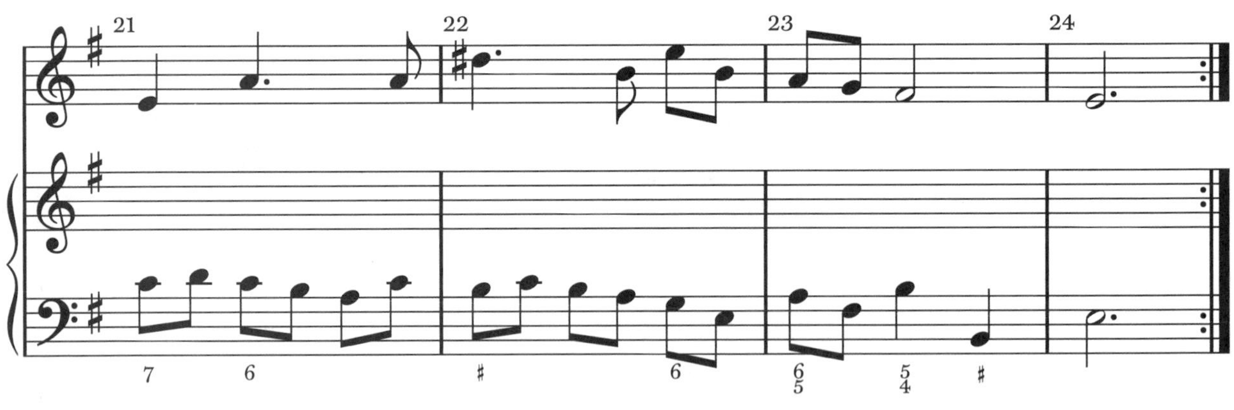

Cadence type: ____________________

Circle any labels that apply:

rounded simple continuous sectional balanced composite binary ternary

Monte *Fonte* *Ponte*

ASSIGNMENT 23.4

Analyzing binary and ternary forms

Listen to the following pieces to determine whether they are binary or ternary. Write uppercase letters in the score to represent the large sections and lowercase to show phrase structure. Label cadences, and be sure to indicate any changes of key.

A. Robert Schumann, "Wilder Reiter"

Provide a Roman numeral analysis.

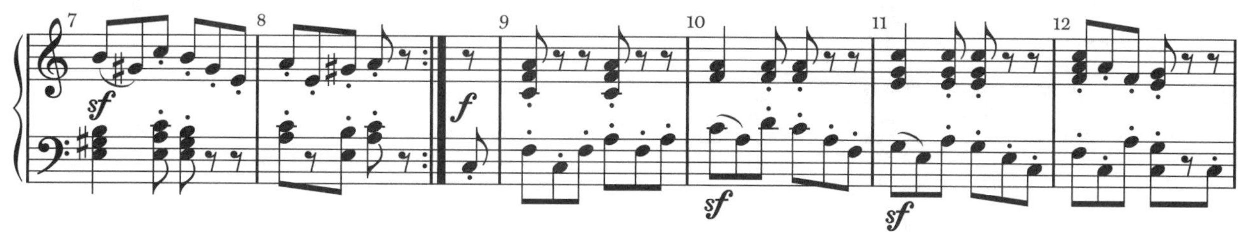

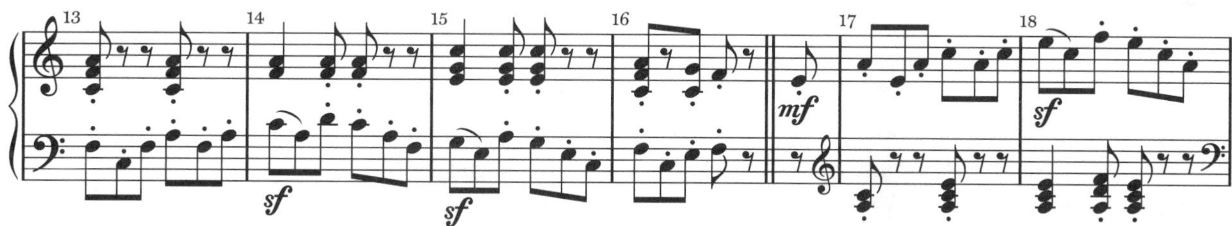

(1) Circle the best term for the form of measures 1–8:

(a) parallel period (b) contrasting period (c) sentence

(2) Compare measures 9–16 with 1–8. What is the same? What is different?

(3) Which of the following best applies to the entire piece?

‖: A :‖ A′ ‖   ‖: A :‖ B ‖   ‖: A :‖ B A′ ‖   ‖: A :‖ B A ‖

(4) Circle any labels that apply to the form of the entire piece:

rounded   simple   continuous   sectional   balanced   composite   binary   ternary

B. Brahms, *Variations on a Theme by Haydn*, theme (two pianos)

Use Anthology 27 to answer the following questions by circling the correct answer or filling in a brief response.

(1) The cadence in measures 4–5 is best described as

(a) an IAC in the tonic key   (b) a HC in the tonic key   (c) a DC in the tonic key

(d) a PAC in the dominant key   (e) not a cadence

(2) The cadence in measures 9–10 is best described as

(a) a PAC in the tonic key   (b) a PAC in the dominant key   (c) a DC in the tonic key

(d) a plagal cadence   (e) not a cadence

(3) The phrase form in measures 1–10 is

(a) one phrase, ten measures long   (b) a parallel period: **a a′**   (c) a contrasting period: **a b**

(d) a repeated phrase: **a a** (same cadence type)

(4) This theme doesn't stray far from the tonic key, but it does move away from it briefly. Where? How does this move fit into the expected harmonic plan in this type of form? What else appears here that is typical of this type of form?

(5) Measures 19–23 present music that should be familiar from earlier in the piece, but there are some changes throughout and a significant change in measure 23. Indicate the measures where this passage appeared before, and briefly describe what has changed.

(6) Briefly describe the formal function of measures 23 to the end of the piece. What is the function of measures 19–29?

(7) Circle any labels that apply to the form of the entire piece:

rounded   simple   continuous   sectional   balanced   composite   binary   ternary

NAME ______________________________

ASSIGNMENT 23.5

Analyzing binary and composite ternary forms

This exercise focuses on the phrase structure, tonal structure, and overall form of a piece; it is not necessary to prepare a complete Roman numeral analysis.

- Listen for the overall formal plan. Look at the score for clues, such as repeat signs. Determine whether the piece is a binary or ternary design. Write uppercase letters in your score to represent the large sections.
- Listen carefully to locate and label each phrase and cadence. Be sure to indicate any changes of key.

Fill in the given charts, and prepare the questions that follow for class discussion (they also provide hints for the analysis). The optional Comments column is a place to write any observations that don't fit in the other spaces.

W. A. Mozart, String Quartet in D Minor, K. 421, mvt. 3 (Anthology 63b)

A. Menuetto (mm. 1–39)

SECTION	MEASURES	PHRASE	CADENCE TYPE	COMMENTS
A	1–10	a	PAC	

Circle any labels that apply to the Menuetto:

rounded   simple   continuous   sectional   balanced   composite   binary   ternary

(1) What is unusual about the phrase structure in measures 1–10?

(2) Indicate the cadence type in measures 28–29, and describe what you hear in measures 11–29. What is the function of these measures, and where do they fit in the formal design?

B. Trio (mm. 40–63)

Considering the Trio on its own, use letters **A** and **B** for this chart; when you make a graph below (part C) for the entire movement, use **C** and **D** for the Trio sections.

SECTION	MEASURES	PHRASE	CADENCE TYPE	COMMENTS
A	40–43	a	HC	I to V

Circle any labels that apply to the Trio:

rounded simple continuous sectional balanced composite binary ternary

C. Menuetto and Trio together

Make a graph showing the overall form of the movement, including the *da capo*. Include section labels for the large form, internal forms, and repeat signs. Then answer the questions that follow.

(1) Compare the texture of the Menuetto with that of the Trio. How do they differ? How are they similar?

(2) What is the key relationship between the Menuetto and Trio?

(3) Circle any labels that apply to the entire movement:

rounded simple continuous sectional balanced composite binary ternary

ASSIGNMENT 23.6

Analyzing rags and marches

These examples focus on the phrase structure, tonal structure, and overall form of a piece; it is not necessary to prepare a complete Roman numeral analysis. For each piece:

- Listen for the overall formal plan. Look at the score for clues, such as repeat signs. Determine whether the piece is a binary or ternary design. Write uppercase letters in your Anthology score to represent the large sections. Identify the composite form and the smaller forms encompassed.
- Listen carefully to locate and label each phrase and cadence. Be sure to indicate any changes of key.

A. Scott Joplin, "Pine Apple Rag" (Anthology 52)

(1) Complete the phrase diagram for measures 1–36.

(2) Measures 5–20 form a (circle one):

contrasting period   parallel period   two phrases (no period)

(3) The cadence at measure 28 implies a HC. How is it similar to, and different from, a HC?

(4) After a return of material from the **A** section, measure 53 initiates a new section. Complete the phrase diagram for measures 53–84.

(5) The form of measures 5–52 is ______________.

(6) The form of measures 53–84 is ______________.

B. John Philip Sousa, "The Washington Post March" (Anthology 90)

Complete the graph. Include large section labels, the measures spanned, and the overall harmonic motion of each section. You do not need to include phrase and cadence information. Indicate which sections are part of the March and which of the Trio.

	March (mm. 1–40)			Trio (mm. 41–80)		
Intro 𝄆	A	:‖:	:‖:	:‖:		:‖
mm. 1–8	9–					
V	G major →					

For the March section, circle any labels that apply:

rounded   simple   continuous   sectional   balanced   composite   binary   ternary

For the Trio section, circle any labels that apply:

rounded   simple   continuous   sectional   balanced   composite   binary   ternary

Prepare the following questions for class discussion (or your teacher may ask you to write a brief essay on one or more of them).

(1) What is the relationship of the different key areas?

(2) The texture is markedly different in measures 57–63. How does that passage fit into the overall scheme of that portion of the march?

(3) How do the melodic ideas of the chromatic introduction return in the following strains?

(4) At the time it was composed (1889), this march was frequently performed at dances, to accompany the two-step, a wildly popular dance of the day. Which rhythmic elements contribute to its dance-like character?

(5) If possible, listen to several recordings of this march. In some performances, it sounds quite dramatic; in others, dance-like; and in still others, like a routine march (meant for actual marching). How are the repeated sections treated in the various performances? Do all of them follow the notated dynamic markings? Would you make the repeats distinctive if you were conducting this march, or would you play them the same? What would the dramatic character be for each section in your ideal performance?

NAME ___

ASSIGNMENT 23.7

I. Part-writing: Binary form B section

In Assignment 22.3, you wrote two two-phrase progressions that, when elaborated, could serve as the first section (**A**) of a binary form. Now write the harmonic progression for a second section (**B**) to complete the harmonic progressions for two small binary compositions in D major and G minor. Write in keyboard style.

A. **B** section of binary piece in D major (with *Monte*)

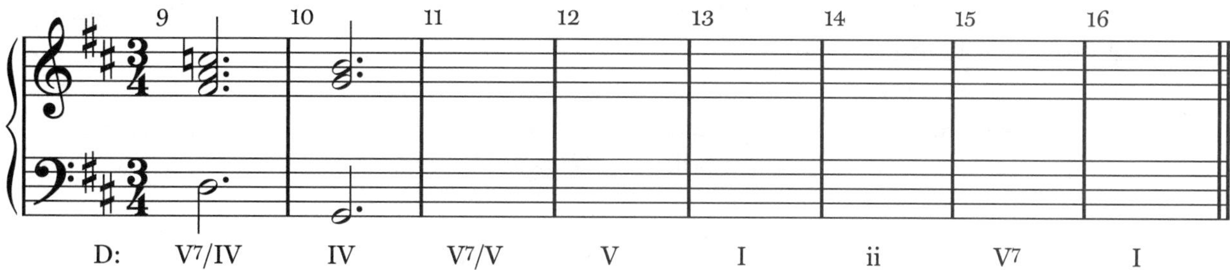

B. **B** section of binary piece in G minor (with sequence)

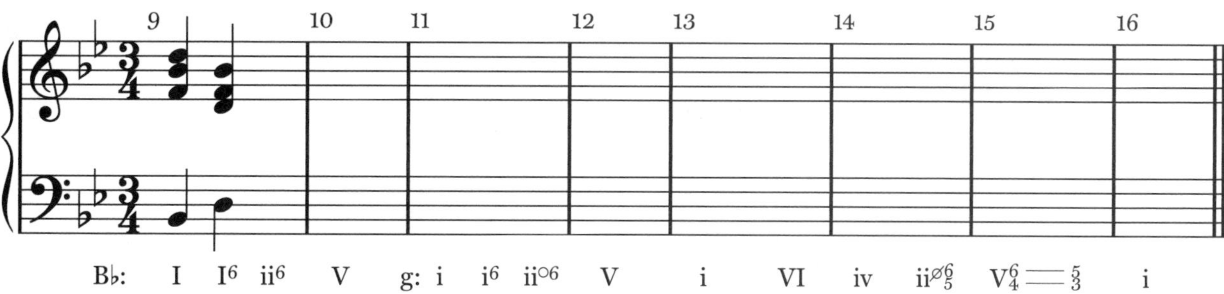

II. Writing a minuet

Write a minuet in Classical style following the guidelines presented here. The goal of this project is to write a piece you will be proud to have performed in class and, in the process, to learn more about Classical style. Aim to make sure all aspects of the composition are stylistically correct and musical.

A. Requirements

- Your minuet should be sixteen measures long in $\frac{3}{4}$ meter.
  - The first section should be eight measures long, with two four-measure phrases *or* a sentence structure;
  - The second section should be eight measures long, with a four-measure harmonic disturbance followed by a four-measure phrase that reestablishes the tonic and ends with an authentic cadence.
- Write repeat signs at the beginning and end of the sections. You may write a first and second ending if you like at the end of the first section, to make the connection smoother from measure 8 back to the beginning and from measure 8 into the second section.
- During the Classical period, major or minor keys with up to two flats or sharps were common, along with C major, C minor, and A minor. Use one of these keys.
- You may compose your own harmonic progression following the models in this chapter, or you may refer back to Assignment 22.3, part I and choose the D major or G minor progression there for your **A** section. Then choose the corresponding progression in part I of this assignment for your second section.

- This composition may be scored for keyboard, keyboard and a melodic instrument, or string quartet, as shown in the models at the bottom of this page. You will not write in chorale style, but you can sketch in block chords to plan your progression and voice leading prior to preparing a stylistic texture based on the models.
- If possible, arrange for a performance in class.

B. Some tips to help you get started

- Make a plan for your model composition, based on information provided in Chapters 22–23. Decide which of the harmonic plans you wish to use from Key Concept boxes in this chapter.
  - The minuet may be sectional (first section does not modulate) or continuous; Assignment 22.3 provides guidance on writing periods with a modulation in the second phrase.
  - The second half will start with a harmonic disturbance. You may use sequential *Monte* or *Fonte* progressions or another sequence pattern (see Chapter 21 for options), or use *Ponte* to prolong the dominant harmony. The harmonic disturbance normally ends harmonically open—on a half cadence or without a clear cadence.
  - The last four measures of the second half return to the tonic and may feature a return of the opening material (rounded) or not (simple).
- Your chord choices, voice leading, and part writing must follow appropriate guidelines for tonal composition. You will not write in chorale style, but will follow an embellished style as demonstrated in the models, using accompaniment patterns in two, three, or four parts, or two-part counterpoint. If you need to review how to construct cadences in two parts, see Chapter 11; for cadences in four parts and accompaniment patterns, see Chapters 12–13; for embellishing patterns, see Chapter 16.
- One way to begin is by laying out the measures and repeat signs for each section on a piece of manuscript paper, prior to entering your score in a music notation software program.
  - Write a tonic chord in measure 1 and the last measure.
  - Write phrase and section labels above the staff for the formal plan you have chosen, indicate the cadence types, then sketch in the cadences.
  - Study the models for the type of binary form you are writing to see how the melodic and bass lines are constructed in regard to intervals, melodic contour, and rhythm, and the type of chords that are used. Then sketch in the chords you want to use or write a melody or bass line for the opening period or sentence structure.
  - Sketch in the chords for the harmonic disturbance you have selected.
- Your composition is meant to model Classical style. The style is conveyed through texture, harmonic choices, location and type of cadences, melodic design, and other features. Closely observe the compositions you are modeling to create your own composition in that style.

Here are some models to emulate for a Classical-style composition besides those in the chapter:

- Haydn, Menuetto and Trio, from String Quartet in D Minor, Op. 76, No. 2 (*Quinten*) (Anthology 43; has Baroque characteristics as well, such as imitation)
- Mozart, Piano Sonata in D Major, K. 284, mvt. 3, Theme (Anthology 60)
- Mozart, *Variations on "Ah, vous dirai-je Maman,"* Theme (Anthology 64)
- Kirnberger, "La Lutine" (Assignment 22.4)

When these steps are completed, you will be well on your way to writing the composition.

Elements of Music

Pitch and Pitch Class

NAME ____________________

In this chapter you'll learn to:

- Use this book and its related materials
- Identify melodic contour and organization
- Identify whole and half steps
- Map pitches to notes, solfège syllables, scale-degree numbers, and letter names
- Use solfège syllables and scale-degree numbers to transpose a melody

---

Dictation and Pattern Recognition

Taking dictation is the process of listening to music and capturing one or more of its elements by memorizing, performing, analyzing, and notating what you hear. These elements—such as pitch, rhythm, harmony, and form—fall into patterns, so pattern recognition is fundamental to understanding music and improving aural skills.

Contextual Listening

Contextual Listening is dictation based on performances of musical literature.

Choosing Audio Playback Equipment

When listening to the playlist, use high-quality earbuds or headphones or connect your device's audio output to an external amplifier and speakers. The built-in speakers on computers, phones, and tablets are inadequate for the careful listening required of these activities.

Solmization

Several systems may be used to sing pitches or represent patterns. While all systems have their pluses and minuses, it is much better to pick a system and use it than to use none.

Movable Systems

Singing with *movable-do* solfège syllables reinforces musical patterns and helps produce the best vocal tone. Singing with *scale-degree numbers* is analogous to using movable *do*. With these movable systems, the tonic pitch is always called *do* ($\hat{1}$) whether the key is major or minor. All *Musician's Guide* materials emphasize the movable-*do* ($\hat{1}$) system.

Another movable system calls the major-key tonic *do* and the minor-key tonic *la*. To use the *do*/*la* system with this book, sing at sight with *do*/*la* syllables and reinforce tonal patterns using scale-degree numbers.

Fixed Systems

In the *fixed-do* system, solfège syllables are associated with specific notes, regardless of the key. The note C is always *do*, the note D is always *re*, and so on. To use fixed *do* with this book, sing at sight with fixed-*do* syllables and reinforce tonal patterns using scale-degree numbers. Singing with letter names is analogous to singing with fixed-*do*.

Mapping Pitches to Notes, Solfège Syllables, Scale Degrees, and Letters

Pitches may be represented as notes on a staff. Pitch classes may be represented as solfège syllables, scale-degree numbers, and letter names. Associating a pitch with a note, syllable, number, or letter is called "mapping." When you sing solfège syllables, sing pure vowels, like those in Spanish or Italian. When you sing numbers, use "*sev*" for scale-degree 7 ($\hat{7}$).

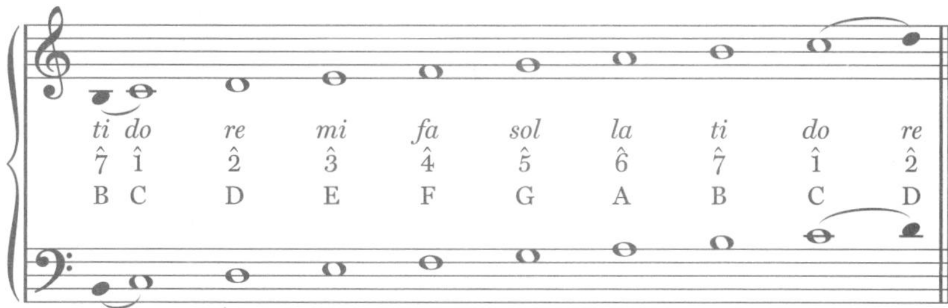

Try it

Try it exercises let you practice skills needed to complete contextual listening.

Contour is melodic shape. Successive pitches repeat, ascend, or descend, creating the simple contours that can be represented as —, ╱, and ╲. Longer melodies create contours such as ╱╲ or ╲╱.

1. Listen to two-pitch patterns and circle the contour (—, ╱, or ╲).
   (a) — ╱ ╲ (b) — ╱ ╲ (c) — ╱ ╲
   (d) — ╱ ╲ (e) — ╱ ╲ (f) — ╱ ╲

2. Listen to three-pitch patterns and circle the contour (— —, ╱╲, or ╲╱).
   (a) — — ╱╲ ╲╱ (b) — — ╱╲ ╲╱ (c) — — ╱╲ ╲╱
   (d) — — ╱╲ ╲╱ (e) — — ╱╲ ╲╱ (f) — — ╱╲ ╲╱

3. Look at the notation and listen to hear half and whole steps (**H** and **W**).

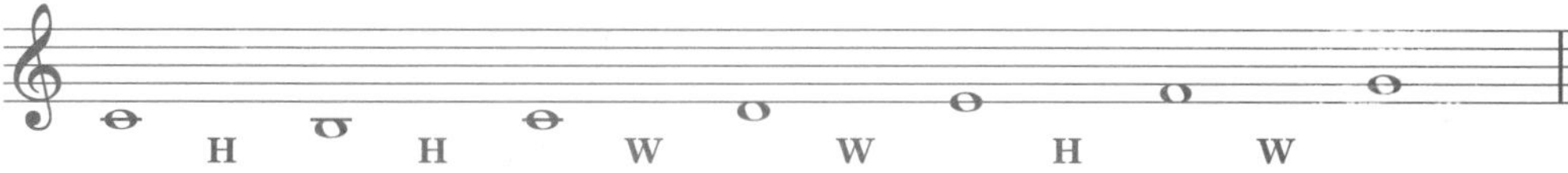

4. Listen to two-pitch patterns. Circle the contour (—, ⁄, or ＼) and **S** for same, **H** for half step, or **W** for whole step.

(a) — ⁄ ＼ **S H W** (b) — ⁄ ＼ **S H W** (c) — ⁄ ＼ **S H W**

(d) — ⁄ ＼ **S H W** (e) — ⁄ ＼ **S H W** (f) — ⁄ ＼ **S H W**

Contextual Listening Strategies

Use these strategies as you work through the Contextual Listening exercises.

- Memorize what you hear as quickly as possible.
- Perform the music in your imagination. Slow it down to figure it out.
- Focus on one element at a time, such as contour or pitch.

NAME ______________________

Contextual Listening 1.1

Listen to a melody consisting of two five-pitch segments. Then complete the exercises.

1. Pitches 1–3 create which contour? — ／ ＼ ︿ ﹀
2. Pitches 3–5 create which contour? — ／ ＼ ︿ ﹀
3. Pitches 6–10 create which contour? — ／ ＼ ︿ ﹀
4. Use the workspace to capture the melody and analyze its construction.
   (a) Beneath the staff in the blanks provided, begin with the given solfège syllable, scale-degree number, and letter name, and write the remaining syllables, numbers, and letters of the melody.
   (b) The starting pitch is C4. In the staff, draw an appropriate clef and notate the melodic pitches using note *heads* only; don't worry about the rhythm. For help, refer to your solfège syllables, scale-degree numbers, and letter names.
   (c) Below the pitch labels, for each pair of pitches write **S** for same pitch, **H** for half step, or **W** for whole step.
   (d) Play *do* ($\hat{1}$) and sing your answer with solfège, numbers, and letters. After singing each note, check the pitch by playing it on a keyboard.

Solfège: *do* ___ ___ ___ ___ ___ ___ ___ ___ ___

Numbers: $\hat{1}$ ___ ___ ___ ___ ___ ___ ___ ___ ___

Letters: C ___ ___ ___ ___ ___ ___ ___ ___ ___

Contour: ___ ___ ___ ___ ___ ___ ___ ___ ___

5. Use the workspace answers in exercise 4 to transpose the melodic pitches to begin on C3. Draw an appropriate clef and use note heads only—don't worry about the rhythm.

6. Use the workspace answers in exercise 4 to transpose the melodic pitches to begin on F4. Draw an appropriate clef and use note heads only—don't worry about the rhythm. Include any necessary accidental(s).

NAME ______________________________

Contextual Listening 1.2

Listen to a melody consisting of four segments and complete the following exercises.

Segment 1, pitches 1–4

1. Pitches 1–4 create which contour? — ⁄ ⁄ ＼ ⁄＼ ＼⁄
2. Between pitches 1–2, which applies? **S** **H** step **W** step
3. Between pitches 2–3, which applies? **S** **H** step **W** step

Segment 2, pitches 5–8

4. Compared with pitches 1–4, pitches 5–8 are: the same similar different

Segment 3, pitches 9–11

5. Pitches 9–11 create which contour? — ⁄ ＼ ⁄＼ ＼⁄
6. Between pitches 9–10, which applies? **S** **H** step **W** step
7. Between pitches 10–11, which applies? **S** **H** step **W** step

Segment 4, pitches 12–14

8. Compared with pitches 9–11, pitches 12–14 are: the same similar different
9. Use the workspace to capture the melody and analyze its construction.
   (a) Beneath the staff in the blanks provided, begin with the given solfège syllable, scale-degree number, and letter name, and write the remaining syllables, numbers, and letters of the melody.
   (b) The starting pitch is C4. In the staff, draw an appropriate clef and notate the melodic pitches using note *heads* only; don't worry about the rhythm. For help, refer to your solfège syllables, scale-degree numbers, and letter names.
   (c) Play *do* ($\hat{1}$) and sing your answer with solfège, numbers, and letters. After singing each note, check the pitch by playing it on a keyboard.

Segment 1 *Segment 2* *Segment 3* *Segment 4*

Solfège: ___ ___ ___ ___ ___ ___ ___ ___ ___ ___ ___ ___ ___ ___

Numbers: ___ ___ ___ ___ ___ ___ ___ ___ ___ ___ ___ ___ ___ ___

Letters: ___ ___ ___ ___ ___ ___ ___ ___ ___ ___ ___ ___ ___ ___

10. Use the workspace answers from exercise 9 to transpose the melody to begin on D3. Draw an appropriate clef and notate the melody using note heads only; don't worry about the rhythm. Include any necessary accidental(s).

Segment 1 *Segment 2* *Segment 3* *Segment 4*

CHAPTER 25

Simple Meters

NAME ______________________________

In this chapter you'll learn to:

- Identify and notate beats and beat divisions in common simple-meter signatures
- Capture accompanied melodies by mapping solfège syllables, scale-degree numbers, letter names, and pitches
- Notate melodies that begin on a pitch other than tonic
- Notate music that begins with an anacrusis or includes syncopation

Try it

1. Conduct or tap in four while performing the four-beat patterns below. Choose a system of rhythm-counting syllables and sing aloud.

Now, listen to a four-beat count-off followed by a melody made from two of the patterns. In the blanks provided, write the rhythm-pattern numbers.

(a) ______ (b) ______ (c) ______ (d) ______

2. Conduct or tap in two while performing the two-beat patterns below. Sing aloud with counting syllables. Note the syncopated rhythms in patterns 7–8.

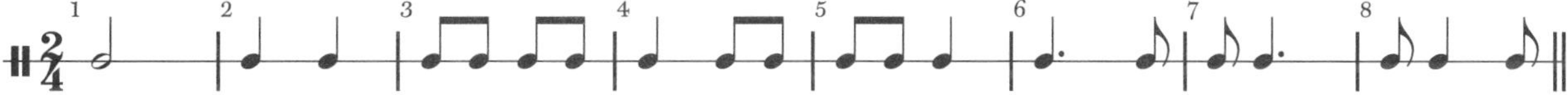

Now, listen to a two-beat count-off followed by a melody made from two of the patterns. In the blanks provided, write the rhythm-pattern numbers.

(a) ______ (b) ______ (c) ______ (d) ______

3. Conduct or tap in three while performing the three-beat patterns below. Sing aloud with counting syllables.

Now, listen to a three-beat count-off followed by a melody made from two of the patterns. In the blanks provided, write the rhythm-pattern numbers.

(a) ______ (b) ______ (c) ______ (d) ______

4. Each of the following melodies is preceded by a count-off. In the staff provided, notate the rhythm, being mindful of any syncopations. Include all bar lines. Sing aloud with counting syllables to compare your notation with the original.

♩ Beat Unit ($\frac{2}{4}$, $\frac{4}{4}$, and $\frac{3}{4}$)

The first exercise is started for you.

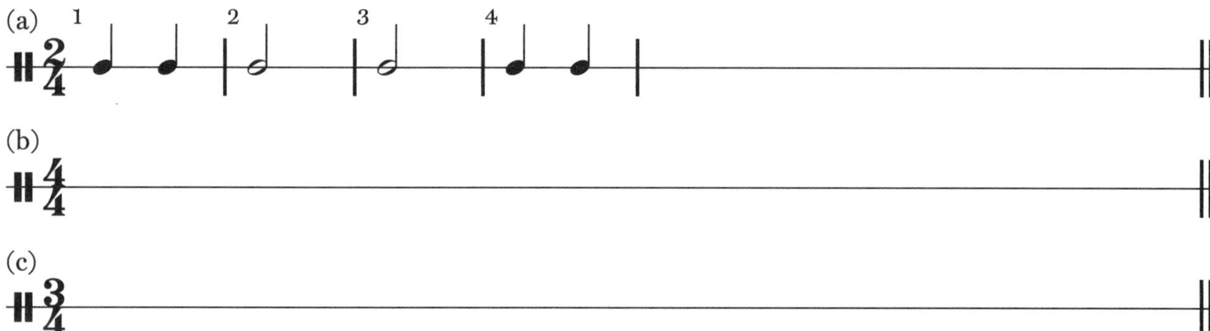

♩ Beat Unit ($\frac{2}{4}$, $\frac{4}{4}$, and $\frac{3}{4}$) with Anacrusis

Each of the following exercises begins with an anacrusis.

The first exercise is started for you.

NAME ______________________________

Contextual Listening 2.1

After a two-measure introduction, exercises 1–3 feature a melody that begins on *do*, *mi*, or *sol* ($\hat{1}$, $\hat{3}$, or $\hat{5}$) and consists of two rhythm patterns. For each melody:

- Determine the starting pitch and circle it. Hint: Listen to the example and then sing *do* ($\hat{1}$). Then sing up or down by step until you match pitch 1.
- Write the rhythm-pattern numbers in the blanks.

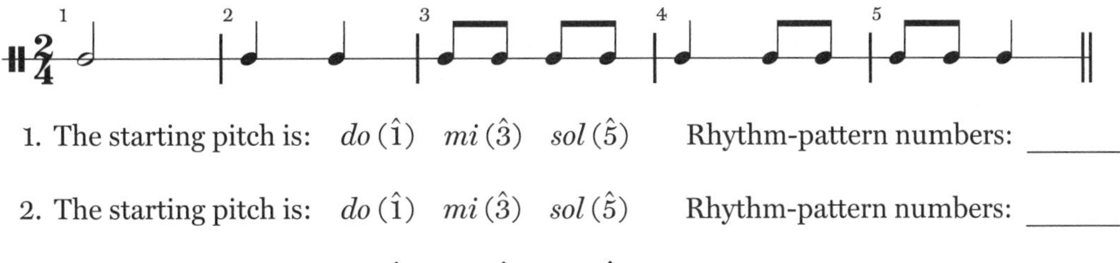

1. The starting pitch is: *do* ($\hat{1}$) *mi* ($\hat{3}$) *sol* ($\hat{5}$) Rhythm-pattern numbers: ______
2. The starting pitch is: *do* ($\hat{1}$) *mi* ($\hat{3}$) *sol* ($\hat{5}$) Rhythm-pattern numbers: ______
3. The starting pitch is: *do* ($\hat{1}$) *mi* ($\hat{3}$) *sol* ($\hat{5}$) Rhythm-pattern numbers: ______

Now, listen to a two-measure introduction, followed by part of a folk song, and complete the remaining exercises.

4. Use the following workspace to capture the melody.
   (a) In the single-line staff, begin with an eighth note and notate the melody's rhythm. Write an appropriate meter signature, beam notes to show beat grouping, and include all bar lines.
   (b) In the blanks provided beneath the single-line staff, begin with the given letter name and write the remaining solfège, numbers, and letters of the melody.
   (c) The starting pitch is E4. In the five-line staff, draw an appropriate clef and meter signature. Notate the melodic pitches using note heads, incorporating the rhythm from the single-line staff. For help with pitches, refer to your solfège syllables, scale-degree numbers, and letter names.
   (d) Play *do* ($\hat{1}$) and sing your answer using solfège, numbers, or letters. After singing each note, check the pitch by playing it on a keyboard.

Solfège: __ __ __ __ __ __ __ __ __ __ __ __

Numbers: __ __ __ __ __ __ __ __ __ __ __ __

Letters: E4 __ __ __ __ __ __ __ __ __ __ __

NAME ______________________________

Contextual Listening 2.2

After a two-measure introduction, exercises 1–3 feature a melody that begins on *do*, *mi*, or *sol* ($\hat{1}$, $\hat{3}$, or $\hat{5}$) and consists of two rhythm patterns. For each melody:

- Determine the starting pitch and circle it. Hint: Listen to the example and then sing *do* ($\hat{1}$). Then sing up or down by step until you match pitch 1.
- Write the rhythm-pattern numbers in the blanks.

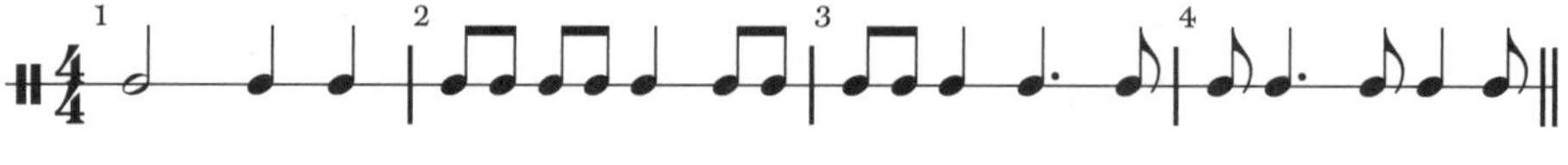

1. The starting pitch is: *do* ($\hat{1}$) *mi* ($\hat{3}$) *sol* ($\hat{5}$) Rhythm-pattern numbers: ______
2. The starting pitch is: *do* ($\hat{1}$) *mi* ($\hat{3}$) *sol* ($\hat{5}$) Rhythm-pattern numbers: ______
3. The starting pitch is: *do* ($\hat{1}$) *mi* ($\hat{3}$) *sol* ($\hat{5}$) Rhythm-pattern numbers: ______

Now, listen to a one-measure count-off followed by a melody from a musical. Then, complete the remaining exercises.

4. Use the following workspace to capture the melody.
   (a) In the single-line staff, begin with an eighth note and notate the melody's rhythm. Write an appropriate meter signature, beam notes to show beat grouping, and include all bar lines.
   (b) In the blanks provided beneath the single-line staff, begin with the given letter name and write the remaining syllables, numbers, and letters of the melody.
   (c) The starting pitch is C3. In the five-line staff, draw an appropriate clef and meter signature. Notate the melodic pitches using note heads and incorporating the rhythm from the single-line staff. For help with pitches, refer to your solfège syllables, scale-degree numbers, and letter names.
   (d) Play *do* ($\hat{1}$) and sing your answer using solfège, numbers, or letters. After singing each note, check the pitch by playing it on a keyboard.

Solfège: _ _ _ _ _   _ _   _ _ _ _ _ _   _ _

Numbers: _ _ _ _ _   _ _   _ _ _ _ _ _   _ _

Letters: C3 _ _ _ _   _ _   _ _ _ _ _ _   _ _

Contextual Listening 2.3

After an introduction, a melody begins on *do*, *mi*, or *sol* ($\hat{1}$, $\hat{3}$, or $\hat{5}$). It consists of two rhythm patterns. For each melody:

- Determine the starting pitch and circle it. Hint: Listen to the example. Sing *do* ($\hat{1}$), then sing up or down by step until you match pitch 1.
- Write the rhythm-pattern numbers in the blanks.

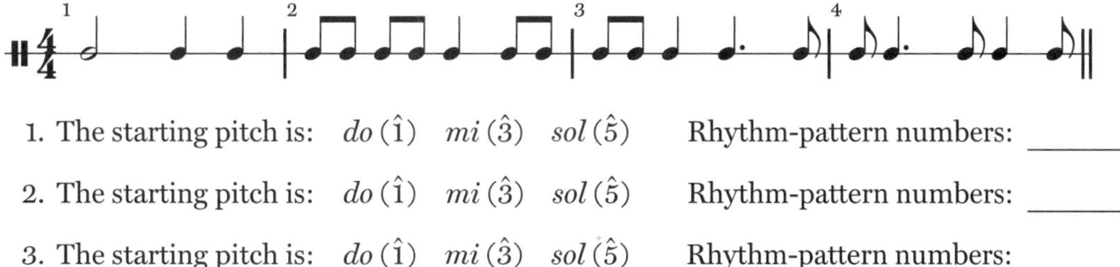

1. The starting pitch is: *do* ($\hat{1}$) *mi* ($\hat{3}$) *sol* ($\hat{5}$) Rhythm-pattern numbers: _______
2. The starting pitch is: *do* ($\hat{1}$) *mi* ($\hat{3}$) *sol* ($\hat{5}$) Rhythm-pattern numbers: _______
3. The starting pitch is: *do* ($\hat{1}$) *mi* ($\hat{3}$) *sol* ($\hat{5}$) Rhythm-pattern numbers: _______

Now, listen to a one-measure count-off followed by a melody from a musical. Then, complete the remaining exercises.

4. Use the following workspace to capture the melody.
   (a) In the single-line staff, begin with an eighth note and notate the melody's rhythm, being mindful of any syncopations. Write an appropriate meter signature, beam notes to show beat grouping, and include all bar lines.
   (b) In the blanks provided beneath the single-line staff, begin with the given letter name and write the remaining syllables, numbers, and letters of the melody.
   (c) The starting pitch is C4. Draw an appropriate clef and meter signature. Notate the melodic pitches using note heads and incorporating the rhythm from the single-line staff. For help with pitches, refer to your solfège syllables, scale-degree numbers, and letter names.
   (d) Play *do* ($\hat{1}$) and sing your answer using solfège, numbers, or letters. After singing each note, check the pitch by playing it on a keyboard.

Solfège: __ __ __ __ __ __ __ __ __ __ __ __ __ __ __

Numbers: __ __ __ __ __ __ __ __ __ __ __ __ __ __ __

Letters: C4 __ __ __ __ __ __ __ __ __ __ __ __ __ __

Pitch Collections, Scales, and Major Keys

NAME ______________________

In this chapter you'll learn to:

- Recognize common pitch collections of the major scale
- Learn to relate notes, solfège syllables, scale-degree numbers, and letters to major keys
- Notate simple-meter melodies in treble, bass, and alto clefs

---

Try it

A one-measure count-off precedes a melody that begins on the pitch given. The smallest note value in the melody is an eighth note.

- In the clef, key, and meter given, notate the melody's pitches and rhythm.
- Beam notes to show beat grouping.
- Notate all bar lines, including a double bar at the end.
- *Strategies*:
    - Memorize the melody and replay it in your mind. Slow it down if necessary.
    - Work quickly, writing a one-stroke "tick" for each note head. Fill it in later.
    - Sketch the rhythm beneath the staff.
    - Sing aloud as you write the solfège syllable or scale degree beneath each note in the rhythm sketch.

1. The major pentachord

(d)

2. The major scale

(a)

(b)

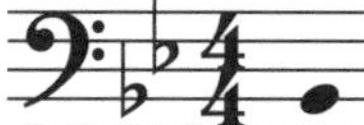

(c)

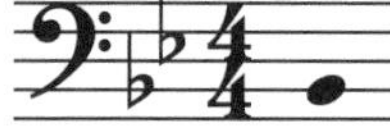

(d)

3. The major pentatonic scale

(a)

(b)

(c)

(d)

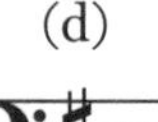

Contextual Listening 3.1

Listen to an excerpt from a traditional song and complete the exercises.

1. Tap the beat. Listen for strong and weak beats to determine beat grouping.
   Tap the beat division.
   Then, conduct while singing the melody from memory.
2. Circle the number of beats in each measure: 2 3 4
3. Circle the melody's lowest note.
   do ($\hat{1}$) *re* ($\hat{2}$) *mi* ($\hat{3}$) *fa* ($\hat{4}$) *sol* ($\hat{5}$) *la* ($\hat{6}$) *ti* ($\hat{7}$) *do* ($\hat{1}$)
4. Circle the melody's highest note.
   do ($\hat{1}$) *re* ($\hat{2}$) *mi* ($\hat{3}$) *fa* ($\hat{4}$) *sol* ($\hat{5}$) *la* ($\hat{6}$) *ti* ($\hat{7}$) *do* ($\hat{1}$)
5. Together, all melodic pitches complete which pattern?
   major pentachord major pentachord scale major scale
6. Use the workspace to capture the excerpt.
   (a) In the single-line rhythm staff, begin with two beamed eighth notes and notate the melody's rhythm. Include the meter signature and bar lines. Beam eighth notes in pairs to show beat grouping.
   (b) Below the rhythm staff and under each note, write the solfège syllables or scale-degree numbers for the melody.
   (c) In the five-line staff, write an appropriate clef, meter signature, and key signature. Begin with C4 and notate both pitches and rhythm.

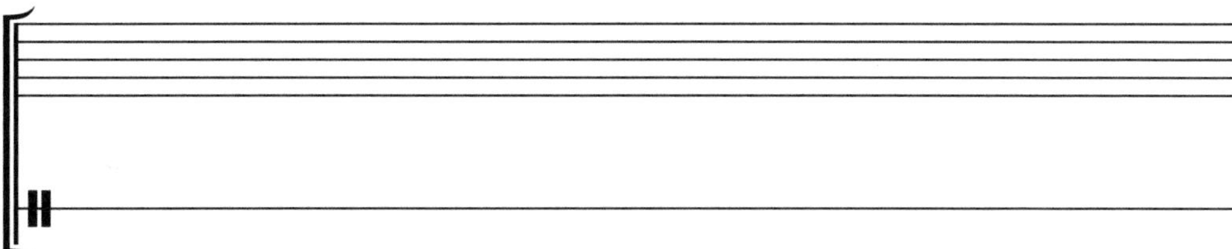

   (d) Play *do* ($\hat{1}$) and sing the first melodic pitch with its syllable or number. Sing pitch 2, then check it by playing. Continue this way, always singing first, then checking by playing.

NAME ______________________________

Contextual Listening 3.2

Listen to part of a holiday song and complete the exercises.

1. Tap the beat. Listen for strong and weak beats to determine beat grouping.
   Tap the beat division.
   Then, conduct while singing the melody from memory.

2. In which meter types might this melody be notated?
   duple or triple duple or quadruple triple or quadruple

3. Sing the last note, *do* ($\hat{1}$). Then, sing up the scale until you match the first note.
   On which pitch does the melody begin? *do* ($\hat{1}$) *mi* ($\hat{3}$) *sol* ($\hat{5}$)

4. Together, all melodic pitches complete which pattern?
   major pentachord major pentachord scale major scale

5. Pitch 6's rhythm is best described as an/a:
   anacrusis syncopation dotted note

6. Use the workspace to capture the excerpt.
   (a) In the single-line rhythm staff, begin with two beamed eighth notes and notate the melody's rhythm. Include the meter signature and bar lines. Beam eighth notes in pairs.
   (b) Below the rhythm staff and under each note, write the solfège syllables or scale-degree numbers for the melody.
   (c) In the five-line staff, write an appropriate clef, meter signature, and key signature. Begin with G3 and notate both pitches and rhythm.

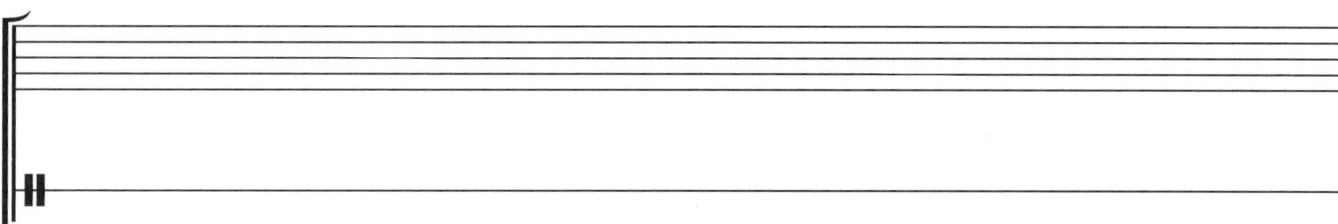

   (d) Sing the melody, then play it on a keyboard.

NAME ______________________________

Contextual Listening 3.3

Listen to part of a folk song and complete the exercises.

1. Tap the beat. Listen for strong and weak beats to determine beat grouping.
   Tap the beat division.
   Then, conduct while singing the melody from memory.
2. Which is the meter type? duple triple quadruple
3. The second beat is the first strong beat. This means the first beat is an/a:
   anacrusis syncopation dotted note
4. Circle the melody's lowest note.
   do ($\hat{1}$) *re* ($\hat{2}$) *mi* ($\hat{3}$) *fa* ($\hat{4}$) *sol* ($\hat{5}$) *la* ($\hat{6}$) *ti* ($\hat{7}$) *do* ($\hat{1}$)
5. Circle the melody's highest note.
   do ($\hat{1}$) *re* ($\hat{2}$) *mi* ($\hat{3}$) *fa* ($\hat{4}$) *sol* ($\hat{5}$) *la* ($\hat{6}$) *ti* ($\hat{7}$) *do* ($\hat{1}$)
6. Together, all melodic pitches complete which pattern?
   major pentachord major scale major pentatonic scale
7. The third-to-last pitch is an/a: anacrusis syncopation dotted note
8. Use the workspace to capture the excerpt.
   (a) Assume a quarter-note beat unit. In the single-line rhythm staff, begin with two beamed eighth notes and notate the rhythm. Include the meter signature and bar lines. Beam eighth notes in pairs.
   (b) Below the rhythm staff and under each note, write the solfège syllables or scale-degree numbers for the melody.
   (c) In the five-line staff, write an appropriate clef, meter signature, and key signature. Begin with C4 and notate both pitches and rhythm.

   (d) Sing the melody, then play it on a keyboard.

CHAPTER 27

Compound Meters

NAME ______________________

In this chapter you'll learn to:

- Hear the difference between simple and compound meters
- Identify and notate beats and beat divisions in compound meters
- Capture accompanied melodies by mapping syllables, numbers, letters, and pitches

Try it

1. Conduct or tap in two while performing the four patterns below. Choose a system of rhythm-counting syllables and sing aloud.

2. Listen to a two-beat count-off followed by a melody made from two of the patterns. In the blanks provided, write the rhythm-pattern numbers.

   (a) ______ (b) ______ (c) ______ (d) ______

3. Following a two-beat count-off, each melody begins with the given pitch(es) and rhythm. Notate the remaining rhythm and pitches. Beam three eighths to show beat grouping.

(a)

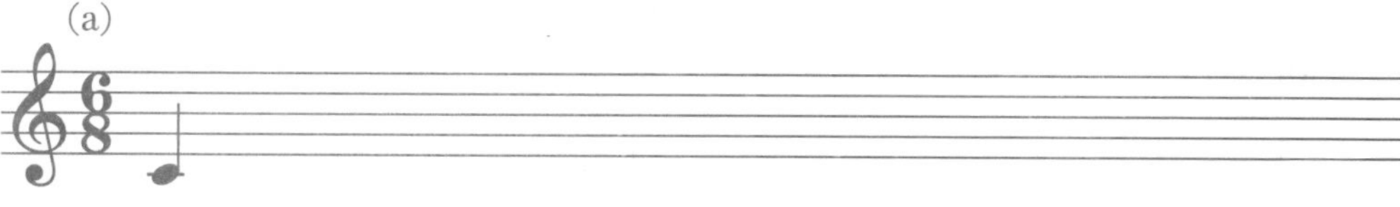

(b)

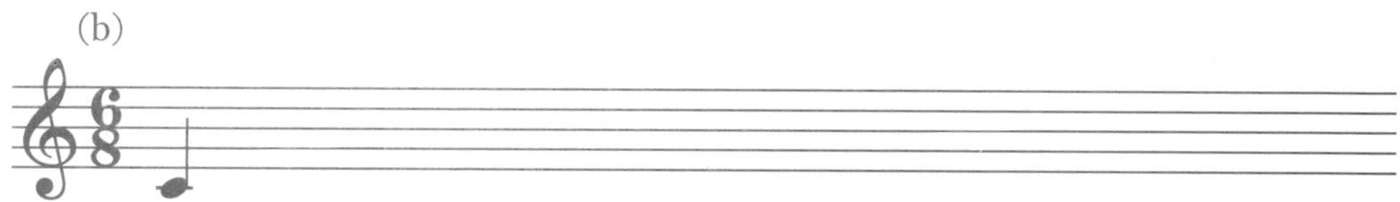

(c)

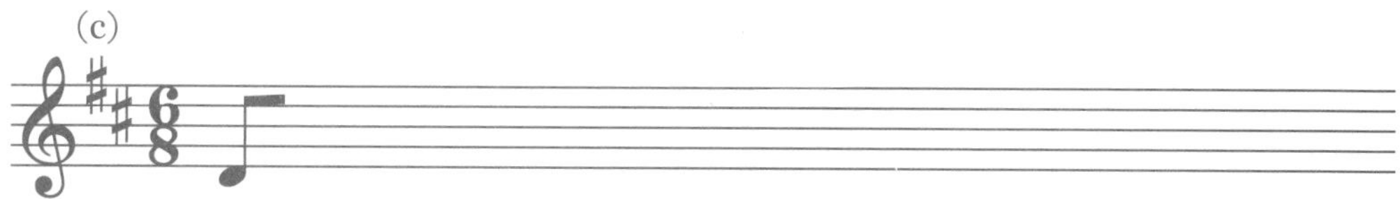

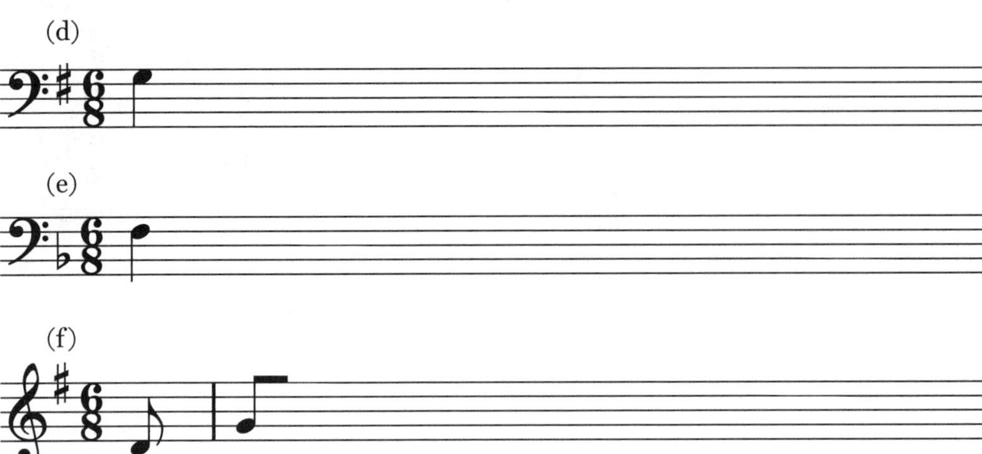

Contextual Listening 4.1

Hearing beat divisions and beat grouping in simple and compound meters:

- As you listen to each excerpt, tap the beat with one hand and beat divisions with the other.
  - If beats divide into twos and fours, circle "simple" in the table below.
  - If beats divide into threes, circle "compound."
- Group beats into measures.
  - For groups of two, circle "duple"; for three, "triple"; for four, "quadruple."
- Check each answer by conducting the beat grouping while tapping the beat division.

	Beat Division		Beat Grouping		
1.	simple	compound	duple	triple	quadruple
2.	simple	compound	duple	triple	quadruple
3.	simple	compound	duple	triple	quadruple
4.	simple	compound	duple	triple	quadruple
5.	simple	compound	duple	triple	quadruple
6.	simple	compound	duple	triple	quadruple
7.	simple	compound	duple	triple	quadruple

NAME ______________________

Contextual Listening 4.2

1. After an introduction, a melody begins on *do*, *mi*, or *sol* ($\hat{1}$, $\hat{3}$, or $\hat{5}$). It consists of two rhythm patterns. Circle the starting pitch and write the rhythm-pattern numbers in the blanks.

   Hint: Sing *do* ($\hat{1}$). Sing up or down by step until you match pitch 1.

   (a) The starting pitch is: *do* ($\hat{1}$) *mi* ($\hat{3}$) *sol* ($\hat{5}$)
   Rhythm-pattern numbers: _______

   (b) The starting pitch is: *do* ($\hat{1}$) *mi* ($\hat{3}$) *sol* ($\hat{5}$)
   Rhythm-pattern numbers: _______

2. After an introduction, a melody begins with an eighth-note anacrusis. Identify melodic pitches 1–2.

   Hint: Sing *do* ($\hat{1}$). Then sing up or down to match the melodic pitches.

   (a) Melodic pitches 1–2 are:
   do-mi ($\hat{1}$-$\hat{3}$) *sol-do* ($\hat{5}$-$\hat{1}$) *mi-sol* ($\hat{3}$-$\hat{5}$) *sol-mi* ($\hat{5}$-$\hat{3}$)

   (b) Melodic pitches 1–2 are:
   do-mi ($\hat{1}$-$\hat{3}$) *sol-do* ($\hat{5}$-$\hat{1}$) *mi-sol* ($\hat{3}$-$\hat{5}$) *sol-mi* ($\hat{5}$-$\hat{3}$)

Now, listen to a traditional song and complete the remaining exercises.

3. Use the workspace to capture the melodic rhythm and pitches.

   (a) In the single-line staff, begin with an eighth-note anacrusis and notate the melody's rhythm. Write an appropriate meter signature, beam notes to show beat grouping, and include all bar lines.

   (b) In the blanks provided beneath the single-line staff, begin with the given letter name, and write the remaining syllables, numbers, and letters of the melody.

   (c) In the treble staff, write appropriate key and meter signatures. Notate the melodic pitches using note heads. For help with pitches, refer to your solfège syllables, scale-degree numbers, and letter names.

   (d) In the treble staff, incorporate the rhythm from the single-line staff. Draw bar lines from the top of the treble staff to the bottom of the bass staff, aligned with the bar lines in the single-line staff.

   (e) Sing the melody, then play it on a keyboard.

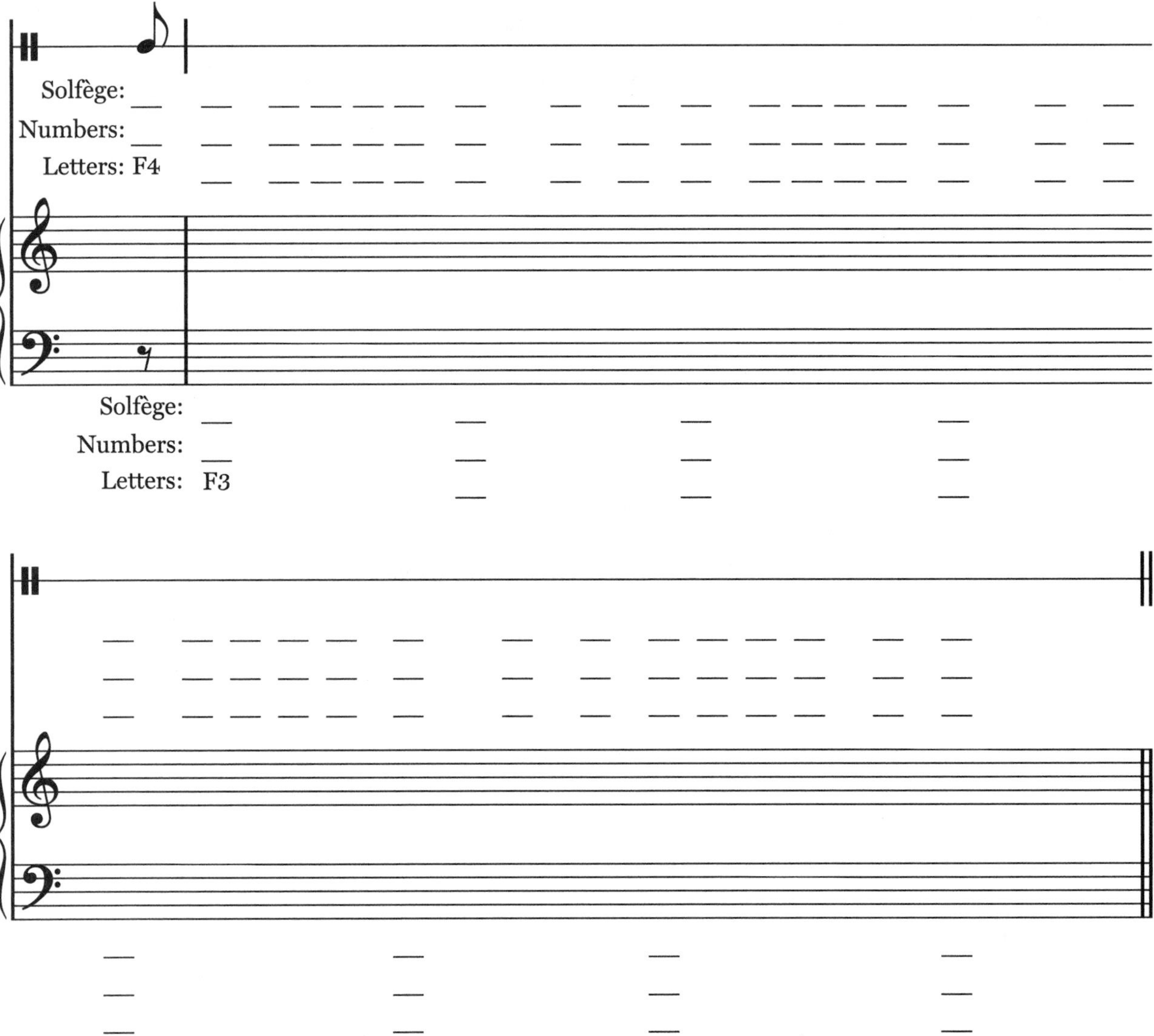

4. Use the workspace in exercise 3 to capture the first bass pitch of every full measure.
   (a) In the blanks provided beneath the bass staff, begin with the given letter name and write the remaining syllables, numbers, and letters of the bass pitches.
   (b) In the bass staff, write appropriate key and meter signatures. Notate the first bass pitch of every measure using note heads only. For help with pitches, refer to your solfège, numbers, and letters.
   (c) Sing the bass line, then play it on a keyboard.

NAME ______________________

Contextual Listening 4.3

1. After an introduction, a melody begins on *do*, *mi*, or *sol* ($\hat{1}$, $\hat{3}$, or $\hat{5}$). It consists of two rhythm patterns. Circle the starting pitch and indicate the pattern numbers.
   Hint: Sing *do* ($\hat{1}$). Sing up or down by step until you match pitch 1.

   (a) The starting pitch is: *do* ($\hat{1}$) *mi* ($\hat{3}$) *sol* ($\hat{5}$)
   Rhythm-pattern numbers: _______

   (b) The starting pitch is: *do* ($\hat{1}$) *mi* ($\hat{3}$) *sol* ($\hat{5}$)
   Rhythm-pattern numbers: _______

2. After an introduction, a melody begins with an eighth-note anacrusis.
   Identify melodic pitches 1–2.
   Hint: Sing *do* ($\hat{1}$). Then sing up or down to match the melodic pitches.

   (a) Melodic pitches 1–2 are:
   do-mi ($\hat{1}$-$\hat{3}$) *sol-do* ($\hat{5}$-$\hat{1}$) *mi-sol* ($\hat{3}$-$\hat{5}$) *sol-mi* ($\hat{5}$-$\hat{3}$)

   (b) Melodic pitches 1–2 are:
   do-mi ($\hat{1}$-$\hat{3}$) *sol-do* ($\hat{5}$-$\hat{1}$) *mi-sol* ($\hat{3}$-$\hat{5}$) *sol-mi* ($\hat{5}$-$\hat{3}$)

Now, listen to a traditional melody and complete the remaining exercises.

3. Use the workspace to capture the melodic rhythm and pitches.
   (a) In the single-line staff, notate the melody's rhythm. Write an appropriate meter signature, beam notes to show beat grouping, and include all bar lines.
   (b) In the blanks provided beneath the single-line staff, begin with the given letter name, and write the remaining syllables, numbers, and letters of the melody. Hint: To identify the pitch after a skip, sing the notes between the first and second note.
   (c) In the treble staff, write appropriate key and meter signatures. Notate the melodic pitches using note heads. For help with pitches, refer to your solfège, numbers, and letters.
   (d) In the treble staff, incorporate the rhythm from the single-line staff. Draw bar lines from the top of the treble staff to the bottom of the bass staff, aligned with the bar lines in the single-line staff.
   (e) Sing the melody, then play it on a keyboard.

Solfège: __

Numbers: __

Letters: C5

Solfège: __

Numbers: __

Letters: C3

4. Use the workspace in exercise 3 to capture the bass pitches.
   (a) In the blanks provided beneath the bass staff, begin with the given letter name and write the remaining syllables, numbers, and letters of the bass pitches.
   (b) In the bass staff, write appropriate key and meter signatures. Notate the pitches and rhythm of the bass line. For help with pitches, refer to your solfège, numbers, and letters. For the rhythm, assume there are no rests.
   (c) Sing the bass line, then play it on a keyboard.

Minor Keys and the Diatonic Modes

NAME ____________________

In this chapter you'll learn to:

- Recognize pitch collections in minor keys and the diatonic modes
- Capture accompanied melodies by mapping syllables, numbers, letters, and pitches
- Notate minor and modal melodies in simple and compound meters
- Transpose melodies to different keys and clefs

Try it

Minor Scale Forms and Aeolian Mode

Often sounds like a minor pentachord, embellished with *ti* ($\hat{7}$) and *le* ($\flat\hat{6}$)

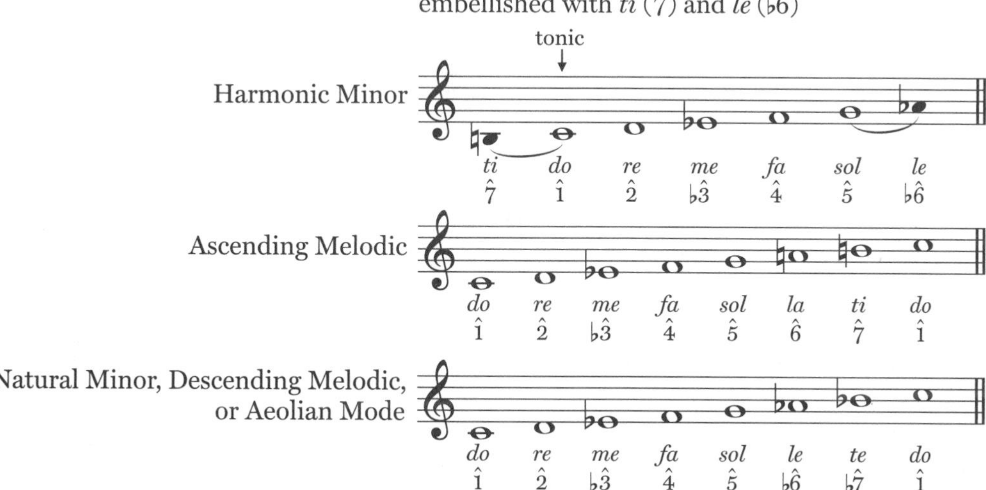

1. A tonic pitch (or modal "final") sounds, followed by silence and then a melody. In the blank, write the pitch-collection name. Then, circle the beat division: simple or compound.

(a) ____________________ simple compound

(b) ____________________ simple compound

(c) ____________________ simple compound

(d) ____________________ simple compound

(e) ____________________ simple compound

(f) ____________________ simple compound

Diatonic Modes

2. Now, listen to melodies in diatonic modes. Write the pitch-collection name in the blank and circle the beat division.

(a) ____________________ simple compound

(b) ____________________ simple compound

(c) ____________________ simple compound

(d) ____________________ simple compound

(e) ____________________ simple compound

(f) ____________________ simple compound

3. Following a count-off, a melody begins with the given pitch and rhythm. Notate the remaining rhythm and pitches. Beam divisions and subdivisions to show beat grouping and include all bar lines.

NAME ______________________

(d)

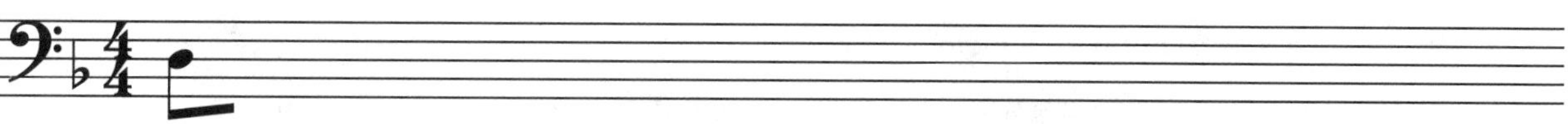

(e)

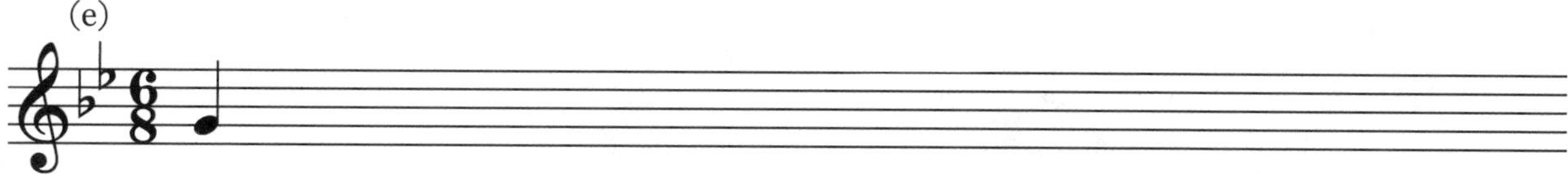

(f)

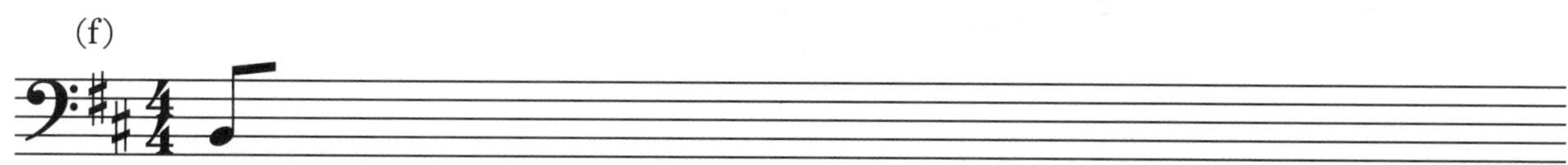

(g)

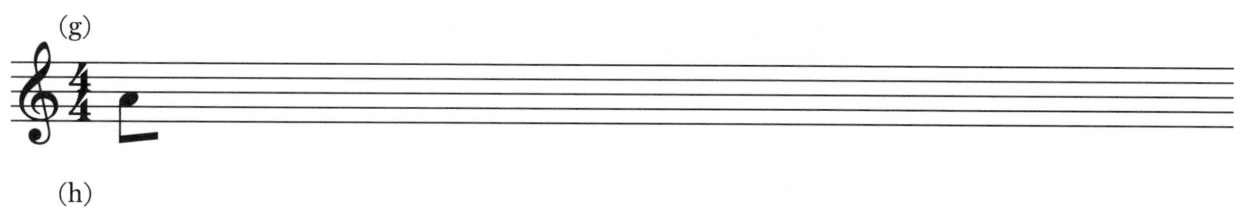

(h)

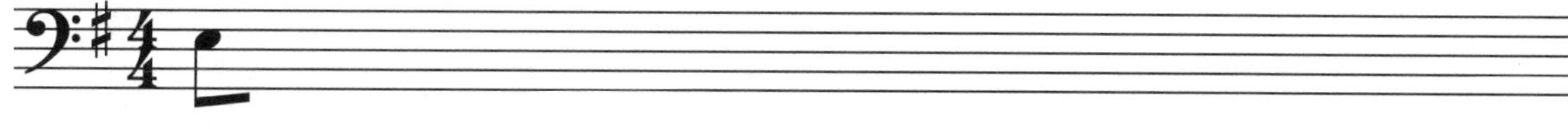

Contextual Listening 5.1

In exercises 1–4, a two-beat introduction precedes a melody that begins on *do* ($\hat{1}$). For each exercise, circle the melodic pitches, the beat division, and the best choice of meter signature.

	Melodic pitches		*Beat division*		*Meter signature*	
1.	*do-re* ($\hat{1}$-$\hat{2}$)	*do-me* ($\hat{1}$-$\flat\hat{3}$)	simple	compound	$\frac{2}{4}$	$\frac{6}{8}$
	do-fa ($\hat{1}$-$\hat{4}$)	*do-sol* ($\hat{1}$-$\hat{5}$)				
2.	*do-re* ($\hat{1}$-$\hat{2}$)	*do-me* ($\hat{1}$-$\flat\hat{3}$)	simple	compound	$\frac{2}{4}$	$\frac{6}{8}$
	do-fa ($\hat{1}$-$\hat{4}$)	*do-sol* ($\hat{1}$-$\hat{5}$)				
3.	*do-re* ($\hat{1}$-$\hat{2}$)	*do-me* ($\hat{1}$-$\flat\hat{3}$)	simple	compound	$\frac{2}{4}$	$\frac{6}{8}$
	do-fa ($\hat{1}$-$\hat{4}$)	*do-sol* ($\hat{1}$-$\hat{5}$)				
4.	*do-re* ($\hat{1}$-$\hat{2}$)	*do-me* ($\hat{1}$-$\flat\hat{3}$)	simple	compound	$\frac{2}{4}$	$\frac{6}{8}$
	do-fa ($\hat{1}$-$\hat{4}$)	*do-sol* ($\hat{1}$-$\hat{5}$)				

Now, focus your listening on the melody from a piano work.

5. Use the workspace to capture the melodic rhythm and pitches.
   (a) In the single-line staff, begin with an eighth note and notate the melody's rhythm in two-beat measures. Write an appropriate meter signature, beam notes to show beat grouping, and include all bar lines.
   (b) In the blanks provided beneath the single-line staff, begin with the given letter name and write the syllables, numbers, and letters of the melody.
   (c) In the treble staff, write appropriate key and meter signatures. Notate the melodic pitches using note heads. For help with pitches, refer to your solfège, numbers, and letters.
   (d) In the treble staff, incorporate the rhythm from the single-line staff, aligning the bar lines with those in the single-line staff.
   (e) Sing the melody, then play it on a keyboard.

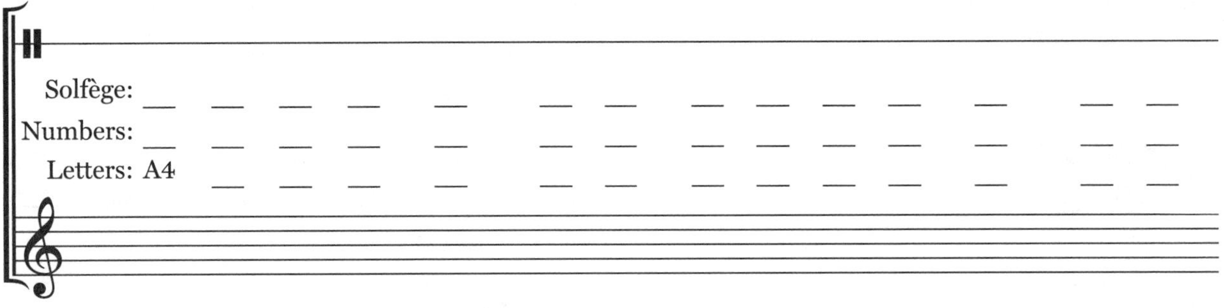

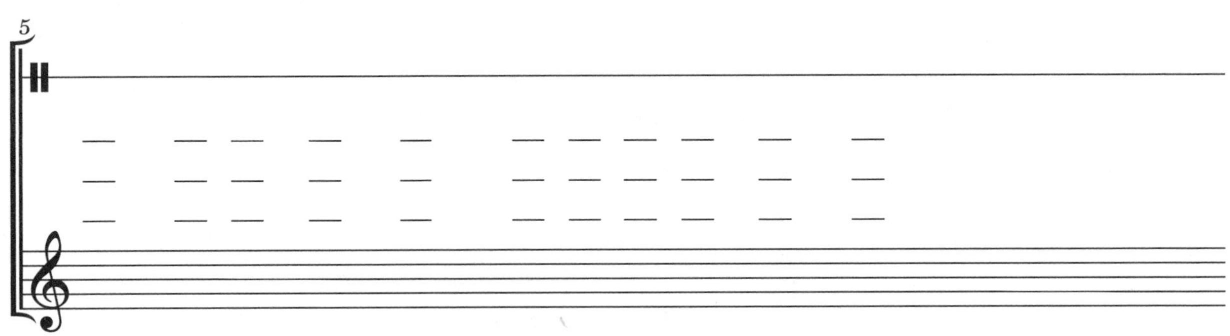

6. Which is the range (lowest pitch to highest pitch) of this melody?

   do-me ($\hat{1}$-$\flat\hat{3}$) *do-fa* ($\hat{1}$-$\hat{4}$) *do-sol* ($\hat{1}$-$\hat{5}$) *do-do* ($\hat{1}$-$\hat{1}$)

7. As a collection, the melodic pitches complete which minor-key pattern?

   pentachord ascending melodc natural (descending melodic) harmonic

NAME ______________________________

Contextual Listening 5.2

In exercises 1-2, a three-beat introduction precedes a melody that begins on *do* ($\hat{1}$). For each exercise, circle the melodic pitches, the beat division, and the best choice of meter signature.

	Melodic Pitches			*Beat Division*		*Meter Signature*	
1.	*do-me* ($\hat{1}$-$\flat\hat{3}$)	*do-sol* ($\hat{1}$-$\hat{5}$)	*do-do* ($\hat{1}$-$\hat{1}$)	simple	compound	$\frac{3}{4}$	$\frac{9}{8}$
2.	*do-me* ($\hat{1}$-$\flat\hat{3}$)	*do-sol* ($\hat{1}$-$\hat{5}$)	*do-do* ($\hat{1}$-$\hat{1}$)	simple	compound	$\frac{3}{4}$	$\frac{9}{8}$

In exercises 3-4, a three-beat count-off precedes a melody that begins on *do* ($\hat{1}$).

3. To which scale do all melodic pitches belong?

   major   ascending melodic   natural minor   harmonic   Dorian

The melodic rhythm includes some of these numbered patterns.

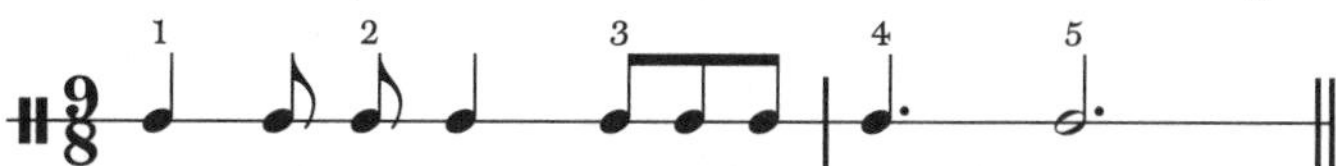

In the blanks, write the pattern number that occurs on the beat indicated.

$\frac{9}{8}$ __ __ __ | __ __ ||

4. To which scale or mode do all melodic pitches belong?

   major   ascending melodic   natural minor   harmonic   Dorian

The melodic rhythm includes some of these numbered patterns.

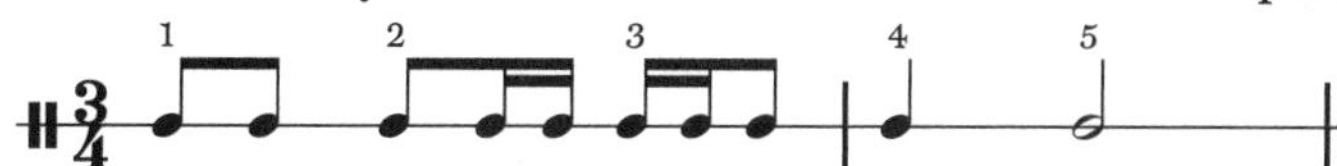

In the blanks, write the pattern number that occurs on the beat indicated.

$\frac{3}{4}$ __ __ __ | __ __ ||

Now, listen to a piano work that begins on *do* ($\hat{1}$).

5. Focus first on melodic pitches 1–2, the beat division, and the meter. Circle the correct answers.

Melodic Pitches 1–2			*Beat Division*		*Meter Signature*	
do-me ($\hat{1}$–$\flat\hat{3}$)	*do-sol* ($\hat{1}$–$\hat{5}$)	*do-do* ($\hat{1}$–$\hat{1}$)	simple	compound	$\frac{3}{4}$	$\frac{9}{8}$

6. Melodic pitches 1–5 belong to which scale or mode?

   harmonic minor natural minor Dorian mode Lydian mode

7. The final three melodic pitches belong to which scale or mode?

   harmonic minor natural minor Dorian mode Lydian mode

8. Use the workspace to capture the melodic rhythm and pitches.
   (a) In the single-line staff, begin with a quarter note and notate the melody's rhythm in three-beat measures. Write an appropriate meter signature, beam notes to show beat grouping, and include all bar lines.
   (b) In the blanks provided beneath the single-line staff, begin with the given letter name and write the syllables, numbers, and letters of the melody.
   (c) In the treble staff, write appropriate key and meter signatures. Notate the melodic pitches using note heads. For help with pitches, refer to your solfège, numbers, and letters.

   Hint: Minor-key music *always* requires an accidental on *ti* ($\hat{7}$).

   (d) In the treble staff, incorporate the rhythm from the single-line staff, aligning the bar lines with those in the single-line staff.
   (e) Sing the melody, then play it on a keyboard.

Solfège: __ __ __ __ __ __ __ __ __ __ __ __ __ __ __ __
Numbers: __ __ __ __ __ __ __ __ __ __ __ __ __ __ __ __
Letters: E3 __ __ __ __ __ __ __ __ __ __ __ __ __ __ __

NAME ___________________________

Contextual Listening 5.3

Listen to a folk song that ends on *do* ($\hat{1}$) and complete the following exercises.

1. The melody begins with which rhythmic feature?

   syncopation   rubato (uneven tempo)   dotted-note values   anacrusis

2. Circle the beat division and best choice of meter signature.

   simple   compound $\begin{smallmatrix}3\\4\end{smallmatrix}$ $\begin{smallmatrix}9\\8\end{smallmatrix}$

3. The melody begins on which pitch?
   Hint: Sing the last pitch, *do* ($\hat{1}$). Then, sing up until you match pitch 1.

   do ($\hat{1}$)   *re* ($\hat{2}$)   *me* ($\flat\hat{3}$)   *sol* ($\hat{5}$)

4. Use the workspace to capture the melodic rhythm and pitches.

   (a) In the single-line staff, begin with an eighth note and notate the melody's rhythm in three-beat measures. Write an appropriate meter signature, beam notes to show beat grouping, and include all bar lines.

   (b) In the blanks provided beneath the single-line staff, begin with the given letter name and write the syllables, numbers, and letters of the melody.

   (c) In the treble staff, draw appropriate key and meter signatures. Notate the melodic pitches using note heads. For help with pitches, refer to your solfège, numbers, and letters.

   (d) In the treble staff, incorporate the rhythm from the single-line staff. Align the bar lines with those in the single-line staff.

Solfège: __ __ __ __ __ __ __ __ __ __ __ __ __ __ __ __ __

Numbers: __ __ __ __ __ __ __ __ __ __ __ __ __ __ __ __ __

Letters: G4 __ __ __ __ __ __ __ __ __ __ __ __ __ __ __ __

5. All melodic pitches belong to which scale or mode?

   major   Dorian mode   harmonic minor   ascending melodic minor

6. Which is the range (lowest pitch to highest pitch) of the melody?

   do-do ($\hat{1}$-$\hat{1}$)   *do-sol* ($\hat{1}$-$\hat{5}$)   *ti-le* ($\hat{7}$-$\flat\hat{6}$)   *sol-sol* ($\hat{5}$-$\hat{5}$)

NAME ______________________

Contextual Listening 5.4

Listen to an accompanied melody for piano and complete the following exercises.

1. Listen low. *Do* ($\hat{1}$), the lowest pitch, sounds on every beat of the accompaniment. Circle the beat division and best choice of meter signature.

   simple   compound $\frac{2}{4}$ $\frac{6}{8}$

2. Listen high. The melody begins with which rhythmic feature?

   syncopation   rubato (uneven tempo)   dotted-note values   anacrusis

3. The melody begins and ends on which pitch?
   Hint: Sing *do* ($\hat{1}$), then sing the scale until you match the first (or last) melodic pitch.

   sol ($\hat{5}$)   *me* ($\flat\hat{3}$)   *re* ($\hat{2}$)   *do* ($\hat{1}$)

4. Use the workspace to capture the melodic rhythm and pitches.
   (a) In the single-line staff, begin with an eighth note and notate the melody's rhythm. Write an appropriate meter signature, beam notes to show beat grouping, and include all bar lines. Hint: Look at the answers to exercises 1–2.
   (b) In the blanks provided beneath the single-line staff, begin with the given letter name and write the syllables, numbers, and letters of the melody.
   (c) In the treble staff, write appropriate key and meter signatures. Notate the melodic pitches using note heads. For help with pitches, refer to your solfège, numbers, and letters.
   (d) In the treble staff, incorporate the rhythm from the single-line staff. Align the bar lines with those in the single-line staff.
   (e) Sing the melody, then play it on a keyboard.

Solfège: __ __ __ __ __ __ __ __ __ __ __ __ __ __ __ __

Numbers: __ __ __ __ __ __ __ __ __ __ __ __ __ __ __ __

Letters: D5 __ __ __ __ __ __ __ __ __ __ __ __ __ __ __

5. All melodic pitches belong to which scale or mode?

   natural minor   Dorian mode   Lydian mode   major scale

6. Which is the range (lowest pitch to highest pitch) of the melody?

   do-do ($\hat{1}$–$\hat{1}$)   *do-sol* ($\hat{1}$–$\hat{5}$)   *ti-le* ($\hat{7}$–$\flat\hat{6}$)   *sol-sol* ($\hat{5}$–$\hat{5}$)

7. Begin on E5 and use the solfège or numbers from exercise 4 to transpose the melody up one whole step to create a B♭ clarinet part. In the staff below, write an appropriate clef, key signature, and meter signature.

B♭ clarinet

NAME ____________________

Contextual Listening 5.5

Translation: The sea glimmered out in the distance by the light of evening's last glow . . .

Listen to part of an art song. Focus first on the accompaniment, then the melody.

1. Listen low. At the beginning, *do* ($\hat{1}$), the lowest pitch, sounds on beat 1 in each measure of the accompaniment. Circle the beat division and best choice of meter signature.

   simple compound $\frac{2}{4}$ $\frac{6}{8}$

2. Listen high. The melody begins with which rhythmic feature?

   syncopation tied note duplet anacrusis

3. Beginning with melodic pitch 3, which describes the recurring rhythmic feature?

   syncopation tied note duplet anacrusis

4. Use the workspace to capture the melodic rhythm and pitches.
   (a) In the single-line staff, begin with an eighth note and notate the melody's rhythm. Write an appropriate meter signature, beam notes to show beat grouping, and include all bar lines. Hint: Look at the answers to exercises 1–2.
   (b) In the blanks provided beneath the single-line staff, begin with the given letter name, and write the syllables, numbers, and letters of the melody.
   (c) In the treble staff, write appropriate key and meter signatures. Notate the melodic pitches using note heads. For help with pitches, refer to your solfège, numbers, and letters.
   (d) In the treble staff, incorporate the rhythm from the single-line staff. Align the bar lines with those in the single-line staff.
   (e) Sing the melody, then play it on a keyboard.

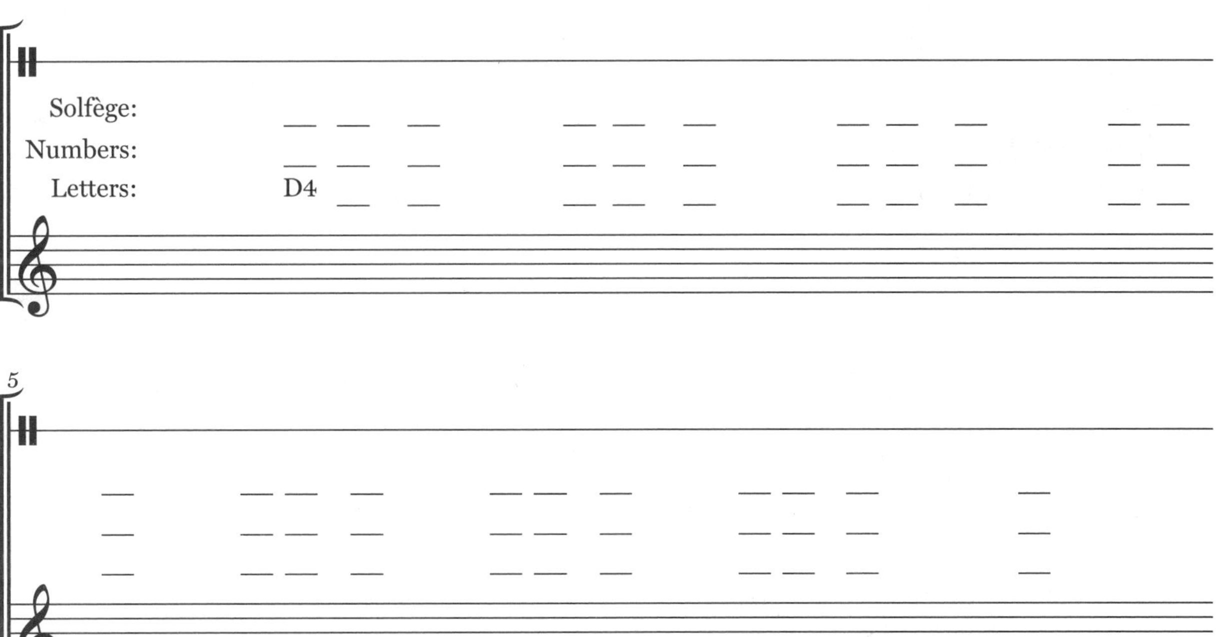

5. The melody ends with which pitch?

   do ($\hat{1}$)   *re* ($\hat{2}$)   *me* ($\flat\hat{3}$)   *sol* ($\hat{5}$)

6. Listen low at the end. The accompaniment ends with which lowest pitch?

   do ($\hat{1}$)   *re* ($\hat{2}$)   *me* ($\flat\hat{3}$)   *sol* ($\hat{5}$)

7. Given your answers to exercise 5, why can you tell this is *not* the end of the song?

Contextual Listening 5.6

Listen again to the work from Contextual Listening 5.1. Focus first on the left-hand accompaniment part. Then, focus on the right-hand melody plus its accompaniment.

1. Which is the rhythm of the accompaniment (the lower parts)?

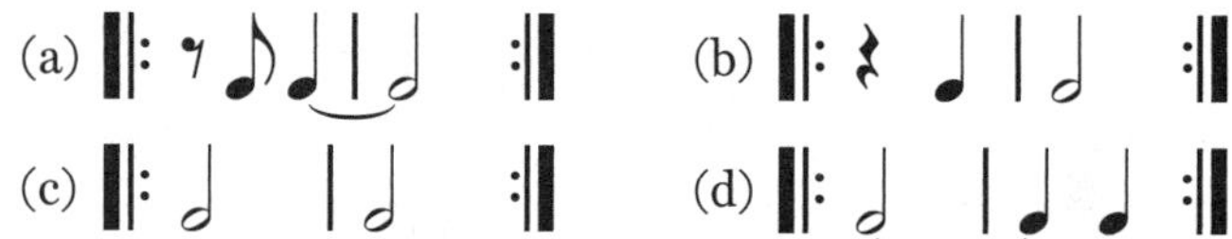

2. The lowest-sounding part of the accompaniment begins on *do* ($\hat{1}$). Which of these represents pitches 1–2? Hint: Sing *do* ($\hat{1}$), then sing up the scale until you match pitch 2.

   do-re ($\hat{1}$–$\hat{2}$)   *do-me* ($\hat{1}$–$\flat\hat{3}$)   *do-fa* ($\hat{1}$–$\hat{4}$)   *do-sol* ($\hat{1}$–$\hat{5}$)

3. The middle part begins on *sol* ($\hat{5}$). Which describes the middle part's next pitch?

   S   **H** below   **W** below   **H** above   **W** above

4. The letter names below represent a scale from which all melodic and accompanying pitch classes are drawn. The first and last are given. After each letter, write the pitch class's accidental: ♮, ♭, or ♯. Write ? after the one note that *isn't* played.

   A♮ ____ ____ ____ ____ ____ ____ A♮

5. To which scale(s) could the melodic and accompanying pitch classes belong? Circle all that apply. Hint: Think of different possibilities for the missing (?) note.

   ascending melodic minor   harmonic minor   natural minor   Dorian mode

CHAPTER 29

Intervals

NAME ______________________________

In this chapter you'll learn to:

- Identify intervals in major- and minor-key music
- Abbreviate solfège syllables
- Think letter names without writing them
- Notate music in simple and compound meters
- Transpose melodies to different keys and clefs

Try it

An introduction precedes a two-measure melody. For each one:

- Circle the beat division—simple or compound.
- Circle the interval formed by the specified melodic pitches. Hint: Map the pitches to syllables or numbers in your head.
- Circle the melody's key—major or minor.
- Refer to the appropriate patterns—compound or simple—and write the rhythm-pattern numbers.

Compound-beat rhythm patterns

1 2 3 4 5

Simple-beat rhythm patterns

1 2 3 4 5 6 7 8

1. Division: simple compound

   Pitches 1-2 form: M3 *do-mi* ($\hat{1}$-$\hat{3}$) P4 *do-fa* ($\hat{1}$-$\hat{4}$) A4 *do-fi* ($\hat{1}$-$\sharp\hat{4}$) P5 *do-sol* ($\hat{1}$-$\hat{5}$)

   Key: major minor

   Patterns: ___ ___ | ___ ___ ||

2. Division: simple compound

   Pitches 1-2 form: M3 *do-mi* ($\hat{1}$-$\hat{3}$) P4 *do-fa* ($\hat{1}$-$\hat{4}$) A4 *do-fi* ($\hat{1}$-$\sharp\hat{4}$) P5 *do-sol* ($\hat{1}$-$\hat{5}$)

   Key: major minor

   Patterns: ___ ___ | ___ ___ ||

3. Division: simple compound

Pitches 1–2 form: M2 m3 P4 P5

do-re ($\hat{1}$–$\hat{2}$) *do-me* ($\hat{1}$–$\flat\hat{3}$) *do-fa* ($\hat{1}$–$\hat{4}$) *do-sol* ($\hat{1}$–$\hat{5}$)

Key: major minor

Patterns: ___ ___ | ___ ___ ||

4. Division: simple compound

Pitches 1–2 form: M3 P4 P5 m6

sol-me ($\hat{5}$–$\flat\hat{3}$) *sol-re* ($\hat{5}$–$\hat{2}$) *sol-do* ($\hat{5}$–$\hat{1}$) *sol-ti* ($\hat{5}$–$\hat{7}$)

Key: major minor

Patterns: ___ ___ | ___ ___ ||

5. Division: simple compound

Pitches 1–2 form: P4 m6 M6 m7

sol-do ($\hat{5}$–$\hat{1}$) *sol-me* ($\hat{5}$–$\flat\hat{3}$) *sol-mi* ($\hat{5}$–$\hat{3}$) *sol-fa* ($\hat{5}$–$\hat{4}$)

Key: major minor

Patterns: ___ ___ | ___ ___ ||

6. In melody 6, focus on melodic pitches 4–5.

Division: simple compound

Pitches 4–5 form: m3 P4 d5 m6

ti-re ($\hat{7}$–$\hat{2}$) *ti-mi* ($\hat{7}$–$\hat{3}$) *ti-fa* ($\hat{7}$–$\hat{4}$) *ti-sol* ($\hat{7}$–$\hat{5}$)

Key: major minor

Patterns: ___ ___ | ___ ___ ||

7. Melody 7 begins with an eighth-note anacrusis, which is given.

Division: simple compound

Pitches 1–2 form: P4 P5 M6 m7

sol-do ($\hat{5}$–$\hat{1}$) *sol-re* ($\hat{5}$–$\hat{2}$) *sol-mi* ($\hat{5}$–$\hat{3}$) *sol-fa* ($\hat{5}$–$\hat{4}$)

Key: major minor

Patterns: ♪ | ___ ___ | ___ ___ ||

8. Melody 8 begins with an eighth-note anacrusis, which is given.

Division: simple compound

Pitches 1–2 form: M3 P5 M6 M7

sol-me ($\hat{5}$–$\flat\hat{3}$) *sol-do* ($\hat{5}$–$\hat{1}$) *sol-te* ($\hat{5}$–$\flat\hat{7}$) *sol-le* ($\hat{5}$–$\flat\hat{6}$)

Key: major minor

Patterns: ♪ | ___ ___ | ___ ___ ||

NAME ____________________

Contextual Listening 6.1

Listen to two melodies. For each, circle melodic pitch 1, the beat division, and the meter signature.

Hint: Sing *do* ($\hat{1}$). Sing up or down until you match the starting pitch.

	Melodic pitch 1			*Beat division*		*Meter signature*	
1.	*do* ($\hat{1}$)	*mi* ($\hat{3}$)	*sol* ($\hat{5}$)	simple	compound	$\frac{2}{4}$	$\frac{6}{8}$
2.	*do* ($\hat{1}$)	*mi* ($\hat{3}$)	*sol* ($\hat{5}$)	simple	compound	$\frac{2}{4}$	$\frac{6}{8}$

Listen to exercises 1–2 again. This time, identify the first and last melodic intervals.

3.	First melodic interval:	M2	M3	P4	P5
	Last melodic interval:	M2	M3	P4	P5
4.	First melodic interval:	M2	M3	P4	P5
	Last melodic interval:	M2	M3	P4	P5

Now, focus your listening on the melody from a piano work.

5. Use the workspace to capture the melodic rhythm and pitches.
   (a) In the single-line staff, begin with a dotted-quarter note and notate the melody's rhythm in two-beat measures. Write an appropriate meter signature, beam notes to show beat grouping, and include all bar lines.
   (b) In the blanks provided beneath the single-line staff, begin with the given letter name, and write the syllables, numbers, and letters of the melody.
   (c) In the treble staff, draw appropriate key and meter signatures. Notate the melodic pitches using note heads. For help with pitches, refer to your syllables, numbers, and letters.
   (d) In the treble staff, incorporate the rhythm from the single-line staff. Align the bar lines with those in the single-line staff.
   (e) Play *do* ($\hat{1}$) and sing your answer with solfège, numbers, and letters. Sing the melody, then play it on a keyboard.
   (f) Beneath the treble staff, beginning with PU, write the interval names between each melodic pitch.

Solfège: __ __ __ __ __ __ __ __ __ __ __ __

Numbers: __ __ __ __ __ __ __ __ __ __ __ __

Letters: G♯4 __ __ __ __ __ __ __ __ __ __ __

Intervals: PU __ __ __ __ __ __ __ __ __ __

6. The melody's pitches belong to which scale?

   ascending melodic minor   natural minor (descending melodic minor)

   harmonic minor   major scale

7. From the melody's lowest pitch to its highest, which is its range?

   do-sol ($\hat{1}$-$\hat{5}$)   *ti-la* ($\hat{7}$-$\hat{6}$)   *do-do* ($\hat{1}$-$\hat{1}$)   *sol-sol* ($\hat{5}$-$\hat{5}$)

8. At the beginning, listen low. The lowest pitches 1–2 form which interval?
   Hint: Sing pitch 1, *do* ($\hat{1}$), then sing down until you match pitch 2.

   m2; *do-ti* ($\hat{1}$-$\hat{7}$)   m3; *do-la* ($\hat{1}$-$\hat{6}$)   P4; *do-sol* ($\hat{1}$-$\hat{5}$)   P5; *do-fa* ($\hat{1}$-$\hat{4}$)

NAME ______________________________

Contextual Listening 6.2

Listen to a melody. Then, circle melodic pitch 1, the beat division, and the meter signature.

Hint: Sing *do* ($\hat{1}$). Then if necessary, sing up or down until you match the starting pitch.

	Melodic pitch 1			*Beat division*		*Meter signature*	
1.	*do* ($\hat{1}$)	*mi* ($\hat{3}$)	*sol* ($\hat{5}$)	simple	compound	C	$\frac{12}{8}$
2.	*do* ($\hat{1}$)	*mi* ($\hat{3}$)	*sol* ($\hat{5}$)	simple	compound	C	$\frac{12}{8}$

Listen to exercises 1–2 again. This time, identify the first and last melodic intervals.

3. First melodic interval: m2 M2 m3 M3
   Last melodic interval: m2 M2 m3 M3
4. First melodic interval: m2 M2 m3 M3
   Last melodic interval: m2 M2 m3 M3

Now, listen to a passage that features violin, viola, and cello. Focus first on the violin melody—the highest part.

5. Violin pitch 1 is: *do* ($\hat{1}$) *mi* ($\hat{3}$) *sol* ($\hat{5}$)
6. The beat division is: simple compound
7. The meter signature is: C $\frac{12}{8}$
8. All violin pitches belong to which scale?
   major scale natural minor (descending melodic minor)
   ascending melodic minor harmonic minor
9. On pitches 1–4, the violin and viola play together.
   The interval between them is a: unison third sixth
   Hint: A unison sounds identical, a third sounds close, and a sixth sounds farther apart.
10. The lowest part is played by the cello. Cello pitch 1 is:
    do ($\hat{1}$) *mi* ($\hat{3}$) *sol* ($\hat{5}$)
11. Cello pitches 1–2 form which interval?
    M3 P5 M6 P8
12. Use the workspace to capture the violin's melodic rhythm and pitches.
    (a) In the single-line staff, begin with a quarter note and notate the melody's rhythm in four-beat measures. Write an appropriate meter signature, beam notes to show beat grouping, and include all bar lines. Notate two measures per staff system.
    (b) In the blanks provided beneath the single-line staff, begin with the given letter name, and write the syllables and numbers of the melody.
    To save time, write only the first letter of a solfège syllable.
    (c) In the treble staff, draw appropriate key and meter signatures. Begin with the given pitch and notate all melodic pitches using note heads.
    Hints: Refer to your syllables and numbers and map them to pitches in the key. *Think* the letter names as you notate, but don't write them out.

(d) In the treble staff, incorporate the rhythm from the single-line staff, aligning the bar lines with those in the single-line staff.

(e) Sing the melody, then play it on a keyboard

Solfège:

Numbers:

B♭4

3

Contextual Listening 6.3

A melody begins on *do* ($\hat{1}$) and features two rhythm patterns. The pitches belong to the top of a minor scale—from *sol* ($\hat{5}$) up to *do* ($\hat{1}$). Identify the pattern numbers and the scale.

Rhythm patterns		*All melodic pitches belong to this minor scale:*		
1.	___ ___	ascending melodic	natural	harmonic
2.	___ ___	ascending melodic	natural	harmonic
3.	___ ___	ascending melodic	natural	harmonic

Now, listen to part of an art song, and complete the remaining exercises.

4. Consult the pattern chart above. Write the rhythm-pattern number for each measure of the singer's rhythm.

   ___ ___ ___ ___ ___ ___ ___ ___

5. The singer's first two and last two pitches form which interval?

   m2 M2 m3 M3

6. The singer's pitch collection belongs to which scale?

   major scale natural minor (descending melodic minor)
   ascending melodic minor harmonic minor

7. Use the workspace to capture the singer's melodic rhythm and pitches.

   (a) In the single-line staff, write the meter signature, then notate the melody's rhythm. Hints: Refer to exercise 4. Notate four measures per staff system.

   (b) In the blanks provided beneath the single-line staff, begin with the given letter name, and write the syllables and numbers of the melody.

   Hint: To save time, write only the first letter of solfège syllables that occur in the major scale. For example, a minor-pentachord melody might look like this: *d t d r me f s le s*.

   (c) In the treble staff, draw appropriate key and meter signatures. Begin with the given pitch and notate all melodic pitches using note heads.

   Hints: Refer to your syllables and numbers and map them to pitches in the key. *Think* the letter names as you notate, but don't write them out.

   (d) In the treble staff, incorporate the rhythm from the single-line staff, aligning the bar lines with those in the single-line staff.

   (e) Sing the melody, then play it on a keyboard.

Solfège: ___ ___ ___ ___ ___ ___ ___ ___ ___ ___ ___ ___

Numbers: ___ ___ ___ ___ ___ ___ ___ ___ ___ ___ ___ ___

C5

5

___ ___ ___ ___ ___ ___ ___ ___ ___ ___ ___ ___

___ ___ ___ ___ ___ ___ ___ ___ ___ ___ ___ ___

Translation: Oh, that you were taken away, never more to return!

NAME ______________________________

Contextual Listening 6.4

Listen to a melody. Then, circle melodic pitch 1, the beat division, and the meter signature. Hint: Sing *do* ($\hat{1}$). Sing up or down until you match the starting pitch.

	Melodic pitch 1			*Beat division*		*Meter signature*	
1.	*do* ($\hat{1}$)	*me* ($\flat\hat{3}$)	*sol* ($\hat{5}$)	simple	compound	$\frac{2}{4}$	$\frac{6}{8}$
2.	*do* ($\hat{1}$)	*me* ($\flat\hat{3}$)	*sol* ($\hat{5}$)	simple	compound	$\frac{2}{4}$	$\frac{6}{8}$

Listen to exercises 1–2 again. This time, identify the first and last melodic intervals.

3. First melodic interval: m2 m3 M3 P4

   Last melodic interval: m2 m3 M3 P4

4. First melodic interval: m2 m3 M3 P4

   Last melodic interval: m2 m3 M3 P4

Now listen to a song from an opera and complete the remaining exercises.

5. Melodic pitches 1–2 form which interval?

   m3 M3 P4 P5

6. Melodic pitches 6–7 form which interval?

   m3 M3 P4 P5

7. The final melodic pitches (pitches 15–16) form which interval?

   m3 M3 P4 P5

8. Melodic pitches 1–8 belong to which pattern?

   major tetrachord minor tetrachord major pentachord minor pentachord

9. The melody's pitch collection belongs to which scale?

   major scale natural minor (descending melodic minor)

   ascending melodic minor harmonic minor

10. Use the workspace to capture the vocal melodic rhythm and pitches.
    (a) In the single-line staff, write an appropriate meter signature. Begin with an eighth note and notate the melody's rhythm in two-beat measures. Beam notes to show beat grouping and include all bar lines. Notate three measures per staff system.
    (b) In the blanks provided beneath the single-line staff, begin with F♯4, and write the syllables and numbers of the melody. Hint: For any major-scale pitch, write only the first letter of its solfège syllable. For other notes, continue writing the entire syllable. A minor-key melody might look like this: *d t d r me f s le s*.
    (c) In the treble staff, draw appropriate key and meter signatures. Begin with the given pitch and notate all melodic pitches using note heads. Hint: Refer to your syllables and numbers and *think* the letter names as you notate, but don't write them out.
    (d) In the treble staff, incorporate the rhythm from the single-line staff, aligning the bar lines with those in the single-line staff.
    (e) Sing the melody, then play it on a keyboard.

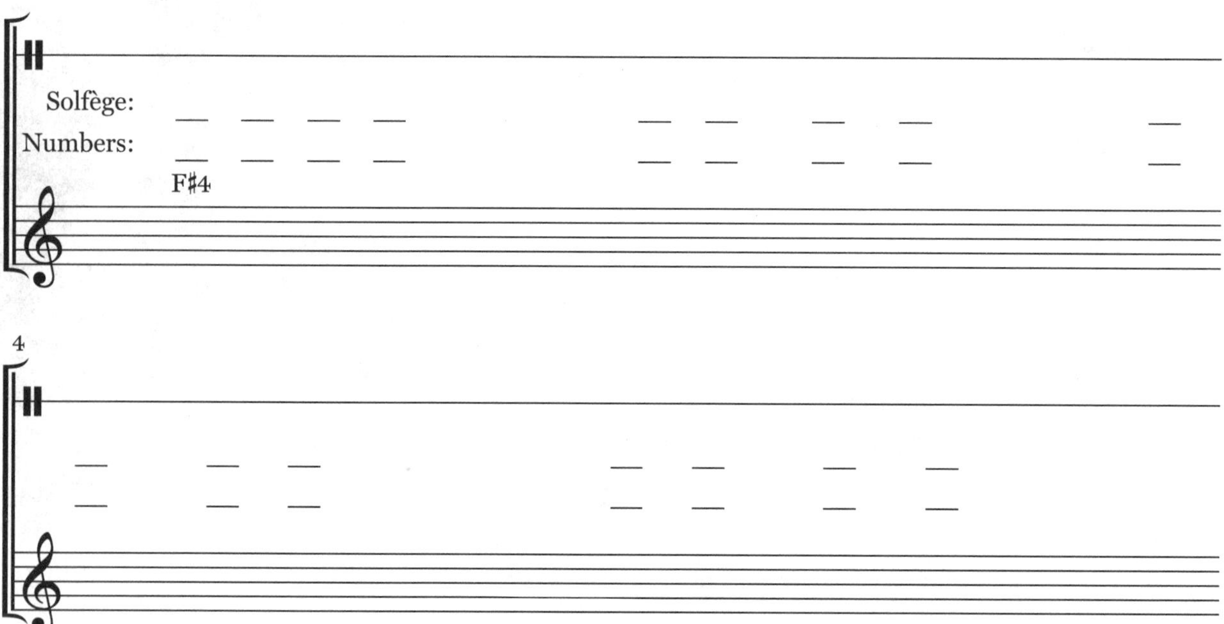

Translation: Black is the night, the wind howls, the spraying sea swells swiftly . . .

CHAPTER 30

Triads

NAME ______________________

In this chapter you'll learn to:

- Identify melodic and harmonic triads in major- and minor-key music
- Notate simple- and compound-meter music that features melodic and harmonic triads

Try it

1. The following eight melodies outline a triad. For each, identify the triad quality and the interval between the last two notes. Choose whether the meter is simple or compound. Then write the pattern numbers for each complete beat of rhythm.

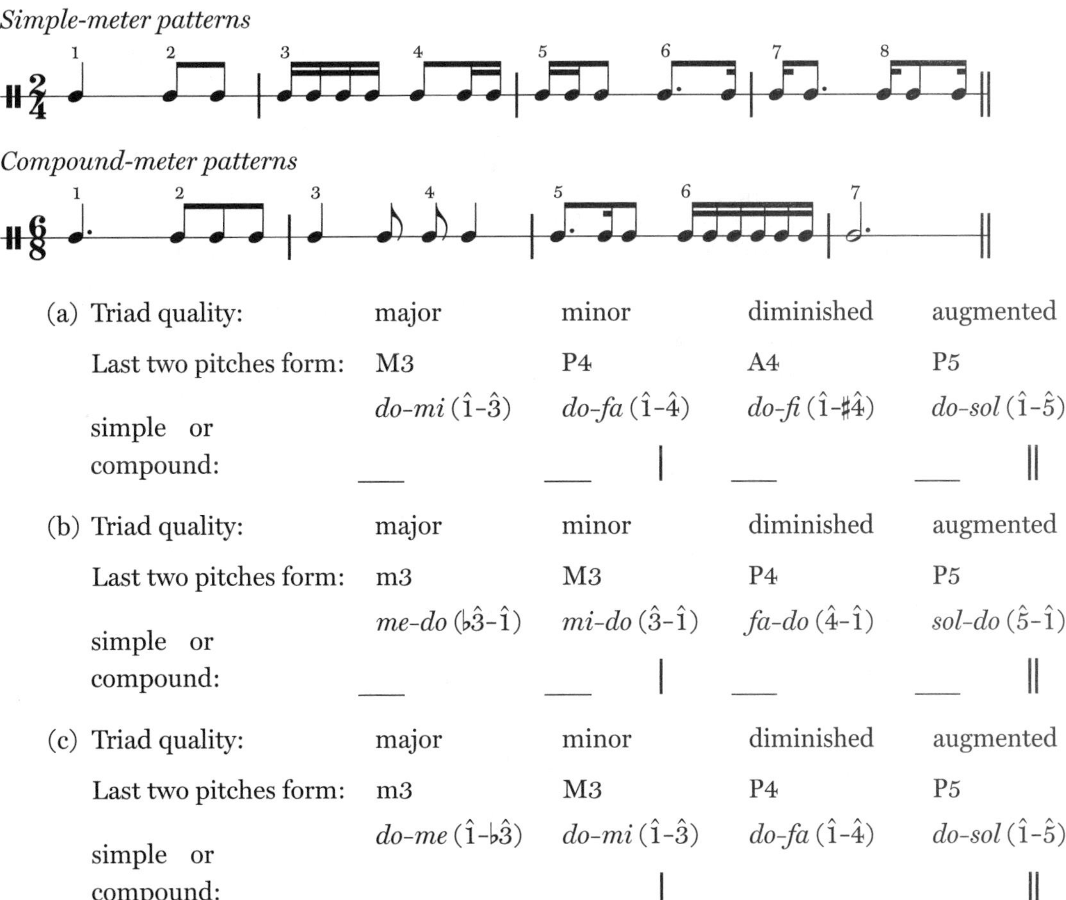

(a) Triad quality: major / minor / diminished / augmented

Last two pitches form: M3 *do-mi* ($\hat{1}$-$\hat{3}$) / P4 *do-fa* ($\hat{1}$-$\hat{4}$) / A4 *do-fi* ($\hat{1}$-$\sharp\hat{4}$) / P5 *do-sol* ($\hat{1}$-$\hat{5}$)

simple or compound: ___ ___ | ___ ___ ||

(b) Triad quality: major / minor / diminished / augmented

Last two pitches form: m3 *me-do* ($\flat\hat{3}$-$\hat{1}$) / M3 *mi-do* ($\hat{3}$-$\hat{1}$) / P4 *fa-do* ($\hat{4}$-$\hat{1}$) / P5 *sol-do* ($\hat{5}$-$\hat{1}$)

simple or compound: ___ ___ | ___ ___ ||

(c) Triad quality: major / minor / diminished / augmented

Last two pitches form: m3 *do-me* ($\hat{1}$-$\flat\hat{3}$) / M3 *do-mi* ($\hat{1}$-$\hat{3}$) / P4 *do-fa* ($\hat{1}$-$\hat{4}$) / P5 *do-sol* ($\hat{1}$-$\hat{5}$)

simple or compound: ___ ___ | ___ ___ ||

(d) Triad quality:

Triad quality:	major	minor	diminished	augmented
Last two pitches form:	m3	M3	P4	P5
	mi-sol ($\hat{3}$–$\hat{5}$)	*me-sol* ($\flat\hat{3}$–$\hat{5}$)	*re-sol* ($\hat{2}$–$\hat{5}$)	*do-sol* ($\hat{1}$–$\hat{5}$)
simple or compound:	___	___ |	___	___ ||

(e) The melody ends on *do* ($\hat{1}$). Identify the quality of the triad outlined by pitches 5–7.

Triad quality:	major	minor	diminished	augmented
Last two pitches form:	m2	m3	M3	P4
	ti-do ($\hat{7}$–$\hat{1}$)	*la-do* ($\hat{6}$–$\hat{1}$)	*le-do* ($\flat\hat{6}$–$\hat{1}$)	*sol-do* ($\hat{5}$–$\hat{1}$)
simple or compound:	___	___ |	___	___ ||

(f) Identify the quality of the triad outlined by pitches 4–6.

Triad quality:	major	minor	diminished	augmented
Last two pitches form:	M3	P4	A4	P5
	do-mi ($\hat{1}$–$\hat{3}$)	*do-fa* ($\hat{1}$–$\hat{4}$)	*do-fi* ($\hat{1}$–$\sharp\hat{4}$)	*do-sol* ($\hat{1}$–$\hat{5}$)
simple or compound:	___	___ |	___	___ ||

(g) Melody 7 begins with an eighth-note anacrusis.

Triad quality:	major	minor	diminished	augmented
Last two pitches form:	M3	P4	P5	M6
	do-mi ($\hat{1}$–$\hat{3}$)	*do-fa* ($\hat{1}$–$\hat{4}$)	*do-sol* ($\hat{1}$–$\hat{5}$)	*do-la* ($\hat{1}$–$\hat{6}$)
simple or compound: ♪ |	___	___ |	___	___ ||

(h) Melody 8 begins with an eighth-note anacrusis.

Triad quality:	major	minor	diminished	augmented
Last two pitches form:	m3	M3	P4	P5
	me-do ($\flat\hat{3}$–$\hat{1}$)	*mi-do* ($\hat{3}$–$\hat{1}$)	*fa-do* ($\hat{4}$–$\hat{1}$)	*sol-do* ($\hat{5}$–$\hat{1}$)
simple or compound: ♪ |	___	___ |	___	___ ||

2. An introduction precedes two triads played first melodically, then harmonically. Identify each chord's quality: **M**ajor, **m**inor, **d**iminished, or **A**ugmented.

(a) Chord 1: ___ Chord 2: ___ (b) Chord 1: ___ Chord 2: ___

(c) Chord 1: ___ Chord 2: ___ (d) Chord 1: ___ Chord 2: ___

(e) Chord 1: ___ Chord 2: ___ (f) Chord 1: ___ Chord 2: ___

(g) Chord 1: ___ Chord 2: ___ (h) Chord 1: ___ Chord 2: ___

(i) Chord 1: ___ Chord 2: ___ (j) Chord 1: ___ Chord 2: ___

NAME ______________________

3. Listen to four chords played harmonically. Identify the quality of each chord.

(a) Chord 1: ___ Chord 2: ___ Chord 3: ___ Chord 4: ___

(b) Chord 1: ___ Chord 2: ___ Chord 3: ___ Chord 4: ___

(c) Chord 1: ___ Chord 2: ___ Chord 3: ___ Chord 4: ___

(d) Chord 1: ___ Chord 2: ___ Chord 3: ___ Chord 4: ___

NAME ______________________

Contextual Listening 7.1

Listen to four chords played harmonically. Identify the quality of each chord as **M**ajor, **m**inor, **d**iminished, or **A**ugmented.

1. Chord 1: ___ Chord 2: ___ Chord 3: ___ Chord 4: ___
2. Chord 1: ___ Chord 2: ___ Chord 3: ___ Chord 4: ___
3. Chord 1: ___ Chord 2: ___ Chord 3: ___ Chord 4: ___

Now, listen to the beginning of a piece played on harpsichord.

4. The key is: major minor
5. Sing *do* ($\hat{1}$). Then, sing up or down from *do* ($\hat{1}$) until you match pitch 1.
   Melodic pitch 1 is: *do* ($\hat{1}$) *mi* ($\hat{3}$) *me* ($\flat\hat{3}$) *sol* ($\hat{5}$)
6. (a) The meter is: duple triple quadruple
   (b) Assume a 𝅗𝅥 beat unit. The meter signature is: $\frac{2}{2}$ $\frac{3}{2}$ $\frac{4}{2}$
7. Use the workspace to capture the melody and the triad qualities of the accompaniment.
   (a) In the single-line staff, write the meter signature. Begin with a half note and notate the melody's rhythm. Bar lines are included.
   (b) In the blanks provided beneath the single-line staff, write the syllables and numbers of the melody.
   (c) Beneath beat 1 of any measure with a "quality" blank, indicate the chord quality by writing "M" for major or "m" for minor.
   (d) In the treble staff, draw appropriate key and meter signatures. Beginning with F4, notate the melodic pitches. Refer to your syllables and numbers.
   (e) In the treble staff, incorporate the rhythm from the single-line staff.
   (f) Sing the melody, then play it on a keyboard.

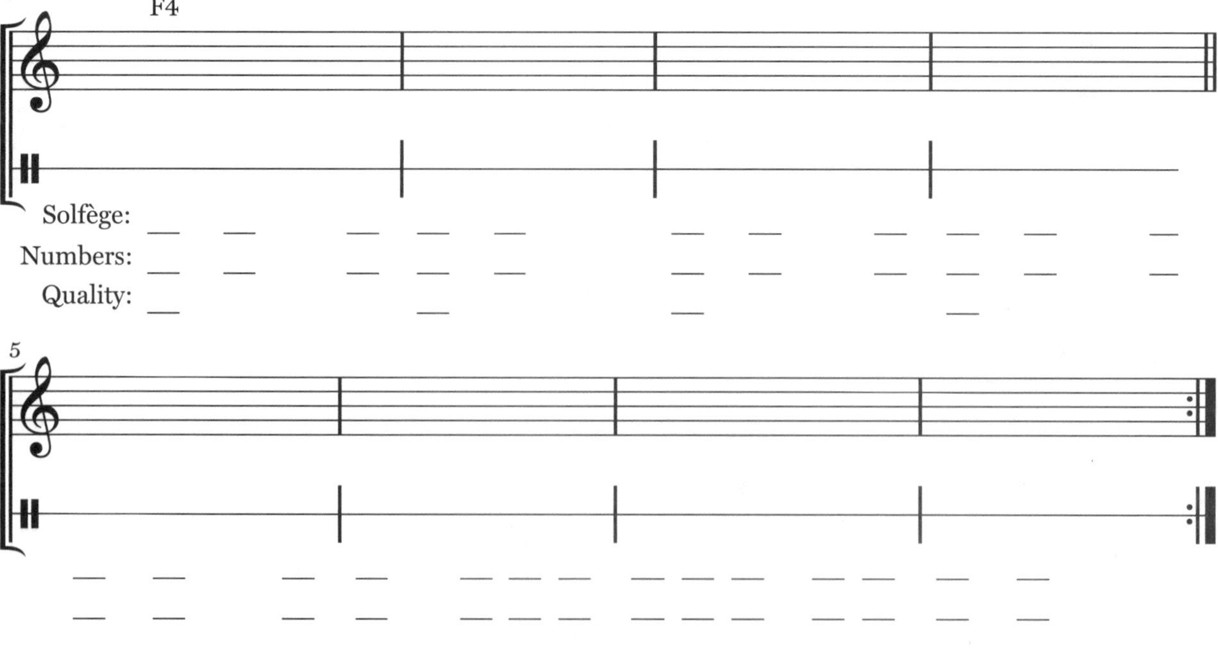

NAME ______________________

Contextual Listening 7.2

Listen to four chords played harmonically. Identify the quality of each chord as **M**ajor, **m**inor, **d**iminished, or **A**ugmented.

1. Chord 1: ___ Chord 2: ___ Chord 3: ___ Chord 4: ___
2. Chord 1: ___ Chord 2: ___ Chord 3: ___ Chord 4: ___
3. Chord 1: ___ Chord 2: ___ Chord 3: ___ Chord 4: ___

Now, listen to the harmonization of an early American melody and complete the following exercises.

4. The key is: major minor
5. Sing *do* ($\hat{1}$). Then, sing up or down from *do* ($\hat{1}$) until you match pitch 1.

   Melodic pitch 1 is: *do* ($\hat{1}$) *mi* ($\hat{3}$) *me* ($\flat\hat{3}$) *sol* ($\hat{5}$)
6. Capture the melody and the triad qualities of the accompaniment.
   (a) Key and meter signatures as well as bar lines are given. In the single-line staff, begin with a half note and notate the melody's rhythm.
   (b) Beneath the single-line staff, write the syllables and numbers of the melody.
   (c) In each "quality" blank, write "M" for major triads and "m" for minor triads.
   (d) In the treble staff, begin with half-note G4 and notate the melodic rhythm and pitches. For help with pitches, refer to your syllables and numbers.
   (e) Sing the melody, then play it on a keyboard.

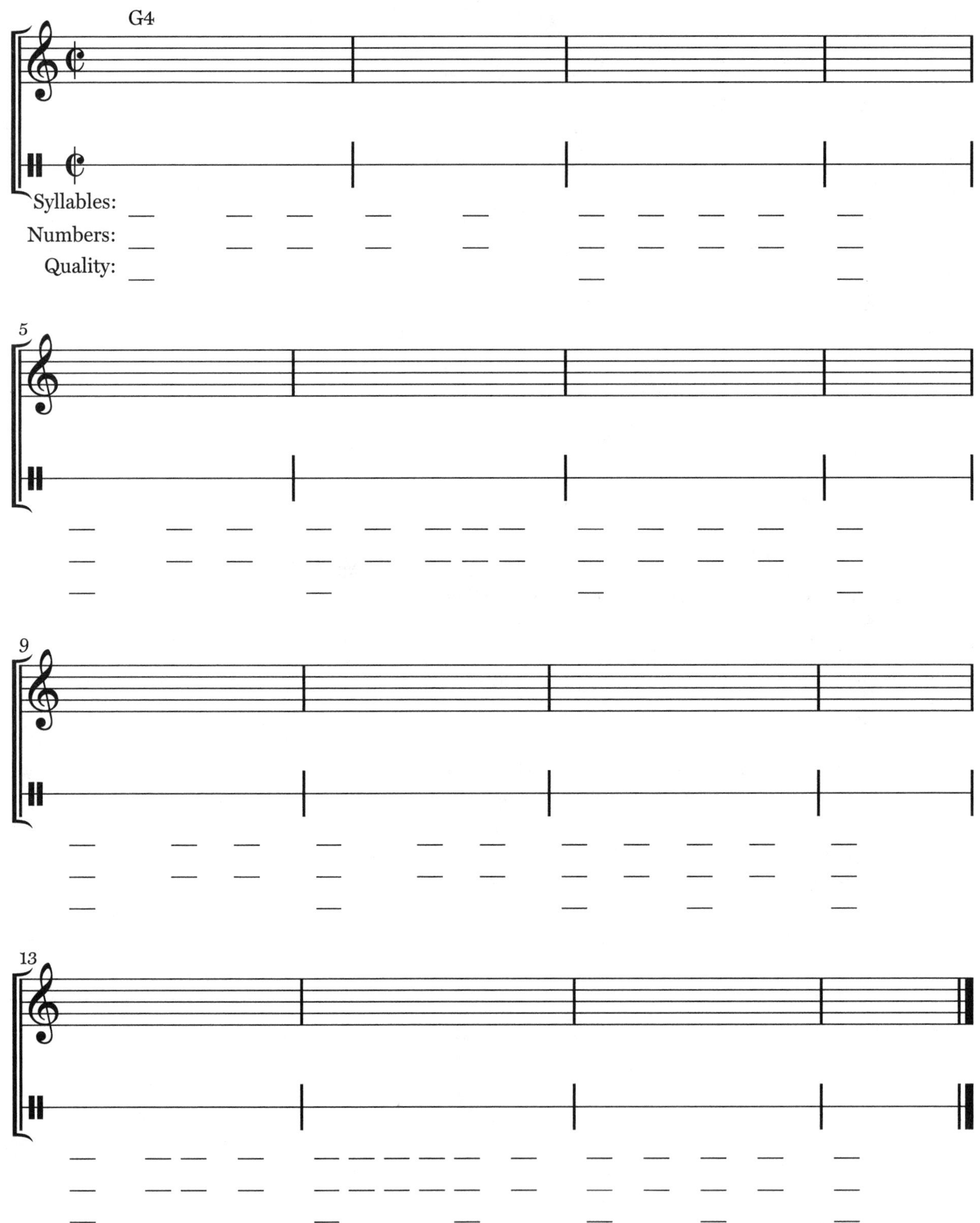
G4
Syllables:
Numbers:
Quality:
5
9
13

Contextual Listening 7.3

A two-beat introduction precedes a melodic triad and two beats of cut-time rhythm. Identify the triad quality as **M**ajor, **m**inor, **d**iminished, or **A**ugmented, and write the rhythm-pattern numbers.

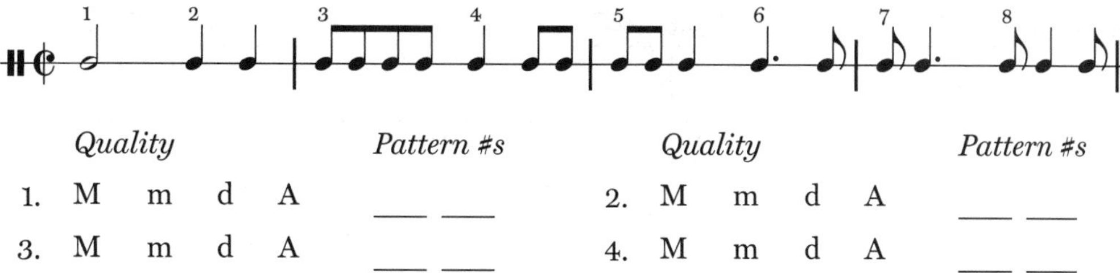

	Quality	*Pattern #s*		*Quality*	*Pattern #s*
1.	M m d A	___ ___	2.	M m d A	___ ___
3.	M m d A	___ ___	4.	M m d A	___ ___

Now, listen to part of a piano work and complete the following exercises.

5. The key is: major minor

6. Sing *do* ($\hat{1}$). Then, sing up or down from *do* ($\hat{1}$) until you match pitch 1.
   Melodic pitch 1 is: *do* ($\hat{1}$) *mi* ($\hat{3}$) *me* ($\flat\hat{3}$) *sol* ($\hat{5}$)

7. Melodic pitches 1–5 belong to a triad of which quality? M m d A

8. Capture the melodic rhythm and pitches.
   (a) Key and meter signatures as well as bar lines are given. In the single-line staff above the piano score, begin with a quarter note and notate the melody's rhythm. The last measure is incomplete; write a quarter note.
   (b) Write the syllables and numbers of the melody beneath the upper single-line staff.
   (c) In the treble staff, begin with quarter-note C4 and notate the melodic rhythm and pitches. For help with pitches, refer to your syllables and numbers. Align your rhythm with that in the single-line staff.
   (d) Sing the melody, then play it on a keyboard.

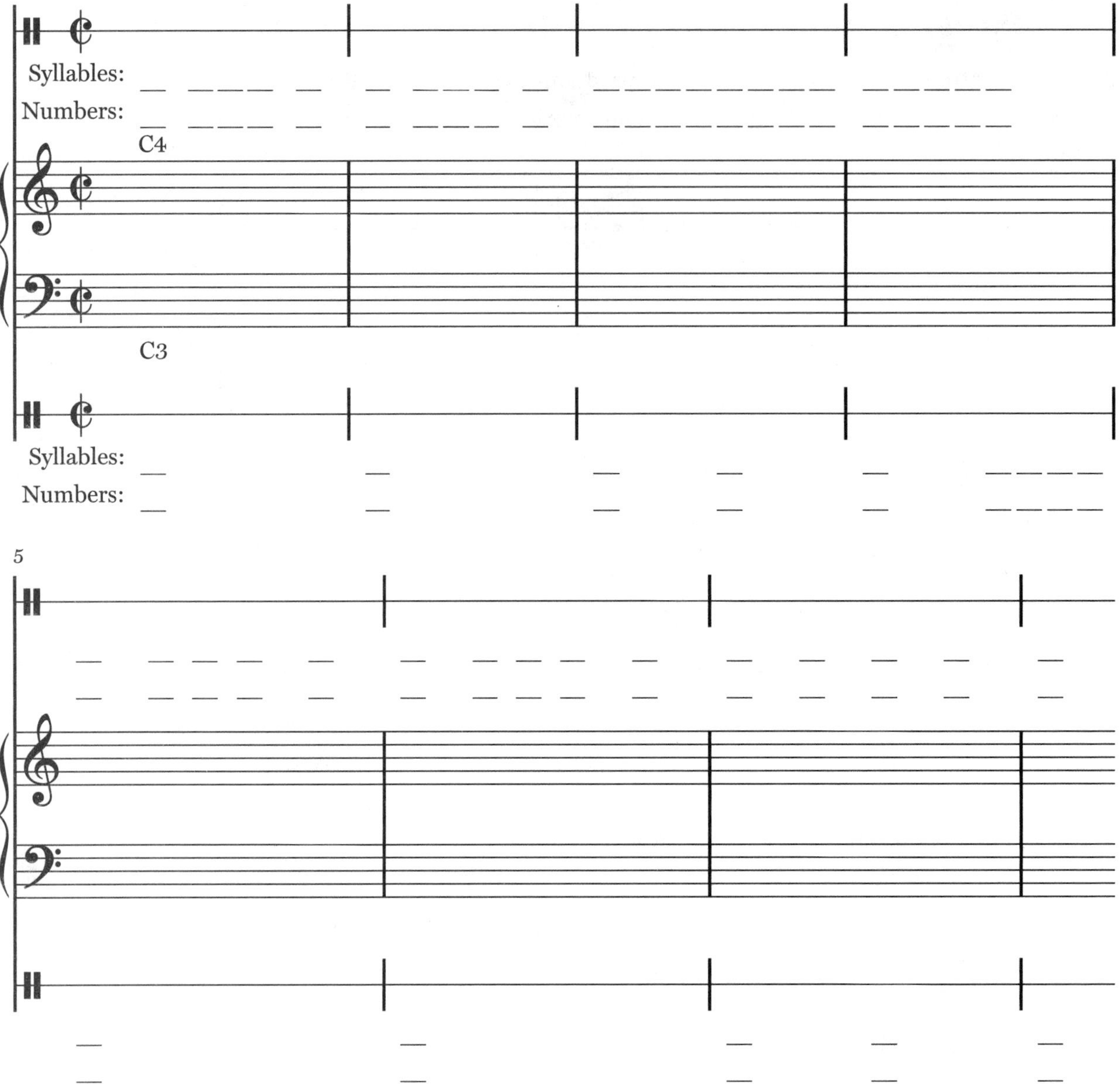

9. At the end, the last five melodic pitches complete which pattern?

   major pentatonic   major pentachord   minor pentatonic   minor pentachord

10. At the end, the melodic pitches are harmonized at which interval?   third   sixth

    Hint: Are the lower pitches close or far away?

11. Use the workspace in exercise 8 to capture the bass line's pitches and rhythm.
    - (a) In the single-line staff below the piano score, begin with a quarter note and notate the bass line's rhythm. The last measure is incomplete; write a quarter note.
    - (b) In the blanks provided beneath the lower single-line staff, write the syllables and numbers of the bass line.
    - (c) In the bass staff, begin with quarter-note C3 and notate the bass line's rhythm and pitches. For help with pitches, refer to your syllables and numbers. Align your rhythm with that in the single-line staff.

NAME ______________________________

Contextual Listening 7.4

A two-beat introduction precedes a melodic triad and two beats of compound-meter rhythm. Identify the triad quality as **M**ajor, **m**inor, **d**iminished, or **A**ugmented, and write the rhythm-pattern numbers.

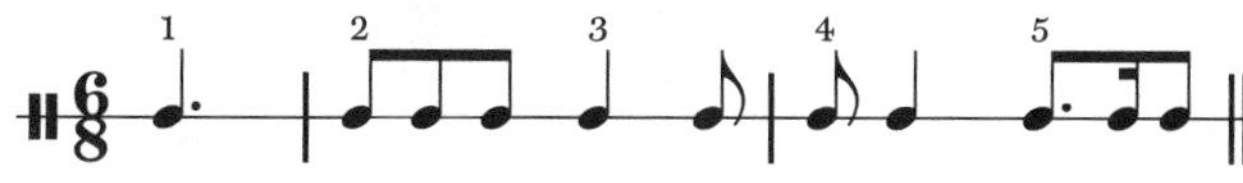

	Quality	*Pattern #s*		*Quality*	*Pattern #s*
1.	M m d A	___ ___	2.	M m d A	___ ___
3.	M m d A	___ ___	4.	M m d A	___ ___

Now, listen to a piano melody and complete the following exercises.

5. Pitches 1–6 belong to a triad of which quality? M m d A

6. The melodic pitches are doubled at which interval?

   m3 M3 M6 P8

7. In the workspace, capture the melodic rhythm and pitches.
   (a) In the single-line staff, write the meter signature. Begin with an eighth-note anacrusis and notate the melody's rhythm.
   (b) Write the syllables and numbers of the melody beneath the single-line staff.
   (c) In the treble staff, write the key and meter signatures. Beginning with eighth-note C4, notate the melodic rhythm and pitches. For help with pitches, refer to your syllables and numbers. Align your rhythm with that in the single-line staff.
   (d) Sing the melody, then play it on a keyboard.

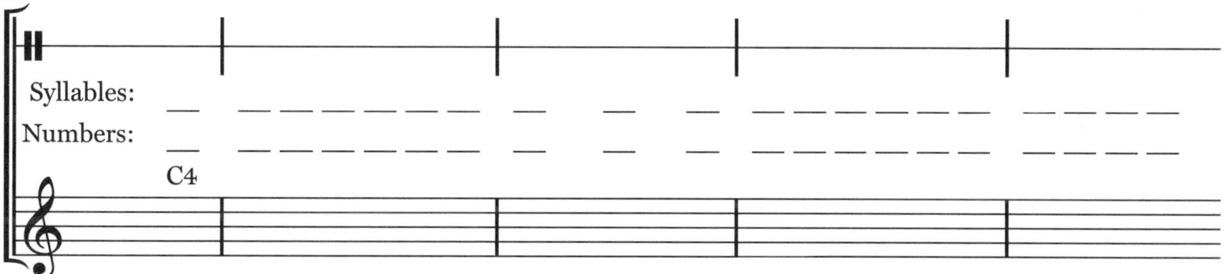

8. All melodic pitches belong to which scale?

   major ascending melodic minor natural minor harmonic minor

9. Between pitches 8–9, the interval is a: PU P4 P5 P8

Seventh Chords

NAME ______________________

In this chapter you'll learn to:

- Identify melodic and harmonic seventh chords in major- and minor-key music
- Label seventh-chord quality and use lead-sheet symbols
- Associate seventh-chord types with specific major- and minor-key scale degrees

Try it

1. To identify root-position seventh chords, listen first for triad quality, then the quality of the seventh.

Triad quality	*7th quality*	*Seventh-chord type*	*Lead-sheet symbol*
M	M	MM7	maj7
M	m	Mm7	7
m	m	mm7	min7
d	m	dm7	ø7
d	d	dd7	o7

Each seventh chord is played melodically, then harmonically. Identify its quality.

(a) MM7 Mm7 mm7 dm7 dd7 (b) MM7 Mm7 mm7 dm7 dd7

(c) MM7 Mm7 mm7 dm7 dd7 (d) MM7 Mm7 mm7 dm7 dd7

(e) MM7 Mm7 mm7 dm7 dd7 (f) MM7 Mm7 mm7 dm7 dd7

The next exercises feature equivalent symbols using lead-sheet notation.

(g) maj7 7 min7 ø7 o7 (h) maj7 7 min7 ø7 o7

(i) maj7 7 min7 ø7 o7 (j) maj7 7 min7 ø7 o7

2. Memorize the seventh chord associated with each major- and minor-key scale degree. Then, listen for the key type and scale degree to recall the chord quality.

Root scale degree	*Major-key seventh chord*	*Minor-key seventh chord*
$\hat{7}$	dm7	dd7
$\flat\hat{7}$	—	Mm7
$\hat{6}$	mm7	MM7
$\hat{5}$	Mm7	Mm7
$\hat{4}$	MM7	mm7
$\hat{3}$	mm7	MM7
$\hat{2}$	mm7	dm7
$\hat{1}$	MM7	mm7

An introduction precedes two seventh chords played first melodically, then harmonically. Identify the quality of each chord.

	Chord 1					*Chord 2*				
(a)	MM7	Mm7	mm7	dm7	dd7	MM7	Mm7	mm7	dm7	dd7
(b)	MM7	Mm7	mm7	dm7	dd7	MM7	Mm7	mm7	dm7	dd7
(c)	MM7	Mm7	mm7	dm7	dd7	MM7	Mm7	mm7	dm7	dd7

The next exercises feature equivalent symbols using lead-sheet notation.

	Chord 1					*Chord 2*				
(d)	maj7	7	min7	ø7	o7	maj7	7	min7	ø7	o7
(e)	maj7	7	min7	ø7	o7	maj7	7	min7	ø7	o7

3. Listen to a series of root-position chords and identify the quality of each.

- For triads, write M, m, d, or A.
- For seventh chords, write MM7, Mm7, mm7, dm7, or dd7.

(a) Chord: 1 2 3 4
Quality: _______ _______ _______ _______

(b) Chord: 1 2 3 4
Quality: _______ _______ _______ _______

(c) Chord: 1 2 3
Quality: _______ _______ _______

(d) Chord: 1 2 3
Quality: _______ _______ _______

(e) Chord: 1 2 3 4 5 6 7 8
Quality: _______ _______ _______ _______ _______ _______ _______ _______

4. Listen again to exercise 3 (a)–(e). After each chord root, write the chord quality using lead-sheet symbols: maj, maj7, min, min7, dim, ø7, or °7.

(a) Chord: 1 2 3 4
Symbol: C ____ A ____ D ____ G ____

(b) Chord: 1 2 3 4
Symbol: C ____ A♭ ____ F ____ G ____

(c) Chord: 1 2 3
Symbol: C♯ ____ D ____ A ____

(d) Chord: 1 2 3
Symbol: F♯ ____ B ____ E ____

(e) Chord: 1 2 3 4 5 6 7 8
Symbol: A ____ D ____ G ____ C ____ F ____ B ____ E ____ A ____

Contextual Listening 8.1

Identify the quality of each chord in a series of root-position seventh chords.

- First, label the triad and seventh quality: MM7, Mm7, mm7, dm7, or dd7.
- Then, use lead-sheet symbols. The root of each chord is given.

1\.

Chord:	1	2	3	4	5	6	7	8
Quality:	______	______	______	______	______	______	______	______
Lead:	1	2	3	4	5	6	7	8
Sheet:	D ______	F ______	G ______	D ______	B♭ ______	E ______	A ______	D ______

2\.

Chord:	1	2	3	4	5	6	7	8
Quality:	______	______	______	______	______	______	______	______
Lead:	1	2	3	4	5	6	7	8
Sheet:	D ______	F♯ ______	G ______	D ______	B ______	E ______	A ______	D ______

Now, listen to the beginning of a piano piece and complete the remaining exercises.

3. The key is: major minor
4. The final bass pitch is *do* ($\hat{1}$). Sing up or down from *do* until you match bass pitch 1.

   Bass pitch 1 is: *do* ($\hat{1}$) *mi* ($\hat{3}$) *fa* ($\hat{4}$) *sol* ($\hat{5}$)
5. Sing up or down from *do* ($\hat{1}$) until you match melodic pitch 1.

   Melodic pitch 1 is: *do* ($\hat{1}$) *mi* ($\hat{3}$) *fa* ($\hat{4}$) *sol* ($\hat{5}$)
6. (a) The meter is: duple triple quadruple

   (b) Assume a ♩ beat unit. The meter signature is: $\frac{2}{4}$ $\frac{3}{4}$ $\frac{4}{4}$
7. In the workspace, capture the chord quality, bass line, and melody. Bar lines are given.

   (a) At the beginning of both single-line staves, write the meter signature.

   - In the lower single-line staff, notate the rhythm of the bass pitch (lowest note).
   - Beneath that staff, write the syllable and number of each bass pitch.
   - Write the seventh-chord quality: MM7, Mm7, mm7, dm7, or dd7.
   - In the upper single-line staff, notate the melodic rhythm.
   - Beneath that staff, write the syllable and number of each melodic pitch.

   (b) In the grand staff, draw appropriate key and meter signatures.

   - Beginning with G2, notate the bass pitches.
   - Beginning with F♯5, notate the melodic pitches.
   - Refer to your syllables and numbers and incorporate the rhythm from the single-line staves.
   - Sing the melody while playing the bass line at a keyboard.

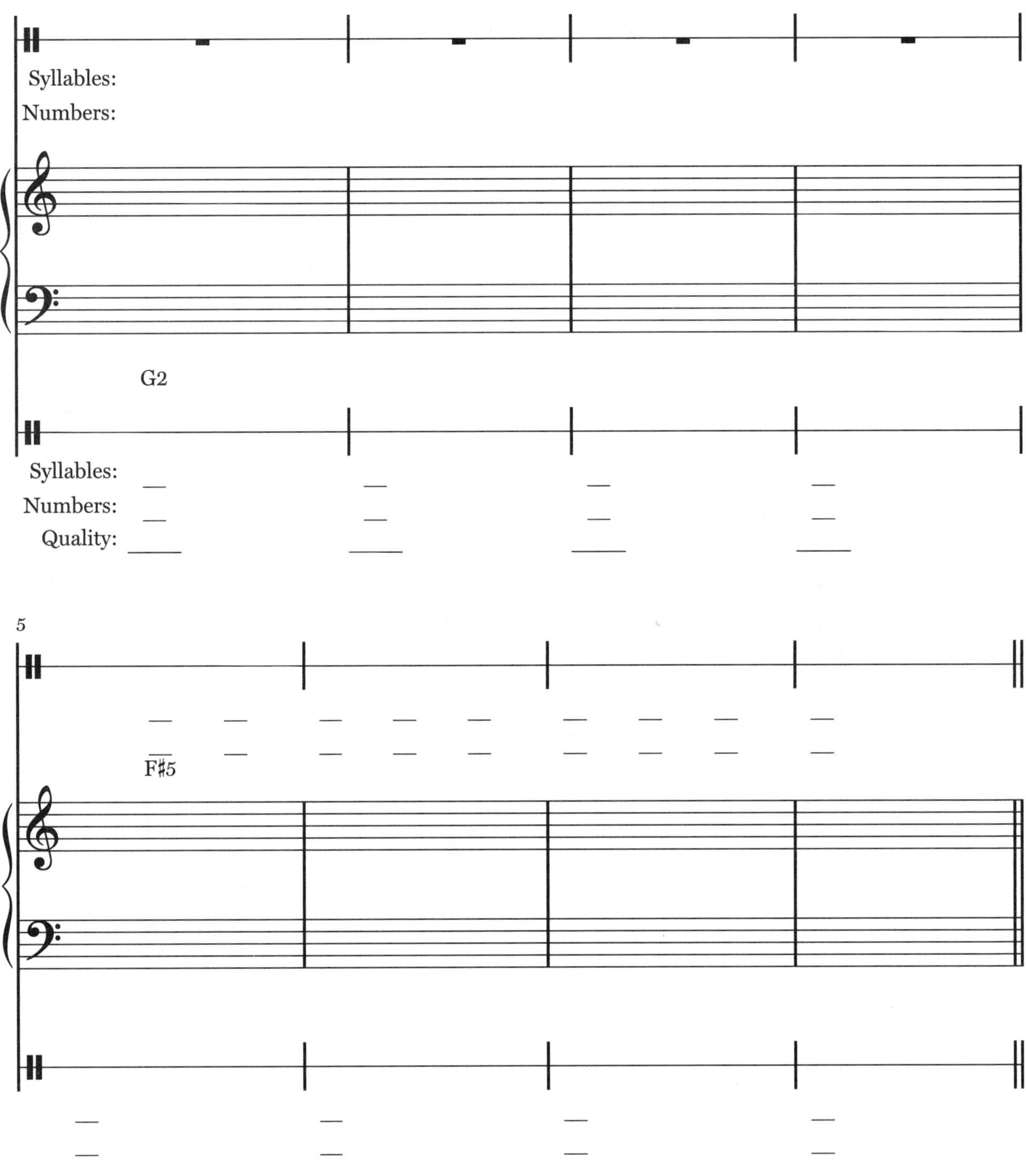
Syllables:
Numbers:
G2
Syllables:
Numbers:
Quality:
5
F♯5

Contextual Listening 8.2

A melody begins with a seventh chord; choose the symbol that matches its chord quality.

1. MM7 Mm7 mm7 dm7 dd7
2. MM7 Mm7 mm7 dm7 dd7
3. MM7 Mm7 mm7 dm7 dd7
4. MM7 Mm7 mm7 dm7 dd7

Now, listen to part of a piano work and complete the remaining exercises.

5. Melodic pitch 1 is *do* ($\hat{1}$). Sing up or down until you match bass pitch 1.
   Bass pitch 1 is: *do* ($\hat{1}$) *mi* ($\hat{3}$) *fa* ($\hat{4}$) *sol* ($\hat{5}$)
6. Compared with bass pitches 1–3, the melody's motion is:
   contrary oblique similar parallel
7. Compared with bass pitches 4–7, the melody's motion is:
   contrary oblique similar parallel
8. Melodic pitches 4–7 outline which seventh chord?
   MM7 Mm7 mm7 dm7 dd7
9. In the workspace, capture the bass and melodic lines. Key and meter signatures, starting pitches, and bar lines are given.
   (a) In the single-line staves, notate the rhythm of the bass and melodic lines. Beneath each staff, write the syllables and numbers of the pitches.
   (b) Beginning with E3 and C5 respectively, notate the pitches and rhythm of the bass and melody. Refer to your syllables and numbers and incorporate the rhythm from the single-line staves.
   (c) Sing the melody while playing the bass line on a keyboard.

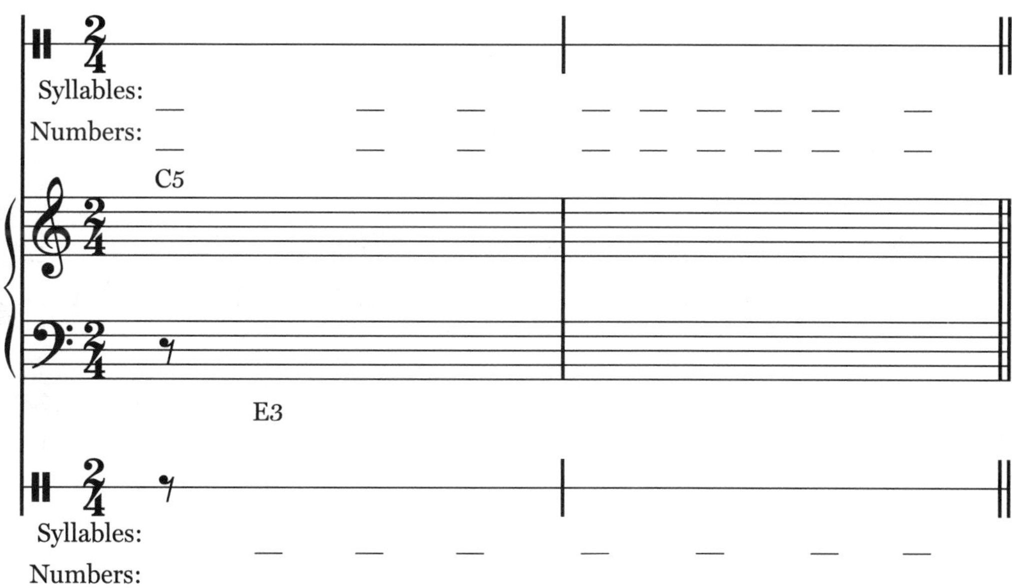

NAME ______________________

Contextual Listening 8.3

A melody begins with a seventh chord. For each exercise, choose the symbol that matches its chord quality.

1. MM7 Mm7 mm7 dm7 dd7
2. MM7 Mm7 mm7 dm7 dd7
3. MM7 Mm7 mm7 dm7 dd7
4. MM7 Mm7 mm7 dm7 dd7

Now, listen to part of a piano work and complete the remaining exercises.

5. The final *bass* pitch is *do* ($\hat{1}$). Sing up or down from *do* until you match melodic pitch 1.

   Melodic pitch 1 is: *do* ($\hat{1}$) *mi* ($\hat{3}$) *fa* ($\hat{4}$) *sol* ($\hat{5}$)

6. Melodic pitches 1–4 outline which seventh chord?

   MM7 Mm7 mm7 dm7 dd7

7. The opening texture is:

   monophonic homophonic heterophonic polyphonic

8. The final bass pitches form which *melodic* interval?

   M3 P4 P5 M6

9. In the workspace, capture the melody's pitches and rhythms. Key and meter signatures as well as bar lines are given.

   (a) In the single-line staff, notate the rhythm of the melody. Beneath the staff, write the syllables and numbers of its pitches.

   (b) Beginning with D♭5, notate the pitches and rhythm of the melody. Refer to your syllables and numbers and incorporate the rhythm from the single-line staff.

   (c) Sing the melody, then play it on a keyboard.

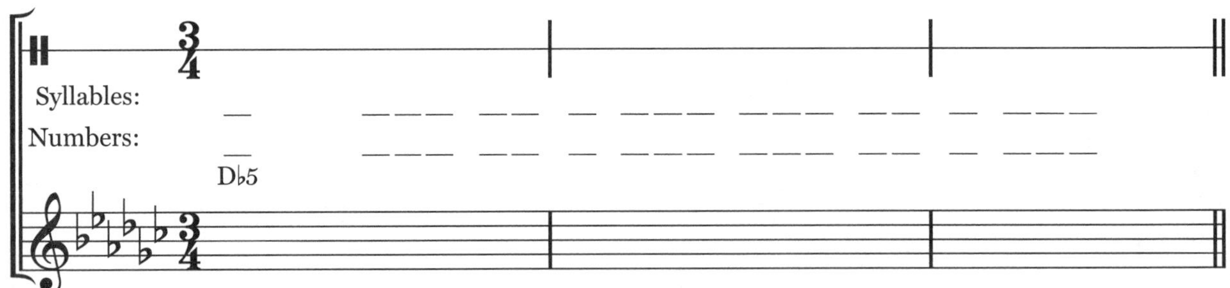

NAME ____________________

Contextual Listening 8.4

1. Listen to a series of root-position seventh chords. After each given root, write the chord quality using lead-sheet symbols: maj7, 7, min7, ø7, or °7.

(a) Chord: 1   2   3   4
Quality: A ____ F ____ C ____ G ____

(b) Chord: 1   2   3   4
Quality: D ____ G ____ C ____ A ____

Now listen to part of a jazz standard and complete the remaining exercises.

2. Use the workspace to capture the bass line, melody, and seventh chords. Key and meter signatures as well as the initial pitches, rhythms, syllables, and numbers are given.
   (a) In the single-line staves, finish notating the rhythm of the bass and melody.
   (b) Below each single-line staff, finish writing the syllables and numbers of the pitches.
   (c) In the grand staff, finish notating the bass line and melody. Refer to your syllables and numbers and incorporate the rhythm from the single-line staves.
   (d) Write chord symbols above the treble staff.
   - In the chord blanks, write the letter name of the chord's root (C, D, E♭, G, etc.). Hint: All chords are root-position seventh chords, so the root is the bass pitch.
   - Listen for the quality of each seventh chord. Then, write it after the letter name using lead-sheet symbols (Cmaj7, Dmin7, etc.).
   (e) Sing the melody while playing the bass line on the keyboard.

3. Melodic pitches 1–2 create which interval?

   m3   M3   P4   P5

4. The last two melodic pitches create which interval?

   P5   m6   M6   m7

5. The last two bass pitches create which interval?

   P8   M6   m6   P4

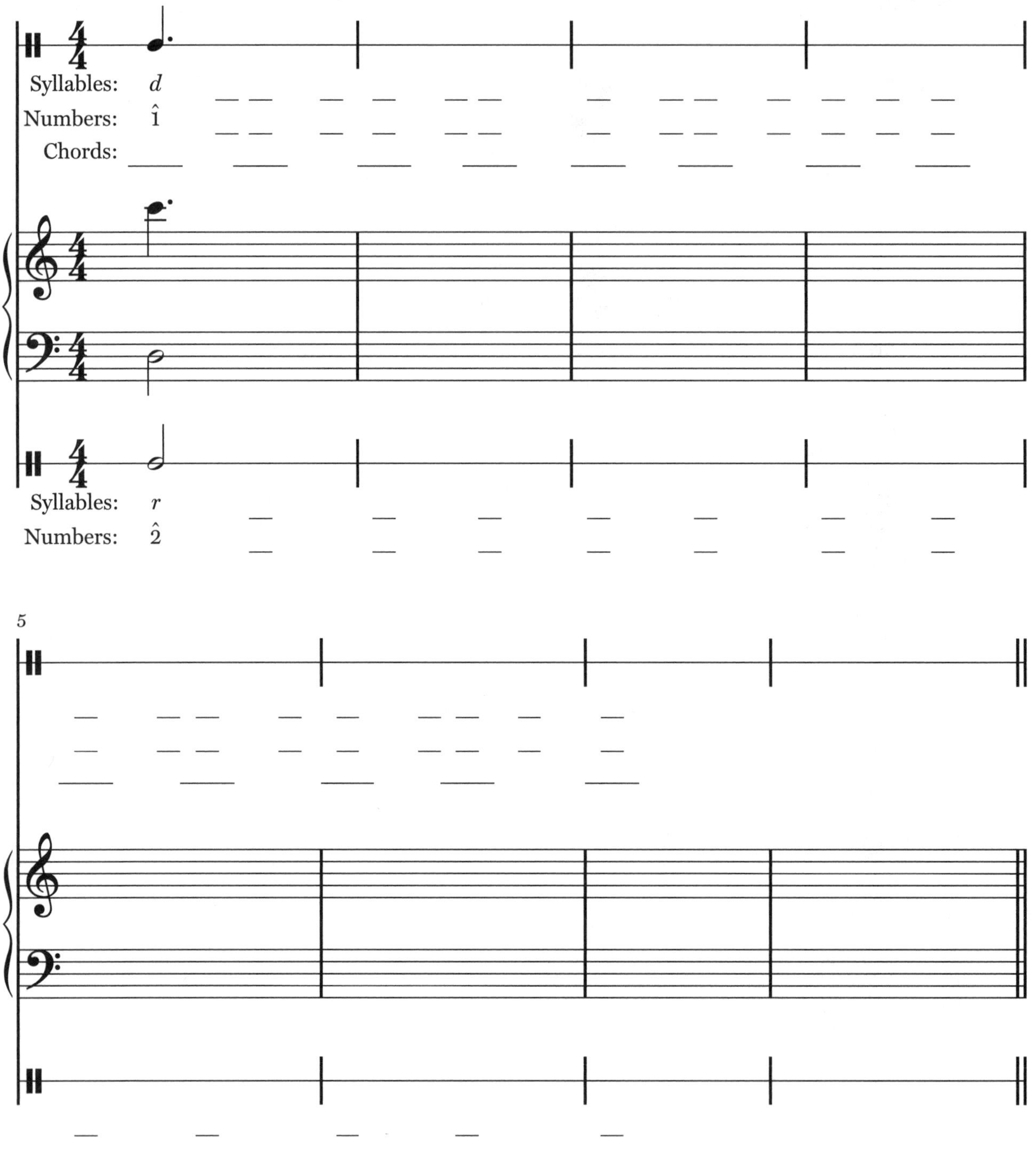
Syllables: d
Numbers: 1̂
Chords:
Syllables: r
Numbers: 2̂
5

Note-to-Note Counterpoint

NAME ______________________________

In this chapter you'll learn to:

- Use contour to identify types of motion in note-to-note (1:1) counterpoint
- Identify harmonic intervals in a two-part contrapuntal texture
- Take dictation of two-part works

Types of Motion

In two-part music, the contours of the two parts interact to create four types of motion.

Type	*How parts move*	*Contour diagrams*
Contrary	Different directions	
Oblique	One part moves, the other stays	
Parallel	Same direction, *same* interval	
Similar	Same direction, *different* interval	

Try it

Listen to six measures of two-part music. Above and below the staff, write the solfège syllables and numbers for each part, then notate the remaining pitches, one whole note per measure. Beneath each measure, write the harmonic interval number. Between the measures, write the type of motion: *contrary*, *oblique*, *parallel*, or *similar*. If neither part moves, write *none*.

1.

Syllables:	*d*	__	__	__	__	__
Numbers:	$\hat{1}$	__	__	__	__	__

Syllables:	*d*	__	__	__	__	__
Numbers:	$\hat{1}$	__	__	__	__	__
Intervals:	U	__	__	__	__	__

Motion: contrary ________ ________ ________ ________

2.

Syllables: *d* __ __ __ __ __

Numbers: $\hat{1}$ __ __ __ __ __

Syllables: *d* __ __ __ __ __

Numbers: $\hat{1}$ __ __ __ __ __

Intervals: U __ __ __ __ __

Motion: contrary ______ ______ ______ ______

3.

Syllables: *d* __ __ __ __ __

Numbers: $\hat{1}$ __ __ __ __ __

Syllables: *d* __ __ __ __ __

Numbers: $\hat{1}$ __ __ __ __ __

Intervals: U __ __ __ __ __

Motion: contrary ______ ______ ______ ______

4.

Syllables: *d* __ __ __ __ __

Numbers: $\hat{1}$ __ __ __ __ __

Syllables: *d* __ __ __ __ __

Numbers: $\hat{1}$ __ __ __ __ __

Intervals: U __ __ __ __ __

Motion: contrary ______ ______ ______ ______

5.

Syllables: *d* __ __ __ __ __

Numbers: $\hat{1}$ __ __ __ __ __

Syllables: *d* __ __ __ __ __

Numbers: $\hat{1}$ __ __ __ __ __

Intervals: 8 __ __ __ __ __

Motion: contrary ______ ______ ______ ______

6.

Syllables: *d* __ __ __ __ __

Numbers: $\hat{1}$ __ __ __ __ __

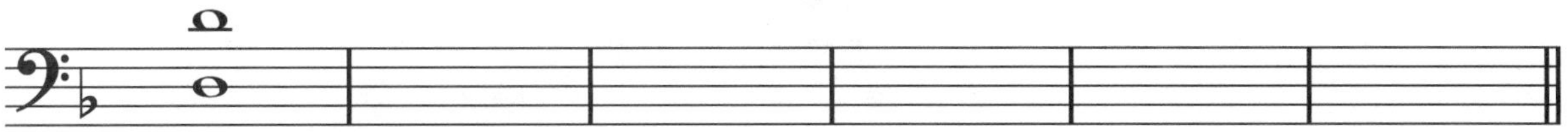

Syllables: *d* __ __ __ __ __

Numbers: $\hat{1}$ __ __ __ __ __

Intervals: 8 __ __ __ __ __

Motion: contrary ________ ________ ________ ________

Exercises 7 and 8 contain eight measures of two-part music.

7.

Syllables: *d* __ __ __ __ __ __ __

Numbers: $\hat{1}$ __ __ __ __ __ __ __

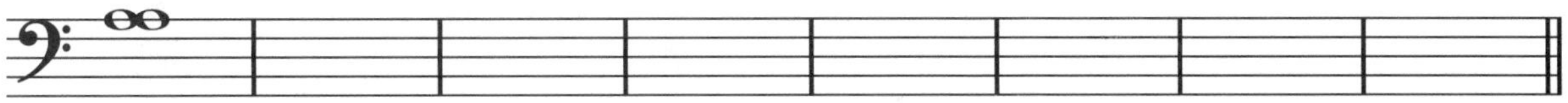

Syllables: *d* __ __ __ __ __ __ __

Numbers: $\hat{1}$ __ __ __ __ __ __ __

Intervals: U __ __ __ __ __ __ __

Motion: contrary ________ ________ ________ ________ ________ ________

8.

Syllables: *d* __ __ __ __ __ __ __

Numbers: $\hat{1}$ __ __ __ __ __ __ __

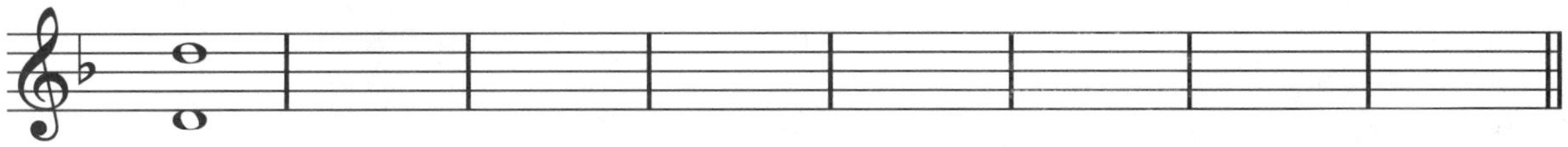

Syllables: *d* __ __ __ __ __ __ __

Numbers: $\hat{1}$ __ __ __ __ __ __ __

Intervals: 8 __ __ __ __ __ __ __

Motion: contrary ________ ________ ________ ________ ________ ________

NAME ______________________________

Contextual Listening 9.1

For exercises 1–4, do the following:

- Write the syllables and numbers of each part.
- On the grand staff, notate the pitches and rhythm of both parts.
- Between the staves, write the numbers for the harmonic intervals.

	1.	2.	3.	4.
Syllables:	*m* __ __ __	__ __ __ __	__ __ __ __	__ __ __ __
Numbers:	$\hat{3}$ __ __ __	__ __ __ __	__ __ __ __	__ __ __ __
Intervals:	3 __ __ __	__ __ __ __	__ __ __ __	__ __ __ __
Syllables:	*d* __ __ __	__ __ __ __	__ __ __ __	__ __ __ __
Numbers:	$\hat{1}$ __ __ __	__ __ __ __	__ __ __ __	__ __ __ __

Refer to exercises 1–4, comparing the contours of the melody and the bass.

5. In exercise 1, the motion between the parts is:

   all contrary   all parallel   contrary, then parallel   parallel, then contrary

6. In exercise 2, the motion between the parts is:

   all contrary   all parallel   contrary, then parallel   parallel, then contrary

7. In exercise 3, the motion between the parts is:

   all contrary   all parallel   contrary, then parallel   parallel, then contrary

8. In exercise 4, the motion between the parts is:

   all contrary   all parallel   contrary, then parallel   parallel, then contrary

Now, listen to the beginning of a piano piece and complete the remaining exercises.

9. In the workspace, begin with the given items and capture the two parts.
   - (a) In the single-line staves, notate the rhythm of each part. Beneath the staves, write the syllables and numbers.
   - (b) In the grand staff, notate the pitches and rhythm of both parts. For help, refer to the single-line staves. Check your work at a keyboard.
   - (c) In the blanks between the treble and bass staves, write the numbers of the harmonic intervals.

In exercises 10–15, compare the contours of the melody and the bass.

10. Between bass pitches 1–3 and the melody, the motion is:

    contrary   oblique   parallel   similar

11. Between bass pitch 3 and the melody, the motion is:

    contrary   oblique   parallel   similar

12. Between bass pitches 4–6 and the melody, the motion is:

    contrary   oblique   parallel   similar

13. Between bass pitches 7–9 and the melody, the motion is:

    contrary   oblique   parallel   similar

14. Between bass pitches 10–11 and the melody, the motion is:

    contrary   oblique   parallel   similar

15. Between the last two bass pitches and the melody, the motion is:

    contrary   oblique   parallel   similar

16. Melodic pitches 2–3 create which interval?

    M3   P4   P5   M6

17. The last two bass pitches create which melodic interval?

    m2   M2   P4   P5

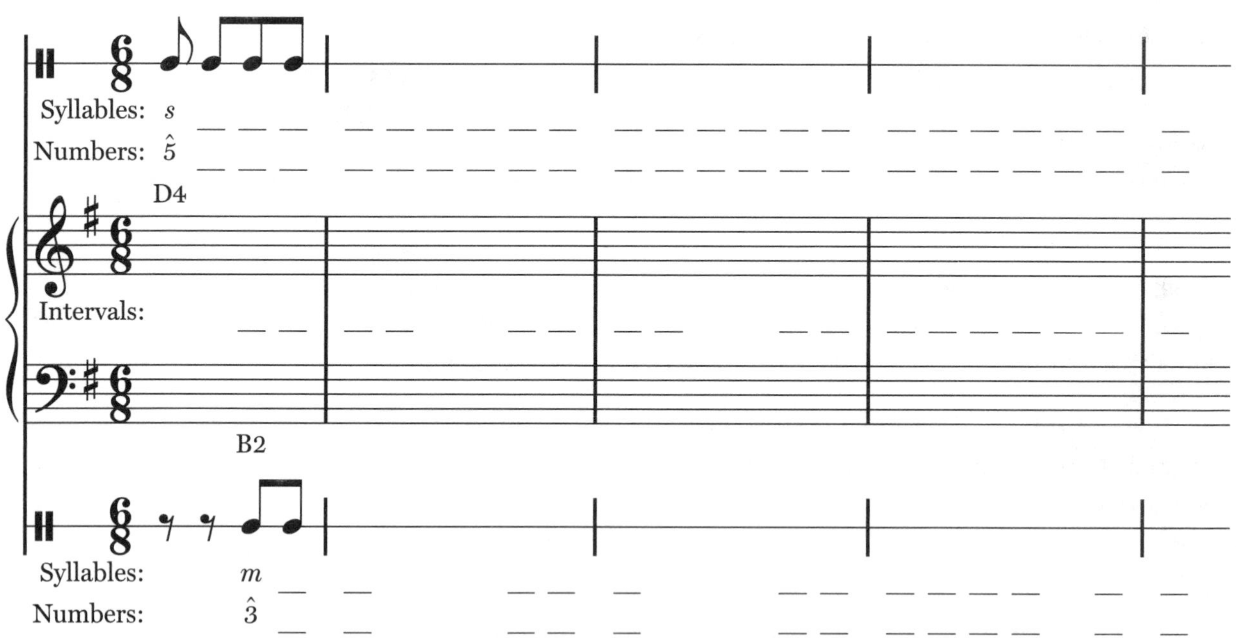

NAME ______________________

Contextual Listening 9.2

Exercises 1–3 are adaptations of a 1:1 counterpoint. For each, begin with the given items and write syllables and numbers for each part. Then, notate the remaining pitches, one whole note per measure. Beneath each measure, write the harmonic interval number. Between the measures, write the type of motion: *contrary*, *oblique*, *parallel*, or *similar*. Refer to your answers to identify the exercise's tonality/modality.

1. The tonality/modality is:

   minor Dorian Phrygian Lydian Mixolydian

Syllables: *d* __ __ __ __ __ __ __ __
Numbers: $\hat{1}$ __ __ __ __ __ __ __ __

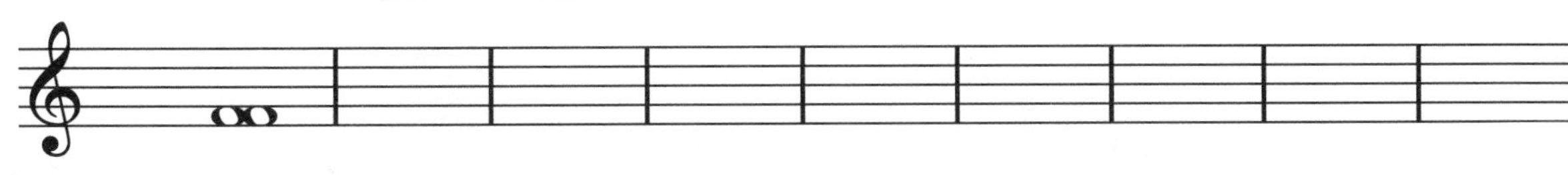

Syllables: *d* __ __ __ __ __ __ __ __
Numbers: $\hat{1}$ __ __ __ __ __ __ __ __
Intervals: U __ __ __ __ __ __ __ __
Motion: ______ ______ ______ ______ ______ ______ ______ ______

2. The tonality/modality is:

   minor Dorian Phrygian Lydian Mixolydian

Syllables: *d* __ __ __ __ __ __ __ __
Numbers: $\hat{1}$ __ __ __ __ __ __ __ __

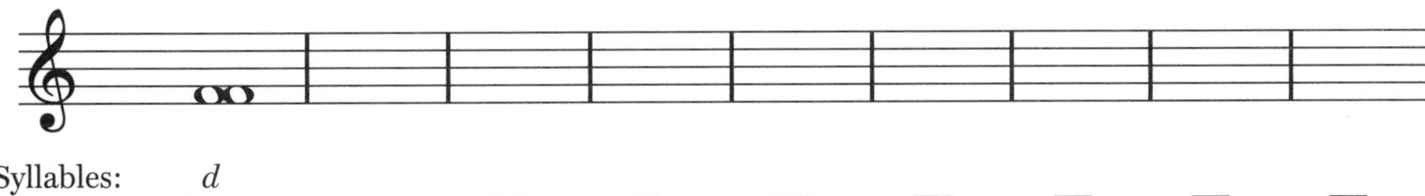

Syllables: *d* __ __ __ __ __ __ __ __
Numbers: $\hat{1}$ __ __ __ __ __ __ __ __
Intervals: U __ __ __ __ __ __ __ __
Motion: ______ ______ ______ ______ ______ ______ ______ ______

3. The tonality/modality is:

   major Dorian Phrygian Lydian Mixolydian

Syllables: *d* __ __ __ __ __ __ __ __
Numbers: $\hat{1}$ __ __ __ __ __ __ __ __

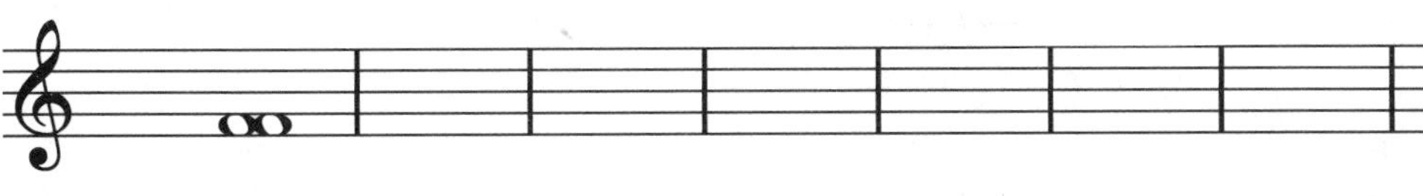

Syllables: *d* __ __ __ __ __ __ __ __
Numbers: $\hat{1}$ __ __ __ __ __ __ __ __
Intervals: U __ __ __ __ __ __ __ __
Motion: ______ ______ ______ ______ ______ ______ ______ ______

Now, listen to the beginning of a string quartet. The excerpt consists of four segments, each eight pitches long.

4. In the workspace, begin with the given items and capture the two parts.
   (a) In the single-line staves, notate the rhythm of each part. Beneath these staves, write the syllables and numbers.
   (b) In the grand staff, notate the pitches and rhythm of both parts. For help, refer to the single-line staves. Check your work at a keyboard.
   (c) In the blanks between the treble and bass staves, write the harmonic interval numbers.

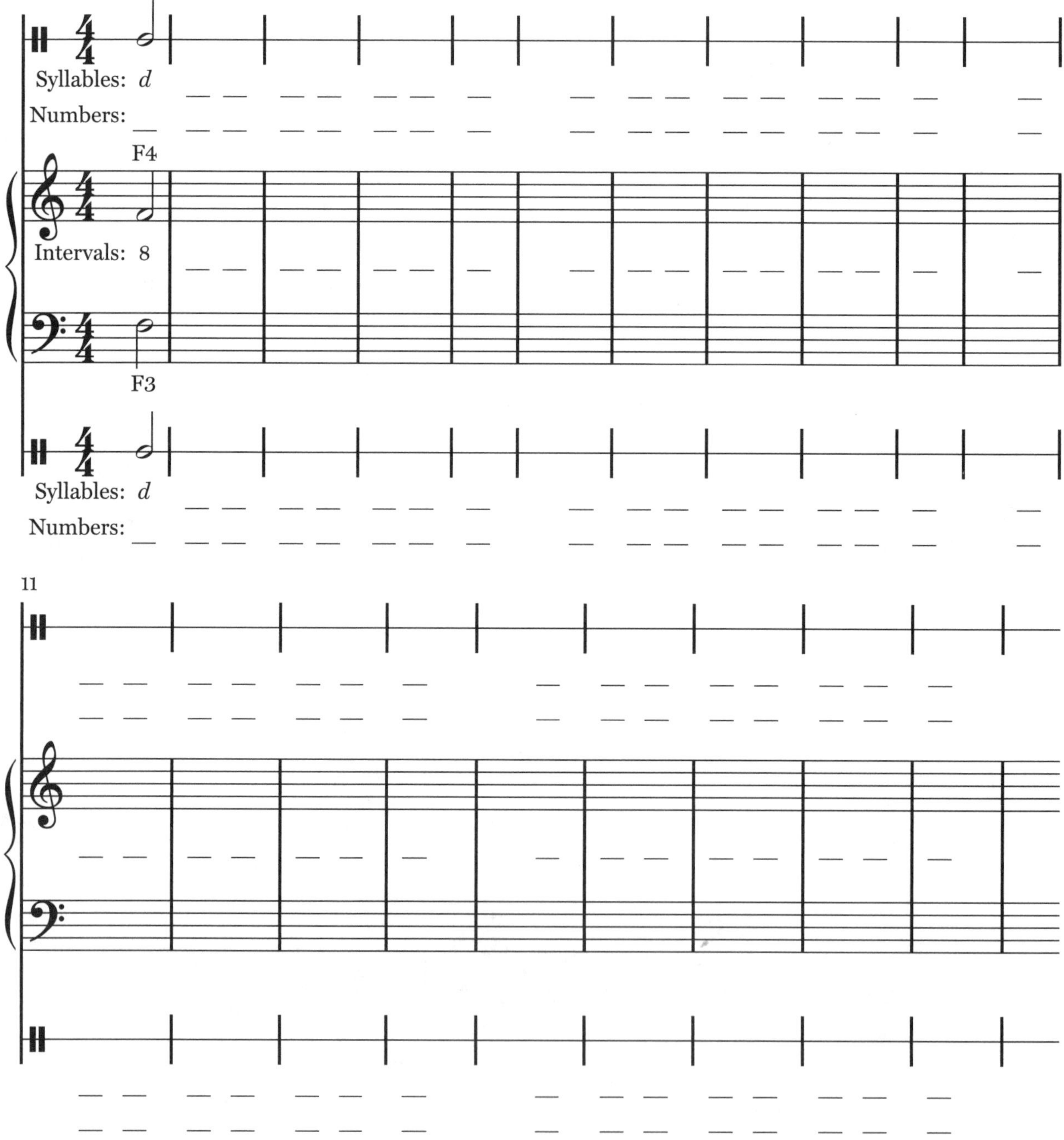

5. Bass pitches 1–3 outline which triad quality?

   major minor diminished augmented

6. Which describes the types of motion in segment 2?

   parallel throughout parallel, then contrary

   contrary, then parallel oblique, then contrary

7. In segment 3, the first two pitches of the melody and bass create which type of motion?

   contrary oblique parallel similar

8. Segment 4 includes which unusual succession of harmonic intervals?
   Hint: Focus on pitches 3–4.

   PU–PU P4–P4 P5–P5 P8–P8

9. The melodic high point occurs at the end of which segment?

   1 2 3 4

10. The excerpt ends with which harmonic intervals?

    m3–M6 M3–m6 P5–P8 M3–P8

11. Which harmonic interval types are heard most frequently in this excerpt?

    thirds and fifths thirds and sixths fifths and octaves sixths and octaves

12. On which tonality or modality is the excerpt based?

    major minor Dorian Lydian

NAME ______________________

Contextual Listening 9.3

Beginning with the given items, write syllables and numbers for each part. Then, notate the remaining pitches, one whole note per measure. Beneath each measure, write the number of the harmonic interval. Between the measures, write the type of motion: *contrary*, *oblique*, *parallel*, or *similar*.

1.

Syllables: *d* __ __ __ __ __ __

Numbers: $\hat{1}$ __ __ __ __ __ __

Syllables: *d* __ __ __ __ __ __

Numbers: $\hat{1}$ __ __ __ __ __ __

Intervals: U __ __ __ __ __ __

Motion: ______ ______ ______ ______ ______ ______

2.

Syllables: *s* __ __ __ __

Numbers: $\hat{5}$ __ __ __ __

Syllables: *s* __ __ __ __

Numbers: $\hat{5}$ __ __ __ __

Intervals: U __ __ __ __

Motion: ______ ______ ______ ______

3.

Syllables: *d* __ __ __ __ __ __

Numbers: $\hat{1}$ __ __ __ __ __ __

Syllables: *d* __ __ __ __ __ __

Numbers: $\hat{1}$ __ __ __ __ __ __

Intervals: 8 __ __ __ __ __ __

Motion: ______ ______ ______ ______ ______ ______

Now, listen to part of a choral work. The six segments are separated by rests. Sopranos sing the higher part and altos sing the lower.

4. In the workspace, begin with the given items and capture the two parts.
   (a) In the single-line staves, notate the rhythm of each part. Beneath these staves, write the syllables and numbers.
   (b) In the treble staves, notate the pitches and rhythm of both parts. For help, refer to the single-line staves. Check your work at a keyboard. Hint: The sopranos' seventh pitch requires an accidental.
   (c) In the blanks between the treble staves, write the numbers of the harmonic intervals.

Translation: If loving Nature or Spirit gave you wings, follow in my light steps, up to the rosy hill.

5. The excerpt's tonality/modality is:

   major minor Dorian Lydian

6. Segments 3 and 4 consist entirely of which type of motion?

   contrary oblique parallel similar

7. Segment 5's beginning ("*folget meiner leichten Spur*") features which motion?

   contrary oblique parallel similar

8. During segment 5, the higher part outlines triads of which qualities?

   minor, minor major, minor major, major diminished, major

9. The last segment begins with sopranos outlining a triad of which quality?

   major minor augmented diminished

10. The last segment's motion is:

    parallel throughout contrary throughout

    parallel, then contrary oblique, then parallel

11. The last segment ends with which harmonic intervals?

    m3–M6 M3–m6 P4–M6 A4–m6

12. The last segment concludes like which earlier segment?

    1 2 3 4 5

13. Which segments consist entirely of note-to-note counterpoint? Choose all that apply.

    1 2 3 4 5 6

14. The harmonic intervals heard most often are:

    thirds and fifths thirds and sixths fifths and octaves sixths and octaves

15. Transpose the excerpt to D major, this time for men's voices. Write appropriate clefs and the key and meter signatures. Include any necessary accidental(s). Between the staves write interval numbers.

Contextual Listening 9.4

In exercises 1–2, identify the tonality/modality. Beneath the rhythm staves, write the syllables and numbers of each part. From the given items, notate the pitches and rhythm of both parts on the grand staff. Below the treble staff, write the harmonic intervals.

1. The tonality/modality is:

   major minor Lydian Mixolydian

2. The tonality/modality is:

   major minor Lydian Mixolydian

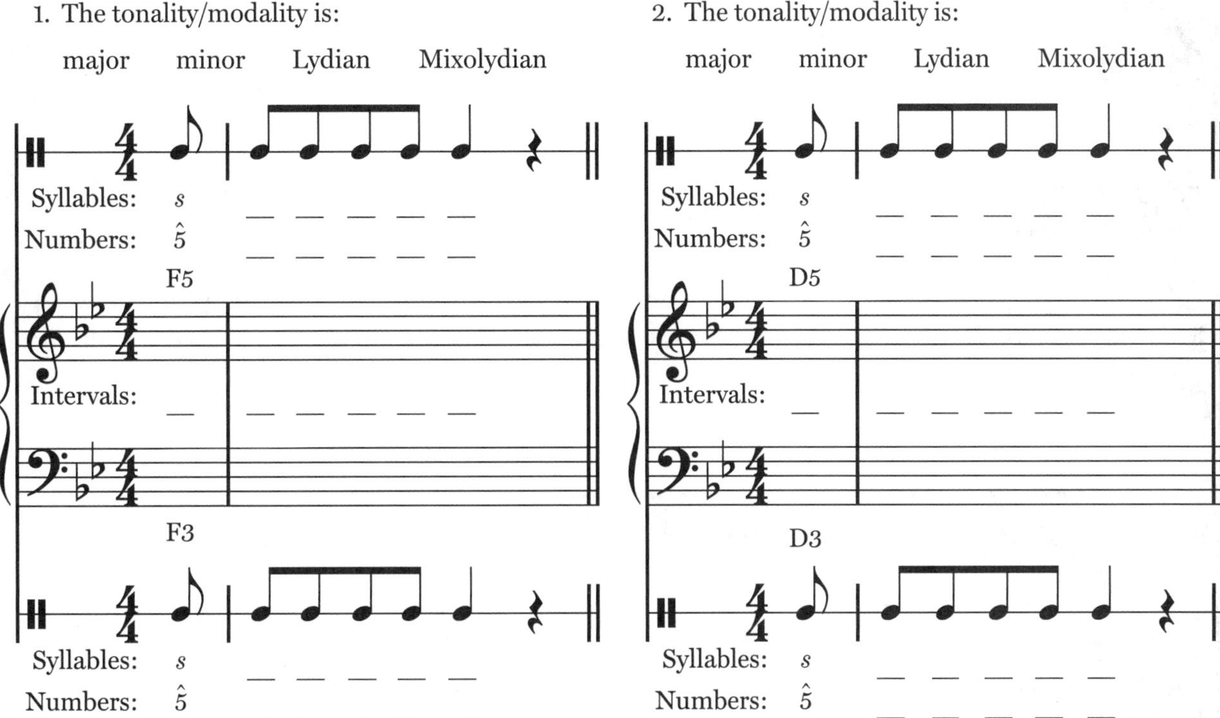

Now, listen to an excerpt from a keyboard work and complete the remaining exercises.

3. The excerpt's tonality/modality is:

   major minor Lydian Mixolydian

4. In the workspace, capture the two parts.
   (a) The rhythm of each part appears in the single-line staves. Beneath each note, write the syllables and numbers.
   (b) In the grand staff, begin with the given items and notate the remaining pitches and rhythm of both parts. Notate the rhythm according to the single-line staves. Check your work at a keyboard.
   (c) Below the treble staff, write the harmonic interval numbers only where blanks appear.

5. Melodic pitches 1–2 create which type of motion against the bass?

   contrary oblique parallel similar

6. Melodic pitches 5–6 create which type of motion against the bass?

   contrary oblique parallel similar

7. Melodic pitches 7–8 create which type of motion against the bass?

   contrary oblique parallel similar

8. Beginning with melodic pitch 14, three triads are outlined. Which are their qualities?

   M-m-d m-M-d d-M-m d-m-M

Embellishment in Two-Part Counterpoint

NAME ______________________________

In this chapter you'll learn to:

- Identify embellishments in two-voice counterpoint
- Convert simple-meter notation to compound meter

Embellishments

Prolongation occurs when embellishment sustains the effect of a pitch, interval, or chord. There are several types of embellishment.

Embellishment	*Definition*	*Original, then embellished idea*
consonant skip (CS) chordal skip (CS)	Skips/leaps within a chord or that create consonant intervals above the bass	 CS
passing tone (P)	Pitch that fills a consonant skip	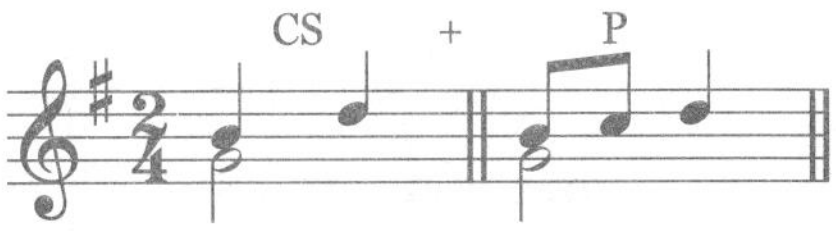 CS + P
neighbor tone (N)	The pitch above (or below) a prolonged pitch	 N
incomplete neighbor (IN)	Neighbor tone that omits the prolonged pitch either before or after	 N
suspension (S)	A strong-beat dissonance that descends by step, delaying the resolution to a consonant interval or chord tone	 S
retardation (S)	A "suspension" that resolves up	 S
voice exchange (VE)	Two voices that "trade places," moving from 3 to 6 or from 6 to 3	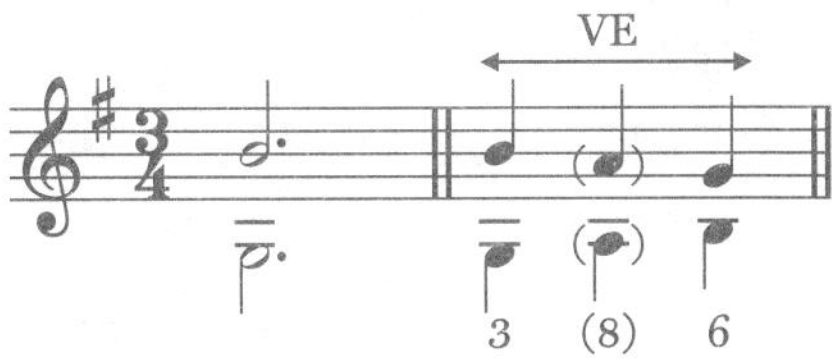 VE 3 (8) 6
anticipation (A)	Pitch that arrives earlier than expected	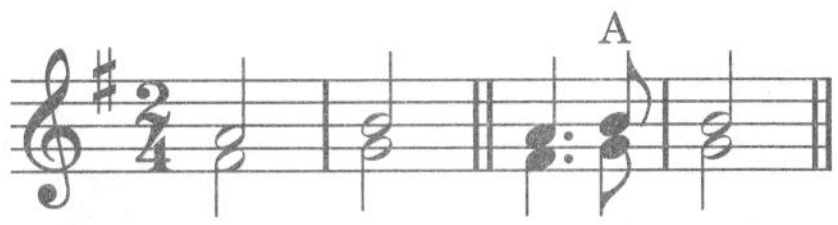 A

Try it

Listen to two-part music and complete the exercises by circling the correct answers.

1. Listen to exercise 1.
   (a) From melodic pitch 1 to 2, the motion between parts is:
   contrary oblique parallel similar
   (b) The initial harmonic intervals are:
   thirds fifths sixths octaves
   (c) The final harmonic interval is a/an:
   unison third fifth octave

2. Listen to exercise 1, then to exercise 2.
   (a) Compared with exercise 1, which part is embellished in exercise 2?
   higher lower both
   (b) The type of embellishment is:
   suspension neighbor tone consonant skip passing tone

3. Listen to exercise 1, then to exercise 3.
   (a) Compared with exercise 1, which part is embellished in exercise 3?
   higher lower both
   (b) The type of embellishment is:
   suspension neighbor tone consonant skip passing tone

4. Listen to exercise 1, then to exercise 4.
   (a) Compared with exercise 1, which part is embellished in exercise 4?
   higher lower both
   (b) The type of embellishment is:
   suspension neighbor tone consonant skip passing tone

5. Listen to exercise 1, then to exercise 5.
   (a) Compared with exercise 1, which part is embellished in exercise 5?
   higher lower both
   (b) The type of embellishment is:
   suspension neighbor tone consonant skip passing tone

6. Listen to exercise 1, then to exercise 6.
   (a) Compared with exercise 1, which part is embellished in exercise 6?
   higher lower both
   (b) The type of embellishment is:
   suspension neighbor tone consonant skip passing tone

7. This time, listen first to exercise 2. Then, listen to exercise 7.
   (a) Compared with exercise 2, which part is embellished in exercise 7?
   higher lower both
   (b) The type of embellishment is:
   suspension neighbor tone consonant skip passing tone

8. Listen to exercise 2, then to exercise 8.
   (a) Compared with exercise 2, the higher part in exercise 8 is embellished with a:
   suspension neighbor tone consonant skip passing tone
   (b) Compared with exercise 2, the lower part in exercise 8 is embellished with a:
   suspension neighbor tone consonant skip passing tone

9. Listen to exercise 9.
   (a) Between melodic pitches 1–2, the motion between parts is:
   contrary oblique parallel similar
   (b) The initial harmonic intervals are:
   thirds fifths sixths octaves
   (c) The final harmonic interval is a/an:
   unison third fifth octave

10. Listen again to exercise 9, then to exercise 10.
   (a) Compared with exercise 9, which part is embellished in exercise 10?
   higher lower both
   (b) The type of embellishment is:
   suspension neighbor tone consonant skip passing tone

11. Listen again to exercise 9, then to exercise 11.
   (a) Compared with exercise 9, which part is embellished in exercise 11?
   higher lower both
   (b) Initially, the type of embellishment is a/an
   suspension incomplete neighbor anticipation voice exchange
   (c) The final embellishment is a/an:
   suspension incomplete neighbor anticipation voice exchange

12. Listen again to exercise 9, then to exercise 12.
   (a) Compared with exercise 9, which part is embellished in exercise 12?
   higher lower both
   (b) The type of embellishment is a/an:
   suspension incomplete neighbor anticipation voice exchange

NAME ______________________________

Contextual Listening 10.1

1. Listen to a series of chords and identify their quality. For triads, write M, m, or d. For seventh chords, write MM7, Mm7, mm7, dm7, or dd7.

Chord:	1	2	3	4	5	6	7
Quality:	____	____	____	____	____	____	____

Now, listen to part of a piano work and complete the following exercises.

2. Capture the excerpt in the workspace.
   (a) In the single-line staves, begin with the given items and notate the rhythm of the outermost parts. Beneath these staves, write the syllables and numbers.
   (b) In the grand staff, begin with the given items and notate the outermost parts' remaining pitches and rhythm. Refer to the syllables and numbers. Check your work at a keyboard.
   (c) Between the staves, write the harmonic interval numbers.
   (d) Circle each dissonant interval and label its function using the abbreviations P (passing tone) or N (neighbor).
   (e) In the blanks marked "Chords," write the chord quality. For triads, write M, m, or d. For seventh chords, write the triad-plus-seventh symbol (MM7, Mm7, etc.). Circle the correct answers below. Hint: Measure 1 is the first complete measure.

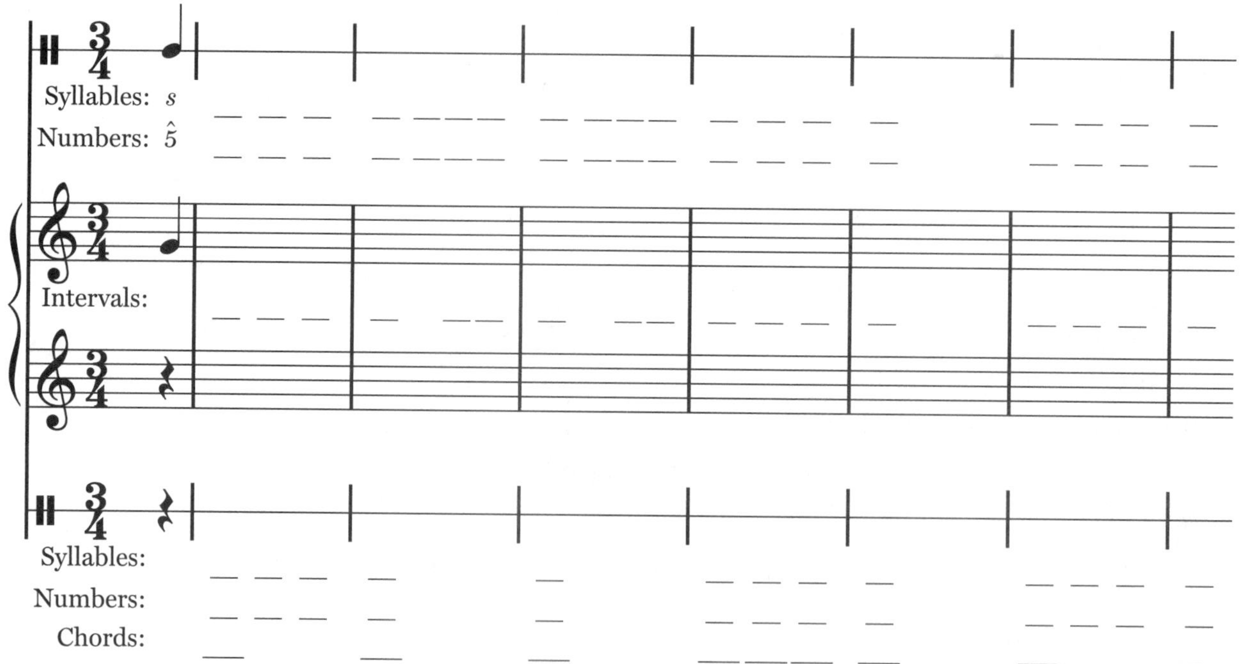

3. In measures 1–3, the motion between the outermost parts is:

   contrary   oblique   parallel   similar

4. Voice exchanges occur during which two measures?

   1 and 3   2 and 4   3 and 5   4 and 6

NAME ___________________________

Contextual Listening 10.2

In each of the following, begin with the given items and notate the remaining pitches and rhythm. Then, complete the exercises.

1. Listen to exercise 1.

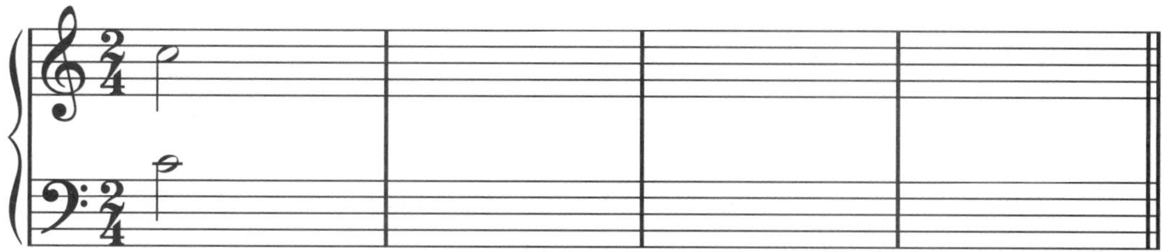

(a) Between melodic pitches 1–2, the motion between the parts is:

contrary oblique parallel similar

(b) Between melodic pitches 2–3, the motion between the parts is:

contrary oblique parallel similar

(c) Between melodic pitches 3–4, the motion between the parts is:

contrary oblique parallel similar

(d) Between melodic pitches 4–5, the motion between the parts is:

contrary oblique parallel similar

2. Listen to exercise 1, then exercise 2. In measure 3, the new embellishments are:

suspensions neighbor tones consonant skips passing tones

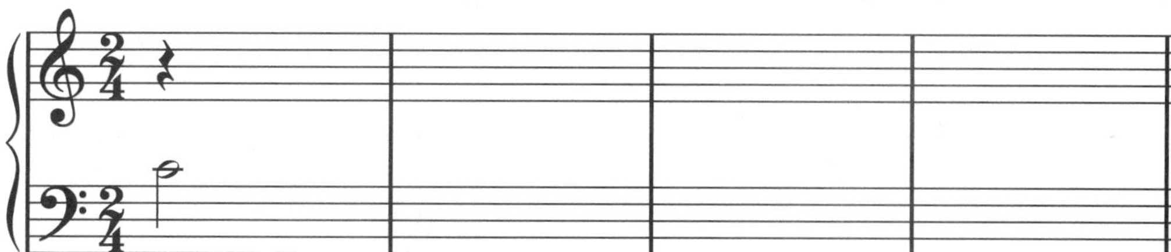

3. Listen to exercise 2, then exercise 3. In measure 2, the new embellishment is a:

suspension neighbor tone consonant skip passing tone

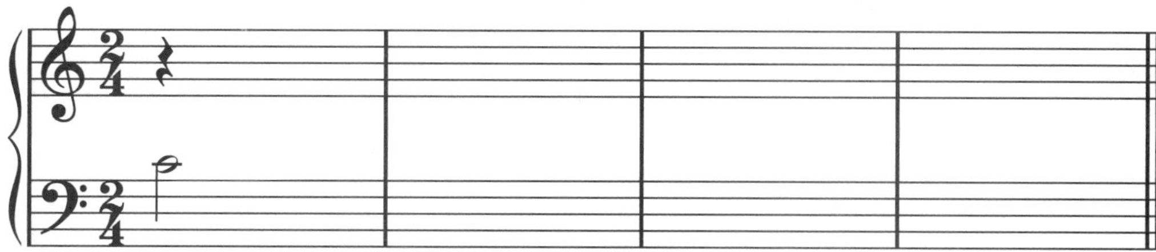

4. Listen to exercise 3, then exercise 4. In measure 3, the new embellishments are:

suspensions   neighbor tones   consonant skips   passing tones

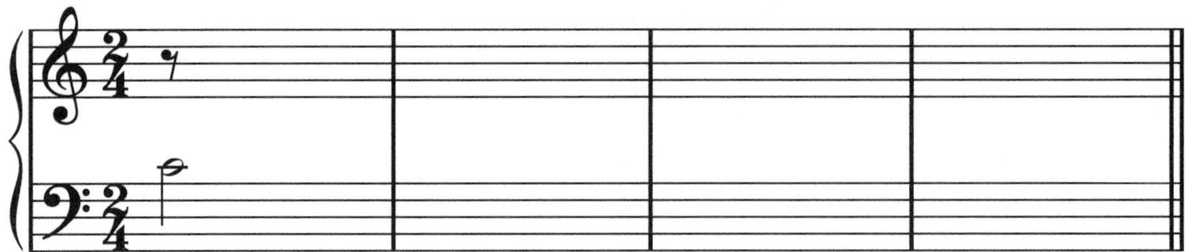

5. Listen to exercise 4, then exercise 5. In measures 1–2, the new embellishments are:

suspensions   neighbor tones   consonant skips   passing tones

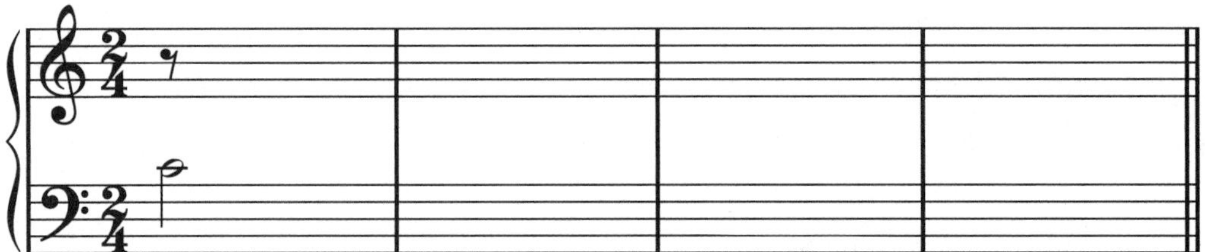

Now, listen to an excerpt from a cantata, and complete the following exercises.

6. Capture the excerpt in the workspace.
   (a) Begin with the given items and notate the remaining pitches and rhythm.
   (b) Between the staves, write the harmonic interval numbers.
   (c) Circle each dissonant interval number and label its function using the abbreviations N (neighbor) and P (passing tone).

Syllables: *d*

Numbers: $\hat{1}$

Intervals:

Syllables: *d*

Numbers: $\hat{1}$

NAME ____________________

Contextual Listening 10.3

Listen to part of an art song, then complete the following exercises.

Translation: Hopping and skipping, happily, whoever can.

1. In the given meter, notate the rhythm of the piano accompaniment for measure 1.

Piano R.H. $\frac{4}{4}$

Piano L.H. $\frac{4}{4}$

2. In the given meter, notate the rhythm of the piano accompaniment for measure 1.

Piano R.H. $\frac{12}{8}$

Piano L.H. $\frac{12}{8}$

3. The composer wrote her music in $\frac{4}{4}$. Are there musical reasons to select one meter signature over another? Could she have chosen $\frac{12}{8}$ instead?

Listen again to the art song excerpt, then focus on chord quality.

4. During beats 1–2, which is the chord quality?

   M triad   m triad   MM7   Mm7   mm7

5. On the downbeats of measures 2 and 3, which is the chord quality?

   M triad   m triad   MM7   Mm7   mm7

6. Which is the final chord's quality?

   M triad   m triad   MM7   Mm7   mm7

NAME ______________________________

Contextual Listening 10.4

In each of the following, begin with the given items and notate the remaining pitches and rhythm. Then, complete the exercises.

1. Listen to exercise 1.

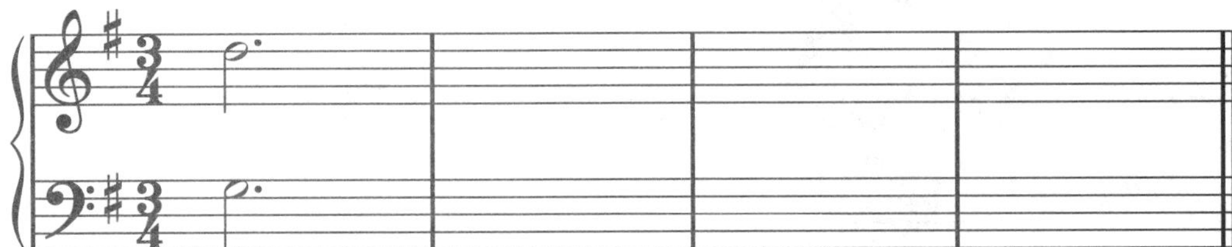

(a) The first harmonic interval is a: M3 P4 d5 P5

(b) The second harmonic interval is a: M3 P4 d5 P5

(c) Between measures 2–3, the motion between the parts is:

contrary oblique parallel similar

(d) Between measures 3–4, the motion between the parts is:

contrary oblique parallel similar

2. Listen to exercise 1, then exercise 2.

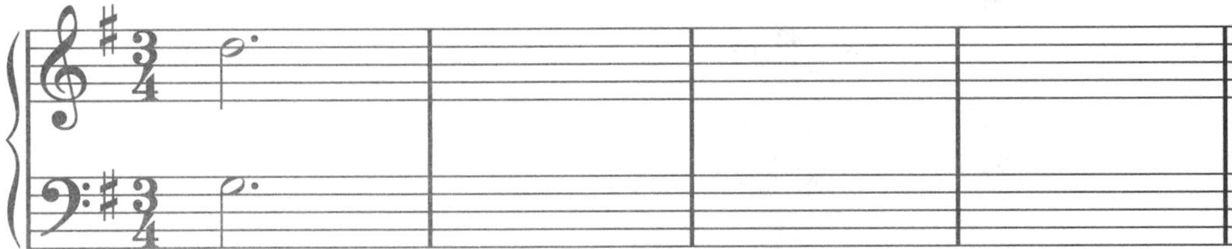

(a) Compared with exercise 1, the lower part is embellished with:

suspensions neighbor tones consonant skips passing tones

(b) Compared with exercise 1, the higher part's embellishment is a/an:

suspension incomplete neighbor consonant skip passing tone

3. Listen to exercise 2, then exercise 3.

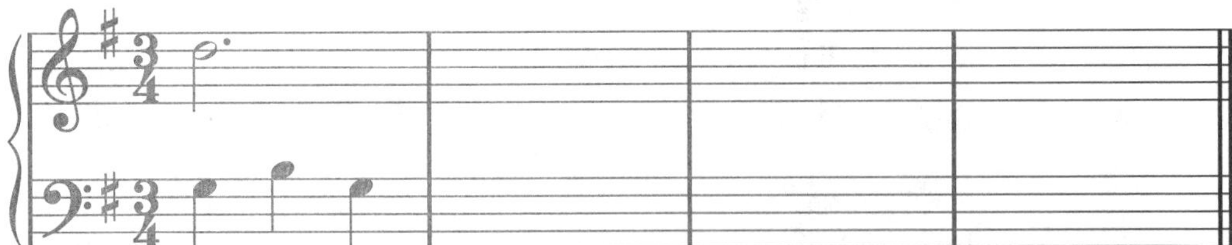

(a) Compared with exercise 2, measures 1–2 are embellished with:

suspensions neighbor tones consonant skips passing tones

(b) In measure 1, all the pitches together create which chord?

major triad minor triad MM7 Mm7

(c) In measure 2, all the pitches together create which chord?

major triad minor triad MM7 Mm7

(d) Compared with exercise 2, measure 3 of the higher part is embellished with a:

suspension neighbor tone consonant skip passing tone

4. Listen to exercise 3, then exercise 4.

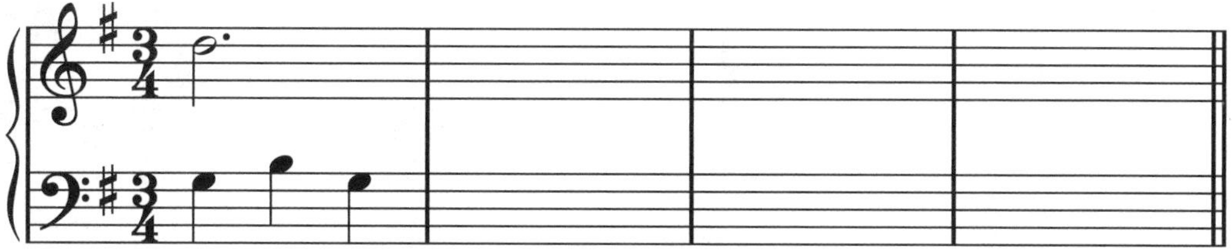

(a) Compared with exercise 3, measure 3 of the higher part is embellished with a:

suspension neighbor tone consonant skip passing tone

(b) Compared with exercise 3, measure 4 of the higher part is embellished with a:

suspension neighbor tone consonant skip passing tone

Now, listen to a string quartet excerpt that features just the violin and cello.

5. Melodic pitches 1–2 create which interval?

P5 m6 M6 m7 M7

6. In measure 1, all the pitches together create which chord?

major triad minor triad MM7 Mm7

7. In measure 2, all the pitches together create which chord?

major triad minor triad MM7 Mm7

8. Begin with the given items and notate the remaining pitches and rhythm.

(a) Between the staves, write the harmonic interval numbers.

(b) Circle each dissonant interval and label its function using the abbreviations S (suspension), IN (incomplete neighbor), or P (passing tone).

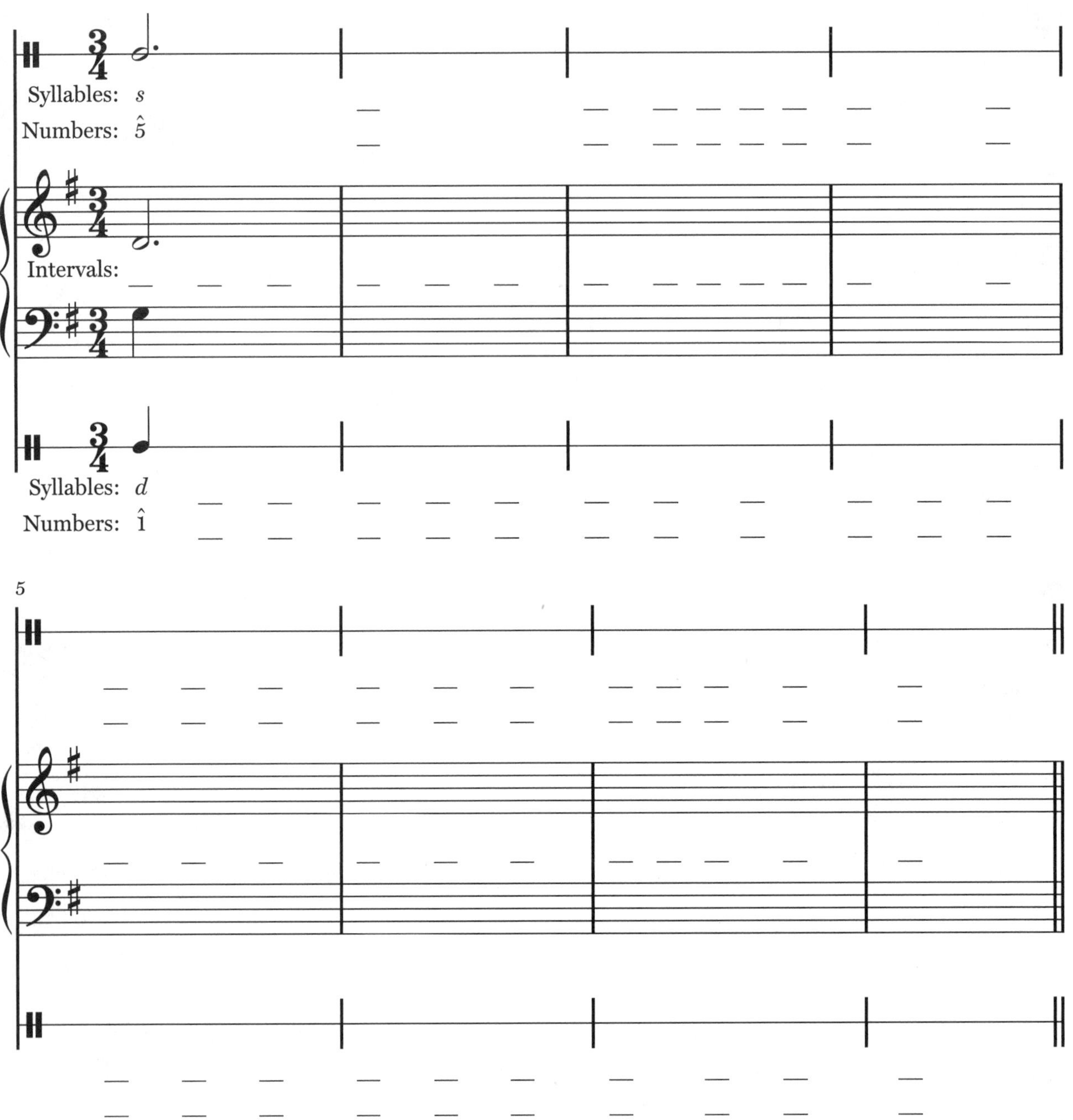

9. In measure 5, the motion between parts creates:

parallel motion a voice exchange rhythmic contrast

Diatonic Harmony and Tonicization

Soprano and Bass Lines in Eighteenth-Century Style

NAME ______________________

In this chapter you'll learn to:

- Classify cadences as conclusive or inconclusive
- Perform and notate the outer parts of eighteenth-century chorales

Phrase and Cadence

A *phrase* is a distinct musical idea that concludes with a cadence. The cadential pitches of the bass (lowest part) and soprano (highest part) determine how conclusive the music sounds.

If the cadential bass pitches are . . .	*And the cadential soprano pitch is . . .*	*The cadence is . . .*
sol–do ($\hat{5}$–$\hat{1}$)	*do* ($\hat{1}$)	conclusive
sol–do ($\hat{5}$–$\hat{1}$)	*mi* or *sol* ($\hat{3}$ or $\hat{5}$)	less conclusive
ti–do ($\hat{7}$–$\hat{1}$)	*do* ($\hat{1}$)	less conclusive
any note to *mi* ($\hat{3}$)	*do* or *sol* ($\hat{1}$ or $\hat{5}$)	less conclusive
any note to *sol* ($\hat{5}$)	*re*, *ti*, or *sol* ($\hat{2}$, $\hat{7}$, or $\hat{5}$)	inconclusive

Try it

Listen to two-part music that concludes with a cadence. Focus on the final bass and soprano pitches to identify the cadence. From the given items, notate the remaining pitches and rhythm of both parts. Include any necessary accidentals and bar lines. Write harmonic interval numbers between the staves.

1. The cadence is:

   conclusive   less conclusive   inconclusive

   Interval: ___ ___ | ___

2. The cadence is:

   conclusive   less conclusive   inconclusive

   Interval: ___ ___ | ___

3. The cadence is:

conclusive   less conclusive   inconclusive

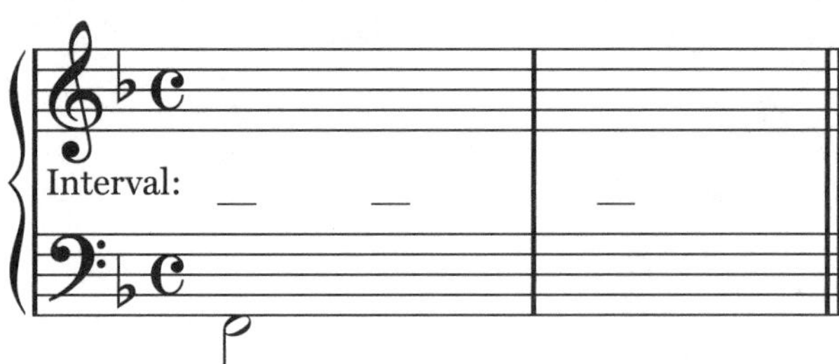

4. The cadence is:

conclusive   less conclusive   inconclusive

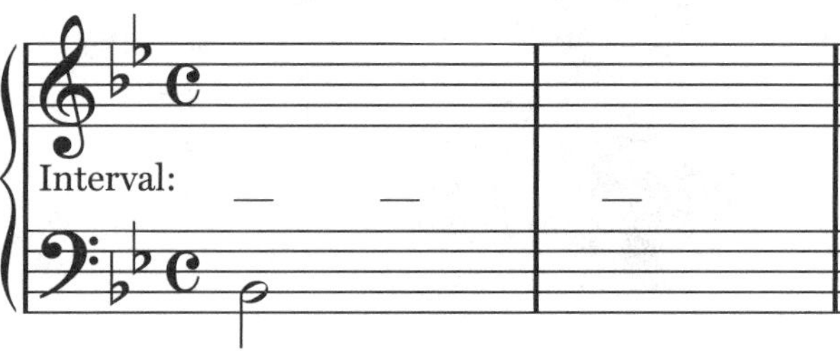

5. The cadence is:

conclusive   less conclusive   inconclusive

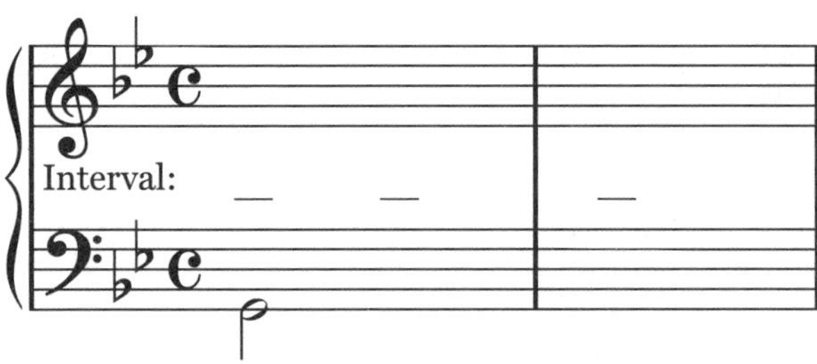

6. The cadence is:

conclusive   less conclusive   inconclusive

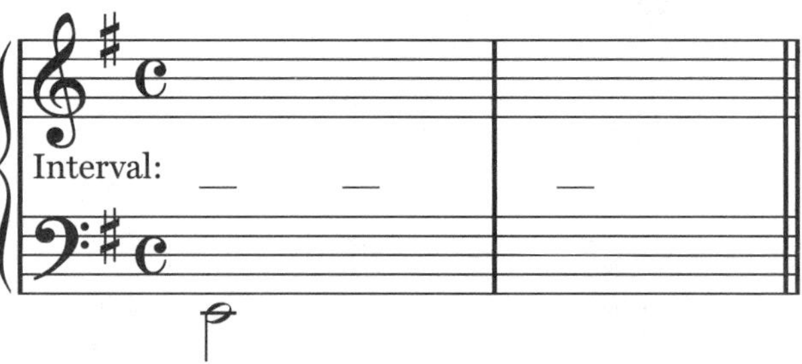

7. The cadence is:

conclusive   less conclusive   inconclusive

8. The cadence is:

conclusive   less conclusive   inconclusive

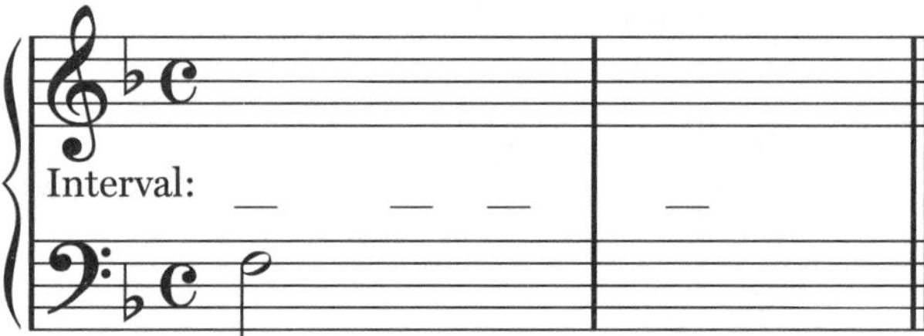

9. The cadence is:

conclusive   less conclusive   inconclusive

10. The cadence is:

conclusive   less conclusive   inconclusive

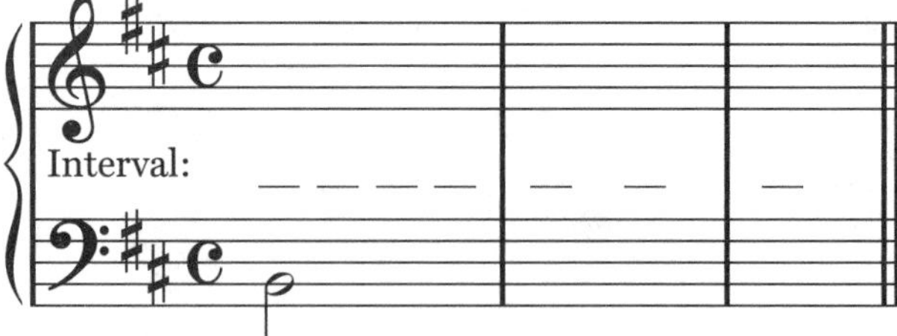

Contextual Listening 11.1

Listen to two-part music and identify the cadence. From the given items, notate the remaining pitches of both parts using whole notes. Include any necessary accidentals. Write harmonic interval numbers between the staves.

1. The cadence is:

   conclusive   less conclusive   inconclusive

2. The cadence is:

   conclusive   less conclusive   inconclusive

3. The cadence is:

   conclusive   less conclusive   inconclusive

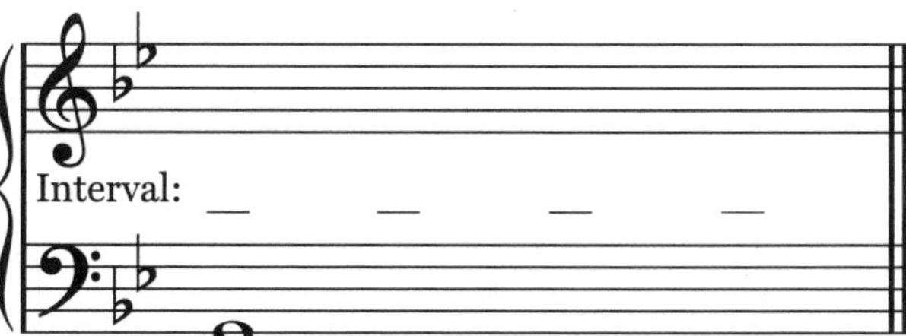

Now, listen to one phrase from a chorale, and complete the following exercises.

4. Beginning with the given items, capture the excerpt in the workspace.
   (a) In the single-line staves, notate the rhythm of the bass and soprano lines.
   (b) Below each note, write the syllables and numbers of the pitches.
   (c) In the grand staff, notate the pitches and rhythm of both parts. Refer to the single-line notation. Check your work at a keyboard.
   (d) Write harmonic interval numbers between the treble and bass staves.

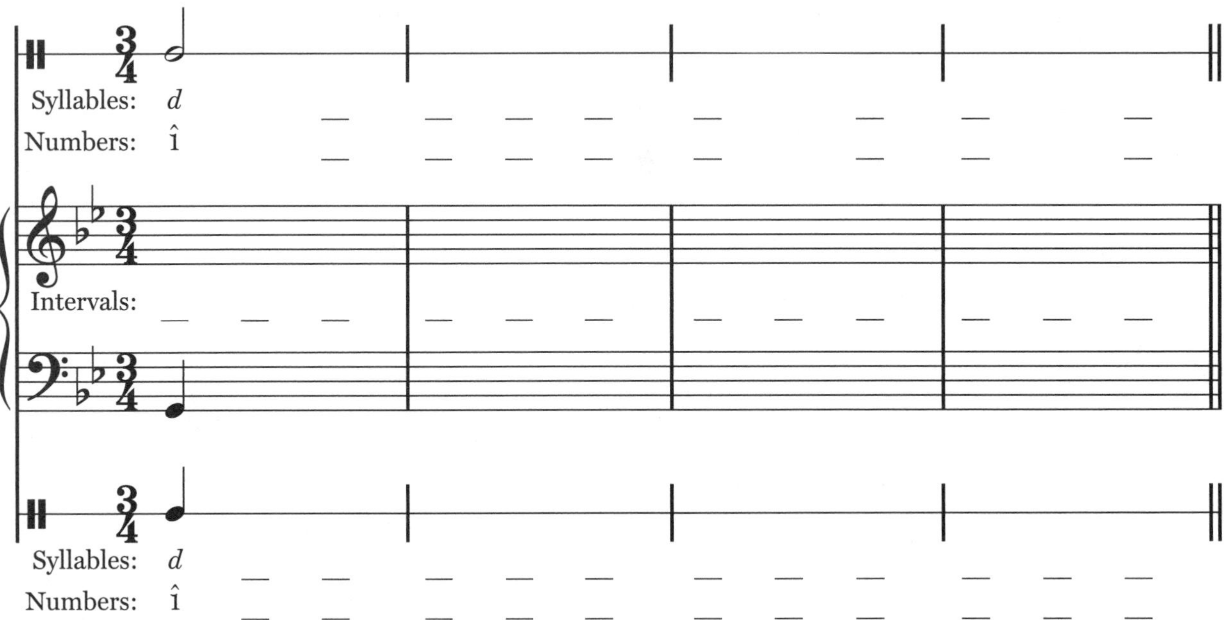

5. Bass pitches 1–2 create which melodic interval?

   P4 P5 M6 P8

6. Bass pitches 6–7 create which melodic interval?

   M3 P4 d5 P5

7. The phrase's cadence is: conclusive less conclusive inconclusive

8. The melody's pitch collection belongs to which pattern?

   major tetrachord minor tetrachord major pentachord minor pentachord

9. The bass line's pitch collection belongs to which scale?

   major natural minor (descending melodic)
   ascending melodic minor harmonic minor

Contextual Listening 11.2

Listen to two-part music and identify the cadence. From the given items, notate the remaining pitches of both parts using whole notes. Include any necessary accidentals. Write harmonic interval numbers between the staves.

1. The cadence is:

   conclusive   less conclusive   inconclusive

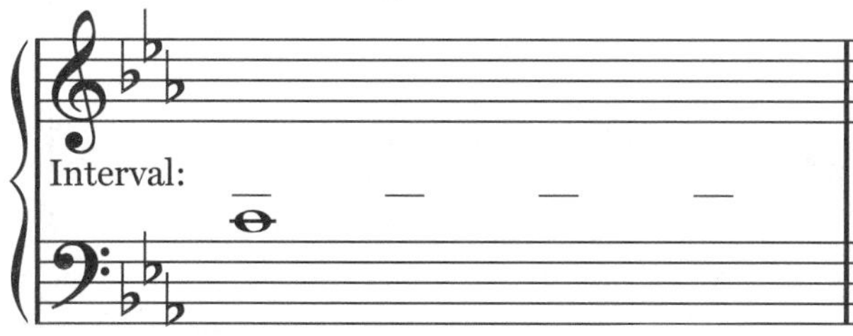

2. The cadence is:

   conclusive   less conclusive   inconclusive

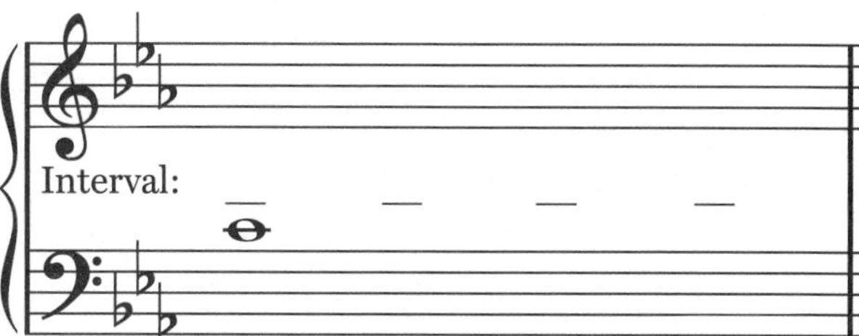

3. The cadence is:

   conclusive   less conclusive   inconclusive

Now, listen to two phrases from a chorale and complete the following exercises.

4. Beginning with the given items, capture the excerpt in the workspace.
   (a) In the single-line staves, notate the rhythm of the bass and soprano lines.
   (b Below each note, write the syllables and numbers of the pitches.
   (c) In the grand staff, notate the pitches and rhythm of both parts. Refer to the single-line notation. Check your work at a keyboard.
   (d) Write harmonic interval numbers between the treble and bass staves.

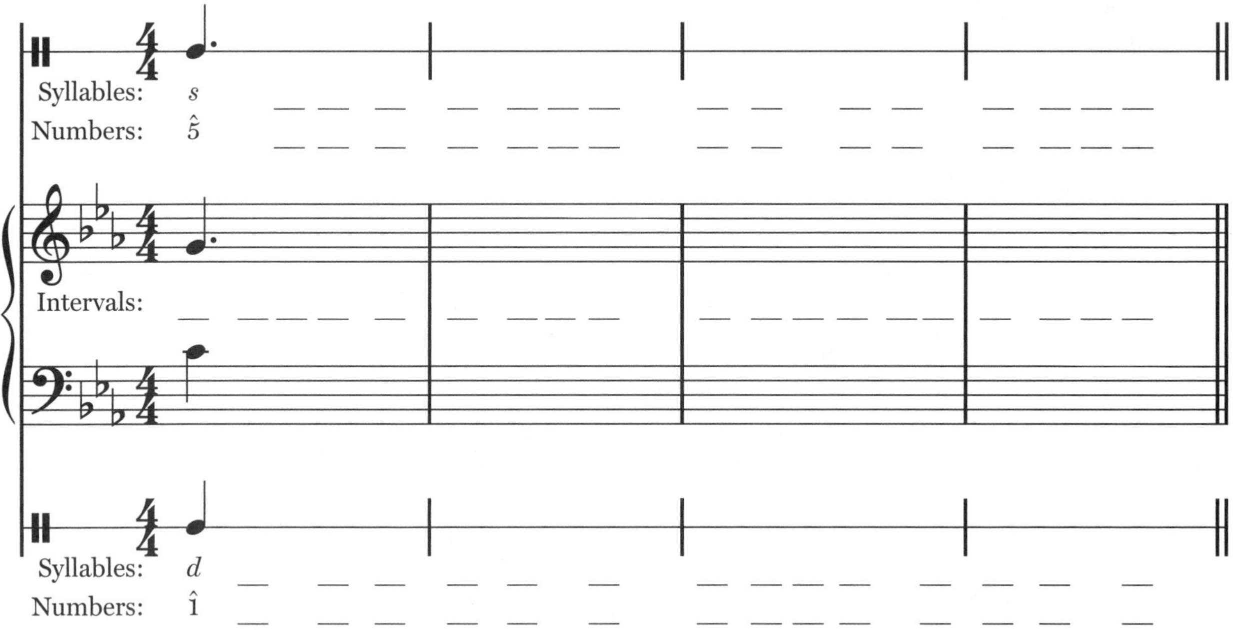

Exercises 5–7 focus only on phrase 1.

5. Soprano pitches 1–2 create which melodic interval?

   m3 P4 P5 m6

6. Between harmonic intervals 3-5, the motion is:

   contrary oblique similar parallel

7. Phrase 1's cadence is: conclusive less conclusive inconclusive

Bonus! From phrase 1's cadential bass pitch, read the line *backward*. Compare this to phrase 1's soprano line read *forward*. How do they relate?

Exercises 8–12 focus only on phrase 2.

8. Between harmonic pitches 1–2, the motion is:

   contrary oblique similar parallel

9. Between the last two harmonic intervals, the motion is:

   contrary oblique similar parallel

10. The final bass pitches create which melodic interval?

    M3 P4 d5 P5

11. Phrase 2's cadence is: conclusive less conclusive inconclusive

12. Phrase 2's bass-line pitch collection belongs to which scale?

    major natural minor (descending melodic)

    ascending melodic minor harmonic minor

Contextual Listening 11.3

Listen to two-part music and identify the cadence. From the given items, notate the remaining pitches of both parts using whole notes. Include any necessary accidentals. Write harmonic intervals between the staves.

1. The cadence is:

   conclusive   less conclusive   inconclusive

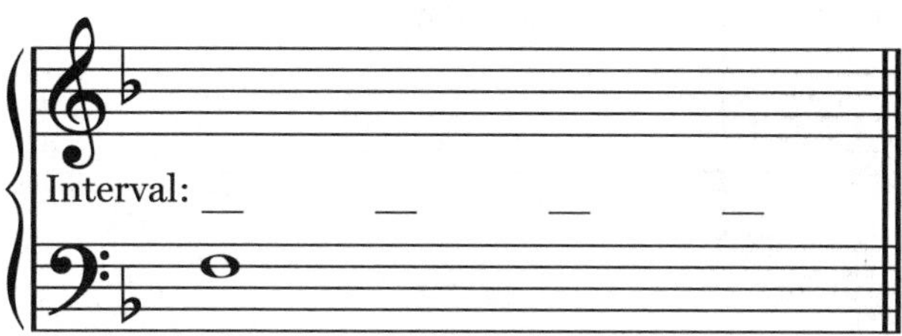

2. 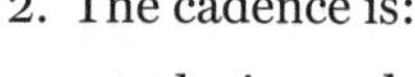
   The cadence is:

   conclusive   less conclusive   inconclusive

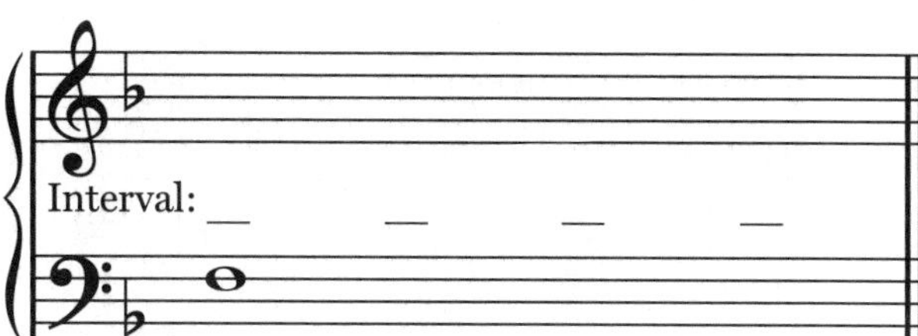

3. The cadence is:

   conclusive   less conclusive   inconclusive

Now, listen to two phrases from a chorale and complete the following exercises.

4. Beginning with the given items, capture the excerpt in the workspace.
   (a) In the single-line staves, notate the rhythm of the bass and soprano lines.
   (b) Below each note, write the syllables and numbers of the pitches.
   (c) In the grand staff, notate the pitches and rhythm of both parts. Refer to the single-line notation. Check your work at a keyboard.
   (d) Write harmonic interval numbers between the treble and bass staves.

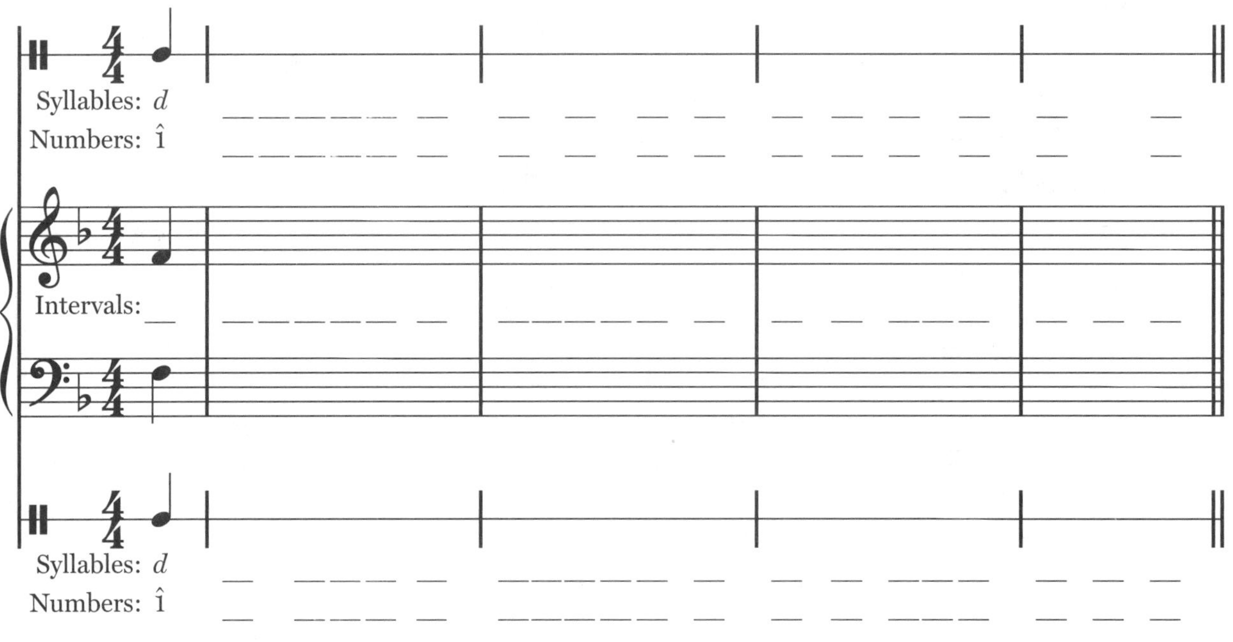

Exercises 5–7 focus only on phrase 1.

5. Soprano pitches 1–2 create which melodic interval?

   m3 P4 P5 m6

6. Harmonic pitches 1–2 produce which type of motion?

   contrary oblique similar parallel

7. Phrase 1's cadence is: conclusive less conclusive inconclusive

Exercises 8–12 focus only on phrase 2.

8. Harmonic pitches 1–4 produce which type of motion?

   contrary oblique similar parallel

9. The last two harmonic pitches produce which type of motion?

   contrary oblique similar parallel

10. The final bass pitches create which melodic interval?

    m3 P4 P5 m6

11. Phrase 2's cadence is: conclusive less conclusive inconclusive

12. The excerpt's pitch collection belongs to which scale?

    major natural minor (descending melodic)

    ascending melodic minor harmonic minor

Contextual Listening 11.4

Listen to two-part music and identify the cadence. From the given items, notate the remaining pitches of both parts using whole notes. Include any necessary accidentals. Write harmonic intervals between the staves.

1. The cadence is:

   conclusive   less conclusive   inconclusive

   Interval: __ __ __ __

2. The cadence is:

   conclusive   less conclusive   inconclusive

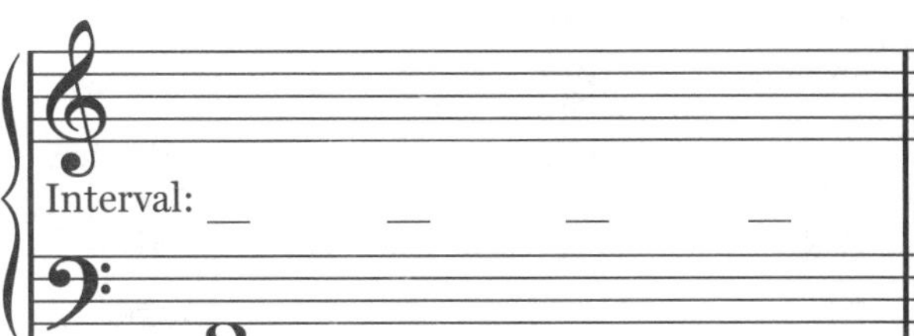

3. The cadence is:

   conclusive   less conclusive   inconclusive

Now, listen to two phrases from a chorale and complete the following exercises.

4. Beginning with the given items, capture the excerpt in the workspace.
   (a) In the single-line staves, notate the rhythm of the bass and soprano lines.
   (b) Below each note, write the syllables and numbers of the pitches.
   (c) In the grand staff, notate the pitches and rhythm of both parts. Refer to the single-line notation. Check your work at a keyboard.
   (d) Write harmonic interval numbers between the treble and bass staves.

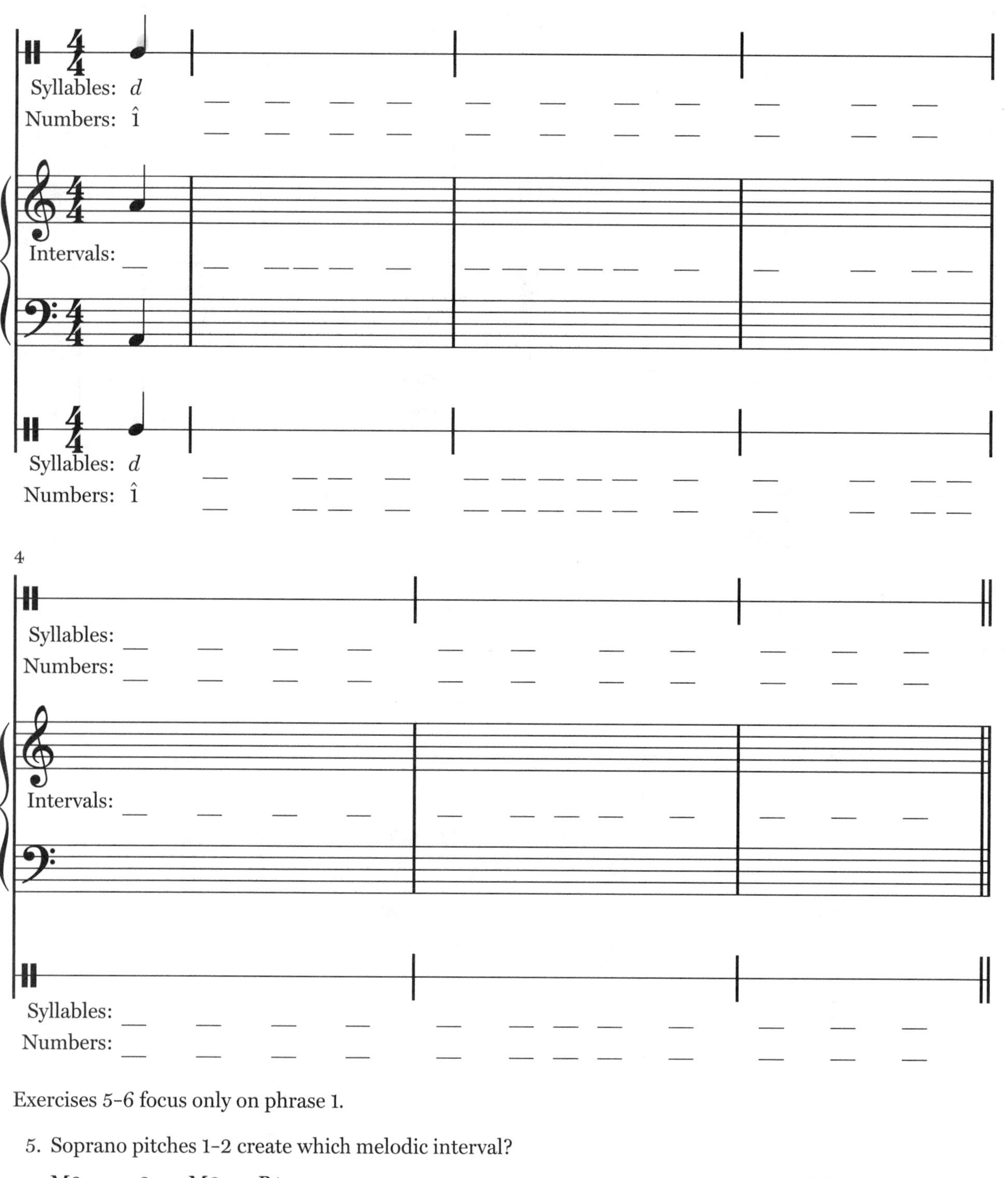

Exercises 5–6 focus only on phrase 1.

5. Soprano pitches 1–2 create which melodic interval?

   M2 m3 M3 P4

6. Phrase 1's cadence is: conclusive less conclusive inconclusive

Exercises 7–8 focus only on phrase 2.

7. Phrase 2's cadence is: conclusive less conclusive inconclusive

8. The final bass pitches create which interval?

   P4 P5 m6 M6

The Basic Phrase in Chorale Style

NAME ____________________

In this chapter you'll learn to:

- Identify harmonies and notate them with Roman numerals and figures
- Identify cadences and label them by type: HC, IAC, PAC
- Transcribe a concert-pitch melody for B♭ clarinet

Tonic–Dominant–Tonic (T–D–T) Roman Numerals and Cadence Types

Focusing on bass pitches helps you determine dominant- and tonic-function chords and their Roman-numeral representations.

If the bass pitch is . . .	*Write*	*And listen above the bass for . . .*	*If present, then write*
sol–do ($\hat{5}$–$\hat{1}$)	V	*sol–fa* ($\hat{5}$–$\hat{4}$)	V^{8-7}
ti ($\hat{7}$)	V^6		
do ($\hat{1}$)	I or i		

Cadential bass pitches help you determine the most common cadence types: half and authentic.

If the bass is . . .	*and the soprano is . . .*	*the ending is . . .*	*and the cadence type is . . .*
sol–do ($\hat{5}$–$\hat{1}$)	*do* ($\hat{1}$)	conclusive	perfect authentic (PAC)
do ($\hat{1}$)	*mi* ($\hat{3}$) or *sol* ($\hat{5}$)	less conclusive	imperfect authentic (IAC)
sol ($\hat{5}$)	*re* ($\hat{2}$), *ti* ($\hat{7}$), or *sol* ($\hat{5}$)	inconclusive	half (HC)

Try it

Look at the given items, then listen to four-part progressions. Sing aloud with syllables or numbers.

- In the blank beneath the bass staff, write the key name and its quality: uppercase for major, lowercase for minor (e.g., C, F, b, g, etc.)
- In the grand staff, notate the pitches and rhythm of the bass and soprano parts.
- Beneath each bass pitch, write the Roman numeral and figure (if needed).
- Circle the cadence type: PAC (perfect authentic), IAC (imperfect authentic), HC (half)
- For an extra challenge, perform and then notate the inner voices.

NAME ____________________

6. Cadence type: PAC IAC HC

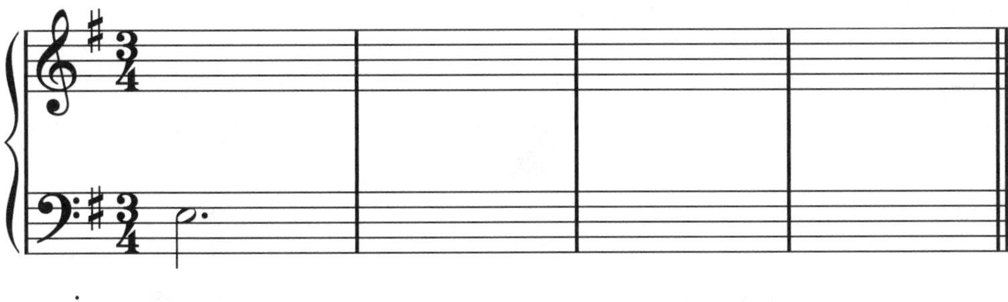

___:

7. Cadence type: PAC IAC HC

8. Cadence type: PAC IAC HC

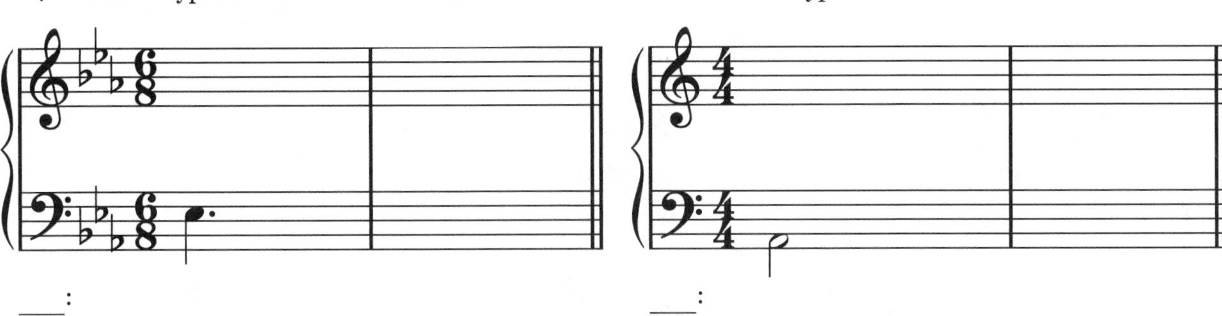

___:

___:

Contextual Listening 12.1

This activity features excerpts from works by three different composers.

CL 12.1A Listen to one phrase from a piano work and focus on the end—a cadence that's extended.

1. The final bass pitch is: *sol* ($\hat{5}$) *do* ($\hat{1}$)
2. The final melodic pitch is: *sol* ($\hat{5}$) *mi* ($\hat{3}$) *re* ($\hat{2}$) *do* ($\hat{1}$) *ti* ($\hat{7}$)
3. The cadence type is: PAC IAC HC

   Hints: HC melodies end on *re* ($\hat{2}$), *ti* ($\hat{7}$), or *sol* ($\hat{5}$). PACs end on *do* ($\hat{1}$) and IACs on *mi* ($\hat{3}$) or *sol* ($\hat{5}$).

CL 12.1B Listen to one phrase from a concerto grosso and focus on the cadence.

4. The final bass pitch is: *sol* ($\hat{5}$) *do* ($\hat{1}$)
5. The final melodic pitch is: *sol* ($\hat{5}$) *mi* ($\hat{3}$) *re* ($\hat{2}$) *do* ($\hat{1}$) *ti* ($\hat{7}$)
6. The cadence type is: PAC IAC HC

CL12.1C Listen to the introduction from an art song and focus on the cadences. Cadence 1 occurs halfway through the excerpt, just before the melody returns.

7. Cadence 1's bass pitch is: *sol* ($\hat{5}$) *do* ($\hat{1}$)
8. Cadence 1's melodic pitch is: *sol* ($\hat{5}$) *mi* ($\hat{3}$) *re* ($\hat{2}$) *do* ($\hat{1}$) *ti* ($\hat{7}$)
9. Cadence 1's type is: PAC IAC HC

Cadence 2 occurs at the end of the excerpt.

10. The final bass pitch is: *sol* ($\hat{5}$) *do* ($\hat{1}$)
11. The final melodic pitch is: *sol* ($\hat{5}$) *mi* ($\hat{3}$) *re* ($\hat{2}$) *do* ($\hat{1}$) *ti* ($\hat{7}$)
12. Cadence 2's type is: PAC IAC HC

Contextual Listening 12.2

Simple-meter patterns *Compound-meter patterns*

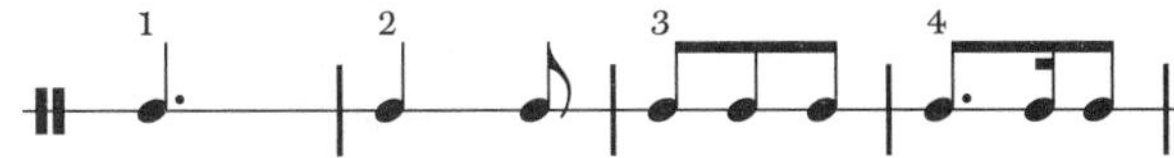

In exercises 1–2, a four-beat count-off precedes four beats of rhythm. Determine whether the meter is simple or compound. Then, from the choices provided, select the pattern number of each beat.

1. (a) The meter type is: simple compound
   (b) Write the correct rhythm-pattern numbers: ___ ___ ___ ___
2. (a) The meter type is: simple compound
   (b) Write the correct rhythm-pattern numbers: ___ ___ ___ ___

In exercises 3–4 a clarinet plays tonic, rests, and then plays a four-beat melody.

3. (a) The meter type is: simple compound
   (b) Write the correct rhythm-pattern numbers: ___ ___ ___ ___
   (c) The triad arpeggiated is: I ii IV V
   (d) Pitches 1–2 form which pitch interval? m3 P4 P5 M6
4. (a) The meter type is: simple compound
   (b) Write the correct rhythm-pattern numbers: ___ ___ ___ ___
   (c) The triad arpeggiated is: tonic supertonic subdominant dominant
   (d) Pitches 1–2 form which pitch interval? m3 P4 P5 M6

Now, listen to two phrases from a twentieth-century ballet and complete the following exercises.

5. Pitches 1–2 form which interval? m3 P4 P5 M6
6. The meter is: simple quadruple compound quadruple
7. Beginning with the given items, capture the excerpt in the workspace.
   (a) In the single-line staff, begin with a half-note anacrusis and notate the melodic rhythm. Include the meter signature and all bar lines. Beam notes to show beat grouping.
   (b) Beginning with *sol* ($\hat{5}$), write the remaining syllables or numbers beneath each note.
   (c) In the five-line staff, begin with C4 and write the appropriate clef, key signature, and meter signature. Refer to the single-line staff and notate the pitches and rhythm of the melody.

Cadence 1 occurs halfway through the excerpt, *just before* the opening idea returns.

8. Cadence 1 features which triad arpeggiation?

   tonic supertonic subdominant dominant

9. Phrase 1's cadence type is: PAC IAC HC

Cadence 2 occurs at the end of the excerpt.

10. The final melodic pitch is: *do* ($\hat{1}$) *re* ($\hat{2}$) *mi* ($\hat{3}$) *sol* ($\hat{5}$)

11. The final pitch implies which chord? I ii V vi

12. The final cadence type is: PAC IAC HC

13. What is the range (lowest pitch to highest pitch) of the melody?

    do-sol ($\hat{1}$-$\hat{5}$) *ti-la* ($\hat{7}$-$\hat{6}$) *do-do* ($\hat{1}$-$\hat{1}$) *sol-sol* ($\hat{5}$-$\hat{5}$)

14. On the given staves, create a part for B♭ clarinet. Notate a new key signature and transpose the concert-pitch melody up a M2. Hint: Refer to your workspace answers.

NAME ___________________________

Contextual Listening 12.3

Simple-meter patterns *Compound-meter patterns*

In exercises 1–2, a two-beat count-off precedes four beats of rhythm.

1. (a) The meter type is: simple compound
   (b) Write the correct rhythm-pattern numbers: ___ ___ ___ ___
2. (a) The meter type is: simple compound
   (b) Write the correct rhythm-pattern numbers: ___ ___ ___ ___

In exercises 3–4 the tonic pitch sounds. After a rest, a woodwind trio performs one phrase.

3. (a) Bass pitch 1 is: *do* ($\hat{1}$) *re* ($\hat{2}$) *mi* ($\hat{3}$) *sol* ($\hat{5}$)
   (b) Soprano pitch 1 is: *do* ($\hat{1}$) *re* ($\hat{2}$) *mi* ($\hat{3}$) *sol* ($\hat{5}$)
   (c) Chord 1 is: I ii IV V
   (d) The final bass pitch is: *do* ($\hat{1}$) *re* ($\hat{2}$) *mi* ($\hat{3}$) *sol* ($\hat{5}$)
   (e) The final chord is Roman numeral: I ii IV V
   (f) The cadence type is: PAC IAC HC

   Hints: For HCs, the bass is *sol* ($\hat{5}$). For IACs, the bass is *do* ($\hat{1}$) and the soprano is either *mi* ($\hat{3}$) or *sol* ($\hat{5}$). A PAC's bass and soprano pitches are both *do* ($\hat{1}$).
4. (a) The final bass pitch is: *do* ($\hat{1}$) *re* ($\hat{2}$) *mi* ($\hat{3}$) *sol* ($\hat{5}$)
   (b) The final soprano pitch is: *do* ($\hat{1}$) *re* ($\hat{2}$) *mi* ($\hat{3}$) *sol* ($\hat{5}$)
   (c) The final chord is Roman numeral: I ii IV V
   (d) The cadence type is: PAC IAC HC

Now, listen to one phrase from a holiday song and complete the following exercises.

5. The meter is: compound duple simple duple
6. The bassoon's first note is: *do* ($\hat{1}$) *re* ($\hat{2}$) *mi* ($\hat{3}$) *sol* ($\hat{5}$)
7. The bassoon's first note implies which chord? I ii IV V
8. The flute melody begins on: *do* ($\hat{1}$) *re* ($\hat{2}$) *mi* ($\hat{3}$) *sol* ($\hat{5}$)
9. During pitches 1–3 the flute and oboe move in which type of motion?
   contrary parallel similar oblique
10. The melody ends on: *do* ($\hat{1}$) *re* ($\hat{2}$) *mi* ($\hat{3}$) *sol* ($\hat{5}$)
11. The bass ends on: *do* ($\hat{1}$) *re* ($\hat{2}$) *mi* ($\hat{3}$) *sol* ($\hat{5}$)
12. The final harmony is: I ii IV V
13. The phrase's cadence type is: PAC IAC HC

Complete your answers to exercises 14–16 in the workspace.

14. Capture the bass line (bassoon part).
    (a) In the single-line bass staff, notate the bass rhythm. Include the meter signature and bar lines. Beam notes to show beat grouping.
    (b) Beneath each note in the single-line bass staff, write the syllables or numbers of the bassoon's pitches.
    (c) In the five-line bass staff, write the key and meter signatures. Begin with D3 and notate the bass line's pitches and rhythm. Refer to your workspace answers.

15. Capture the essential harmonies.
    (a) Beneath each bass-pitch *do* ($\hat{1}$), write Roman numeral I.
    (b) Beneath bass-pitch *sol* ($\hat{5}$), write V. If a pitch repeats, don't rewrite its Roman numeral.
    (c) For each bass-pitch *sol* ($\hat{5}$), if you hear *fa* ($\hat{4}$) above it, write V^7.
    If you hear *sol-fa* ($\hat{5}$–$\hat{4}$), write V^{8-7}.

16. Capture the soprano line (flute part).
    (a) In the single-line treble staff, notate the soprano rhythm. Include the meter signature and bar lines. Beam notes to show beat grouping.
    (b) Beneath each note in the single-line treble staff, write the syllables or numbers of the flute's pitches.
    (c) In the five-line treble staff, write the appropriate key and meter signatures. Begin with A5 and notate the soprano line's pitches and rhythm. Refer to the workspace answers.

Dominant Sevenths and Predominants

NAME ______________________

In this chapter you'll learn to:

- Associate bass pitches with chords and chord inversions
- Identify dominant seventh and predominant chords in harmonic progressions
- Identify authentic and half cadences that are prepared with predominant chords

More Tonic-Dominant-Tonic (T-D-T) Progressions

Focusing on bass pitches helps you determine dominant- and tonic-function chords and their Roman-numeral representations.

If the bass pitch is . . .	*Write*	*And listen above the bass for . . .*	*If present, then write*
sol ($\hat{5}$)	V	*sol-fa* ($\hat{5}$–$\hat{4}$)	V^{8-7}
ti ($\hat{7}$)	V^6	*fa* ($\hat{4}$)	V^6_5
re ($\hat{2}$)	V^4_3		
fa-mi ($\hat{4}$–$\hat{3}$)	V^4_2–I^6		
fa-me ($\hat{4}$–$\flat\hat{3}$)	V^4_2–i^6		

Tonic-Chord Listening Strategies

If the bass pitch is . . .	*Write*
do ($\hat{1}$)	I for major; i for minor
mi ($\hat{3}$) or *me* ($\flat\hat{3}$)	I^6 or i^6

Try it 1

Look at the given items, then listen to four-part progressions. Sing each part.

- Write the key name and quality: uppercase for major, lowercase for minor (e.g., C or g).
- Notate the pitches and rhythm of the bass and soprano.
- In the blanks beneath the bass pitches, write the Roman numeral and figure (if needed) that represents the harmony.

- Identify the cadence type.
- For an extra challenge, perform and then notate the inner voices.

NAME ______________________

Contextual Listening 13.1

- Beginning with the given items, capture the excerpt in the workspace.
- Between the treble staves, write harmonic interval numbers.
- In each chord blank specified, write the Roman numeral and figure (if needed) that represents the harmony.
- Hint: If a harmony is sustained, write a figure that matches the chord's lowest-sounding pitch.

1. The phrase ends with which cadence type? PAC IAC HC

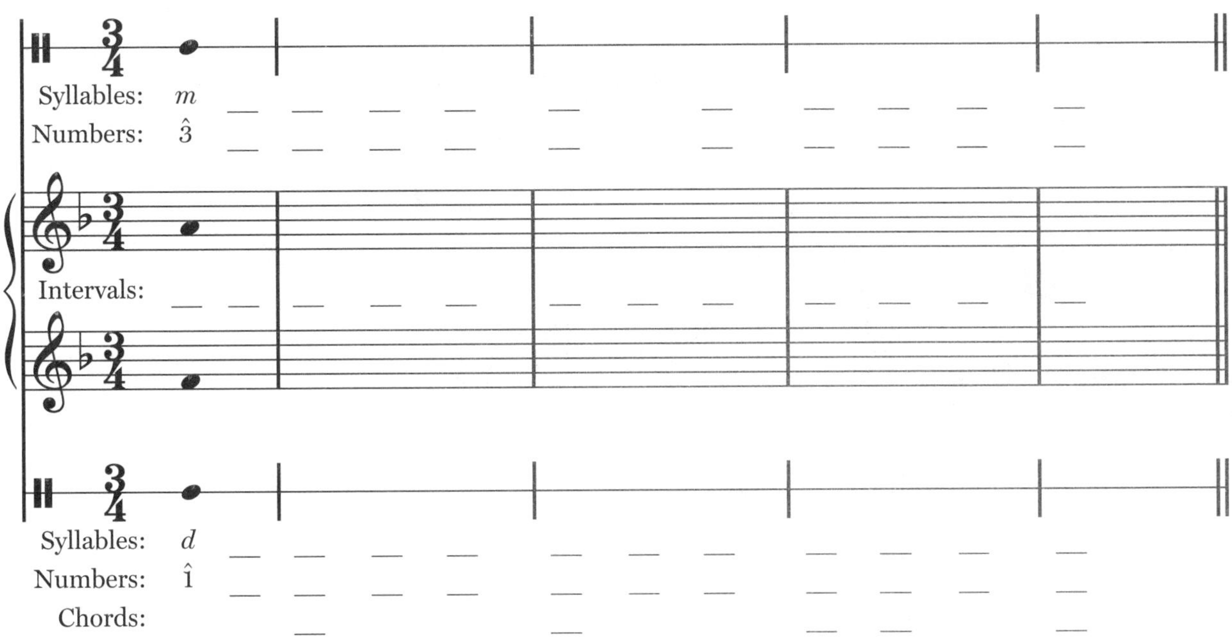

2. The phrase ends with which cadence type? PAC IAC HC

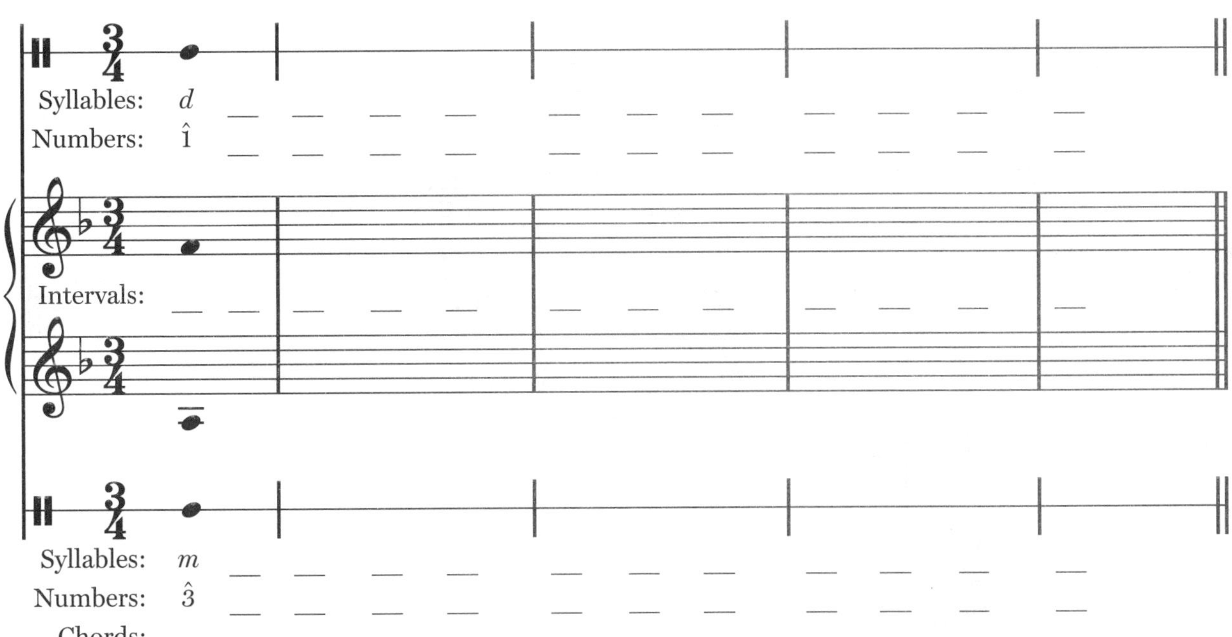

Now, listen to two phrases from a piano sonata and complete the remaining exercises.

3. Beginning with the given items, capture the excerpt in the workspace.
   (a) In the single-line staves, notate the rhythm of the bass and soprano lines.
   (b) Below each note, write the syllables and numbers of the pitches.
   (c) In the grand staff, notate the pitches and rhythm of both parts. Refer to the single-line notation. Check your work at a keyboard.
   (d) In each chord blank, write the Roman numeral and figure (if needed) that represents the harmony.

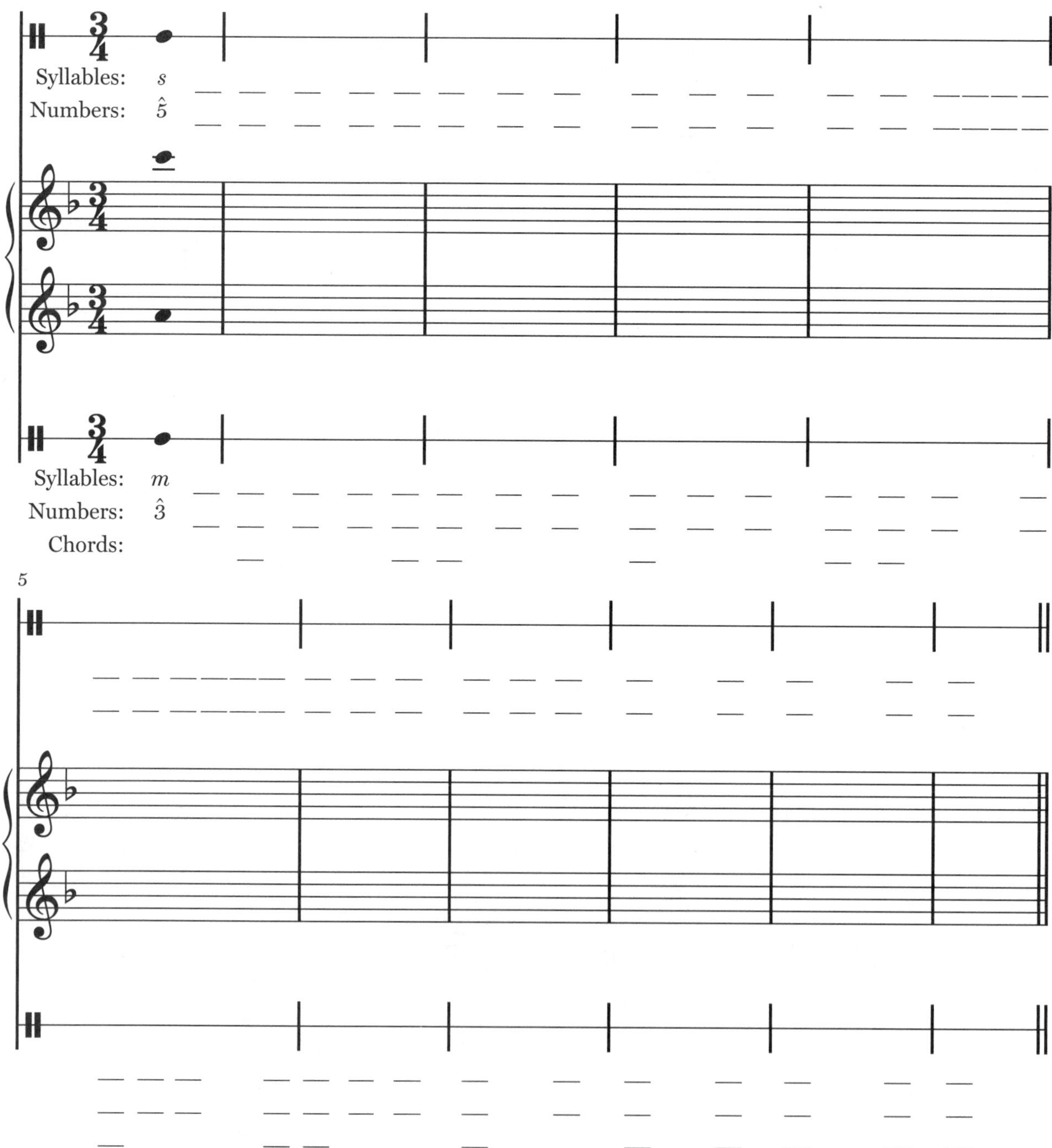

NAME ______________________________

4. At the beginning, the bass and middle pitch form which harmonic interval?

   unison   third   fifth   sixth

5. Phrase 1 ends with which cadence type?   PAC   IAC   HC
   Hint: Listen for cadential pitches in both the bass and the soprano.

6. Phrase 2's first melodic pitch is embellished with an/a:

   upper neighbor   lower neighbor   consonant skip   passing tone

7. Phrase 2 ends with which cadence type?   PAC   IAC   HC

8. Measure 8 sounds final, but the music continues. Measures 9–10 feature which of the following?

   tonic prolongation   cadential extension

   contrary-motion octaves   all of these

NAME ____________________

Contextual Listening 13.2

Exercises 1-3 each feature a three-chord progression. Focus especially on the bass and soprano and refer to the *Try it* listening strategies.

1. (a) Chords 1 and 3 are: i i^6 V^{8-7} V^6_5 V^4_3 V^4_2

   (b) Chord 2 is: i i^6 V^{8-7} V^6_5 V^4_3 V^4_2

   (c) The progression ends with the cadence type: PAC IAC HC

2. (a) Chord 1 is: i i^6 V^{8-7} V^6_5 V^4_3 V^4_2

   (b) Chord 2 is: i i^6 V^{8-7} V^6_5 V^4_3 V^4_2

   (c) Chord 3 is: i i^6 V^{8-7} V^6_5 V^4_3 V^4_2

3. (a) Chord 1 is: i i^6 V^{8-7} V^6_5 V^4_3 V^4_2

   (b) Chord 2 is: i i^6 V^{8-7} V^6_5 V^4_3 V^4_2

   (c) Chord 3 is: i i^6 V^{8-7} V^6_5 V^4_3 V^4_2

Now, listen to a folk song arrangement and complete the remaining exercises.

4. Beginning with the given items, capture the excerpt in the workspace.
   (a) In the single-line staves, notate the rhythm of the bass and soprano lines.
   (b) Below each note, write the syllables and numbers of the pitches.
   (c) In the grand staff, notate the pitches and rhythm of both parts. Refer to the single-line notation. Check your work at a keyboard.
   (d) In each chord blank, write the Roman numeral and figure (if needed) that represents the harmony.

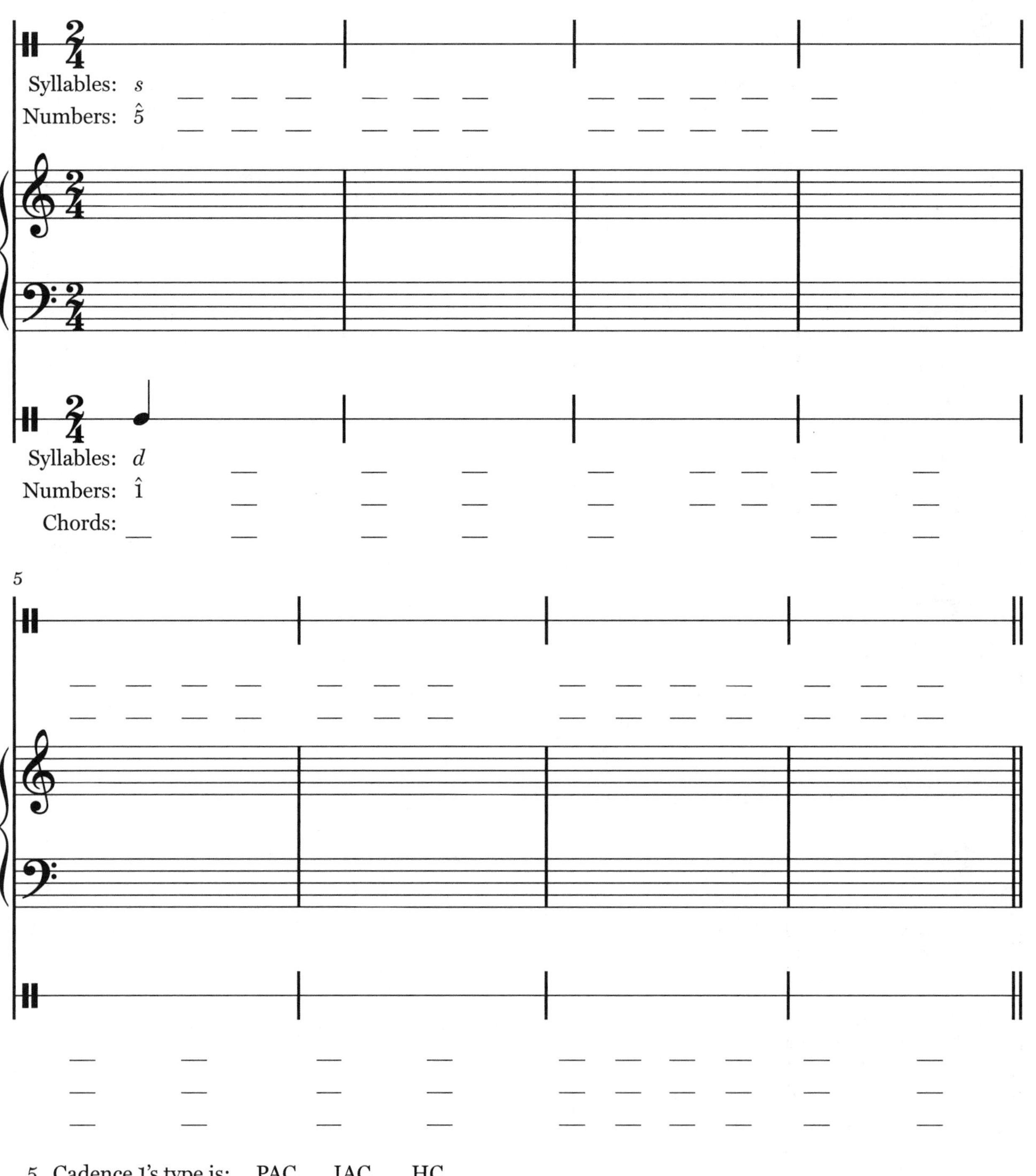

5. Cadence 1's type is: PAC IAC HC

6. Cadence 2's type is: PAC IAC HC

NAME ______________________________

Predominant Chords

When bass pitch *fa* ($\hat{4}$) rises to *sol* ($\hat{5}$), the function of the chord above *fa* ($\hat{4}$) is predominant. For now, we focus on the most common predominant-function chords: ii^6, ii^6_5, and IV.

Above fa ($\hat{4}$), *if you hear . . .*	*in major write*	*in minor write*	*then beneath* sol ($\hat{5}$), *write*
re ($\hat{2}$)	ii^6	$\text{ii}^{\circ 6}$	V
re + *do* ($\hat{2}$ + $\hat{1}$)	ii^6_5	$\text{ii}^{\varnothing 6}_{\ 5}$	V
only *do* ($\hat{1}$)	IV	iv	V

Try it 2

1. Cadence type: PAC IAC HC

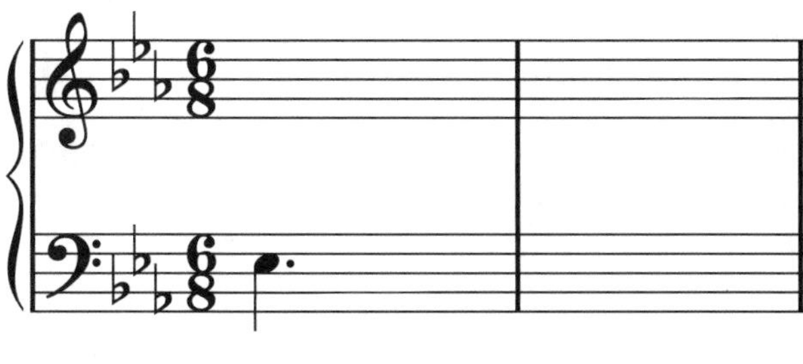

___: ___ ___ ___ ___ ___

2. Cadence type: PAC IAC HC

___: ___ ___ ___ ___

3. Cadence type: PAC IAC HC

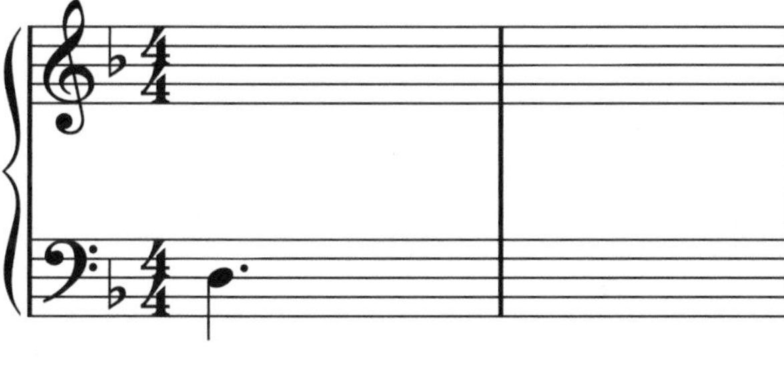

___: ___ ___ ___ ___ ___

4. Cadence type: PAC IAC HC

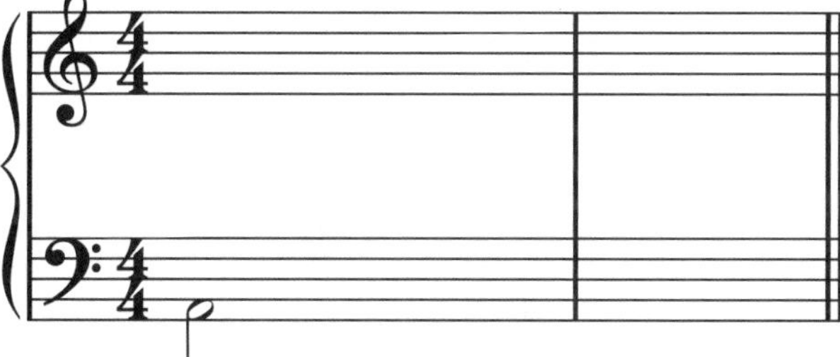

___: ___ ___ ___ ___

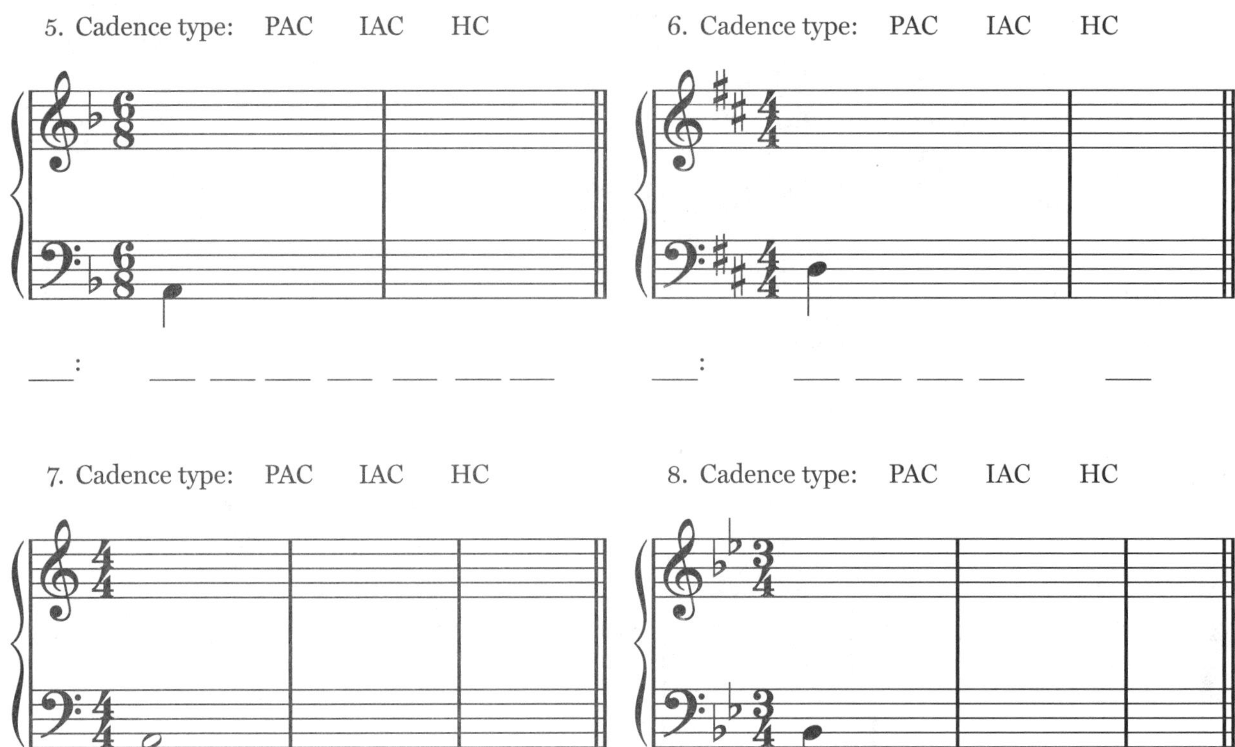
5. Cadence type: PAC IAC HC
6. Cadence type: PAC IAC HC
7. Cadence type: PAC IAC HC
8. Cadence type: PAC IAC HC

NAME ______________________

Contextual Listening 13.3

Exercises 1–2 feature short progressions. Focus especially on the bass and soprano and refer to the *Try it* listening strategies.

1. (a) Chords 1 and 4 are: I V V^{8-7} V^{6}_{5} V^{4}_{3} V^{4}_{2}
   (b) Chord 2 is: ii^{6} ii^{6}_{5} IV
   (c) Chord 3 is: I V V^{8-7} V^{6}_{5} V^{4}_{3} V^{4}_{2}
   (d) The progression ends with which cadence type? PAC IAC HC
2. (a) Chord 1 is: I V V^{8-7} V^{6}_{5} V^{4}_{3} V^{4}_{2}
   (b) Chord 2 is: ii^{6} ii^{6}_{5} IV
   (c) Chord 3 is: I V V^{8-7} V^{6}_{5} V^{4}_{3} V^{4}_{2}
   (d) The progression ends with which cadence type? PAC IAC HC

Now, listen to two phrases from an arrangement of an American spiritual.

3. Beginning with the given items, capture the excerpt in the workspace.
   (a) In the single-line staves, notate the rhythm of the bass and soprano lines.
   (b) Below each note, write the syllables and numbers of the pitches.
   (c) In the grand staff, notate the pitches and rhythm of both parts. Refer to the single-line notation. Check your work at a keyboard.
   (d) In each chord blank, write the Roman numeral and figure (if needed) that represents the harmony.

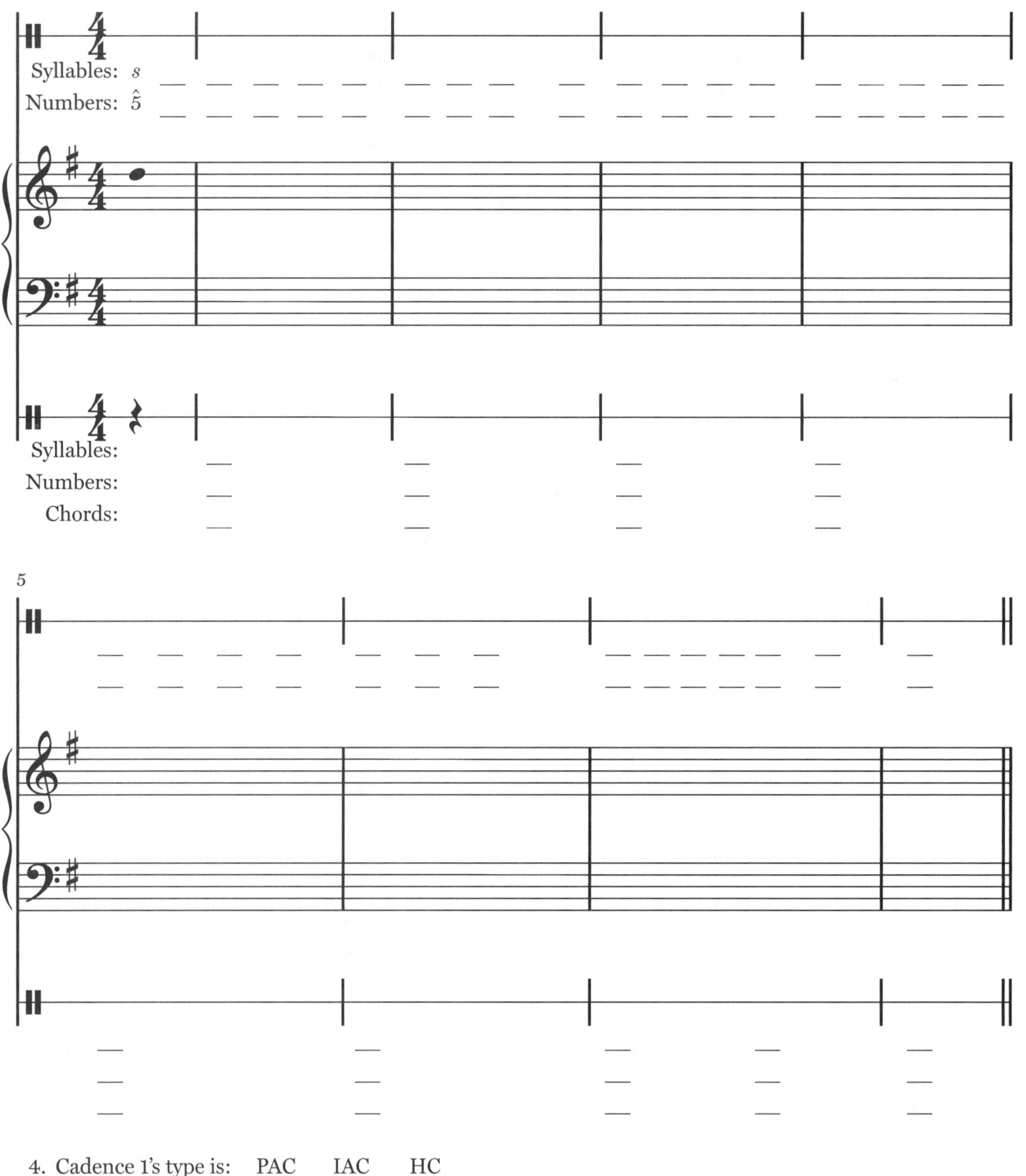

4. Cadence 1's type is: PAC IAC HC

5. Cadence 2's type is: PAC IAC HC

NAME ______________________

Contextual Listening 13.4

Exercises 1–2 each consist of one phrase of two-part counterpoint.

1. (a) The beat division is: simple compound
   (b) Which rhythmic device is featured? anacrusis syncopation triplets
   (c) The predominant chord implied is: ii^6 ii^6_5 IV
   (d) The cadence type is: PAC IAC HC
2. (a) Chords 1–2 are represented by which pair?
   I–V V–I ii^6–V IV–V
   (b) The predominant chord implied is: ii^6 ii^6_5 IV
   (c) The cadence type is: PAC IAC HC

Now, listen to one phrase from a piano sonata and complete the remaining exercises.

3. Beginning with the given items, capture the excerpt in the workspace.
   (a) In the single-line staves, notate the rhythm of the bass and soprano lines.
   (b) Below each note, write the syllables and numbers of the pitches.
   (c) In the grand staff, notate the pitches and rhythm of both parts. Refer to the single-line notation. Check your work at a keyboard.
   (d) In each chord blank, write the Roman numeral and figure (if needed) that represents the harmony.

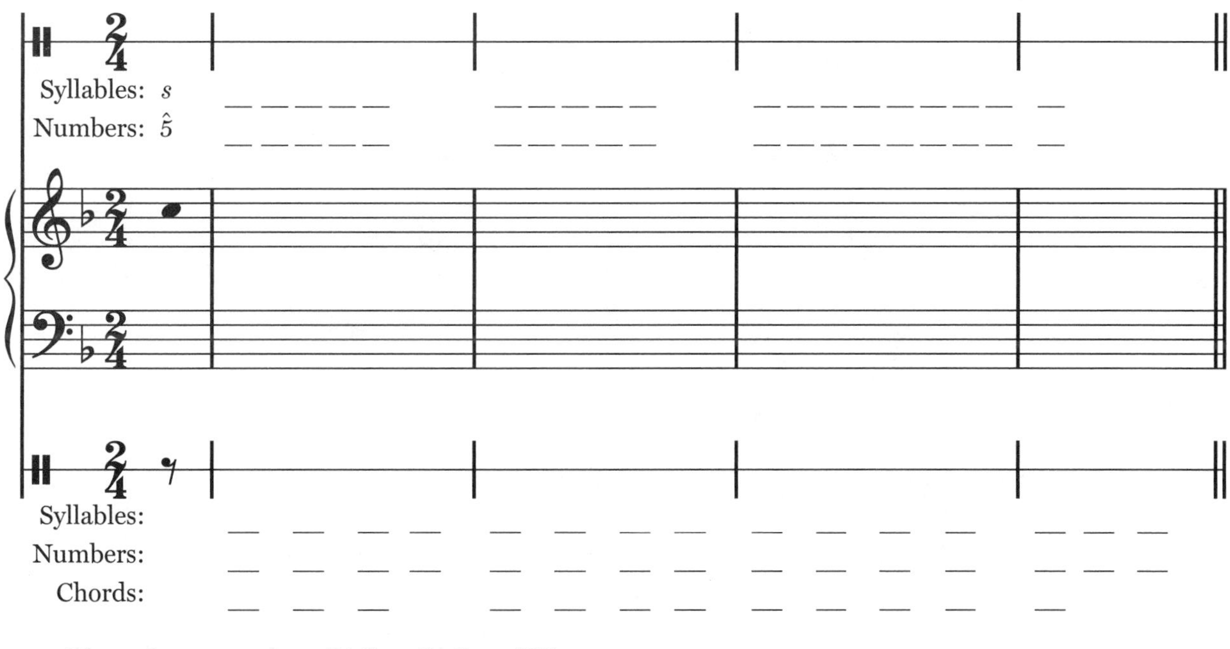

4. The cadence type is: PAC IAC HC

Expanding Harmonies with $^6_4$ Chords

NAME ______________________________

In this chapter you'll learn to:

- Identify $^6_4$ harmonies typical of Common Practice compositions

Expanding Harmonies with $^6_4$ Chords

In Common Practice music, $^6_4$ chords appear only in these four ways.

$^6_4$ type	*What it does*	*Listen for . . .*
Passing	harmonizes the passing tone in a voice exchange	tonic expansions to feature *do-re-mi* and *mi-re-do* $\hat{1}$-$\hat{2}$-$\hat{3}$ and $\hat{3}$-$\hat{2}$-$\hat{1}$
Neighboring (Pedal)	prolongs a triad's third and fifth with their upper neighbors	*mi-fa-mi* and *sol-la-sol* $\hat{3}$-$\hat{4}$-$\hat{3}$ and $\hat{5}$-$\hat{6}$-$\hat{5}$ over bass pitch *do* ($\hat{1}$)
Cadential	delays the resolution to the third and fifth of the V chord	*mi* → *re* ($\hat{3} \rightarrow \hat{2}$) *do* → *ti* ($\hat{1} \rightarrow \hat{7}$) over bass pitch *sol* ($\hat{5}$)
Arpeggiated	describes a moment where a triad's fifth is the lowest pitch	bass arpeggiation of a chord's root, third, fifth

Try it

Listen to four-part progressions. Sing each part aloud. In each exercise, identify beat division, predominant chord, type of $^6_4$ chords used, and cadence type.

1. (a) Beat division: simple compound
   (b) Predominant: ii^6 ii$^6_5$ IV
   (c) First $^6_4$: passing neighboring cadential
   (d) Second $^6_4$: passing neighboring cadential
   (e) Cadence type: PAC IAC HC

2. (a) Beat division: simple compound
   (b) Predominant: ii^6 ii^6_5 IV
   (c) First $^6_4$: passing neighboring cadential
   (d) Second $^6_4$: passing neighboring cadential
   (e) Cadence type: PAC IAC HC

3. (a) Beat division: simple compound
   (b) Predominant: $ii^{\circ 6}$ ii^6_5 iv
   (c) First $^6_4$: passing neighboring cadential
   (d) Second $^6_4$: passing neighboring cadential
   (e) Cadence type: PAC IAC HC

4. (a) Beat division: simple compound
   (b) Predominant: $ii^{\circ 6}$ $ii^{\varnothing 6}_5$ iv
   (c) First $^6_4$: passing neighboring cadential
   (d) Second $^6_4$: passing neighboring cadential
   (e) Cadence type: PAC IAC HC

5. (a) Beat division: simple compound
   (b) Predominant: ii^6 ii^6_5 IV
   (c) First $^6_4$: passing neighboring cadential
   (d) Second $^6_4$: passing neighboring cadential
   (e) Cadence type: PAC IAC HC

6. (a) Beat division: simple compound
   (b) Predominant: $ii^{\circ 6}$ $ii^{\varnothing 6}_5$ iv
   (c) First $^6_4$: passing neighboring cadential
   (d) Second $^6_4$: passing neighboring cadential
   (e) Cadence type: PAC IAC HC

7. (a) Beat division: simple compound
   (b) Predominant: $ii^{\circ 6}$ $ii^{\varnothing 6}_5$ iv
   (c) First $^6_4$: passing neighboring cadential
   (d) Second $^6_4$: passing neighboring cadential
   (e) Cadence type: PAC IAC HC

8. (a) Beat division: simple compound
   (b) Predominant: ii^6 ii^6_5 IV
   (c) First $^6_4$: passing neighboring cadential
   (d) Second $^6_4$: passing neighboring cadential
   (e) Cadence type: PAC IAC HC

NAME ______________________________

Contextual Listening 14.1

In exercises 1–3, write the syllables and numbers of the bass part. Beneath them, write the Roman numeral and figure (if needed) that represents the harmony.

1. Bass pitch:	1	2	3	4	5
Syllable:					
Number:					
Roman numeral:					

2. Bass pitch:	1	2	3	4	5
Syllable:					
Number:					
Roman numeral:					

3. Bass pitch:	1	2	3	4	5
Syllable:					
Number:					
Roman numeral:					

Now, listen to one phrase from a piano work and complete the remaining exercises.

4. Beginning with the given items, capture the excerpt in the workspace.
   (a) In the single-line staves, notate the rhythm of the bass and soprano lines.
   (b) Below each note, write the syllables and numbers of the pitches.
   (c) In the grand staff, notate the pitches and rhythm of both parts. Refer to the single-line notation. Check your work at a keyboard.
   (d) Between treble and bass staves, write the harmonic interval numbers.
   (e) In each chord blank, write the Roman numeral and figure (if needed) that represents the harmony.

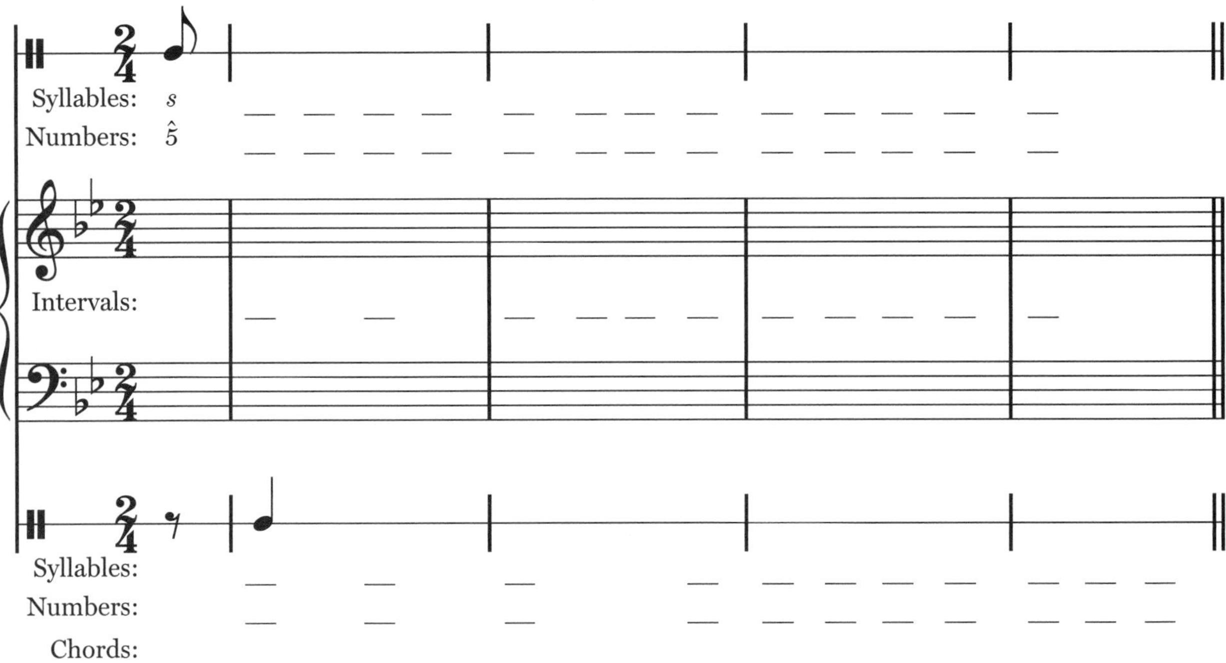

5. The type of $^6_4$ chord is: neighboring passing cadential

6. The phrase ends with which cadence type? PAC IAC HC

NAME ____________________

Contextual Listening 14.2

1. (a) Listen to two measures of music. Identify the bass pitches, harmonies, and $^6_4$ types.

Bass pitch:	1	2	3	4	5
Syllable:					
Number:					
Roman numeral:					

(b) In chords 1–3, the motion between bass and soprano is:

contrary oblique similar parallel

(c) Chord 2's $^6_4$ type is: passing neighboring cadential

(d) Chord 4's $^6_4$ type is: passing neighboring cadential

(e) The progression ends with which cadence type? PAC IAC HC

2. (a) Listen to two measures of music. Identify the bass pitches, harmonies, and $^6_4$ type.

Bass pitch:	1	2	3	4	5	6
Syllable:						
Number:						
Roman numeral:						

(b) In chords 1–3, the motion between bass and soprano is:

contrary oblique similar parallel

(c) Chord 4's $^6_4$ type is: passing neighboring cadential

(d) The progression ends with which cadence type? PAC IAC HC

Now, listen to the first phrase of a piano sonata and complete the remaining exercises.

3. (a) Identify the bass pitches, harmonies, and $^6_4$ type. Ignore chord 5.

Bass pitch:	1	2	3	4	5	6
Syllable:						
Number:						
Roman numeral:						

(b) In chords 2–4, the motion between bass and soprano is:

contrary oblique similar parallel

(c) Chord 3's $^6_4$ type is: passing neighboring cadential

(d) The progression ends with which cadence type? PAC IAC HC

NAME ____________________

Contextual Listening 14.3

1. (a) Listen to two measures of music. Identify bass pitches 1-5, their harmonies, the $^6_4$ type, and the cadence.

Bass pitch:	1	2	3	4	5
Syllable:					
Number:					
Roman numeral:					

(b) During chords 1–3, the motion between bass and soprano is:

contrary oblique similar parallel

(c) Melodic pitches 1–3 feature which embellishment?

consonant skip neighboring tone passing tone

(d) Chord 2's $^6_4$ type is: passing neighboring cadential

(e) The progression ends with which cadence type? PAC IAC HC

2. (a) Listen to two measures of music. Identify bass pitches 1-5, their harmonies, the $^6_4$ type, and the cadence.

Bass pitch:	1	2	3	4	5
Syllable:					
Number:					
Roman numeral:					

(b) During chords 1–3, the motion between bass and soprano is:

contrary oblique similar parallel

(c) Chord 4's $^6_4$ type is: passing neighboring cadential

(d) The progression ends with which cadence type? PAC IAC HC

Now, listen to one phrase from a chorale and complete the remaining exercises.

3. Beginning with the given items, capture the excerpt in the workspace.
   (a) In the single-line staves, notate the rhythm of the bass and soprano lines.
   (b) Below each note, write the syllables and numbers of the pitches.
   (c) In the grand staff, notate the pitches and rhythm of both parts. Refer to the single-line notation. Check your work at a keyboard.
   (d) Between treble and bass staves, write the harmonic interval numbers that occur on each beat.
   (e) In each chord blank, write the Roman numeral and figure (if needed) that represents the harmony.

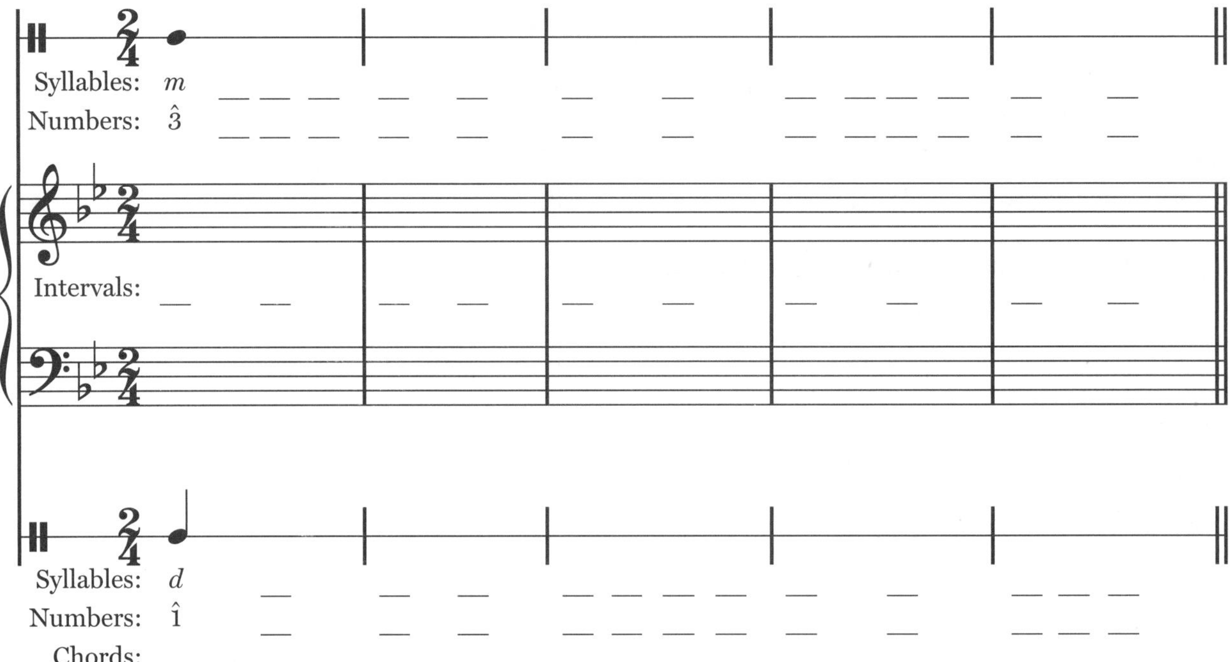

4. The type of $\substack{6\\4}$ chord heard in the first measure is:

   passing   neighboring   cadential

5. The phrase ends with which cadence type?   PAC   IAC   HC

Contextual Listening 14.4

Exercises 1–2 consist of two measure of music.

1. Listen to two measures of music. Identify the harmonies and $^6_4$ type.

   (a) What is the harmony in measure 1? I ii^6 IV V$^{8-7}$ V$^{6-5}_{4-3}$

   (b) In measure 2, which represents the harmony? I ii^6 IV V$^{8-7}$ V$^{6-5}_{4-3}$

   (c) The $^6_4$ chord type is: passing neighboring cadential

   (d) The progression ends with which cadence type? PAC IAC HC

2. Listen to two measures of music. For bass pitches 1–5, write the syllable and number. Beneath, write the Roman numeral that represents the harmony.

Bass pitch:	1	2	3	4	5
Syllable:					
Number:					
Roman numeral:					

   (a) The $^6_4$ chord type is: passing neighboring cadential

   (b) The progression ends with which cadence type? PAC IAC HC

Now, listen to one phrase from a piano sonata and complete the remaining exercises. For ease of dictation, the phrase is notated in the key of C (i.e., the dominant of F major).

3. Beginning with the given items, capture the excerpt in the workspace.
   (a) In the single-line staves, notate the rhythm of the bass and soprano lines.
   (b) Below each note, write the syllables and numbers of the pitches.
   (c) In the grand staff, notate the pitches and rhythm of both parts. Refer to the single-line notation. Check your work at a keyboard.
   (d) In each chord blank, write the Roman numeral and figure (if needed) that represents the harmony.

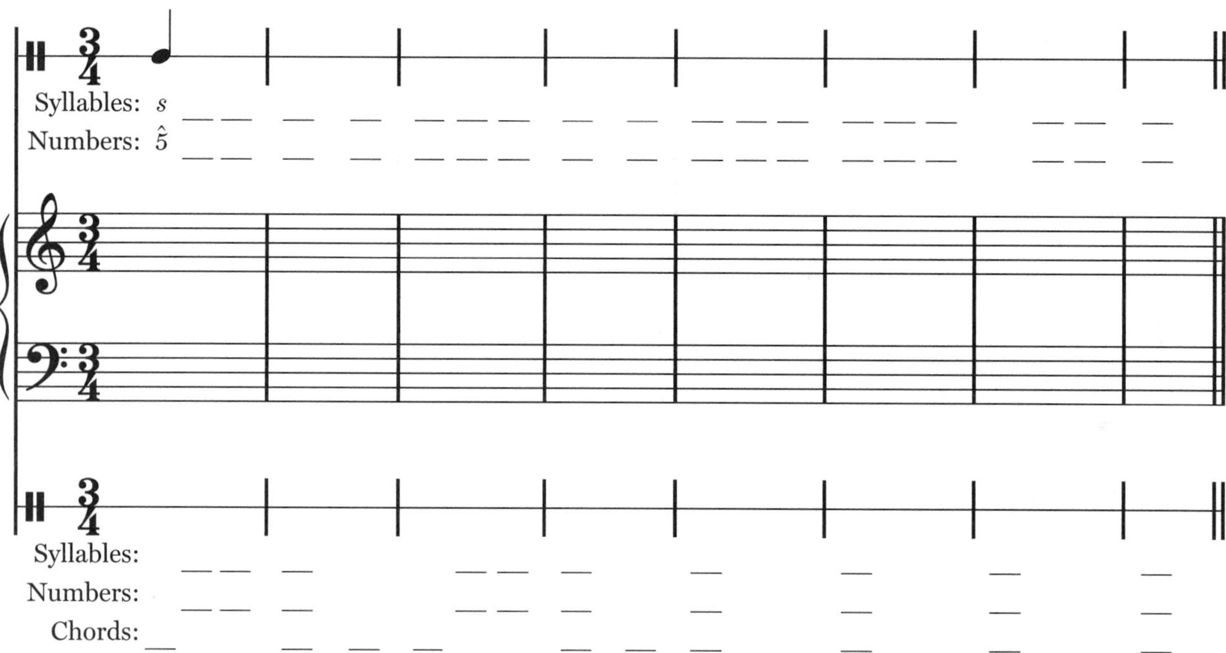

4. The phrase ends with which cadence type? PAC IAC HC

New Cadence Types

NAME ______________________

In this chapter you'll learn to:

- Recognize Phrygian, deceptive, and plagal cadences and resolutions
- Associate all cadence types with bass lines and their syllables and numbers

Deceptive, Plagal, and Phrygian Cadences and Resolutions

The Phrygian half cadence occurs frequently in minor-key works. Deceptive and plagal cadences are somewhat rare, but deceptive and plagal resolutions are common. Deceptive resolutions occur mid-phrase and delay the arrival of an authentic cadence. Plagal resolutions often extend or prolong an authentic cadence. Cadential bass pitches help you determine these progressions.

If cadential bass pitches are . . .	*the cadence or resolution is called . . .*
le–sol ($\flat\hat{6}$–$\hat{5}$)	Phrygian (PHC)
sol–la ($\hat{5}$–$\hat{6}$)	deceptive (DC)
fa–do ($\hat{4}$–$\hat{1}$)	plagal (PC)

Try it

Listen to four-part progressions. Sing each part aloud. In each exercise, identify beat division, predominant chord, the type of $^6_4$ chord or V chord specified, and the cadence type.

1. (a) Beat division: simple compound
   (b) Predominant: ii^6 ii$^6_5$ IV
   (c) $^6_4$ type: passing neighboring cadential
   (d) Cadence type: PAC IAC HC PHC DC PC
2. (a) Beat division: simple compound
   (b) Predominant: ii^6 ii$^6_5$ IV
   (c) $^6_4$ type: passing neighboring cadential
   (d) Cadence type: PAC IAC HC PHC DC PC

3. (a) Beat division: simple compound
   (b) Predominant: ii^{o6} $ii^{ø6}_{5}$ iv^6
   (c) $^6_4$ type: passing neighboring cadential
   (d) Cadence type: PAC IAC HC PHC DC PC

4. (a) Beat division: simple compound
   (b) Predominant: ii^6 ii^6_5 IV
   (c) $^6_4$ type: passing neighboring cadential
   (d) Cadence type: PAC IAC HC PHC DC PC

5. (a) Beat division: simple compound
   (b) Predominant: ii^{o6} $ii^{ø6}_{5}$ iv
   (c) Chord 2 is: V V^6_5 V^6_4 V^4_3 V^4_2
   (d) $^6_4$ type: passing neighboring cadential
   (e) Cadence type: PAC IAC HC PHC DC PC

6. (a) Beat division: simple compound
   (b) Predominant: ii^{o6} $ii^{ø6}_{5}$ iv^6
   (c) Chord 2 is: V V^6_5 V^6_4 V^4_3 V^4_2
   (d) Cadence type: PAC IAC HC PHC DC PC

7. (a) Beat division: simple compound
   (b) Predominant: ii^6 ii^6_5 IV
   (c) Chord 2 is: V V^6_5 V^6_4 V^4_3 V^4_2
   (d) $^6_4$ type: passing neighboring cadential
   (e) Cadence type: PAC IAC HC PHC DC PC

8. (a) Beat division: simple compound
   (b) Predominant: ii^{o6} $ii^{ø6}_{5}$ iv^6
   (c) Chord 4 is: V V^6_5 V^6_4 V^4_3 V^4_2
   (d) $^6_4$ type: passing neighboring cadential
   (e) Cadence type: PAC IAC HC PHC DC PC

NAME ______________________

Contextual Listening 15.1

Exercises 1–3 feature two-part counterpoint.

1. (a) The parallel harmonic intervals are of which size? 3 5 6 8

   (b) The cadence type is: PAC IAC HC PHC DC PC

2. (a) The first harmonic interval is which size? 3 5 6 8

   (b) The recurring suspensions create which interval pattern?

   2–3 4–3 7–6 9–8

   (c) The cadence type is: PAC IAC HC PHC DC PC

3. (a) The recurring harmonic intervals are: 3–3 3–4 3–5 3–6

   (b) The cadence type is: PAC IAC HC PHC DC PC

Now, listen to four two-measure phrases consisting of the outer parts from a chorale. Then, complete the remaining exercises.

4. Beginning with the given items, capture the excerpt in the workspace.
   (a) In the single-line staves, notate the rhythm of the bass and soprano lines.
   (b) Below each note, write the syllables and numbers of the pitches.
   (c) In the grand staff, notate the pitches and rhythm of both parts. Refer to the single-line notation. Check your work at a keyboard.
   (d) Between the treble and bass staves, write the harmonic interval numbers.

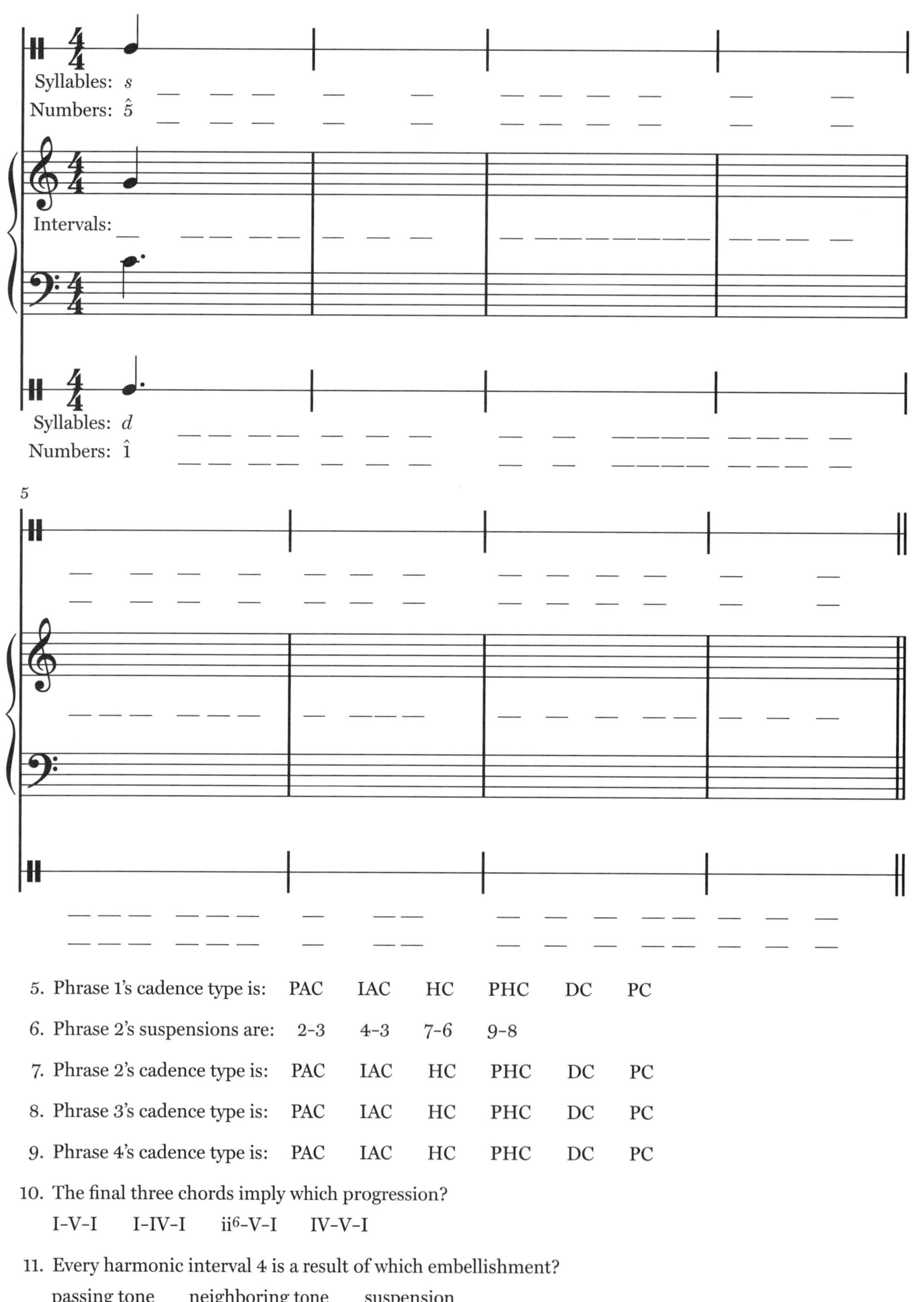

5. Phrase 1's cadence type is: PAC IAC HC PHC DC PC
6. Phrase 2's suspensions are: 2–3 4–3 7–6 9–8
7. Phrase 2's cadence type is: PAC IAC HC PHC DC PC
8. Phrase 3's cadence type is: PAC IAC HC PHC DC PC
9. Phrase 4's cadence type is: PAC IAC HC PHC DC PC
10. The final three chords imply which progression?
    I–V–I I–IV–I ii^6–V–I IV–V–I
11. Every harmonic interval 4 is a result of which embellishment?
    passing tone neighboring tone suspension

NAME ______________________________

Contextual Listening 15.2

Listen to a four-part progression. Sing each part aloud. In each exercise, identify the requested items.

1. Cadence type: PAC IAC HC PHC DC PC

2. (a) Predominant: $ii^{\circ 6}$ $ii^{\varnothing 6}_{5}$ iv^{6}
   (b) $^{6}_{4}$ type: passing neighboring cadential
   (c) Cadence type: PAC IAC HC PHC DC PC

3. (a) Predominant: $ii^{\circ 6}$ $ii^{\varnothing 6}_{5}$ iv^{6}
   (b) $^{6}_{4}$ type: passing neighboring cadential
   (c) Cadence type: PAC IAC HC PHC DC PC

Now, listen to the first phrase of a Baroque dance.

4. Beginning with the given items, capture the excerpt in the workspace.
   (a) In the single-line staves, notate the rhythm of the bass and soprano lines.
   (b) Below each note, write the syllables and numbers of the pitches.
   (c) In the grand staff, notate the pitches and rhythm of both parts. Refer to the single-line notation. Check your work at a keyboard.
   (d) In each chord blank, write the Roman numeral and figure (if needed) that represents the harmony.

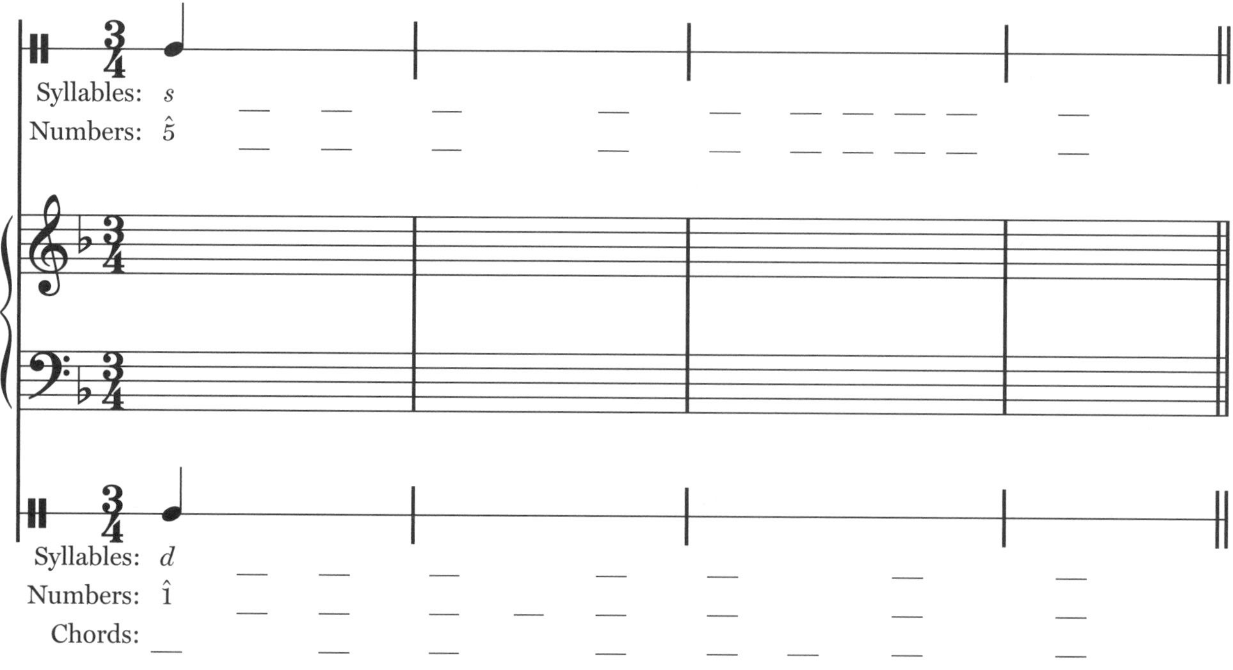

Syllables: *d*
Numbers: $\hat{1}$
Chords:

5. Measure 1, beat 3 features which $^6_4$ type? passing neighboring cadential
6. Which of the following occurs on measure 3, beat 1?
   PAC IAC HC PHC DC PC
7. Phrase 1's cadence type is:
   PAC IAC HC PHC DC PC

Listen to phrase 1 again, now followed by a second phrase.

8. The final cadence type is:
   PAC IAC HC PHC DC PC

NAME ______________________________

Contextual Listening 15.3

Listen to a four-part progression. Sing each part aloud. In each exercise, identify the requested items.

1. (a) Chord 2 is: V V^6_5 V^6_4 V^4_3 V^4_2
   (b) Chord 3 is: V V^6_5 V^6_4 V^4_3 V^4_2
   (c) Cadence type: PAC IAC HC PHC DC PC
2. (a) Chord 2 is: V V^6_5 V^6_4 V^4_3 V^4_2
   (b) $^6_4$ type: passing neighboring cadential
   (c) Cadence type: PAC IAC HC PHC DC PC
3. (a) Predominant: ii^6 ii^6_5 IV
   (b) $^6_4$ type: passing neighboring cadential
   (c) Cadence type: PAC IAC HC PHC DC PC

Now, listen to one phrase from a piano sonata and complete the remaining exercises.

4. Beginning with the given items, capture the excerpt in the workspace.
   (a) In the single-line staves, notate the rhythm of the bass and soprano lines.
   (b) Below each note, write the syllables and numbers of the pitches.
   (c) In the grand staff, notate the pitches and rhythm of both parts. Refer to the single-line notation. Check your work at a keyboard.
   (d) In each chord blank, write the Roman numeral and figure (if needed) that represents the harmony.

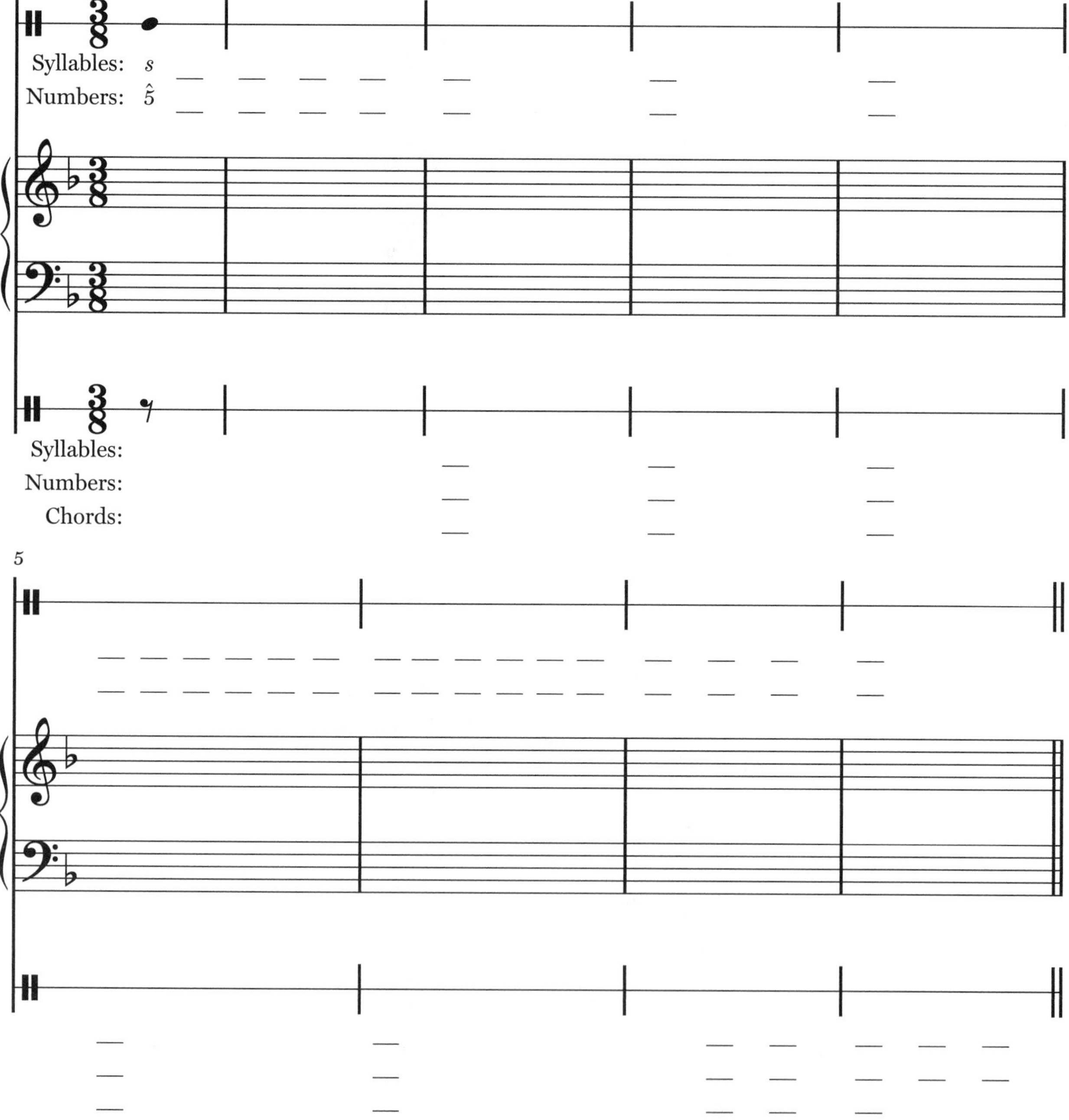

5. In measure 6, the chord's function is: predominant dominant tonic

Embellishing Tones

NAME ______________________________

In this chapter you'll learn to:

- Identify the rhythmic displacements anticipations, suspensions, and retardations
- Identify incomplete neighbor tones, pedal points, chromatic and bass-voice passing tones

Rhythmic Displacement, Incomplete Neighbor Tones, and Pedal Points

Some harmonic intervals anticipate or delay resolution to the expected pitch.

Does a pitch . . .		*You hear an/a . . .*
Anticipate the expected pitch?		Anticipation (A)
Delay the expected pitch? Then, does it . . .	*Fall* to resolve?	Suspension (S)
	Rise to resolve?	Retardation (also S)

Incomplete neighbor tones (N) appear as appoggiaturas or escape tones. Upper parts moving over a stationary bass pitch—usually the dominant or tonic—create a pedal point.

Appoggiatura (N)
Strong-beat neighbor tone
Weak-beat resolution

Escape Tone (N)
Strong-beat preparation
Weak-beat neighbor tone
Strong-beat resolution

Try it

Listen to four-part progressions. Sing each part aloud. Identify the items specified.

1. (a) Beat division: simple compound
   (b) Predominant: ii^6 ii^6_5 IV
   (c) Melodic pitches 2 and 4 are: CS N P
   (d) Melodic pitch 6 is an/a: anticipation (A) suspension/retardation (S)
   (e) Cadence type: PAC IAC HC PHC DC PC

2. (a) Beat division: simple compound
   (b) Predominant: ii^{o6} $ii^{ø6}_5$ iv^6
   (c) Melodic pitch 3 is an/a: anticipation (A) suspension/retardation (S)
   Choose figure(s): 2-3 4-3 7-6 7-8 9-8
   (d) Cadence type: PAC IAC HC PHC DC PC

3. (a) Beat division: simple compound
   (b) Predominant: ii^{o6} $ii^{ø6}_5$ iv iv^6
   (c) The final measure includes an/a: anticipation (A) suspension/retardation (S)
   Choose figure(s): 2-3 4-3 7-6 7-8 9-8
   (d) $^6_4$ type: passing neighbor cadential
   (e) Cadence type: PAC IAC HC PHC DC PC

4. (a) Beat division: simple compound
   (b) Predominant: ii^6 ii^6_5 IV
   (c) Melodic pitch 5 is an/a: anticipation (A) suspension/retardation (S)
   Choose figure(s): 2-3 4-3 7-6 7-8 9-8
   (d) $^6_4$ type: passing neighbor cadential
   (e) Cadence type: PAC IAC HC PHC DC PC

5. (a) Beat division: simple compound
   (b) Bass pitch 2 is a: CS N P chromatic P
   (c) Melodic pitch 3 is a: CS N P chromatic P
   (d) The final measure includes an/a: anticipation (A) suspension/retardation (S)
   Choose figure(s): 2-3 4-3 7-6 7-8 9-8
   (e) Cadence type: PAC IAC HC PHC DC PC

NAME ________________________________

Contextual Listening 16.1

Listen to four-part progressions. Sing each part aloud. Identify the items specified.

1. (a) Beat division: simple compound
   (b) Chord 1 is: V V^7 V^6_5 V^4_3 V^4_2
   (c) Melodic pitches 4, 7, 10 are which type of N: appoggiaturas escape tones
   (d) $^6_4$ type: passing neighbor cadential
   (e) The final measure includes an/a: anticipation (A) suspension/retardation (S)
   Choose figure(s): 2–3 4–3 7–6 7–8 9–8
   (f) Cadence type: PAC IAC HC PHC DC PC

2. (a) Beat division: simple compound
   (b) $^6_4$ type: passing neighbor cadential
   (c) Melodic pitch 6 is an/a: anticipation (A) suspension/retardation (S)
   (d) Cadence type: PAC IAC HC PHC DC PC

Now, listen to one phrase from a choral work and complete the remaining exercises.

3. Beginning with the given items, capture the excerpt in the workspace.
   (a) In the single-line staves, notate the rhythm of the bass and soprano lines.
   (b) Below each note, write the syllables and numbers of the pitches.
   (c) In the grand staff, notate the pitches and rhythm of both parts. Refer to the single-line notation. Sing aloud to check your work.
   (d) In each chord blank, write the Roman numeral and figure (if needed) that represents the harmony.

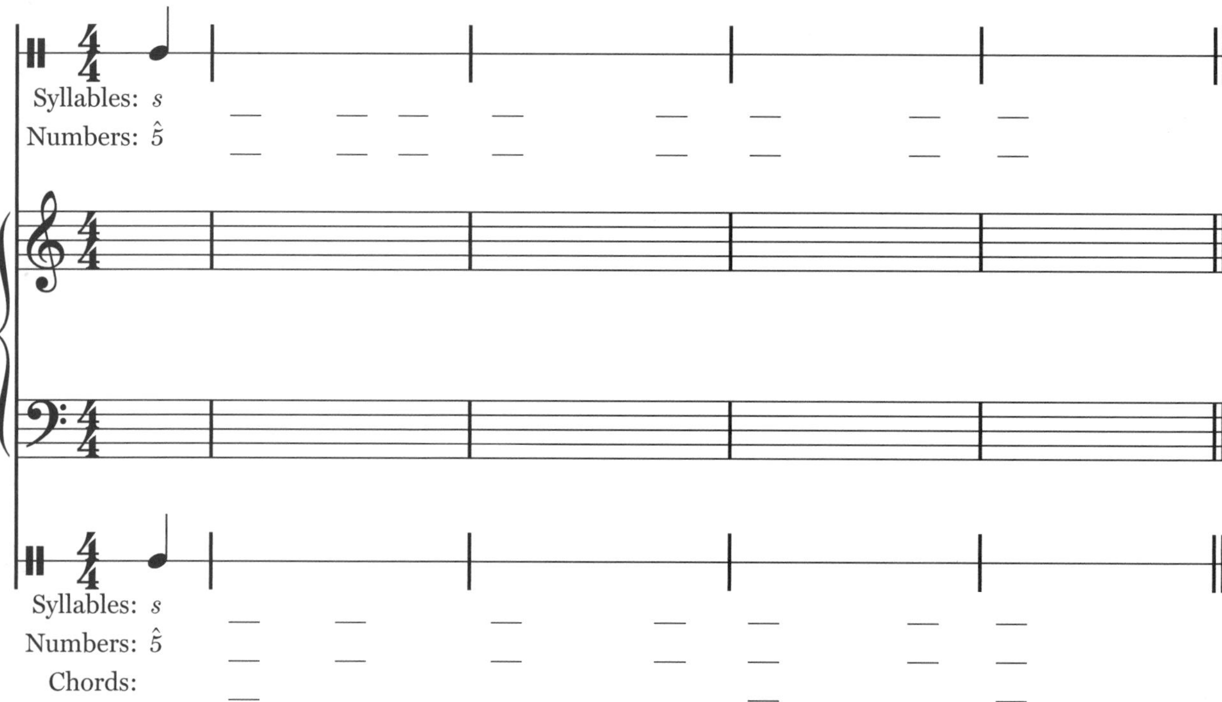

Translation: How hopeful is the world around.

4. Over bass pitch 6, which dissonance occurs?

   anticipation (A) 4-3 suspension (S)

   incomplete neighbor tone (N) chromatic passing tone (P)

5. The next-to-last melodic pitch is which type of dissonance?

   anticipation (A) 4-3 suspension (S)

   incomplete neighbor tone (N) chromatic passing tone (P)

6. The cadence type is:

   PAC IAC HC PHC DC PC

NAME ______________________

Contextual Listening 16.2

Listen to two progressions. Sing each part aloud. Identify the items specified.

1. (a) Beat division: simple compound
   (b) Melodic pitch 1 is embellished with a/an: upper N lower N incomplete N
   (c) The bass throughout is a/an: arpeggiating $^6_4$ pedal point CS
2. (a) Beat division: simple compound
   (b) Melodic pitches 2 and 5 are which type of N? appoggiaturas escape tones
   (c) Chord 2 is: V^6 V^6_5 V^4_3 V^4_2
   (d) $^6_4$ type: passing neighbor cadential
   (e) Cadence type: PAC IAC HC PHC DC PC

Now, listen to two, four-measure phrases for piano and complete the remaining exercises.

3. Write syllables and numbers for melodic pitches 1–7.

   m __ __ __ __ __ __
   $\hat{3}$ __ __ __ __ __ __
4. Melodic pitch 1, *mi* ($\hat{3}$), is embellished with an/a:
   upper N lower N incomplete N CS
5. Melodic pitch 5, *re* ($\hat{2}$), is which embellishment?
   upper N lower N incomplete N CS
6. Melodic pitches 6–7 are which embellishment?
   upper N lower N incomplete N CS
7. During most of phrase 1, the bass line's role is:
   tonic pedal point dominant pedal point
8. Phrase 1's cadence type is: PAC IAC HC PHC DC PC
9. Near the end, the $^6_4$ type is: passing neighbor cadential
10. The final two chords are: I–V IV–V V–I V^7–I
11. Phrase 2's cadence type is: PAC IAC HC PHC

Sketch space

NAME ______________________________

Contextual Listening 16.3

Listen to three-chord progressions and complete the exercises.

1. (a) The bass-line scale degrees are: $\hat{1}$-$\hat{2}$-$\hat{3}$ $\hat{1}$-$\hat{4}$-$\hat{3}$ $\hat{1}$-$\hat{7}$-$\hat{1}$ $\hat{3}$-$\hat{2}$-$\hat{1}$
   (b) Which of these is present between the bass line and an upper part?
   parallel 6ths parallel 10ths a voice exchange a suspension
   (c) Chord 2 is: V^6_4 V^4_3 V^6 V^6_5

2. (a) The bass-line scale degrees are: $\hat{1}$-$\hat{2}$-$\hat{3}$ $\hat{1}$-$\hat{4}$-$\hat{3}$ $\hat{1}$-$\hat{7}$-$\hat{1}$ $\hat{3}$-$\hat{2}$-$\hat{1}$
   (b) Which of these is present between the bass line and an upper part?
   parallel 6ths parallel 10ths a voice exchange a suspension
   (c) Chord 2 is: V^6_4 V^4_3 V^6 V^6_5

3. (a) The bass-line scale degrees are: $\hat{1}$-$\hat{2}$-$\hat{3}$ $\hat{1}$-$\hat{4}$-$\hat{3}$ $\hat{1}$-$\hat{7}$-$\hat{1}$ $\hat{3}$-$\hat{2}$-$\hat{1}$
   (b) Chord 2 is: V^6_4 V^4_3 V^6 V^6_5

Now, listen to two phrases from a piano work and complete the remaining exercises.

4. Beginning with the given items, capture the excerpt in the workspace.
   (a) In the single-line staves, notate the rhythm of the bass and soprano lines.
   (b) Below each note, write the syllables and numbers of the pitches.
   (c) Write harmonic interval numbers between the treble and bass staves. Identify each dissonant interval number (2, 4, or 7) by writing N for neighbor tone or S for suspension.
   (d) In the grand staff, notate pitches and rhythm of both parts. Refer to the single-line notation. Check your work at a keyboard.
   (e) In the given chord blanks, write the Roman numeral and figure (if needed) that represents the harmony.

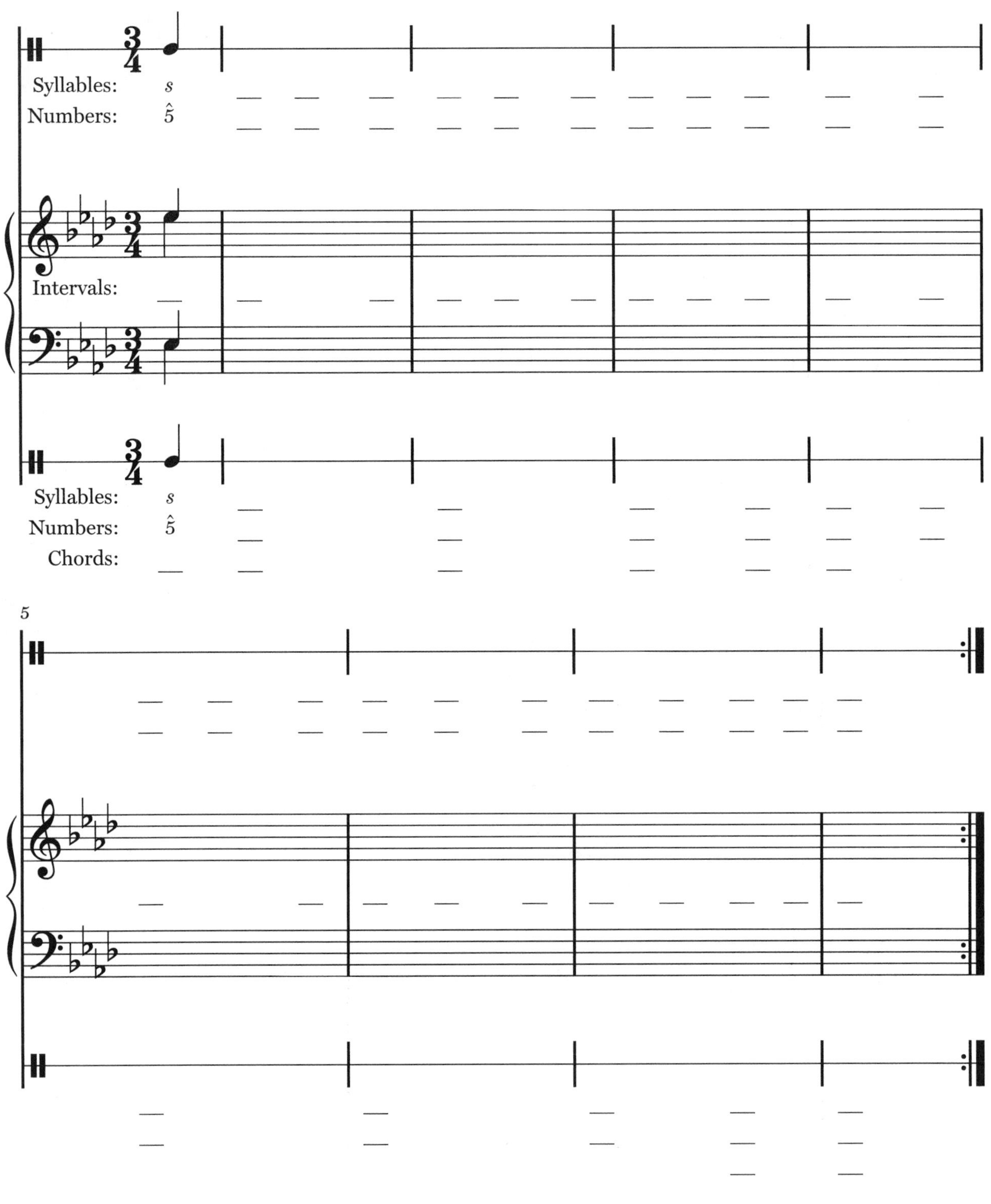

5. Phrase 1's cadence type is: PAC IAC HC PHC DC PC

6. The third-to-last melodic pitch is which type of neighbor tone?

   upper lower appoggiatura escape tone

7. Phrase 2's cadence type is: PAC IAC HC PHC DC PC

More Dominant-Function Harmonies

NAME ______________________________

In this chapter you'll learn to:

- Distinguish between V7 and vii°7 and their inversions
- Distinguish between vii°6 and V^6_4

Dominant-Function Seventh Chords and Their Tonic-Chord Resolutions (D–T)

Dominant-function seventh chords V7 and vii°7 both lead to tonic. Here are four examples of dominant-function seventh chords with their resolutions. The following observations can help you identify these D–T progressions.

- The V7 and vii°7 bass lines in 1-3 are identical: *ti-do* ($\hat{7}$-$\hat{1}$); *fa-me* ($\hat{4}$-$\flat\hat{3}$); and *re-do* ($\hat{2}$-$\hat{1}$).
- Example 4—*sol* ($\hat{5}$) in V7 or *le* ($\flat\hat{6}$) in vii°7—resolves to *sol* ($\hat{5}$).
- Certain bass-line scale degrees imply specific chords and resolutions: for example, *ti-do* ($\hat{7}$-$\hat{1}$) in the bass implies either V^6_5-i or vii°7-i.
- To hear the voice leading, sing the bass line as a four-part canon.

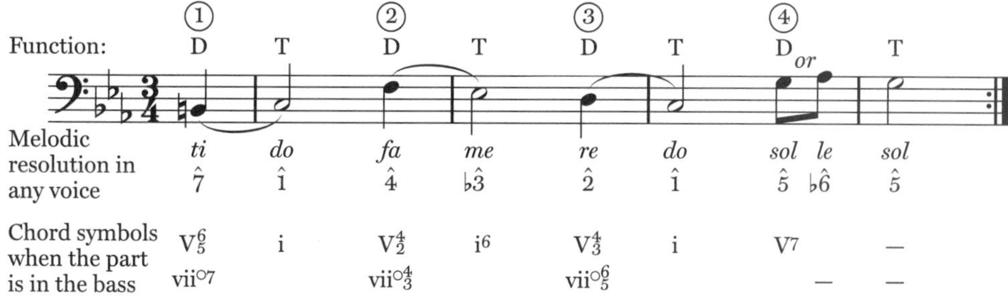

- Because V7 and vii°7 share *ti-re-fa* ($\hat{7}$-$\hat{2}$-$\hat{4}$), the differences shown here can help you determine which chord you heard.

Chord	V7	vii°7
Chord quality	dominant	fully diminished
Common tone with i	yes	no
Distinct pitch	*sol* ($\hat{5}$)	*le* ($\flat\hat{6}$)
Tritone(s)	1	2

Try it 1

Use the strategies you just learned to identify V7 and vii°7 in these paired, four-part progressions.

1. (a) Chord 2 is: V^6_5 vii°7
   (b) Chord 4 is: V^4_2 $vii^{\circ 4}_{3}$
   (c) Predominant: ii°6 $ii^{ø6}_{5}$ iv iv6
   (d) Cadence type: PAC IAC HC PHC

2. (a) Chord 2 is: V^6_5 vii°7
   (b) Chord 4 is: V^4_2 $vii^{\circ 4}_{3}$
   (c) Predominant: ii°6 $ii^{ø6}_{5}$ iv iv6
   (d) Cadence type: PAC IAC HC PHC

3. (a) Chord 2 is: V^4_3 $vii^{\circ 6}_{5}$
   (b) Chord 4 is: V^6_5 vii°7
   (c) Predominant: ii°6 $ii^{ø6}_{5}$ iv iv6
   (d) Cadence type: PAC IAC HC PHC

4. (a) Chord 2 is: V^4_3 $vii^{\circ 6}_{5}$
   (b) Chord 4 is: V^6_5 vii°7
   (c) Predominant: ii°6 $ii^{ø6}_{5}$ iv iv6
   (d) Cadence type: PAC IAC HC PHC

5. (a) Chord 2 is: V^4_2 $vii^{\circ 4}_{3}$
   (b) Chord 4 is: V^4_3 $vii^{\circ 6}_{5}$
   (c) Predominant: ii°6 $ii^{ø6}_{5}$ iv iv6
   (d) Cadence type: PAC IAC HC PHC

6. (a) Chord 2 is: V^4_2 $vii^{\circ 4}_{3}$
   (b) Chord 4 is: V^4_3 $vii^{\circ 6}_{5}$
   (c) Predominant: ii°6 $ii^{ø6}_{5}$ iv iv6
   (d) Cadence type: PAC IAC HC PHC

7. The meter type of exercises 1–6 is: simple compound

Dominant-Function Triads vii$^{\circ 6}$ and V$^{6}_{4}$

Triads vii$^{\circ 6}$ and V$^{6}_{4}$ both lead to tonic and often harmonize the passing tone in a voice exchange. Because they share *ti-re* ($\hat{7}$-$\hat{2}$), these differences help you determine which chord you heard.

Chord	V$^{6}_{4}$	vii$^{\circ 6}$
Chord quality	major	diminished
Common tone with i	yes	no
Distinct pitch	*sol* ($\hat{5}$)	*fa* ($\hat{4}$)
Tritone	0	1

Try it 2

Use the strategies you just learned to identify V$^{6}_{4}$ and vii$^{\circ 6}$ in these paired, four-part progressions. Near the end, listen for an embellishment.

1. (a) Chord 2 is: V$^{6}_{4}$ vii$^{\circ 6}$
   (b) Predominant: ii$^{\circ 6}$ ii$^{\varnothing 6}_{5}$ iv iv^{6}
   (c) Embellishment: CS N S P
   (d) Cadence type: PAC IAC HC PHC

2. (a) Chord 2 is: V$^{6}_{4}$ vii$^{\circ 6}$
   (b) Predominant: ii$^{\circ 6}$ ii$^{\varnothing 6}_{5}$ iv iv^{6}
   (c) Embellishment: CS N S P
   (d) Cadence type: PAC IAC HC PHC

3. (a) Chord 2 is: V$^{6}_{4}$ vii$^{\circ 6}$
   (b) Predominant: ii$^{\circ 6}$ ii$^{\varnothing 6}_{5}$ iv iv^{6}
   (c) Embellishment: CS N S P
   (d) Cadence type: PAC IAC HC PHC

4. (a) Chord 2 is: V$^{6}_{4}$ vii$^{\circ 6}$
   (b) Predominant: ii$^{\circ 6}$ ii$^{\varnothing 6}_{5}$ iv iv^{6}
   (c) Embellishment: CS N S P
   (d) Cadence type: PAC IAC HC PHC

NAME ______________________________

Contextual Listening 17.1

Identify dominant-function chords in these paired, four-part progressions. At the cadence, listen for an embellishment.

1. (a) Chord 2 is: V^6_4 $vii^{\circ 6}$
   (b) Predominant: $ii^{\circ 6}$ $ii^{\varnothing 4}_3$ iv iv^6
   (c) Embellishment: CS N S P
   (d) Cadence type: PAC IAC HC PHC

2. (a) Chord 2 is: V^6_4 $vii^{\circ 6}$
   (b) Predominant: $ii^{\circ 6}$ $ii^{\varnothing 6}_5$ iv iv^6
   (c) Embellishment: CS N S P
   (d) Cadence type: PAC IAC HC PHC

Now, listen to one phrase from a classical piano sonata and complete the remaining exercises.

3. Beginning with the given items, capture the music in the workspace.
   (a) In the single-line staves, notate the rhythm of the bass and soprano lines.
   (b) Below each note, write the syllables and numbers of the pitches.
   (c) In the grand staff, notate pitches and rhythm of both parts. Refer to the single-line notation. Check your work at a keyboard.

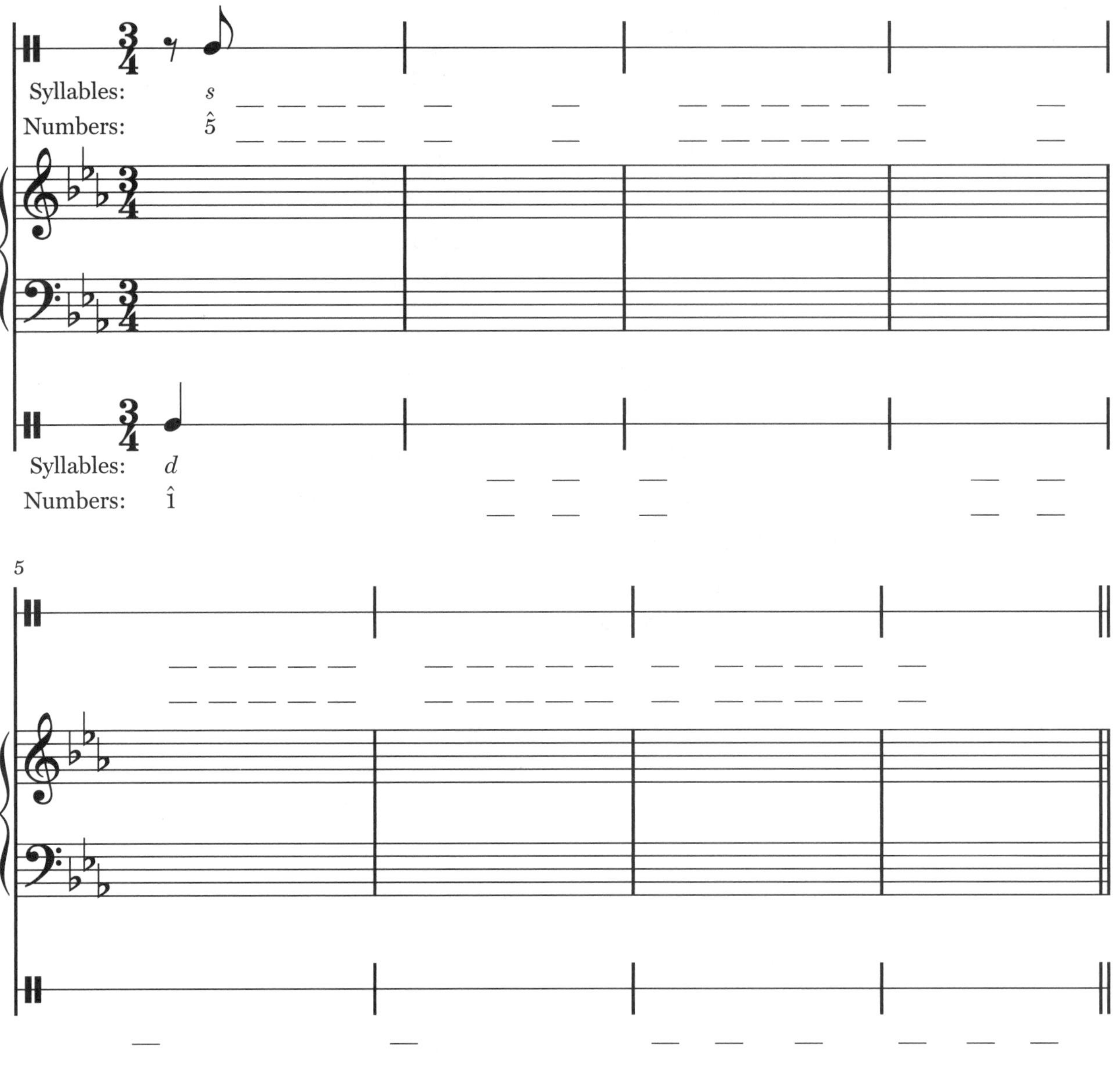

4. The progression in measures 1–4 is:

   i–V⁷–i⁶   i–ii°–i⁶   i–vii°⁶–i⁶

5. The four chords implied in measures 7–8 are:

   i–v⁶–iv⁶–V   i–VI–iv–V   i⁶–ii°⁶–V–i

NAME ____________________

Contextual Listening 17.2

Identify dominant-function seventh chords in these four-chord progressions.

1. (a) Chord 2 is: V^4_3 $vii^{\circ 6}_5$
   (b) Chord 3 is: V^4_2 $vii^{\circ 4}_3$

2. (a) Chord 2 is: V^4_3 $vii^{\circ 6}_5$
   (b) Chord 4 is: V^4_3 $vii^{\circ 6}_5$

Now, listen to one phrase from a classical piano sonata and complete the remaining exercises.

3. Beginning with the given items, capture the music in the workspace.
   (a) In the single-line staves, notate the rhythm of the bass and soprano lines.
   (b) Below each note, write the syllables and numbers of the pitches.
   (c) In the grand staff, notate pitches and rhythm of both parts. Refer to the single-line notation. Sing aloud to check your work.
   (d) Beneath each bass pitch, write the Roman numeral and figure (if needed) that represents the harmony.

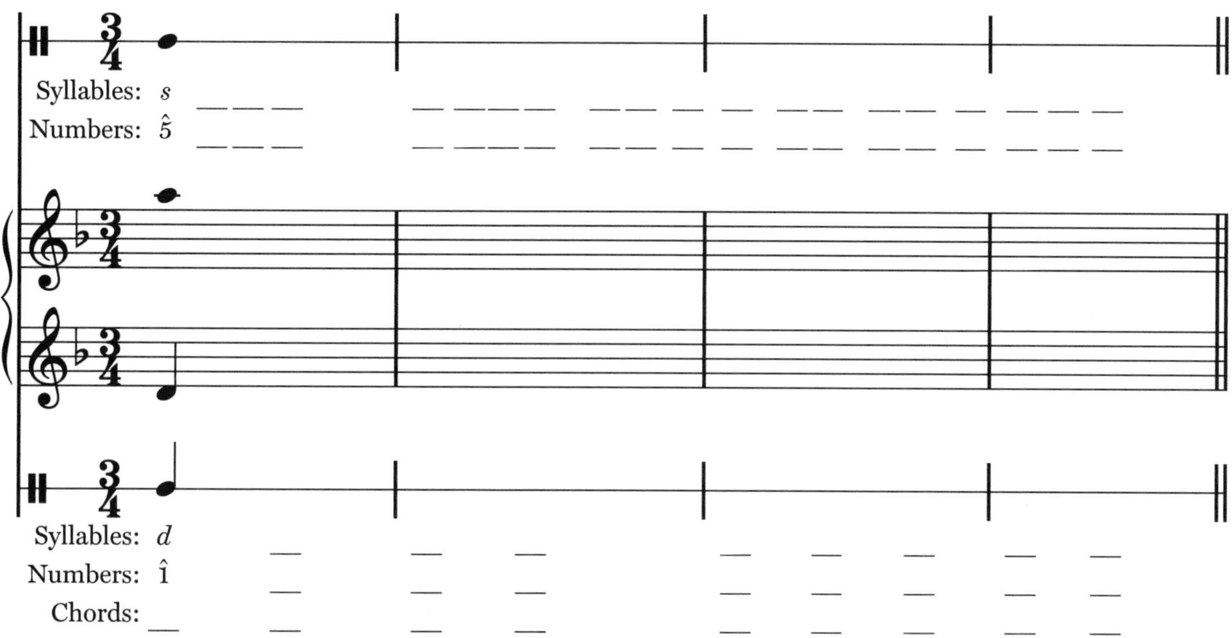

4. Near the end, the embellishment is a: CS N S P

5. The cadence type is: PAC IAC HC PHC

NAME ____________________

Contextual Listening 17.3

Identify dominant-function seventh chords in these four-chord progressions.

1. (a) Predominant: ii°6   iiø$^4_3$ iv   iv6
   (b) Chord 3 is: V$^6_5$ vii°7

2. (a) Chords 1–2 are: i$^{5-6}_{3-4}$ i–iv
   (b) Chord 3 is: V$^6_5$ vii°7

Now, listen to an instrumental adaptation of a choral work and complete the remaining exercises.

3. Beginning with the given items, capture the music in the workspace.
   (a) In the single-line staves, notate the rhythm of the bass and soprano lines.
   (b) Below each note, write the syllables and numbers of the pitches.
   (c) In the grand staff, notate pitches and rhythm of both parts. Refer to the single-line notation. Sing aloud to check your work.
   (d) Beneath each bass pitch, write the Roman numeral and figures (if needed) that represents the harmony.

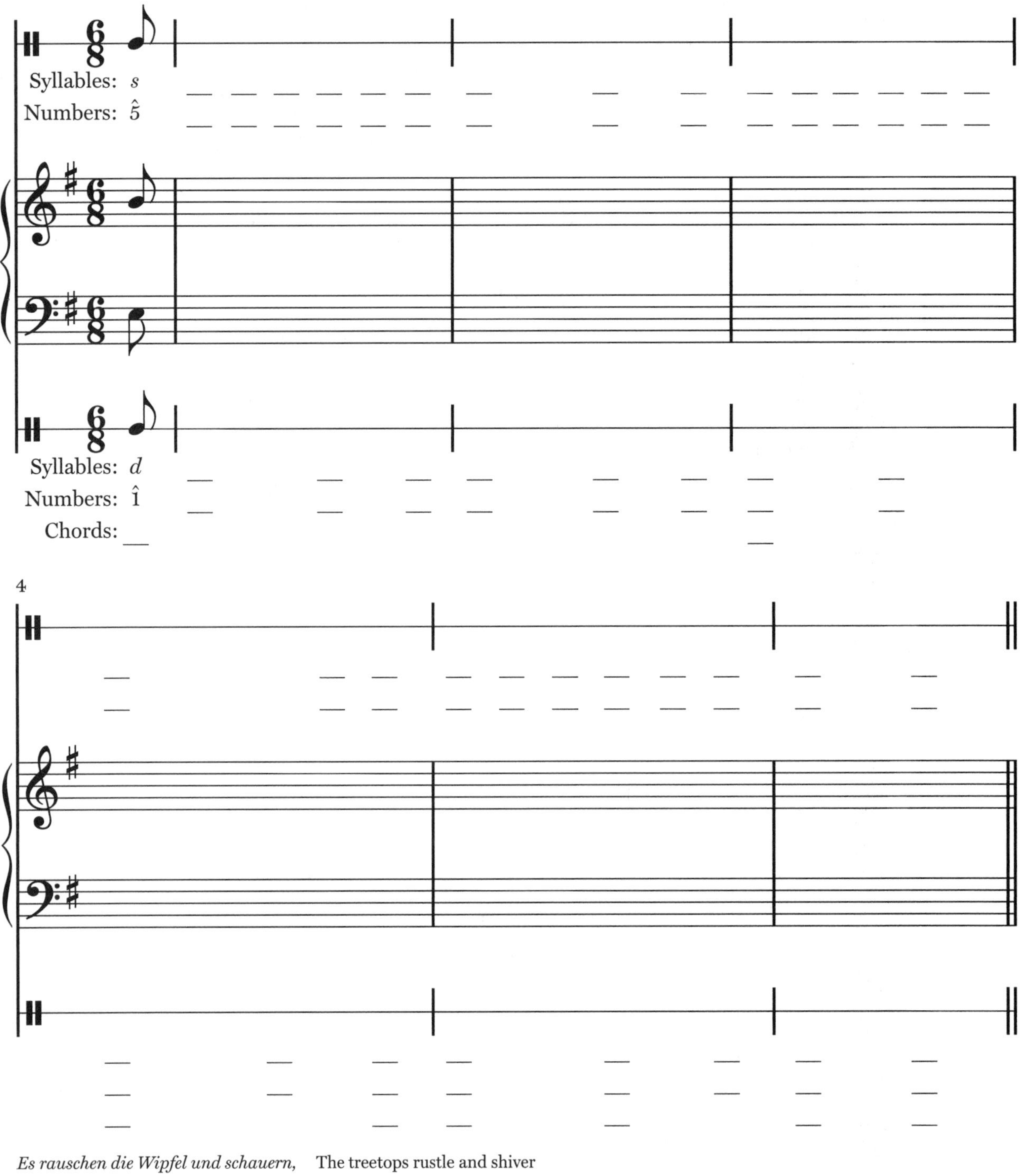

Es rauschen die Wipfel und schauern,
Als machten zu dieser Stund
Um die halbverfallenen Mauern
Die alten Götter die Rund.

The treetops rustle and shiver
as if at this hour
about the half-crumbled walls
the old gods are making their rounds.

Phrase Structure and Motivic Analysis

NAME ______________________

In this chapter you'll learn to:

- Identify subphrase, motive, sentence, and independent phrase
- Identify parallel and contrasting periods
- Diagram phrase structures

Phrase Subdivisions, Sentence, and Independent Phrase

Phrases can contain smaller units called subphrases, which themselves may consist of or contain a motive.

Phrase: the smallest complete idea that ends with a cadence
Subphrase: a cohesive part of a phrase
Motive: a recurring idea with distinct rhythm and contour

A phrase made from three subphrases with the proportion 1:1:2 is called a sentence.

| x^1 | x^2 | x^3 or y → | → cadence |
1 ——— + 1 ——— + 2 ———————

An isolated phrase that ends with a PAC is called an independent phrase.

Try it 1

Listen to part of a string quartet and complete the following exercises.

1. At the end, the $^6_4$ chord type is: passing neighboring cadential
2. The next-to-last melodic pitch is which embellishment?
   consonant skip passing tone retardation
3. The excerpt ends with a/an: PAC IAC HC

Identify which term or terms apply to the specified portion. More than one answer may apply.

4. Melodic pitches 1–5:

   motive subphrase phrase sentence independent phrase

5. Melodic pitches 6–10:

   motive subphrase phrase sentence independent phrase

6. Melodic pitches 11–end:

   motive subphrase phrase sentence independent phrase

7. The entire excerpt:

   motive subphrase phrase sentence independent phrase

Periods and Phrase Diagrams

Phrases often group in pairs called a period. Same or similar melodic beginnings receive the same letter name. A contrasting beginning receives a new letter name.

Phrase	*Phrase name*	*Cadence*	*Melodic beginnings*	*Letter name*	*Type of period*
1	antecedent	inconclusive, often a HC	initial motive	**a**	
2	consequent	always a PAC	same/similar to Phrase 1 different from Phrase 1	**a** or **a′** **b**	parallel contrasting

Phrase diagrams show structural levels, cadences, and unit names.

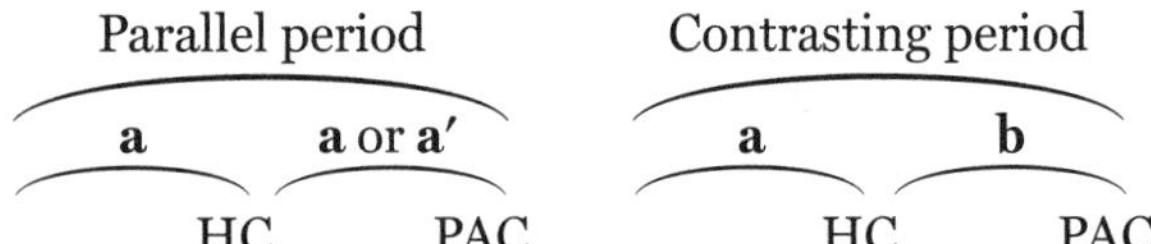

This diagram shows a parallel period comprising two phrases, each a three-subphrase sentence.

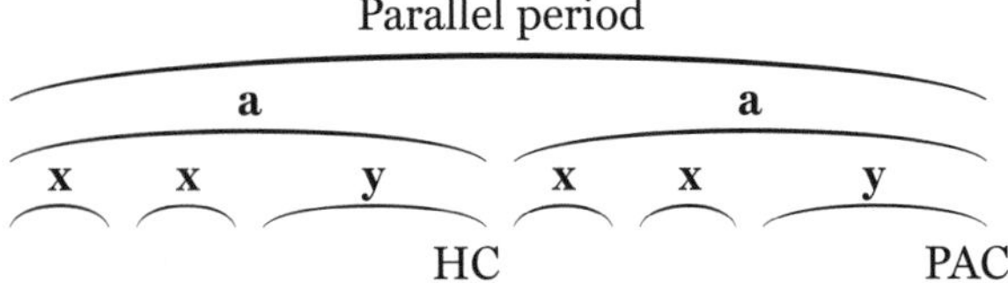

Try it 2

1. Listen to a two-phrase excerpt and complete the exercises.

   (a) Identify which term or terms apply to the specified portion. More than one answer may apply.

   (1) Melodic pitches 1–5:

   motive   subphrase   phrase   sentence   independent phrase

   (2) Melodic pitches 6–10:

   motive   subphrase   phrase   sentence   independent phrase

   (3) Melodic pitches 11–19:

   motive   subphrase   phrase   sentence   independent phrase

   (4) Melodic pitches 1–19:

   motive   subphrase   phrase   sentence   independent phrase

   (b) Phrase 1 ends with a/an: PAC   IAC   HC

   (c) Phrase 2 ends with a/an: PAC   IAC   HC

   (d) Phrases 1–2 complete which pattern?

   motive   subphrase   sentence   period

   (e) Compare phrase 2's beginning with that of phrase 1. Phrase 2 begins:

   the same or similarly (**a** or **a′**)   differently (**b**)

   (f) Which diagram represents the excerpt's structure?

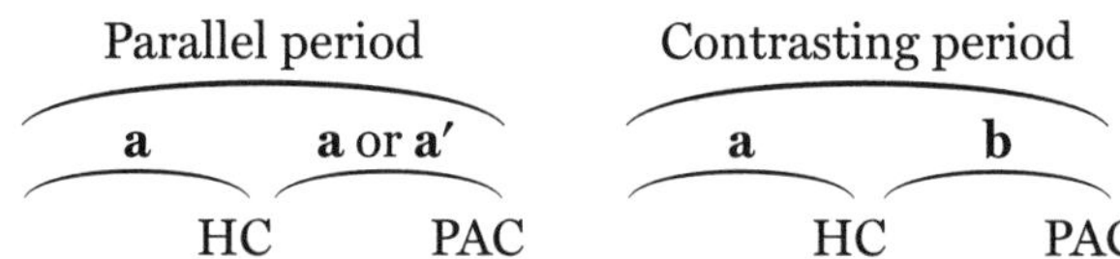

2. Listen to a two-phrase excerpt and complete the exercises.

   (a) Phrase 1 ends with a/an: PAC   IAC   HC

   (b) Phrase 2 ends with a/an: PAC   IAC   HC

   (c) Phrases 1–2 complete which pattern?

   motive   subphrase   sentence   period

   (d) Compare phrase 2's beginning with that of phrase 1. Phrase 2 begins:

   the same or similarly (**a** or **a′**)   differently (**b**)

   (e) Which diagram matches the excerpt's structure?

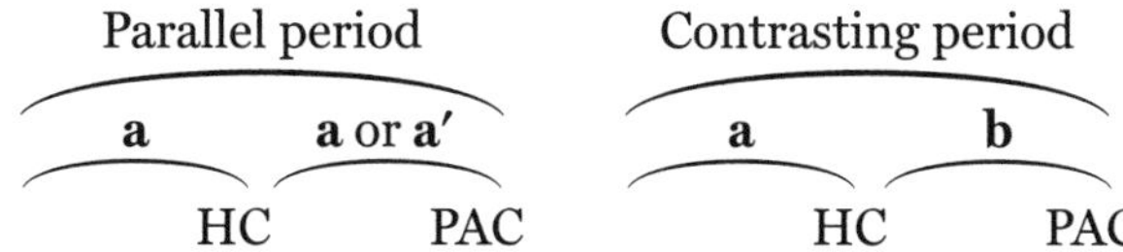

3. Locate and listen online to the initial vocal phrases of Billy Joel's "Piano Man."

   (a) The beat division is: simple compound

   (b) The lyrics "It's nine o'clock on a Saturday" complete a:

   motive subphrase sentence period

   (c) Compare phrase 2's beginning with that of phrase 1. Phrase 2 begins:

   the same or similarly (**a** or **a′**) differently (**b**)

   (d) The excerpt's structure is a:

   sentence parallel period contrasting period

NAME ______________________________

Contextual Listening 18.1

Listen to an eight-measure excerpt of a keyboard work and complete the following exercises.

1. The beat grouping is: duple triple quadruple
2. The beat division is: simple compound
3. The motive lasts how many measures? 1 2 3 4
4. The excerpt consists of how many subphrases? 1 2 3 4
5. The excerpt ends with which cadence? PAC IAC HC PHC
6. The excerpt's structure is a/an:
   phrase sentence independent phrase period

Listen to a different eight-measure excerpt of a keyboard work and complete the following exercises.

7. The beat grouping is: duple triple
8. The beat division is: simple compound
9. The motive lasts how many measures? 1 2 3 4
10. Phrase 1 ends with a/an: PAC IAC HC PHC
11. Phrase 2 ends with a/an: PAC IAC HC PHC
12. Compare phrase 2's beginning with that of phrase 1. Phrase 2 begins:
    the same or similarly (**a** or **a′**) differently (**b**)
13. Which diagram matches the excerpt's structure?

Parallel period

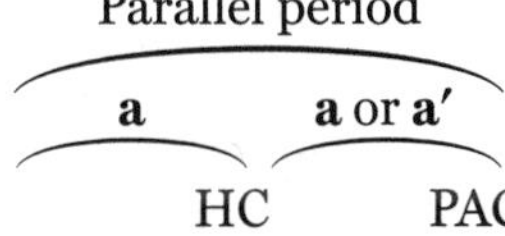

Contrasting period

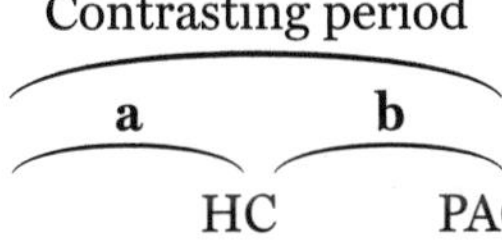

Contextual Listening 18.2

Listen to a two-phrase trumpet melody and complete the following exercises. Recall that melodic pitches can imply harmony.

1. The motive consists of how many pitches? 1 2 3 4 5 6 7 8
2. Phrase 1 ends with a: PAC IAC HC PHC
3. Phrase 1 consists of how many subphrases? 1 2 3 4
4. Phrase 1 is a/an: sentence period independent phrase
5. Phrase 2 ends with a/an: PAC IAC HC PHC
6. Which diagram represents the excerpt's structure?

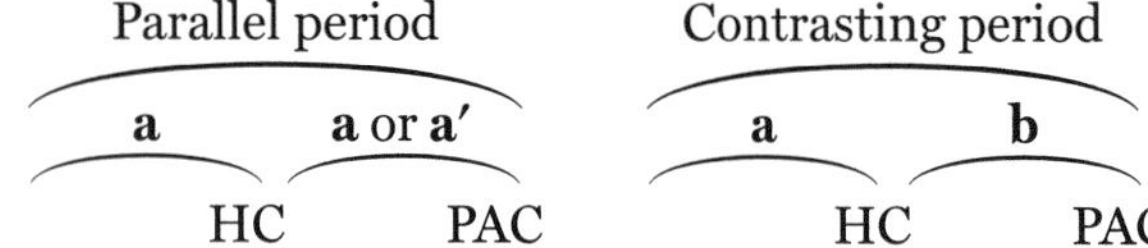

7. Beginning with the given items, capture the melody in the workspace.

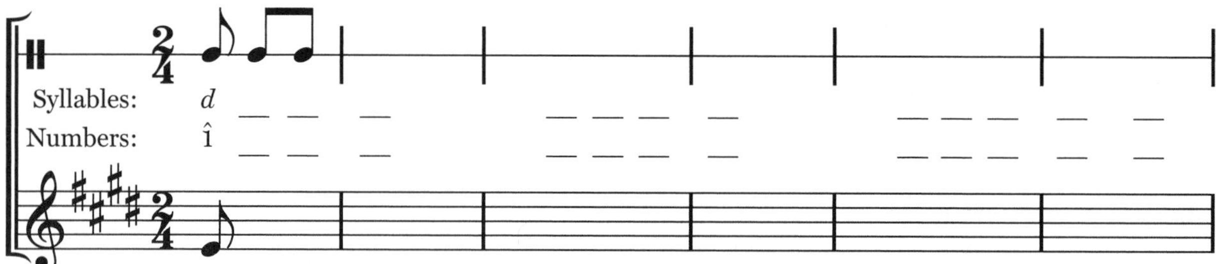

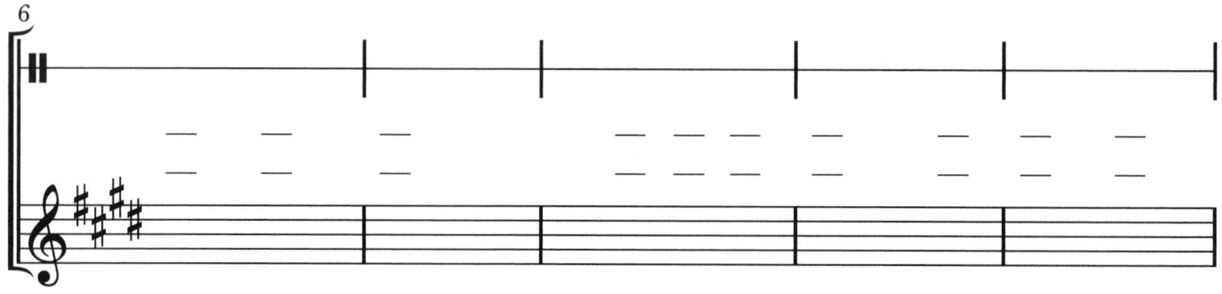

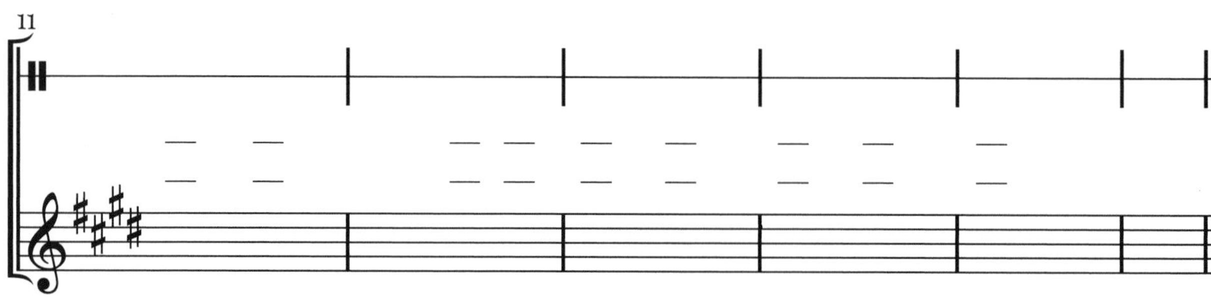

NAME ______________________________

Contextual Listening 18.3

Listen to eight measures from a piano work. Then complete the exercises.

1. The beat grouping is: duple triple quadruple
2. The beat division is: simple compound
3. The motive consists of how many pitches? 1 2 3 4 5 6 7 8
4. In measure 4, beat 1, phrase 1 ends with a: PAC IAC HC PHC
5. Phrase 1 consists of how many subphrases? 1 2 3 4
6. Phrase 1 is a/an: sentence period independent phrase
7. Phrase 2 ends with a/an: PAC IAC HC PHC
8. Which diagram represents the excerpt's structure?

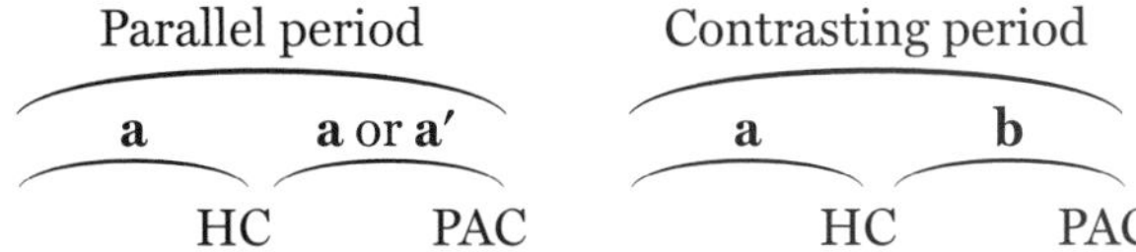

9. Each phrase includes which type of phrase expansion?

   introduction deceptive resolution cadential extension

10. Beginning with the given items, capture phrase 1's melody in the workspace. Include key and meter signatures. For help, refer to previous answers.

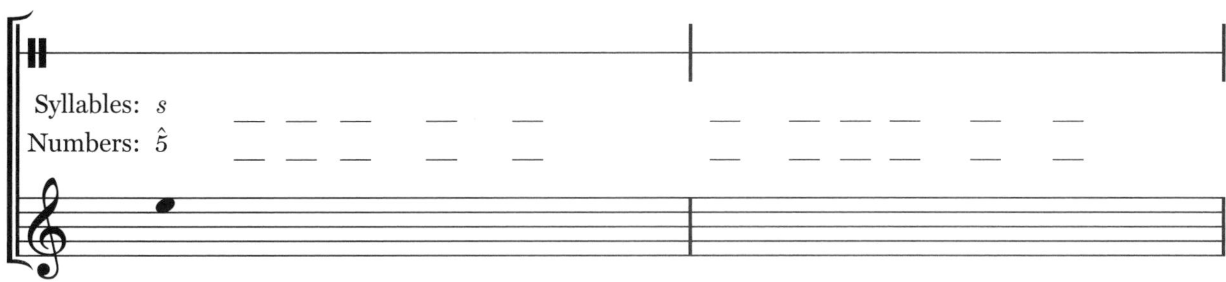

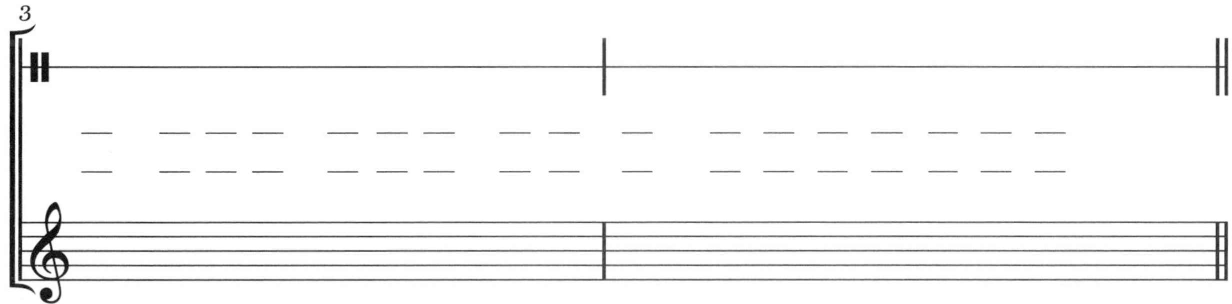

NAME ___________________________

Contextual Listening 18.4

Listen to four measures from a piano work. Then, complete the exercises.

1. The beat division is: simple compound
2. Phrase 1 ends with a: PAC IAC HC PHC
3. Phrase 1 consists of how many subphrases? 1 2 3 4
4. Phrase 2 ends with a/an: PAC IAC HC PHC
5. The excerpt's structure is a: parallel period contrasting period
6. Beginning with the given items, capture the melodic and bass lines in the workspace.
   (a) In the single-line staves, notate the rhythm. Below each note, write the syllables and numbers of the pitches.
   (b) In the grand staff, notate the pitches and rhythm of melody and the bass. (There is no need to double the bass one octave lower.)
   (c) In each chord blank, write the Roman numeral and figure (if needed) that represents the harmony.

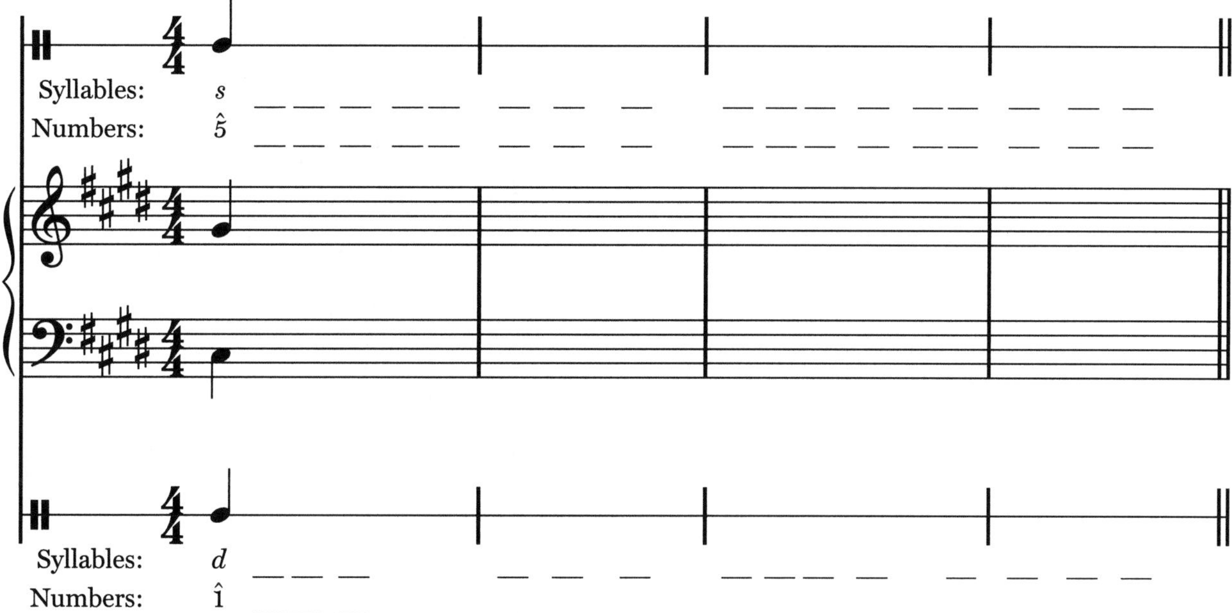

Double Periods

Typically, a double period is a four-phrase period. When the first consequent phrase begins the same or similarly as the first antecedent, the period is parallel. Otherwise, it is contrasting.

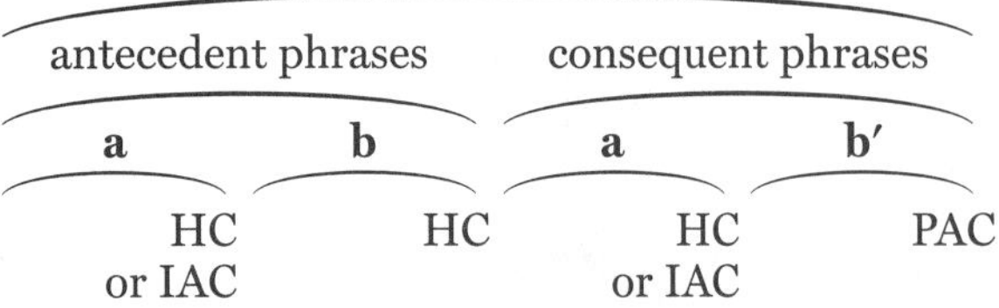

Asymmetrical periods have an unequal number of antecedent and consequent phrases.

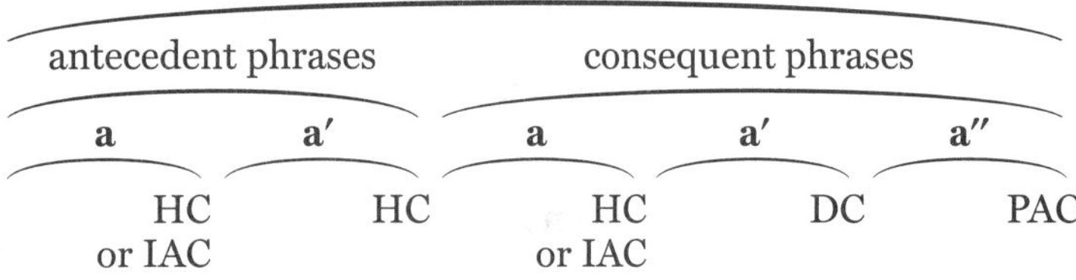

Try it 3

1. Listen to a piano work and complete the following exercises.

   (a) The bass rhythm is given. Below each note, write the syllables and numbers of the bass pitch. In each chord blank, write the Roman numeral and figure (if needed).

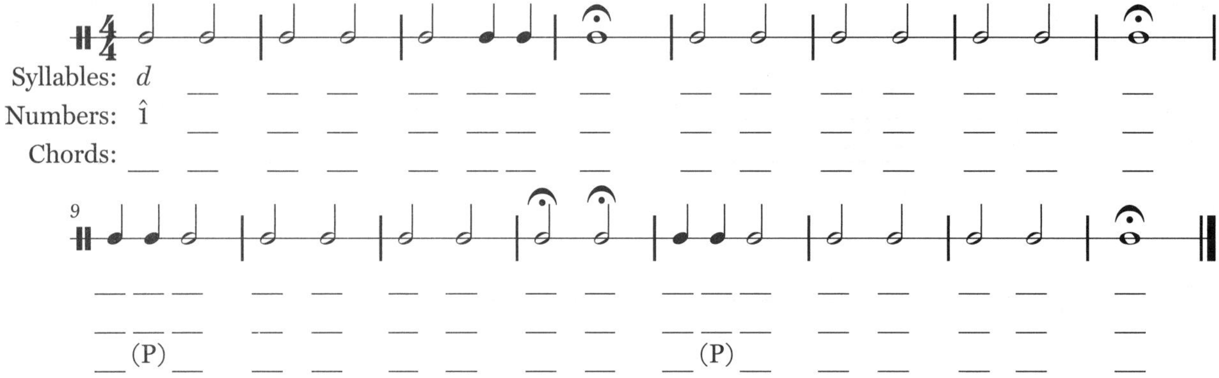

   (b) Diagram the structure. Follow the models given earlier and label each unit.

2. Listen to a different excerpt and diagram the structure. Label each unit.

NAME ______________________

Contextual Listening 18.5

Listen to a string duo and complete the following exercises.

1. The phrase design letters are: **a a a a** **a b a a′** **a b a b′**
2. Phrase 1's melody ends with: *do* ($\hat{1}$) *re* ($\hat{2}$) *mi* ($\hat{3}$) *sol* ($\hat{5}$)
3. (a) Phrase 2's melody ends with: *do* ($\hat{1}$) *re* ($\hat{2}$) *mi* ($\hat{3}$) *sol* ($\hat{5}$)
   (b) Phrase 2 has how many subphrases? 1 2 3 4
   (c) Phrase 2's structure is a/an: sentence independent phrase period
4. Phrase 3's melody ends with: *do* ($\hat{1}$) *re* ($\hat{2}$) *mi* ($\hat{3}$) *sol* ($\hat{5}$)
5. Phrase 4's melody ends with: *do* ($\hat{1}$) *re* ($\hat{2}$) *mi* ($\hat{3}$) *sol* ($\hat{5}$)
6. The cadences occur in which order? Hint: Focus on cadential bass pitches and the answers to exercises 2–5.

   HC–HC–HC–PAC HC–IAC–HC–PAC

   IAC–HC–IAC–PAC IAC–IAC–IAC–PAC
7. The excerpt's phrase structure is:

   parallel period contrasting period

   parallel double period contrasting double period
8. Draw a diagram of the excerpt's phrase structure. Label cadences, phrase design letters, and the overall structure (the answers to exercises 1, 6, and 7).

CHAPTER 42

Secondary Dominant-Function Chords of V

NAME ______________________________

In this chapter you'll learn to:

- Identify secondary dominant-function chords V^7/V and $\text{vii}^{\circ 7}/\text{V}$ and their inversions
- Notate music that includes secondary dominant-function chords

Secondary Dominant-Function Chords of V

Sometimes, *fi* ($\sharp\hat{4}$) is a melodic embellishment, like a chromatic neighbor tone. Other times, it is the leading tone of a dominant-function chord in the key of V. Bracket, slash, and colon notation are three ways to show secondary dominant-function chords.

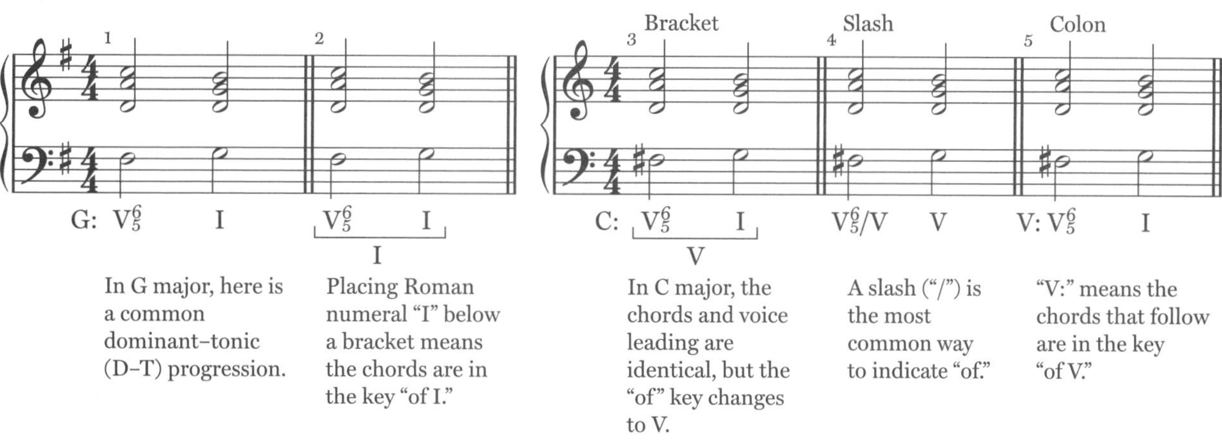
Bracket
Slash
Colon
1
2
3
4
5
G: V^6_5 I
V^6_5 I
I
C: V^6_5 I
V
V^6_5/V V
V: V^6_5 I
In G major, here is a common dominant–tonic (D–T) progression.
Placing Roman numeral "I" below a bracket means the chords are in the key "of I."
In C major, the chords and voice leading are identical, but the "of" key changes to V.
A slash ("/") is the most common way to indicate "of."
"V:" means the chords that follow are in the key "of V."

Try it

Listen to four-part progressions that include dominant-function chords of the tonic (e.g., V^6_5 and $\text{vii}^{\circ 7}$) and of the dominant (e.g., V^6_5/V and $\text{vii}^{\circ 7}/\text{V}$) and answer the following.

1. (a) Meter type: simple compound
   (b) Chord 2 is: V^6_5 $\text{vii}^{\circ 7}$ V^4_3 $\text{vii}^{\circ 6}_{\ 5}$
   (c) Chord 5 is: ii^6 ii^6_5 IV IV^6
   (d) Chord 6 is: V^7/V V^6_5/V V^4_3/V
   (e) Cadence type: PAC IAC HC DC

2. (a) Meter type: simple compound
   (b) Chord 2 is: V^6_5 $\text{vii}^{\circ 7}$ V^4_3 $\text{vii}^{\circ 6}_{\ 5}$
   (c) Chord 5 is: $\text{ii}^{\circ 6}$ $\text{ii}^{\varnothing 6}_{\ 5}$ iv iv^6
   (d) Chord 6 is: V^7/V V^6_5/V V^4_3/V
   (e) Cadence type: PAC IAC HC DC

3. (a) Meter type: simple compound
   (b) Chord 2 is: V$^4_3$ vii$^{\circ 6}_{5}$ V$^4_2$ vii$^{\circ 4}_{3}$
   (c) Chord 4 is: V^7/V V$^6_5$/V vii^{ø7}/V
   (d) $^6_4$ type: neighboring passing cadential
   (e) Cadence type: PAC IAC HC DC

4. (a) Meter type: simple compound
   (b) Chord 2 is: V$^6_5$ vii$^{\circ 7}$ V$^4_3$ vii$^{\circ 6}_{5}$
   (c) Chord 4 is: V^7/V V$^6_5$/V vii$^{\circ 7}$/V
   (d) $^6_4$ type: neighboring passing cadential
   (e) Cadence type: PAC IAC HC DC

5. (a) Meter type: simple compound
   (b) Chord 4 is: ii$^{\circ 6}$ ii$^{ø6}_{5}$ iv iv^6
   (c) Chord 5 is: V^7/V V$^6_5$/V vii$^{\circ 7}$/V
   (d) $^6_4$ type: neighboring passing cadential
   (e) Cadence type: PAC IAC HC PHC

6. (a) Meter type: simple compound
   (b) Chord 4 is: ii$^{\circ 6}$ ii$^{ø6}_{5}$ iv iv^6
   (c) Chord 6 is: V^7/V V$^6_5$/V vii$^{\circ 7}$/V
   (d) $^6_4$ type: neighboring passing cadential
   (e) Cadence type: PAC IAC HC PHC

7. (a) Meter type: simple compound
   (b) Chord 2 is: V$^4_3$ vii$^{\circ 6}$ V$^4_2$ vii$^{ø4}_{3}$
   (c) Chord 4 is: V^7/V V^6/V vii$^{\circ 7}$/V
   (d) Cadence type: PAC IAC HC PHC

8. (a) Meter type: simple compound
   (b) Chord 2 is: V$^6_4$ vii$^{\circ 6}$ V$^4_2$ vii$^{\circ 6}_{5}$
   (c) Chord 5 is: V^7/V V^6/V vii$^{\circ 7}$/V
   (d) Cadence type: PAC IAC HC PHC

NAME ______________________

Contextual Listening 19.1

CL 19.1A Listen to two phrases from a chorale and complete the following exercises.

1. Phrase 1's cadence type is: PAC IAC HC DC
2. Phrase 2's cadence type is: PAC IAC HC DC
3. Diagram the excerpt's structure. Draw curves for phrases. Label each phrase, cadence, and the entire structure.

4. In the top row of blanks, write phrase 2's bass pitches using syllables or numbers.

____ ____ ____ ____ ____ ____

____ ____ ____ ____ ____

5. Beneath the answers to exercise 4, write the Roman numerals and figures (if needed). Indicate secondary dominant-function chords using bracket, slash, or colon notation.

CL 19.1B Listen to two phrases from a chorale and complete the following exercises.

6. Phrase 1's melody ends with:

   mi-fa ($\hat{3}$–$\hat{4}$) *fi-sol* ($\sharp\hat{4}$–$\hat{5}$) *si-la* ($\sharp\hat{5}$–$\hat{6}$) *ti-do* ($\hat{7}$–$\hat{8}$)
7. Phrase 1's final two chords are: I–V IV–V V/V–V V–I
8. Phrase 2's cadence type is: PAC IAC HC DC
9. In the top row of blanks, write the final three bass pitches with syllables or numbers.

____ ____ ____

____ ____ ____

10. Beneath the answers to exercise 9, write the Roman numerals and figures (if needed). Indicate secondary dominant-function chords using bracket, slash, or colon notation.

CL 19.1C Listen to one phrase from a chorale and complete the following exercises.

11. The cadence type is: PAC IAC HC DC
12. In the top row of blanks, write the final three bass pitches using syllables or numbers.

____ ____ ____

____ ____ ____

13. Beneath the answers to exercise 12, write the Roman numerals and figures (if needed). Indicate secondary dominant-function chords using bracket, slash, or colon notation.

Contextual Listening 19.2

CL 19.2A Near the end of CL 19.2A, listen for *fi* ($\sharp\hat{4}$) in the inner voice.

1. The final three bass pitches are:

   re-sol-do ($\hat{2}$–$\hat{5}$–$\hat{1}$) *mi-sol-do* ($\hat{3}$–$\hat{5}$–$\hat{1}$) *fa-sol-do* ($\hat{4}$–$\hat{5}$–$\hat{1}$) *sol-sol-do* ($\hat{5}$–$\hat{5}$–$\hat{1}$)

2. The last three chords are: ii–V–I IV–V–I V7/V–V7–I ii–V^6_5–I

CL 19.2B Listen to a phrase from a string quartet. At the end, focus on the bass line.

3. The final three bass pitches are:

   do-mi-sol ($\hat{1}$–$\hat{3}$–$\hat{5}$) *re-sol-do* ($\hat{2}$–$\hat{5}$–$\hat{1}$) *fa-fi-sol* ($\hat{4}$–$\sharp\hat{4}$–$\hat{5}$) *ti-sol-sol* ($\hat{7}$–$\hat{5}$–$\hat{5}$)

4. *Fi* ($\sharp\hat{4}$) is part of which chord? Hint: Listen for the next-to-last melodic pitch.

   I7 ii7 V7/V vii^{ø7}/V

CL 19.2C Listen to a phrase from a song. Focus especially on the bass pitches.

Translation: Beside the brook grow many small flowers, gazing out of bright blue eyes.

5. Chords 1–3 form which progression?

   I–V–I I–V^6_4–I6 I–V^4_3–I6 I–ii–I6

6. Bass pitches 4–6 are:

   do-di-re ($\hat{1}$–$\sharp\hat{1}$–$\hat{2}$) *re-ri-mi* ($\hat{2}$–$\sharp\hat{2}$–$\hat{3}$) *mi-fa-sol* ($\hat{3}$–$\hat{4}$–$\hat{5}$) *fa-fi-sol* ($\hat{4}$–$\sharp\hat{4}$–$\hat{5}$)

7. *Fi* ($\sharp\hat{4}$) is harmonized with which chord? ii7 V7 V^6_5/V vi

NAME ______________________

Contextual Listening 19.3

Listen to short excerpts and choose the progression played.

1. I–V7–I   I–V^6_5–I   I–V^4_3–I6   I–V^4_2–I6
2. I–V7–I   I–V^6_5–I   I–V^4_3–I6   I–V^4_2–I6
3. I–V7–I   I–V^6_5–I   I–V^4_3–I6   I–V^4_2–I6

Now, listen to two phrases from a piano work and complete the remaining exercises.

4. Which meter signature is most likely? $\frac{3}{4}$ $\frac{6}{8}$ $\frac{9}{8}$
5. Initially, the two lower parts are doubled at which harmonic interval?

   third   fifth   sixth   octave
6. Phrase 1's cadence type is: PAC   IAC   HC   DC
7. Phrase 2's cadence type is: PAC   IAC   HC   DC
8. Diagram the excerpt's structure. Draw curves for phrases. Label each phrase, cadence, and the entire structure.

9. Beginning with the given items, capture the excerpt in the workspace.
   (a) In the single-line staves, notate the rhythm of the melody and bass. Below each note, write the syllables and numbers of the pitches.
   (b) In the grand staff, notate the pitches and rhythm of the melody and bass lines.
   (c) In the chord blanks specified, write the Roman numeral and figure (if needed) that represents the harmony.

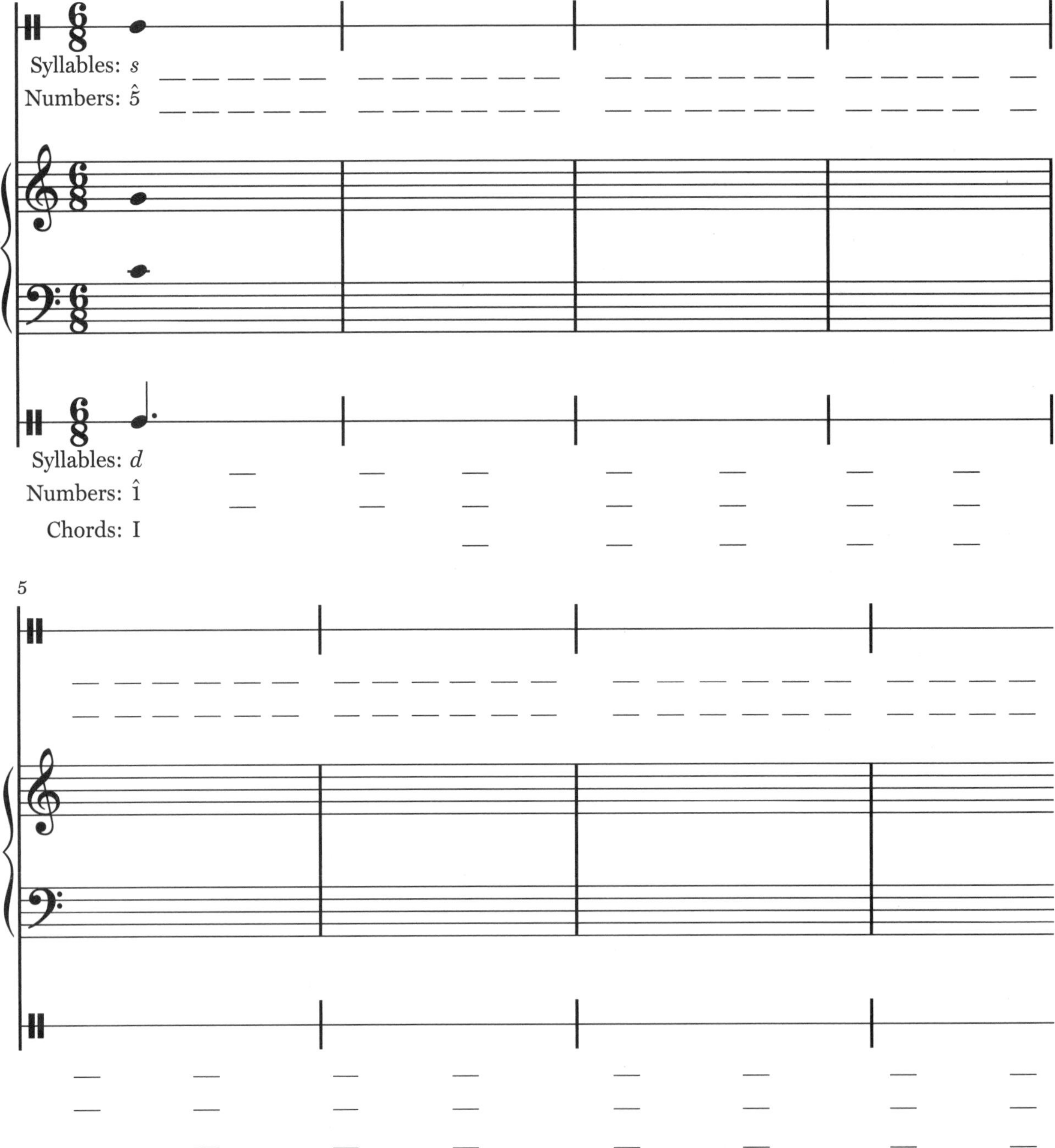

NAME ______________________________

Contextual Listening 19.4

Listen to short excerpts and choose the progression played.

1.	I–vi–ii^{6}–V	I–IV–I–V	I–ii^{6}–I^{6}–V
2.	V–V^{7}–I^{6}	V–V$^{6}_{5}$–I^{6}	V–V$^{4}_{2}$–I^{6}
3.	I–vi–ii^{6}–V	I–vi–V^{7}/V–V	I–IV–V$^{6}_{5}$/V–V

Now, listen to two phrases from a piano work and complete the remaining exercises.

4. Phrase 1's cadence chord is: I V vi
5. Phrase 2's cadence chord is: I V vi
6. The phrase design letters are: **a a** **a a′** **a b**
7. Beginning with the given items, capture the excerpt in the workspace.
   (a) In the single-line staves, notate the rhythm of the melody and bass. Below each note, write the syllables and numbers of the pitches.
   (b) In the grand staff, notate the pitches and rhythm of the melody and bass lines.
   (c) In each chord blank, write the Roman numeral and figure (if needed) that represents the harmony.

Syllables:
s s
Numbers:
$\hat{5}$ $\hat{5}$
Syllables:
d
Numbers:
$\hat{1}$
Chords:
I
5
(P)
(P)

NAME ______________________________

Contextual Listening 19.5

A pizzicato-chord accompaniment begins on tonic before changing to a different chord. Focus on the strong-beat bass pitches and choose the correct progression.

1. i–$\text{ii}^{\varnothing 6}_{5}$ i–iv i–V7 i–V^{4}_{3} i–V7/V
2. i–$\text{ii}^{\varnothing 6}_{5}$ i–iv i–V7 i–V^{4}_{3} i–V7/V
3. i–$\text{ii}^{\varnothing 6}_{5}$ i–iv i–V7 i–V^{4}_{3} i–V7/V
4. i–$\text{ii}^{\varnothing 6}_{5}$ i–iv i–V7 i–V^{4}_{3} i–V7/V

Now, listen to an arrangement of a song. After a two-measure introduction, you will hear a melody that consists of four segments.

5. Which meter signature is most likely? $\substack{2\\4}$ $\substack{6\\8}$ $\substack{9\\8}$
6. The melodic design letters are: **a a b a** **a b a b** **a b a c** **a b c d**
7. Beginning with the given items, capture the music in the workspace.
   (a) In the single-line staff, notate the melodic rhythm. Below each note, write the syllables and numbers of the pitches.
   (b) In the treble staff, notate the pitches and rhythm of the melody.
   (c) From the chord choices given, circle the one that represents the implied harmony.

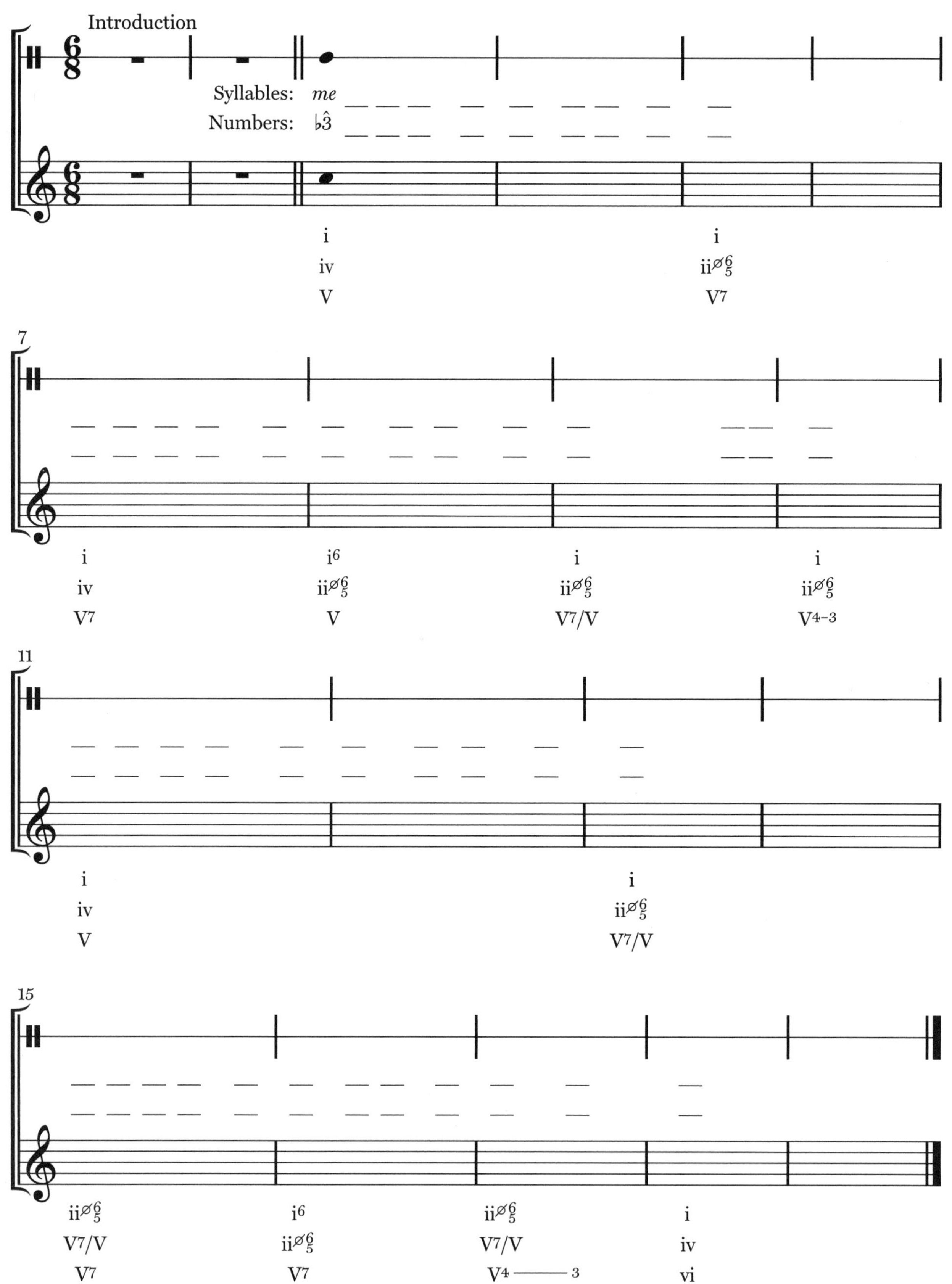
Introduction
Syllables: me
Numbers: ♭$\hat{3}$
i
iv
V
i
ii⌀$^6_5$
V7
7
i
iv
V7
i6
ii⌀$^6_5$
V
i
ii⌀$^6_5$
V7/V
i
ii⌀$^6_5$
V4–3
11
i
iv
V
i
ii⌀$^6_5$
V7/V
15
ii⌀$^6_5$
V7/V
V7
i6
ii⌀$^6_5$
V7
ii⌀$^6_5$
V7/V
V4 —— 3
i
iv
vi

Tonicizing Scale Degrees Other Than $\hat{5}$

NAME ________________________________

In this chapter you'll learn to:

- Identify tonicizations of scale degrees other than $\hat{5}$
- Notate music that includes secondary dominant-function chords and their inversions

Tonicizing Scale Degrees Other Than $\hat{5}$

Any major or minor triad may be tonicized. Here, a dominant-tonic progression is transposed repeatedly, tonicizing chords ii, iii, IV, V, and vi. Each tonicization appears in bracket notation with the D-T progression shown over the Roman numeral of the tonicized chord.

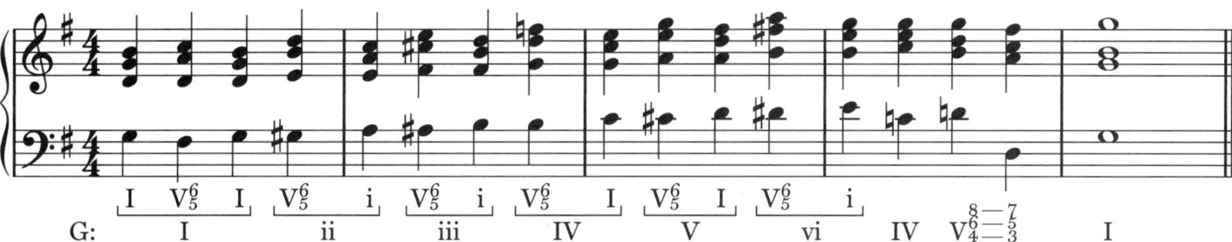

Tonicization can also be shown using slash notation (V^6_5/ii–ii, etc.) or colon notation (ii: V^6_5–ii, etc.).

Listening Strategies

Chromatic pitches often imply tonicization. Raised pitches rise, and can sound like *ti* ($\hat{7}$). Lowered pitches fall, and can sound like *fa* ($\hat{4}$), *le* ($\flat\hat{6}$), or *ra* ($\flat\hat{2}$).

Ti ($\hat{7}$) functions as a diatonic pitch in both major and minor, even though in minor keys it requires an accidental. Canceling *ti* ($\hat{7}$)'s accidental so that it becomes *te* ($\flat\hat{7}$) can signal movement away from tonic.

Major keys *If you hear . . .*	*the chord tonicized is . . .*
fi–sol ($\sharp\hat{4}$–$\hat{5}$)	V (most common)
si–la ($\sharp\hat{5}$–$\hat{6}$)	vi (common)
di–re ($\sharp\hat{1}$–$\hat{2}$)	ii (somewhat common)
ri–mi ($\sharp\hat{2}$–$\hat{3}$)	iii (rare)
te–la ($\flat\hat{7}$–$\hat{6}$)	IV (very common)

Minor keys *If you hear . . .*	*the chord tonicized is . . .*
fi–sol ($\sharp\hat{4}$–$\hat{5}$)	V or v (very common)
mi–fa ($\natural\hat{3}$–$\hat{4}$)	iv (very common)
te, not *ti* ($\flat\hat{7}$, not $\hat{7}$)	III (most common)
te and *ra* ($\flat\hat{7}$ and $\flat\hat{2}$)	VI (common)

Try it

A three-chord progression establishes the key. Chords 4–5 create a tonicization. Identify the initial progression, the chromatic pitch(es), and the tonicized chord. Then, write the tonicization (chords 4–5) using bracket, slash, and colon notation.

1. (a) The initial progression is: I–V7–I I–V^6_5–I I–V^4_3–I6 I–V^4_2–I6
   (b) The chromatic pitch is: *di* ($\sharp\hat{1}$) *fi* ($\sharp\hat{4}$) *si* ($\sharp\hat{5}$) *te* ($\flat\hat{7}$)
   (c) The tonicized chord is: ii IV V vi
   (d) Write the tonicization (chords 4–5) using bracket, slash, and colon notation.
   Bracket *Slash* *Colon*

2. (a) The initial progression is: I–V7–I I–V^6_5–I I–V^4_3–I6 I–V^4_2–I6
   (b) The chromatic pitch is: *di* ($\sharp\hat{1}$) *fi* ($\sharp\hat{4}$) *si* ($\sharp\hat{5}$) *te* ($\flat\hat{7}$)
   (c) The tonicized chord is: ii IV V vi
   (d) Write the tonicization (chords 4–5) using bracket, slash, and colon notation.
   Bracket *Slash* *Colon*

3. (a) The initial progression is: I–V7–I I–V^6_5–I I–V^4_3–I6 I–V^4_2–I6
   (b) The chromatic pitch is: *di* ($\sharp\hat{1}$) *fi* ($\sharp\hat{4}$) *si* ($\sharp\hat{5}$) *te* ($\flat\hat{7}$)
   (c) The tonicized chord is: ii IV V vi
   (d) Write the tonicization (chords 4–5) using bracket, slash, and colon notation.
   Bracket *Slash* *Colon*

NAME ______________________________

4. (a) The initial progression is: I–V–I   I–V^6_5–I   I–V^4_3–I^6 I–V^4_2–I^6
   (b) The chromatic pitch is: *di* (♯$\hat{1}$)   *fi* (♯$\hat{4}$)   *si* (♯$\hat{5}$)   *te* (♭$\hat{7}$)
   (c) The tonicized chord is: ii   IV   V   vi
   (d) Write the tonicization (chords 4–5) using bracket, slash, and colon notation.
   Bracket   *Slash*   *Colon*

5. (a) The initial progression is: i–V^7–i   i–V^6_5–i   i–V^4_3–i^6 i–V^4_2–i^6
   (b) The chromatic pitch(es) is (are): *ra* (♭$\hat{2}$)   *mi* (♮$\hat{3}$)   *fi* (♯$\hat{4}$)   *te* (♭$\hat{7}$)
   (c) The tonicized chord is: III   iv   V or v   VI
   (d) Write the tonicization (chords 4–5) using bracket, slash, and colon notation.
   Bracket   *Slash*   *Colon*

6. (a) The initial progression is: i–V–i   i–V^6_5–i   i–V^4_3–i^6 i–V^4_2–i^6
   (b) The chromatic pitch(es) is (are): *ra* (♭$\hat{2}$)   *mi* (♮$\hat{3}$)   *fi* (♯$\hat{4}$)   *te* (♭$\hat{7}$)
   (c) The tonicized chord is: III   iv   V or v   VI
   (d) Write the tonicization (chords 4–5) using bracket, slash, and colon notation.
   Bracket   *Slash*   *Colon*

7. (a) The initial progression is: i–vii$^{\circ 7}$–i   i–vii$^{\circ 6}_{\ 5}$–i^6 i–vii$^{\circ 4}_{\ 3}$–i^6
   (b) The chromatic pitch(es) is (are): *ra* (♭$\hat{2}$)   *mi* (♮$\hat{3}$)   *fi* (♯$\hat{4}$)   *te* (♭$\hat{7}$)
   (c) The tonicized chord is: III   iv   V or v   VI
   (d) Write the tonicization (chords 4–5) using bracket, slash, and colon notation.
   Bracket   *Slash*   *Colon*

Contextual Listening 20.1

Listen to three-chord progressions that begin on tonic and complete the exercises.

1. (a) Bass pitches 1–3 are scale degrees:

   ($\hat{1}$-$\hat{5}$-$\hat{1}$)   ($\hat{1}$-$\hat{7}$-$\hat{1}$)   ($\hat{1}$-$\hat{2}$-$\hat{3}$)   ($\hat{1}$-$\hat{4}$-$\hat{3}$)

   (b) Melodic pitches 3 and 6 are which type of embellishment?

   neighbor   consonant skip   passing tone   suspension

   (c) Melodic pitches 4 and 7 are which type of embellishment?

   incomplete neighbor   consonant skip   passing tone   suspension

   (d) The chromatic pitch is: none   *di* (♯$\hat{1}$)   *fi* (♯$\hat{4}$)   *si* (♯$\hat{5}$)   *te* (♭$\hat{7}$)

   (e) The tonicized chord is: only I   ii   IV   V   vi

   (f) Write the progression. If there is a tonicization, use bracket, slash, and colon notation.

   Bracket   *Slash*   *Colon*

2. (a) Bass pitches 1–3 are scale degrees:

   ($\hat{1}$-$\hat{5}$-$\hat{1}$)   ($\hat{1}$-$\hat{7}$-$\hat{6}$)   ($\hat{1}$-$\hat{2}$-$\hat{3}$)   ($\hat{1}$-$\hat{4}$-$\hat{3}$)

   (b) Melodic pitches 3 and 6 are which type of embellishment?

   neighbor   consonant skip   passing tone   suspension

   (c) Melodic pitches 4 and 7 are which type of embellishment?

   incomplete neighbor   consonant skip   passing tone   suspension

   (d) The chromatic pitch is: none   *di* (♯$\hat{1}$)   *fi* (♯$\hat{4}$)   *si* (♯$\hat{5}$)   *te* (♭$\hat{7}$)

   (e) The tonicized chord is: only I   ii   IV   V   vi

   (f) Write the progression. If there is a tonicization, use bracket, slash, and colon notation.

   Bracket   *Slash*   *Colon*

3. (a) The chromatic bass pitch is: none   *di* (♯$\hat{1}$)   *fi* (♯$\hat{4}$)   *si* (♯$\hat{5}$)   *te* (♭$\hat{7}$)

   (b) The tonicized chord is: only I   ii   IV   V   vi

   (c) Write the progression. If there is a tonicization, use bracket, slash, and colon notation.

   Bracket   *Slash*   *Colon*

Now, listen to two phrases from a piano work and complete the remaining exercises.

4. Beginning with the given items, capture only phrase 2 in the workspace.
   (a) In the single-line staves, notate the rhythm of the bass and melody.
   (b) Below each note, write the syllables and numbers of the pitches.
   (c) In the grand staff, notate pitches and rhythm of both parts. Refer to the single-line notation.

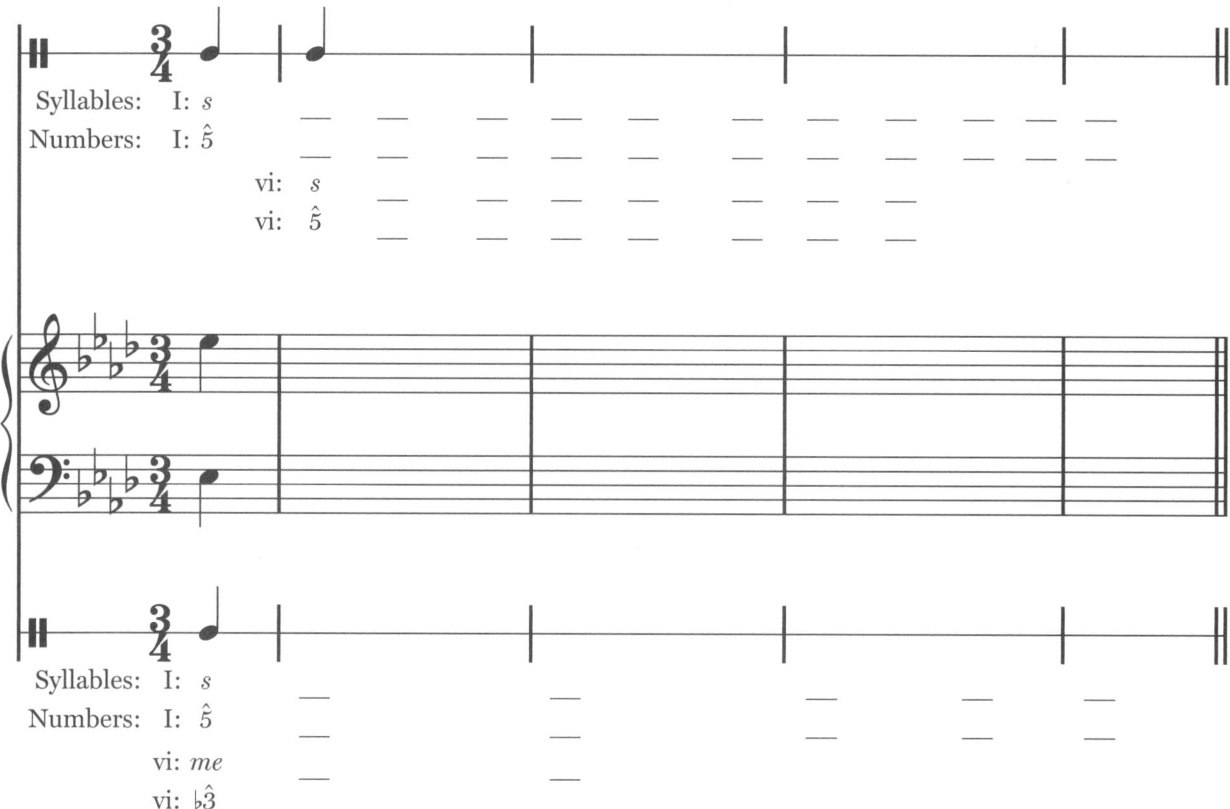

5. Bass pitch 3 supports which type of seventh chord?

   MM7 Mm7 mm7 dm7 (ø7)

6. Bass pitches 3–4 create which progression?

   V^4_3/vi–vi vii^{o6}_5/vi–vi V^7/V–V vii^{o7}/V–V

NAME ______________________________

Contextual Listening 20.2

Listen to short progressions that begin on tonic and complete the exercises.

1. (a) The next-to-last melodic pitch is which embellishment?

   incomplete neighbor   consonant skip   passing tone   suspension

   (b) The chromatic pitch(es) is (are):

   none   *ra* (♭$\hat{2}$)   *mi* (♮$\hat{3}$)   *fi* (♯$\hat{4}$)   *te* (♭$\hat{7}$)

   (c) The tonicized chord is: only i   III   iv   V or v   VI

   (d) Write the progression. If there is a tonicization, use bracket, slash, and colon notation.

   Bracket   *Slash*   *Colon*

2. (a) The next-to-last melodic pitch is which type of suspension?

   9–8   7–6   4–3

   (b) The chromatic pitch(es) is (are):

   none   *ra* (♭$\hat{2}$)   *mi* (♮$\hat{3}$)   *fi* (♯$\hat{4}$)   *te* (♭$\hat{7}$)

   (c) The tonicized chord is: only i   III   iv   V or v   VI

   (d) Write the progression. If there is a tonicization, use bracket, slash, and colon notation.

   Bracket   *Slash*   *Colon*

3. (a) The next-to-last melodic pitch is which type of suspension?

   9–8   7–6   4–3

   (b) The chromatic pitch(es) is (are):

   none   *ra* (♭$\hat{2}$)   *mi* (♮$\hat{3}$)   *fi* (♯$\hat{4}$)   *te* (♭$\hat{7}$)

   (c) The tonicized chord is: only i   III   iv   V or v   VI

   (d) Write the progression. If there is a tonicization, use bracket, slash, and colon notation.

   Bracket   *Slash*   *Colon*

4. (a) The next-to-last melodic pitch is which type of suspension?

   9–8   7–6   4–3

   (b) The chromatic pitch(es) is (are):

   none   *ra* (♭$\hat{2}$)   *mi* (♮$\hat{3}$)   *fi* (♯$\hat{4}$)   *te* (♭$\hat{7}$)

   (c) The tonicized chord is: only i   III   iv   V or v   VI

   (d) Write the progression. If there is a tonicization, use bracket, slash, and colon notation.

   Bracket   *Slash*   *Colon*

Now, listen to twelve measures from a piano work and complete the remaining exercises.

5. Phrase 1's cadence type is: PAC IAC HC PHC
6. In the middle, a pedal point occurs on which scale degree?
   tonic subdominant dominant
7. The final cadence type is: PAC IAC HC PHC
8. Beginning with the given items, capture the music in the workspace.
   (a) In the single-line staves, notate the rhythm of the bass and soprano lines.
   (b) Below each note, write the syllables and numbers of the pitches.
   (c) In the grand staff, notate pitches and rhythm of both parts. Refer to the single-line notation.
   (d) In each chord blank, write the Roman numeral and figure (if needed) that represents the harmony. Indicate any tonicization with bracket, slash, or colon notation.

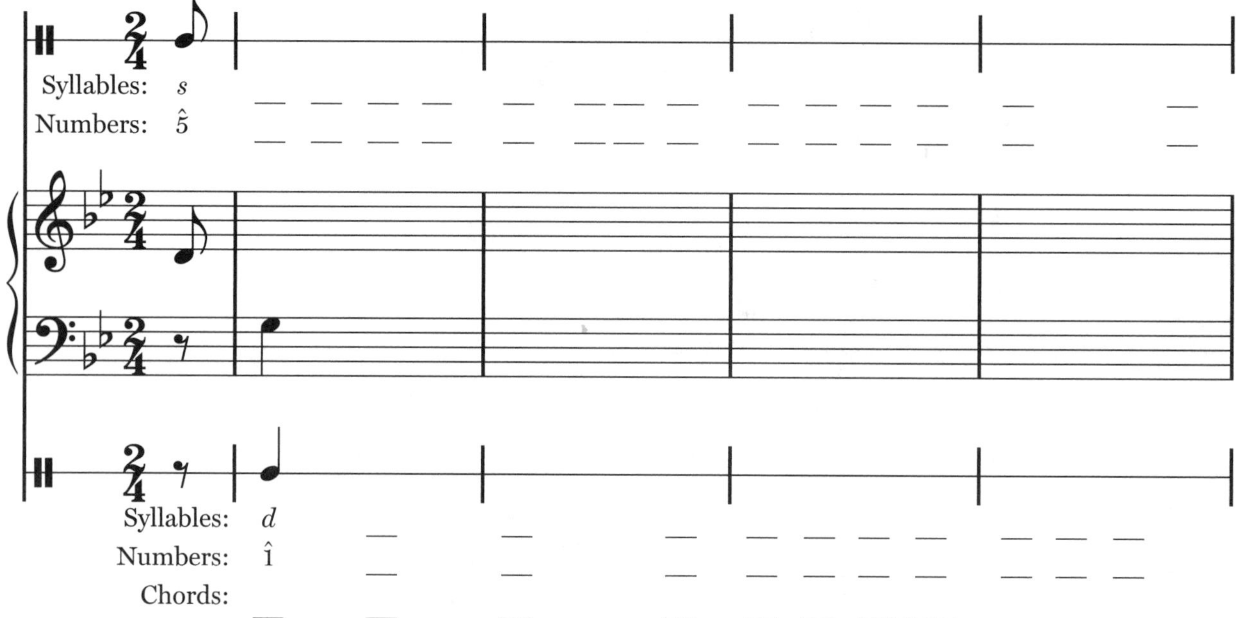

NAME ___________________

5

Syllables:
Numbers:

Syllables:
Numbers:
Chords:

9

Syllables:
Numbers:

Syllables in i:
Numbers in i:
Syllables in iv:
Numbers in iv:

Contextual Listening 20.3

Listen to short progressions that begin on tonic and complete the exercises.

1. (a) Melodic pitch 3 is which embellishment?

   incomplete neighbor   consonant skip   passing tone   suspension

   (b) The chromatic pitch is: *ra* (♭$\hat{2}$) *mi* (♮$\hat{3}$) *fi* (♯$\hat{4}$) *te* (♭$\hat{7}$)

   (c) The tonicized chord is: III iv V or v VI

   (d) Write the progression. If there is a tonicization, use bracket, slash, and colon notation.

   Bracket   *Slash*   *Colon*

2. (a) Melodic pitch 3 is which embellishment?

   incomplete neighbor   consonant skip   passing tone   suspension

   (b) The chromatic pitch is: *ra* (♭$\hat{2}$) *mi* (♮$\hat{3}$) *fi* (♯$\hat{4}$) *te* (♭$\hat{7}$)

   (c) The tonicized chord is: III iv V or v VI

   (d) Write the progression. If there is a tonicization, use bracket, slash, and colon notation.

   Bracket   *Slash*   *Colon*

3. (a) Melodic pitch 3 is which embellishment?

   incomplete neighbor   consonant skip   passing tone   suspension

   (b) The chromatic pitch is: *ra* (♭$\hat{2}$) *mi* (♮$\hat{3}$) *fi* (♯$\hat{4}$) *te* (♭$\hat{7}$)

   (c) The tonicized chord is: III iv V or v VI

   (d) Write the progression. If there is a tonicization, use bracket, slash, and colon notation.

   Bracket   *Slash*   *Colon*

Now, listen to two phrases from a Baroque dance and complete the remaining exercises. First, focus only on phrase 1. During it, a five-pitch melodic motive repeats four times.

4. Melodic pitch 3 is which embellishment?

   incomplete neighbor consonant skip passing tone suspension

5. Phrase 1's cadence type is: PAC IAC HC PHC

6. Phrase 1's next-to-last chord includes which suspension? 9–8 7–6 4–3

7. Beginning with the given items, capture phrase 1 in the workspace.
   (a) In the single-line staves, notate the rhythm of the bass and melody.
   (b) Below each note, write the syllables and numbers of the pitches.
   (c) In the grand staff, notate pitches and rhythm of both parts. Refer to the single-line notation.
   (d) In each chord blank, write the Roman numeral and figure (if needed) that represents the chord. Indicate any tonicization with bracket, slash, or colon notation.

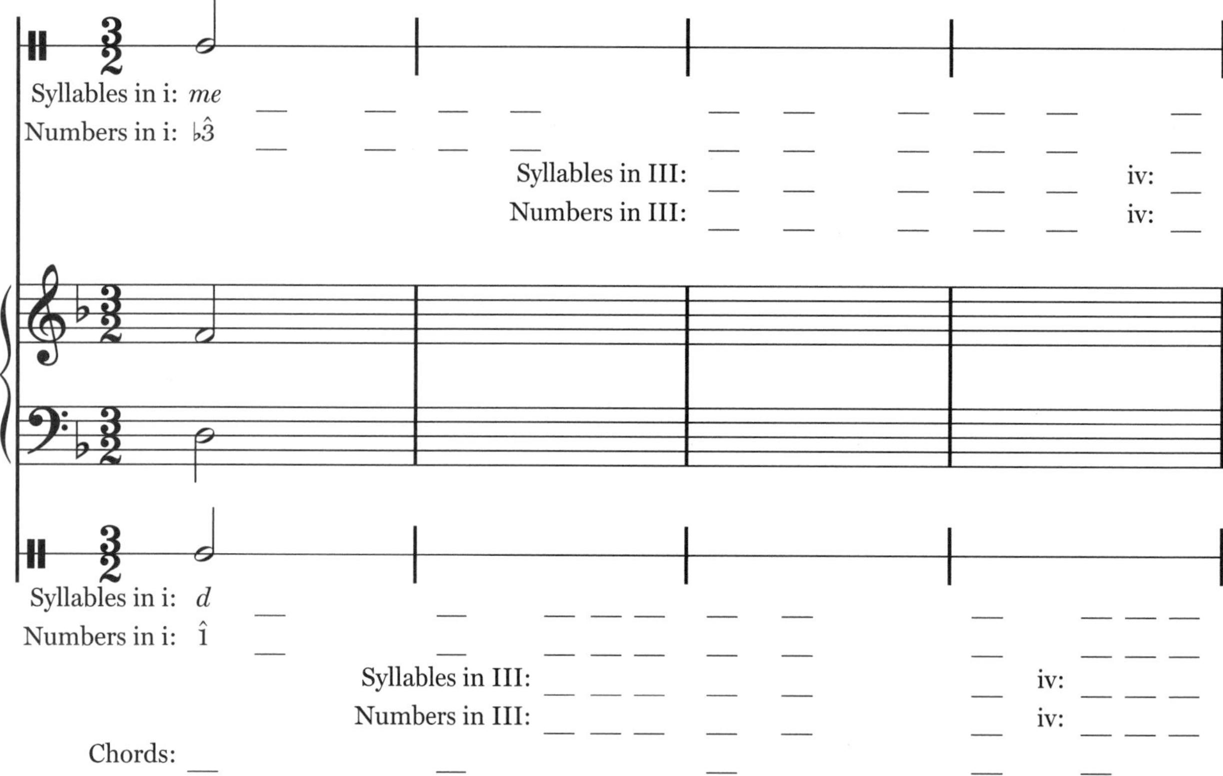

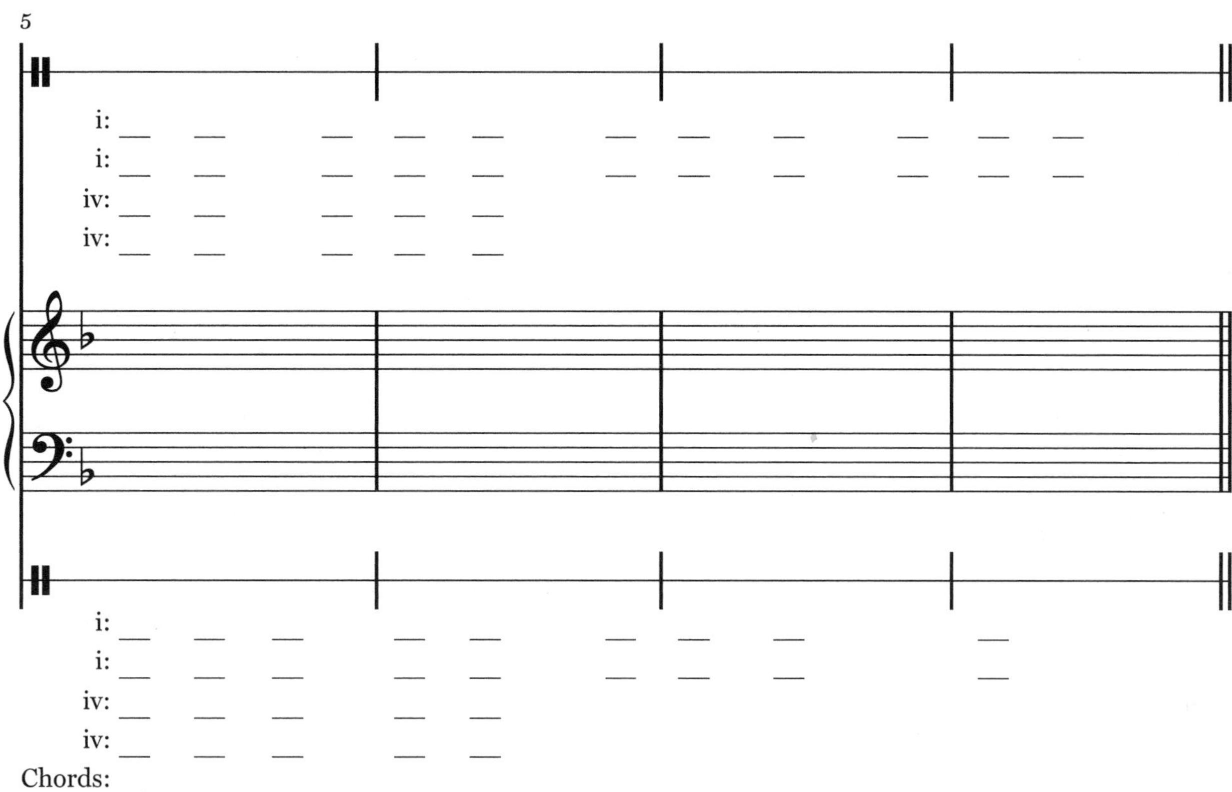

8. Now, listen again to the entire excerpt. Diagram its phrase structure. Draw curves for phrases and label each cadence. Include phrase design letters and the overall structure name.

NAME ______________________________

Contextual Listening 20.4

Listen to three-chord progressions that begin on tonic and complete the exercises.

1. (a) Melodic pitch 2 is which embellishment?

   incomplete neighbor   consonant skip   passing tone   retardation

   (b) The chromatic pitch(es) is (are):

   none   *di* (♯$\hat{1}$)   *fi* (♯$\hat{4}$)   *si* (♯$\hat{5}$)   *te* (♭$\hat{7}$)

   (c) The tonicized chord is: only I   ii   IV   V   vi

   (d) Write the progression. If there is a tonicization, use bracket, slash, and colon notation.

   Bracket   *Slash*   *Colon*

2. (a) The chromatic pitch(es) is (are):

   none   *di* (♯$\hat{1}$)   *fi* (♯$\hat{4}$)   *si* (♯$\hat{5}$)   *te* (♭$\hat{7}$)

   (b) The tonicized chord is: only I   ii   IV   V   vi

   (c) Write the progression. If there is a tonicization, use bracket, slash, and colon notation.

   Bracket   *Slash*   *Colon*

3. (a) The chromatic pitch(es) is (are):

   none   *di* (♯$\hat{1}$)   *fi* (♯$\hat{4}$)   *si* (♯$\hat{5}$)   *te* (♭$\hat{7}$)

   (b) The tonicized chord is: only I   ii   IV   V   vi

   (c) Write the progression. If there is a tonicization, use bracket, slash, and colon notation.

   Bracket   *Slash*   *Colon*

4. (a) The chromatic pitch(es) is (are):

   none   *di* (♯$\hat{1}$)   *fi* (♯$\hat{4}$)   *si* (♯$\hat{5}$)   *te* (♭$\hat{7}$)

   (b) The tonicized chord is: only I   ii   IV   V   vi

   (c) Melodic pitch 5 is which embellishment?

   incomplete neighbor   consonant skip   passing tone   retardation

   (d) Write the progression. If there is a tonicization, use bracket, slash, and colon notation.

   Bracket   *Slash*   *Colon*

Now, listen to eight measures from a piano work and complete the remaining exercises.

5. On beat 2, the $^6_4$ type is:

   cadential passing neighboring arpeggiating

6. Melodic pitch 5 is which embellishment?

   incomplete neighbor consonant skip passing tone retardation

7. The next-to-last melodic pitch is which embellishment?

   incomplete neighbor consonant skip passing tone retardation

8. (a) The next-to-last melodic pitch is: *di* (♯$\hat{1}$) *fi* (♯$\hat{4}$) *si* (♯$\hat{5}$) *te* (♭$\hat{7}$)

   (b) The tonicized chord is: ii IV V vi

9. Near the end, the $^6_4$ type is:

   cadential passing neighboring arpeggiating

10. Beginning with the given items, capture the music in the workspace.
    (a) In the single-line staves, notate the rhythm of the bass and soprano lines.
    (b) Below each note, write the syllables and numbers of the pitches.
    (c) In the grand staff, notate pitches and rhythm of both parts. Refer to the single-line notation.
    (d) In each chord blank, write the Roman numeral and figure (if needed) that represents the chord. Indicate any tonicization with bracket, slash, or colon notation.

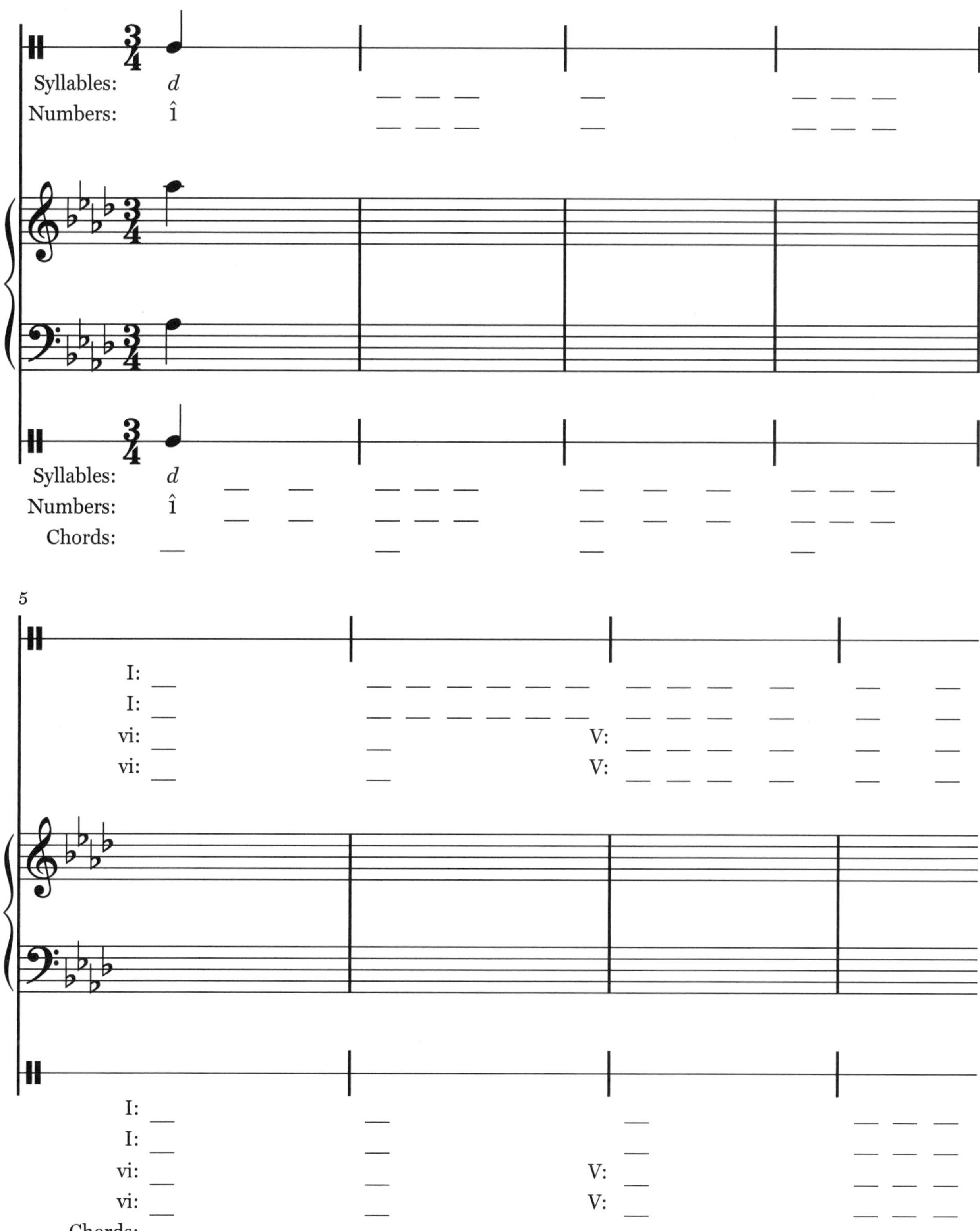
Syllables:
Numbers:
Syllables:
Numbers:
Chords:
5
I:
I:
vi:
vi:
V:
V:
Chords:

Diatonic Sequences

NAME ______________________

In this chapter you'll learn to:

- Identify a sequence's attributes and name
- Recognize common melodic and harmonic patterns of diatonic sequences

Sequences

Sequences repeatedly transpose a unit of music down or up by the same interval and always include at least the beginning of a third repetition. A two-repetition unit that ascends is called *monte* and one that descends is called *fonte*.

Sequences can be identified by listening for six attributes: (1) key, (2) unit, (3) direction, (4) interval, (5) number of repetitions (reps), and (6) soprano-bass intervals (linear-intervallic pattern, or LIP).

Identifying a Sequence's Attributes

	What is the . . .	*Listen for . . .*	*Think or write . . .*
1	key?	*mi* ($\hat{3}$) or *me* ($\flat\hat{3}$)	in a major key . . . in the key of D minor . . . etc.
2	unit?	how much music is transposed	two-chord units . . . one-chord units . . . etc.
3	direction?	overall contour	descend or ascend
4	interval?	how much lower (higher) unit 2 is than unit 1	by second . . . by third . . . etc.
5	number of reps?	how many times the unit repeats	in four reps . . . in three reps . . . etc.
6	LIP?	unit 1's soprano and bass notes e.g., *mi-fa* ($\hat{3}$-$\hat{4}$) over *do-fa* ($\hat{1}$-$\hat{4}$); *sol-la* ($\hat{5}$-$\hat{6}$) over *do-fa* ($\hat{1}$-$\hat{4}$)	with a . . . 10-8 LIP 5-6 LIP

Use a model sentence to guide your listening. For example, if you hear the following sequence, filling in the model's blanks will describe it.

In the key of C ___________ (1) major or minor?, ___________ (2) how many? -chord units ___________ (3) descend or ascend?

by ___________ (4) interval? in ___________ (5) number? reps with a ____-____ (6) intervals between S and B? LIP.

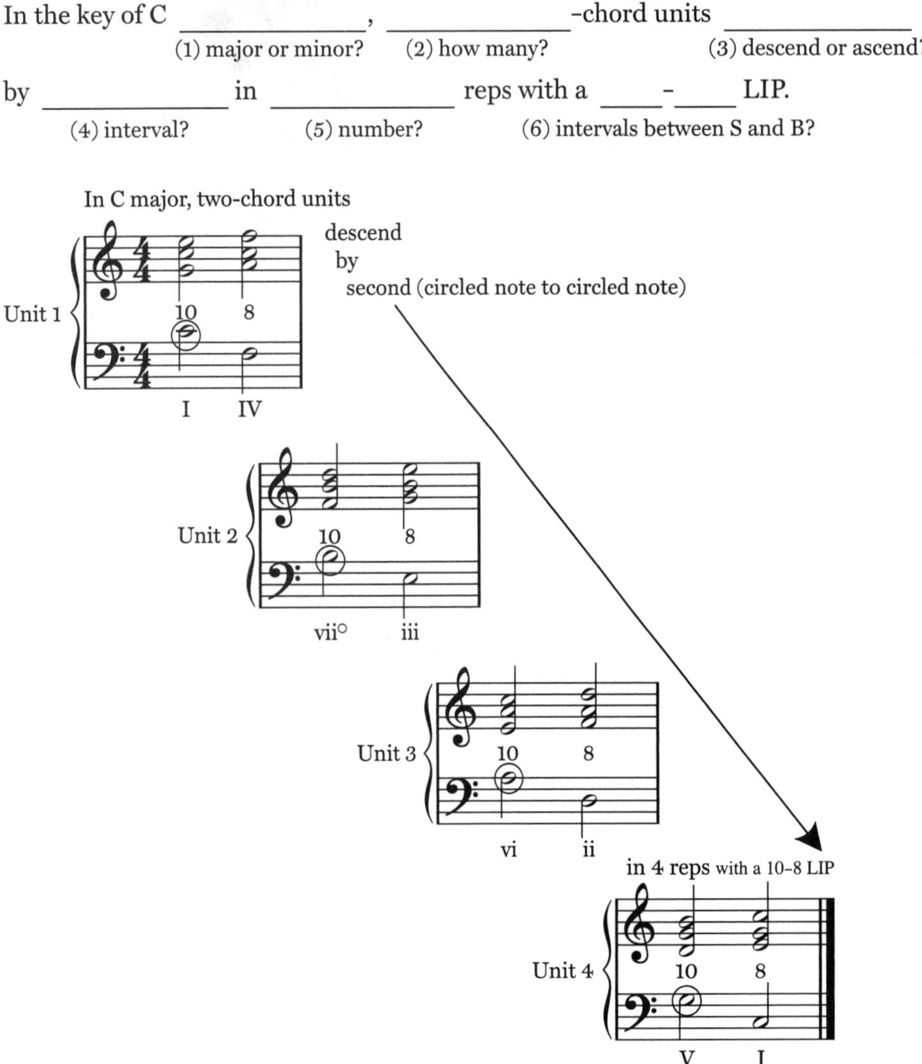

Identifying Common Sequences by Name

Sequence name	*Units*	*Reps*	*Interval*	*Common melodies*	*Chord labels*
Descending fifth	2-chord	four	second	*mi-fa* ($\hat{3}$-$\hat{4}$) *re-mi* ($\hat{2}$-$\hat{3}$)... *sol-la* ($\hat{5}$-$\hat{6}$) *fa-sol* ($\hat{4}$-$\hat{5}$)...	I-IV, vii°-iii, vi-ii, V-I
Descending third	2-chord	three	third	*mi-re* ($\hat{3}$-$\hat{2}$) *do-ti* ($\hat{1}$-$\hat{7}$)... *do-ti* ($\hat{1}$-$\hat{7}$) *la-sol* ($\hat{6}$-$\hat{5}$)...	I-IV, vi-iii, IV-I
Parallel $^6_3$	1-chord	varies	second	descending scale... ascending scale...	e.g., i$^{5-6}$ v$^{7-6}$ iv$^{7-6}$... e.g., I^6 ii^6 iii^6 IV^6...
Ascending 5-6	2-chord	varies	second	*sol-la* ($\hat{5}$-$\hat{6}$) *la-ti* ($\hat{6}$-$\hat{7}$)...	I$^{5-6}$ ii$^{5-6}$ iii$^{5-6}$ IV$^{5-6}$ or I-vi^6 ii-vii°^{6} iii-I^6 IV-ii^6

NAME ______________________

Try it

1. Each exercise begins on tonic. Use the tables to identify the sequence's attributes and name.

   (a) In a ______ (major or minor?) key, ______ (how many?) -chord units ______ (descend or ascend?) by ______ (interval?) in ______ (number?) reps with a ___-___ (intervals between S and B?) LIP to create a(n) ______ (sequence name?).

   (b) In a ______ (major or minor?) key, ______ (how many?) -chord units ______ (descend or ascend?) by ______ (interval?) in ______ (number?) reps with a ___-___ (intervals between S and B?) LIP to create a(n) ______ (sequence name?).

   (c) In a ______ (major or minor?) key, ______ (how many?) -chord units ______ (descend or ascend?) by ______ (interval?) in ______ (number?) reps with a ___-___ (intervals between S and B?) LIP to create a(n) ______ (sequence name?).

   (d) In a ______ (major or minor?) key, ______ (how many?) -chord units ______ (descend or ascend?) by ______ (interval?) in ______ (number?) reps with a ___-___ (intervals between S and B?) LIP to create a(n) ______ (sequence name?).

2. Each exercise begins on tonic and with the given items. Write the key name and quality, notate the bass and soprano, and write Roman numerals and LIP numbers.

   (a) Sequence name: ______________

   Syllables: __ __ __ __ __ __ __ __

   Numbers: __ __ __ __ __ __ __ __

   LIP: __ __ __ __ __ __ __ __

   Syllables: *d* __ __ __ __ __ __ __

   Numbers: $\hat{1}$ __ __ __ __ __ __ __

   ______: __ __ __ __ __ __ __ __

   (b) Sequence name: ______________

   Syllables: __ __ __ __ __ __

   Numbers: __ __ __ __ __ __

   LIP: __ __ __ __ __ __

   Syllables: *d* __ __ __ __ __

   Numbers: $\hat{1}$ __ __ __ __ __

   ______: __ __ __ __ __ __

(c) Sequence name: ______________________

Syllables: __ __ __ __ __ __ __ __

Numbers: __ __ __ __ __ __ __ __

LIP: __ __ __ __ __ __ __ __

Syllables: *d* __ __ __ __ __ __ __

Numbers: $\hat{1}$ __ __ __ __ __ __ __

________: __ __ __ __ __ __ __ __

(d) Sequence name: ______________________

Syllables: __ __ __ __ __ __ __

Numbers: __ __ __ __ __ __ __

LIP: __ __ __ __ __ __ __

Syllables: *d* __ __ __

Numbers: $\hat{1}$ __ __ __

________: __ __ __ __

(e) Sequence name: ______________________

Syllables: __ __ __ __ __ __ __ __ __

Numbers: __ __ __ __ __ __ __ __ __

LIP: __ __ __ __ __ __ __ __ __

Syllables: *d* __ __ __ __

Numbers: $\hat{1}$ __ __ __ __

________: __ __ __ __ __

NAME ______________________________

Contextual Listening 21.1

In exercises 1–3 the initial bass pitch is C4. Identify the sequence's attributes and name. Hint: On beat 1 of every measure, identify the bass and soprano (violin 1 and cello) using syllables or numbers; for example, if you hear *do–mi* ($\hat{1}$–$\hat{3}$), the interval is 10.

1. In the key of C ____________ (major or minor?), ____________ (how many?) -chord units ____________ (descend or ascend?) by ____________ (interval?) in ____________ (number?) reps with a _____–_____ (intervals between S and B?) LIP to create a(n) ______________________ (sequence name?).

2. In the key of C ____________ (major or minor?), ____________ (how many?) -chord units ____________ (descend or ascend?) by ____________ (interval?) in ____________ (number?) reps with a _____–_____ (intervals between S and B?) LIP to create a(n) ______________________ (sequence name?).

3. In the key of C ____________ (major or minor?), ____________ (how many?) -chord units ____________ (descend or ascend?) by ____________ (interval?) in ____________ (number?) reps with a _____–_____ (intervals between S and B?) LIP to create a(n) ______________________ (sequence name?).

Now, listen to one phrase from a string quartet and complete the remaining exercises.

4. In the key of C ____________ (major or minor?), ____________ (how many?) -chord units ____________ (descend or ascend?) by ____________ (interval?) in ____________ (number?) reps with a _____–_____ (intervals between S and B?) LIP to create a(n) ______________________ (sequence name?).

5. Beginning with the given items, capture the music in the workspace.
   (a) In the single-line staves, notate the rhythm of the outer voices, cello and violin 1.
   (b) Below each note, write the syllables or numbers of the pitches.
   (c) In the grand staff, notate the pitches and rhythm of the outer voices. Refer to the single-line notation.
   (d) In each chord blank provided, write the Roman numeral and figure (if needed) that represents the harmony.

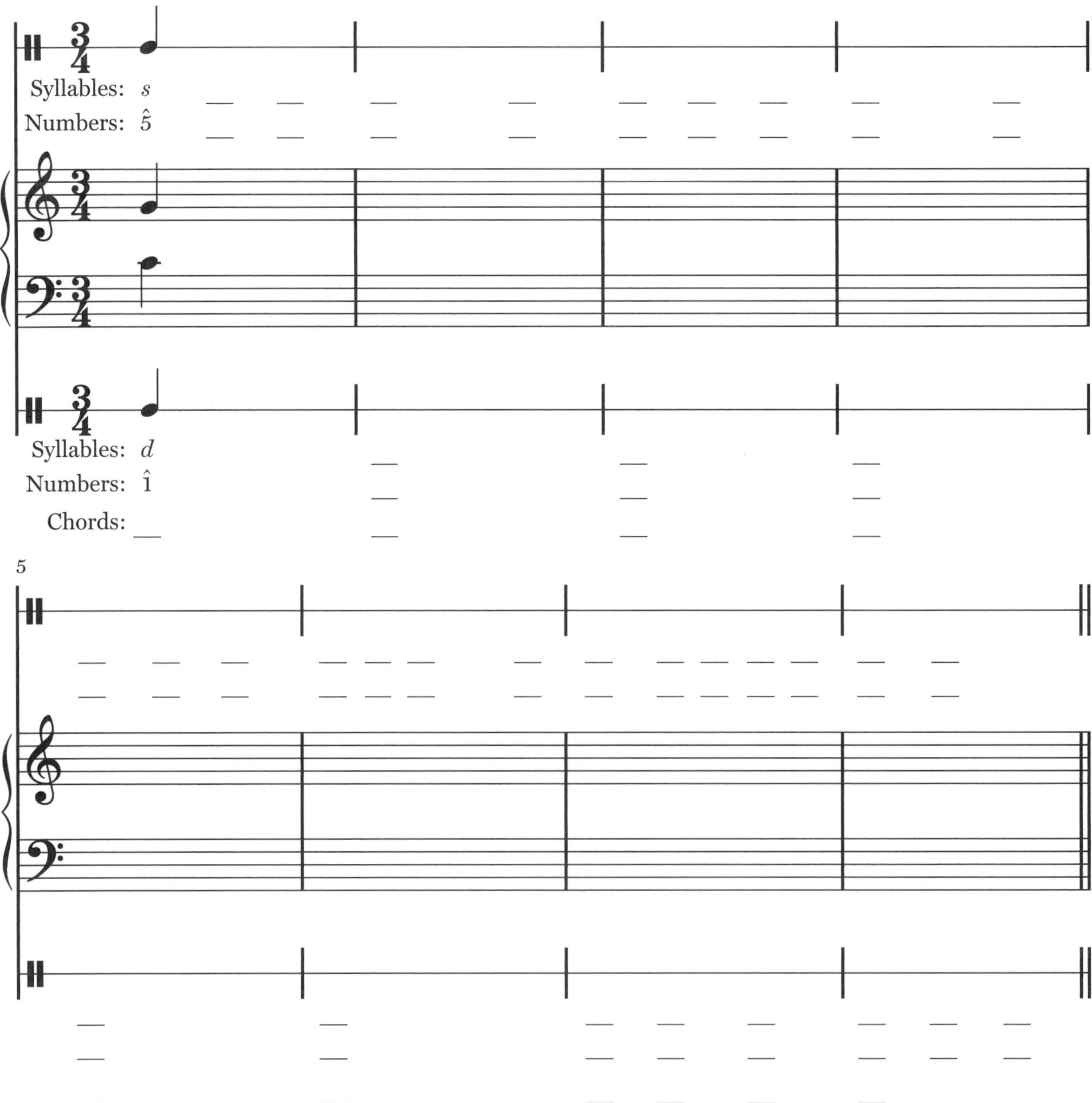

6. Near the end, the $^6_4$ chord type is: cadential passing neighbor

7. The next-to-last melodic pitch is which embellishment?
   neighbor tone consonant skip passing tone retardation

8. The cadence type is: PAC IAC HC PHC

NAME ______________________________

Contextual Listening 21.2

In exercises 1–2 the initial bass pitch is G. Identify the sequence's attributes and name.
Hint: At every chord change, identify the outer parts using syllables or numbers; for example, if you hear *do-sol* ($\hat{1}$–$\hat{5}$), the interval is 5.

1. In the key of G ____________ (major or minor?), ____________ (how many?) -chord units ____________ (descend or ascend?) by ____________ (interval?) in ____________ (number?) reps with a ____–____ (intervals between S and B?) LIP to create a(n) ______________________ (sequence name?).

2. In the key of G ____________ (major or minor?), ____________ (how many?) -chord units ____________ (descend or ascend?) by ____________ (interval?) in ____________ (number?) reps with a ____–____ (intervals between S and B?) LIP to create a(n) ______________________ (sequence name?).

Now, listen to part of a carol and complete the remaining exercises.

3. Beginning with the given items, capture the music in the workspace.
   (a) In the single-line staves, notate the rhythm of the outer voices, basses and sopranos.
   (b) Below each note, write the syllables or numbers of the pitches.
   (c) In the grand staff, notate the pitches and rhythm of the outer voices parts. Refer to the single-line notation.
   (d) In each chord blank provided, write the Roman numeral and figure (if needed) that represents the harmony.

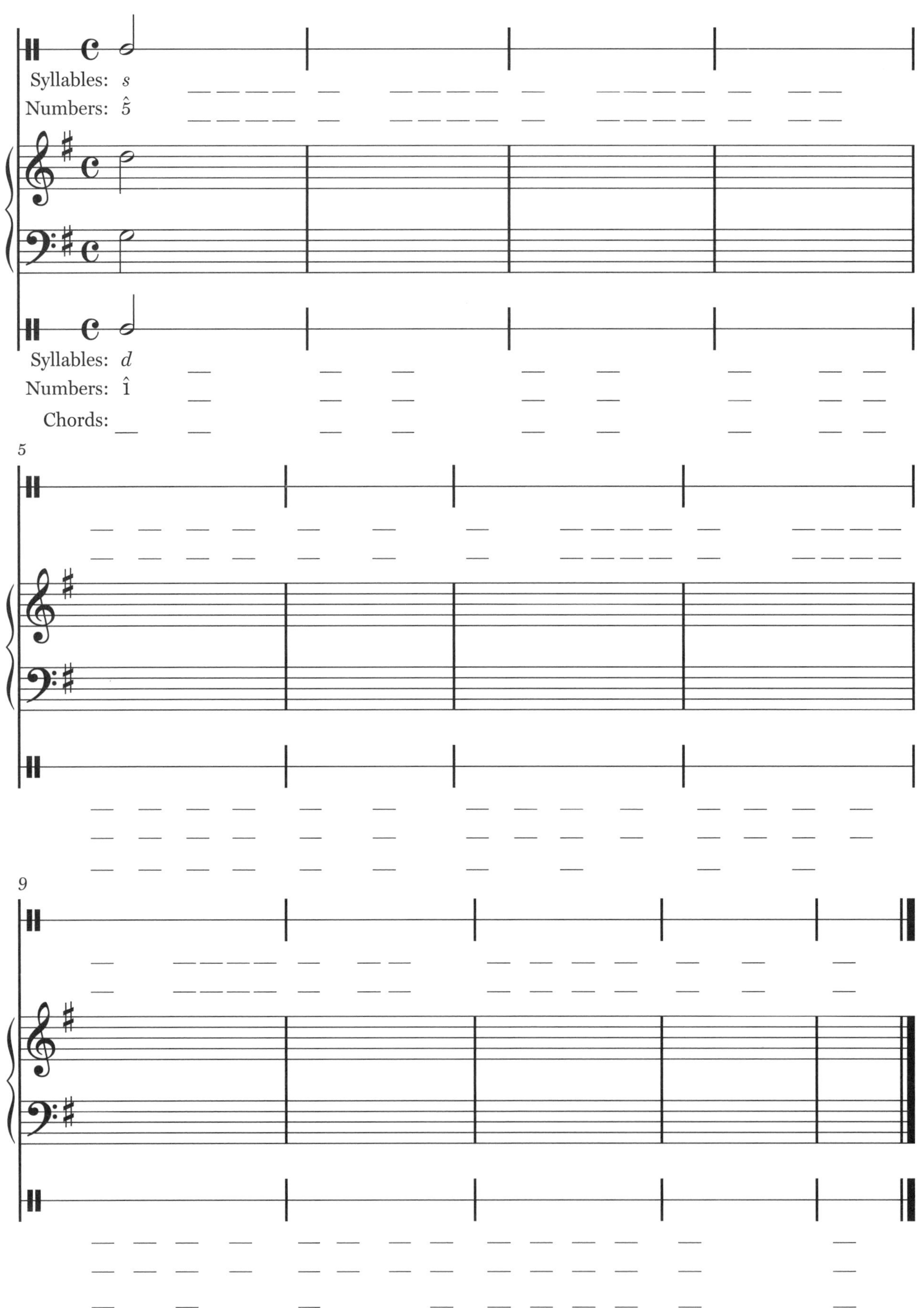

Translation: Glory be to God in the highest!

NAME ______________________

4. Phrase 1's cadence type is: PAC IAC HC PHC
5. Phrase 2's cadence type is: PAC IAC HC PHC
6. Diagram the phrase structure. Draw curves for phrases. Write cadence types, the design letter for each phrase, and the name for the overall structure.

7. During the words "*in excelsis*," the $^6_4$ chord type is:
   Hint: Listen carefully to the outer voices.

   cadential passing neighbor
8. The final cadence features which embellishment?

   consonant skips double neighbor tones anticipation suspension
9. Each time the word "*Deo*" occurs, the $^6_4$ type is:

   cadential passing neighbor
10. From phrase 1's end ("*Deo*") to phrase 2's beginning ("*Gloria*"), which error occurs?

    parallel octaves parallel fifths

    similar motion to an octave similar motion to a fifth

NAME ______________________________

Contextual Listening 21.3

In exercises 1–3 the initial bass pitch is B♭. Identify the sequence's attributes and name.

Hint: At every chord change, identify the outer parts using syllables or numbers; for example, if you hear *do*-*mi* ($\hat{1}$-$\hat{3}$), the interval is 10.

1. In the key of B♭ ____________ (major or minor?), ____________ (how many?) -chord units ____________ (descend or ascend?) by ____________ (interval?)

   in ____________ (number?) reps with a ____-____ (intervals between S and B?) LIP to create a(n) ________________________ (sequence name?).

2. In the key of B♭ ____________ (major or minor?), ____________ (how many?) -chord units ____________ (descend or ascend?) by ____________ (interval?)

   in ____________ (number?) reps with a ____-____ (intervals between S and B?) LIP to create a(n) ________________________ (sequence name?).

3. In the key of B♭ ____________ (major or minor?), ____________ (how many?) -chord units ____________ (descend or ascend?) by ____________ (interval?)

   in ____________ (number?) reps with a ____-____ (intervals between S and B?) LIP to create a(n) ________________________ (sequence name?).

Now, listen to part of a carol and complete the remaining exercises.

4. In the key of B♭ ____________ (major or minor?), ____________ (how many?) -chord units ____________ (descend or ascend?) by ____________ (interval?)

   in ____________ (number?) reps with a ____-____ (intervals between S and B?) LIP to create a(n) ________________________ (sequence name?).

5. Beginning with the given items, capture the music in the workspace.

   (a) In the single-line staves, notate the rhythm of the outer voices, basses and sopranos.

   (b) Below each note, write the syllables or numbers of the pitches.

   (c) In the grand staff, notate the pitches and rhythm of the outer voices parts. Refer to the single-line notation.

   (d) In each chord blank provided, write the Roman numeral and figure (if needed) that represents the harmony.

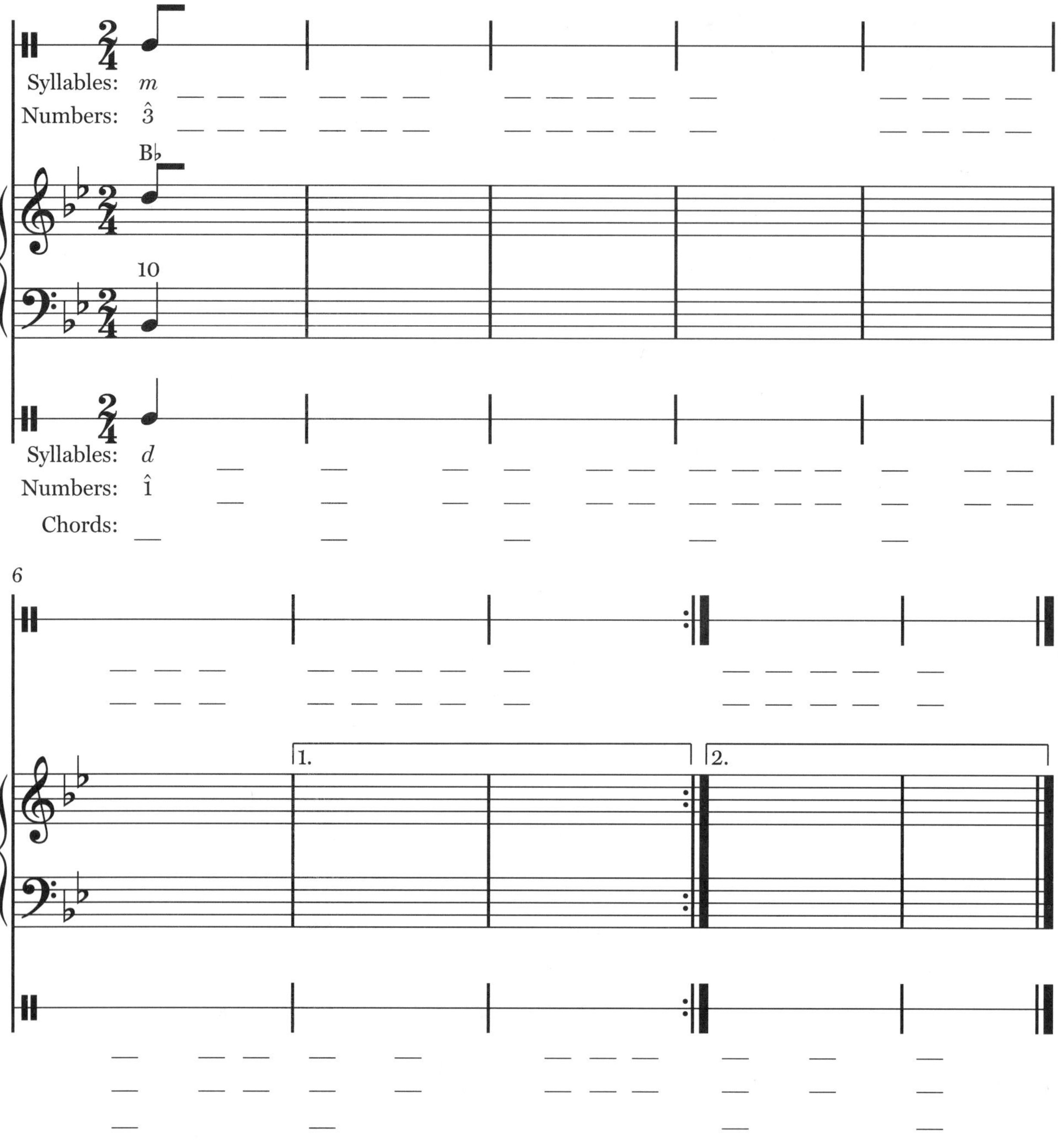

6. Bass pitch 4 is which type of chromatic embellishing tone?

passing   neighbor   appoggiatura   anticipation

7. At each phrase end, the highest parts move in parallel:

thirds   fourths   fifths   sixths

NAME ______________________

Contextual Listening 21.4

In exercises 1–3 the initial bass pitch is C. Identify the sequence's attributes and name.

Hint: At every chord change, identify the bass and soprano (violin 1 and cello) using syllables or numbers; for example, if you hear *do-me* ($\hat{1}$–$\flat\hat{3}$), the interval is 10.

1. In the key of C ____________ (major or minor?), ____________ (how many?) -chord units ____________ (descend or ascend?) by ____________ (interval?) in ____________ (number?) reps with a ____-____ (intervals between S and B?) LIP to create a(n) ______________________ (sequence name?).

2. (a) In the key of C ____________ (major or minor?), ____________ (how many?) -chord units ____________ (descend or ascend?) by ____________ (interval?) in ____________ (number?) reps.

   (b) At each chord change, record the outer interval. Think syllables or scale degrees.

   ____ ____ ____ ____ ____ ____ ____ ____

   (c) On which chord does the recurring interval pattern begin?

3. In the key of C ____________ (major or minor?), ____________ (how many?) -chord units ____________ (descend or ascend?) by ____________ (interval?) in ____________ (number?) reps with a ____-____ (intervals between S and B?) LIP to create a(n) ______________________ (sequence name?).

Now, listen to one phrase from a chamber-orchestra work and complete the remaining exercises.

4. Beginning with the given items, capture the outer voices in the workspace.
   (a) In the single-line staves, notate the rhythm of the outer voices, cello and violin 1.
   (b) Below each note, write the syllables or numbers of the pitches.
   (c) In the grand staff, notate the pitches and rhythm of the outer voices parts. Refer to the single-line notation.

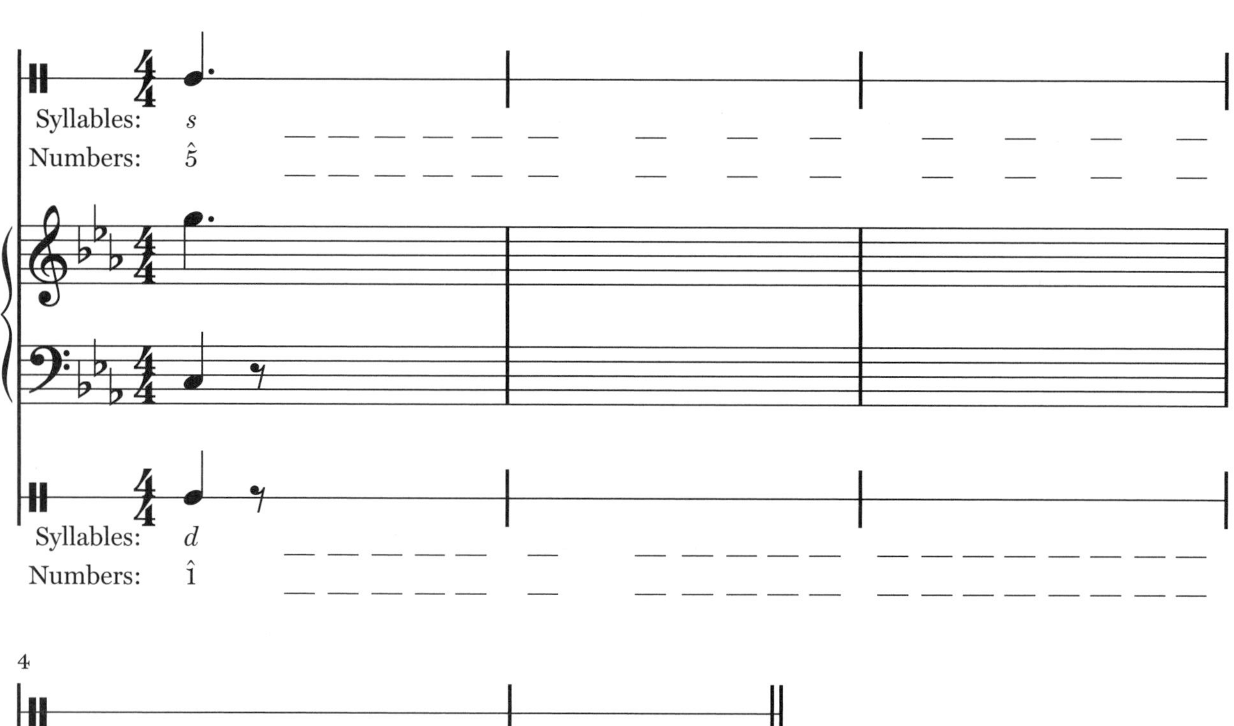

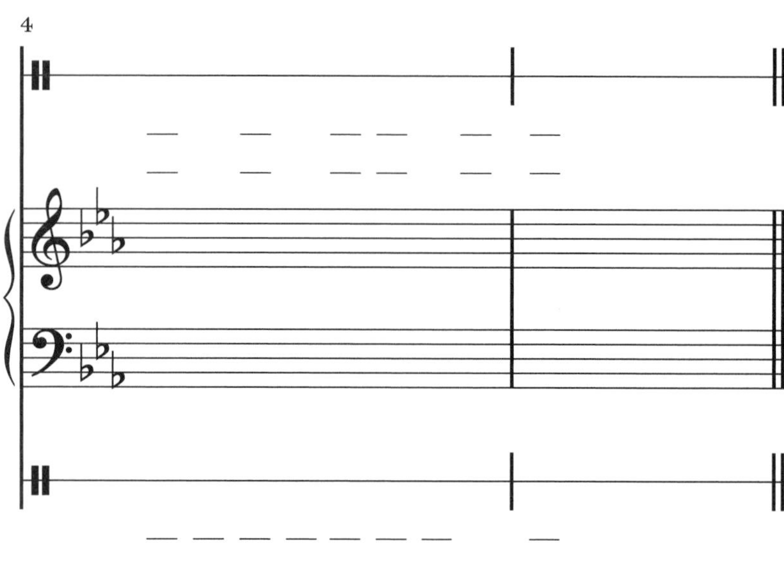

5. During pitches 1–7, which harmonies alternate? Hint: Focus on the bass line.
   i–III   i–iv^6 i–V^6 i–VI

6. Melodic pitch 8 and following feature which rhythmic device?
   syncopation   triplets   hemiola   anacruses

7. From bass pitch 8 to the end, all bass pitches belong to which scale?
   chromatic   major   ascending melodic   descending melodic

Bass pitch 9 begins a sequence.

8. In the key of C ____________ (major or minor?), ____________ (how many?) -chord units ____________ (descend or ascend?) by ____________ (interval?)
   in ____________ (number?) reps with a ____-____ (intervals between S and B?) LIP to create a(n) ______________________ (sequence name?).

9. The sequence includes which type of embellishment?
   passing tones   suspensions   neighbor tones

10. The concluding bass pitches are:
    do-sol ($\hat{1}$–$\hat{5}$)   *re-sol* ($\hat{2}$–$\hat{5}$)   *le-sol* ($\hat{6}$–$\hat{5}$)   *sol-do* ($\hat{5}$–$\hat{1}$)

11. The cadence type is: PAC   IAC   HC   PHC

Chromatic Harmony and Form

Modulation

NAME ______________________________

In this chapter you'll learn to:

- Identify and notate phrases and periods that begin in one key and modulate to another
- Identify and notate pivot chords

Modulation

Modulation occurs when music begins in one key and ends in another. Like tonicization, modulation employs secondary-dominant-function harmony. Thus, a chromatic pitch or, in minor keys, the cancelation of *ti* ($\hat{7}$), can signal a modulation.

Major keys *If you hear . . .*	*the modulation is to . . .*
fi-sol ($\sharp\hat{4}$-$\hat{5}$)	V (most common)
si-la ($\sharp\hat{5}$-$\hat{6}$)	vi (common)
di-re ($\sharp\hat{1}$-$\hat{2}$)	ii (somewhat common)
ri-mi ($\sharp\hat{2}$-$\hat{3}$)	iii (rare)
te-la ($\flat\hat{7}$-$\hat{6}$)	IV (very common)

Minor keys *If you hear . . .*	*the modulation is to . . .*
fi-sol ($\sharp\hat{4}$-$\hat{5}$)	v (very common)
mi-fa ($\hat{3}$-$\hat{4}$)	iv (very common)
te, not *ti* ($\flat\hat{7}$, not $\hat{7}$)	III (most common)
te and *ra* ($\flat\hat{7}$ and $\flat\hat{2}$)	VI (common)

Often, composers pivot between the origin and destination keys using a common chord or common tone. Colon notation identifies the keys. A bent bracket shows the pivot chord.

Pivot-chord notation	*Interpretation*
I: I IV V I ⌋	The I chord pivots to become
⌈ V: IV V I	IV in the key of the dominant.

Try it 1

Each exercise begins on tonic and then modulates. The initial questions guide your listening and prepare you to notate the music as follows. Notate the key signature. For bass and soprano parts, write the syllables or numbers as well as pitches and rhythm. Indicate the keys with colon notation and the pivot chord at the bent bracket. Write Roman numerals and figures (if needed) beneath the bass staff. Use exercise 1 as a model for where to place your answers.

1. (a) The initial progression is:

	I–V$^{8-7}$–I	I–ii$^6_5$–V–I	i–V$^{8-7}$–i	i–ii$^{ø6}_5$–V–i
Bass:	*d-s-s-d*	*d-f-s-d*	*d-s-s-d*	*d-f-s-d*
	$\hat{1}$-$\hat{5}$-$\hat{5}$-$\hat{1}$	$\hat{1}$-$\hat{4}$-$\hat{5}$-$\hat{1}$	$\hat{1}$-$\hat{5}$-$\hat{5}$-$\hat{1}$	$\hat{1}$-$\hat{4}$-$\hat{5}$-$\hat{1}$

(b) The chromatic pitch is: *fi* (♯$\hat{4}$) *te* (♭$\hat{7}$)

(c) The exercise modulates to the key of: V III

(d) The example ends with which progression?

I–V$^{8-7}$–I I–ii$^6_5$–V–I i–V$^{8-7}$–i i–ii$^{ø6}_5$–V–i

I: *m*($\hat{3}$) ___ ___ ___

: ___ ___ ___ ___ ___ ___ ___

d ($\hat{1}$) ___ ___ ___

I: I ___ ___ ___

___ ___ ___ ___ ___ ___

: ___ ___ ___ ___ ___ ___ ___

2. (a) The initial progression is:

	I–vi–ii$^6_5$–V$^{8-7}$–I	I–ii^6–V$^{8-7}_{6-5}{}^{}_{4-3}$–I
Bass:	*d - l - f - s - d*	*d - f - s - s - d*
	$\hat{1}$ - $\hat{6}$ - $\hat{4}$ - $\hat{5}$ - $\hat{1}$	$\hat{1}$ - $\hat{4}$ - $\hat{5}$ - $\hat{5}$ - $\hat{1}$
	i–VI–ii$^{ø6}_5$–V$^{8-7}$–i	i–ii^{o6}–V$^{8-7}_{6-5}{}^{}_{4-3}$–i
Bass:	*d - le - f - s - d*	*d - f - s - s - d*
	$\hat{1}$ - ♭$\hat{6}$ - $\hat{4}$ - $\hat{5}$ - $\hat{1}$	$\hat{1}$ - $\hat{4}$ - $\hat{5}$ - $\hat{5}$ - $\hat{1}$

(b) The chromatic pitch is: *fi* (♯$\hat{4}$) *te* (♭$\hat{7}$)

(c) The exercise modulates to the key of: V III

(d) The example ends with which progression?

I–vi–ii$^6_5$–V$^{8-7}$–I I–ii^6–V$^{8-7}_{6-5}{}^{}_{4-3}$–I i–VI–ii$^{ø6}_5$–V$^{8-7}$–i i–ii^{o6}–V$^{8-7}_{6-5}{}^{}_{4-3}$–i

i: *me*(♭$\hat{3}$) ___ ___ ___ ___ ___ ___ ___

: ___ ___ ___ ___ ___ ___ ___ ___

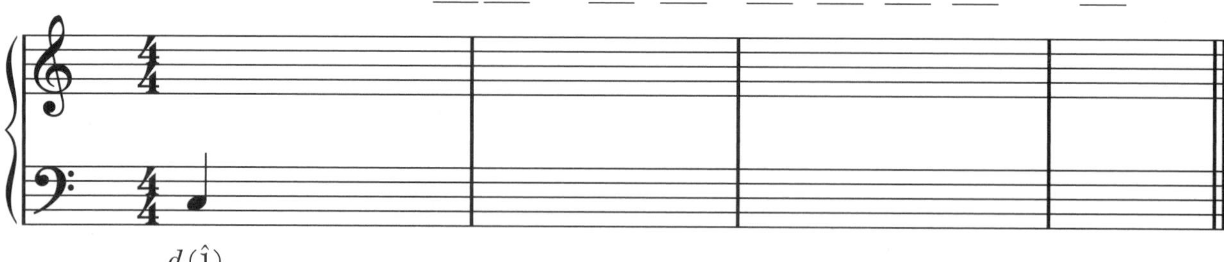

d ($\hat{1}$) ___ ___ ___ ___ ___ ___

i: i ___ ___ ___ ___

___ ___ ___ ___ ___ ___ ___

: ___ ___ ___ ___ ___ ___ ___

3\. (a) The initial progression is:

	I–V^6_5–I–ii^6–V^{6-5}_{4-3}–I	I–V^4_2–I^6–ii^6–$V^{8-7}_{\substack{6-5\\4-3}}$–I
Bass:	*d - t - d - f - s - s - d*	*d - f - m - f - s - s - d*
	$\hat{1}$ - $\hat{7}$ - $\hat{1}$ - $\hat{4}$ - $\hat{5}$ - $\hat{5}$ - $\hat{1}$	$\hat{1}$ - $\hat{4}$ - $\hat{3}$ - $\hat{4}$ - $\hat{5}$ - $\hat{5}$ - $\hat{1}$
	i–V^6_5–i–ii^{o6}–V^{6-5}_{4-3}–i	i–V^4_2–i^6–ii^{o6}–$V^{8-7}_{\substack{6-5\\4-3}}$–I
Bass:	*d - t - d - f - s - s - d*	*d - f - me - f - s - s - d*
	$\hat{1}$ - $\hat{7}$ - $\hat{1}$ - $\hat{4}$ - $\hat{5}$ - $\hat{5}$ - $\hat{1}$	$\hat{1}$ - $\hat{4}$ - $\flat\hat{3}$ - $\hat{4}$ - $\hat{5}$ - $\hat{5}$ - $\hat{1}$

(b) The chromatic pitch is: *di* ($\sharp\hat{1}$) *fi* ($\sharp\hat{4}$) *si* ($\sharp\hat{5}$) *te* ($\flat\hat{7}$)

(c) The exercise modulates to the key of: ii IV V vi

(d) The example ends with which progression?

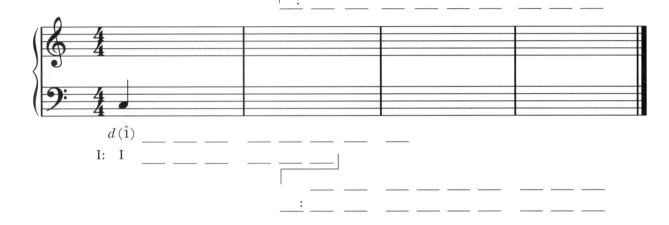

I–V^6_5–I– ii^6–V^{6-5}_{4-3}–I I–V^4_2–I^6– ii^6–$V^{8-7}_{\substack{6-5\\4-3}}$–I

i–V^6_5–i–ii^{o6}–V^{6-5}_{4-3}–i i–V^4_2–i^6– ii^{o6}–$V^{8-7}_{\substack{6-5\\4-3}}$–I

I: *m* ($\hat{3}$) ___ ___ ___ ___ ___ ___ ___ ___

: ___ ___ ___ ___ ___ ___ ___ ___ ___ ___

d ($\hat{1}$) ___ ___ ___ ___ ___ ___ ___ ___

I: I ___ ___ ___ ___ ___ ___

___ ___ ___ ___ ___ ___ ___ ___ ___

: ___ ___ ___ ___ ___ ___ ___ ___ ___ ___

4. The initial and concluding bass lines are identical in their respective keys. Focus on the soprano to identify the progression.

(a) The initial progression is:

	m - f - s . . .	*m - r - d . . .*
Sop.:	I–V^4_3–I^6–ii^6–$V^{8-7}_{6-5\,4-3}$–I	I–V^6_4–I^6–ii^6–V^{6-5}_{4-3}–I
	$\hat{3}$ - $\hat{4}$ - $\hat{5}$	$\hat{3}$ - $\hat{2}$ - $\hat{1}$
	me - f - s . . .	*m - r - d . . .*
Sop.:	i–V^4_3–i^6–ii^{o6}–$V^{8-7}_{6-5\,4-3}$–i	i–V^6_4–i^6–ii^6–V^{6-5}_{4-3}–i
	$\flat\hat{3}$ - $\hat{4}$ - $\hat{5}$	$\hat{3}$ - $\hat{2}$ - $\hat{1}$

(b) The chromatic pitch is: *di* ($\sharp\hat{1}$) *fi* ($\sharp\hat{4}$) *si* ($\sharp\hat{5}$) *te* ($\flat\hat{7}$)

(c) The exercise modulates to the key of: ii IV V vi

(d) The example ends with which progression?

I–V^4_3–I^6–ii^6–$V^{8-7}_{6-5\,4-3}$–I I–V^6_4–I^6–ii^6–V^{6-5}_{4-3}–I

i–V^4_3–i^6–ii^{o6}–$V^{8-7}_{6-5\,4-3}$–i i–V^6_4–i^6–ii^6–V^{6-5}_{4-3}–i

m($\hat{3}$) ___ ___ ___ ___ ___ ___ ___ ___

___ : ___ ___ ___ ___ ___ ___ ___ ___ ___

d ($\hat{1}$) ___ ___ ___ ___ ___ ___ ___

I: I ___ ___ ___ ___ ___ ___

___ ___ ___ ___ ___ ___ ___ ___ ___

___ : ___ ___ ___ ___ ___ ___ ___ ___ ___

NAME ____________________

Contextual Listening 22.1

Exercises 1–2 begin on tonic and then modulate. To identify progressions, focus on the bass.

1. (a) The initial progression is:

	I–V^{8-7}–I	I–ii^6_5–V–I	i–V^{8-7}–i	i–$ii^{ø6}_5$–V–i
Bass:	*d-s-s-d*	*d-f-s-d*	*d-s-s-d*	*d-f-s-d*
	$\hat{1}$-$\hat{5}$-$\hat{5}$-$\hat{1}$	$\hat{1}$-$\hat{4}$-$\hat{5}$-$\hat{1}$	$\hat{1}$-$\hat{5}$-$\hat{5}$-$\hat{1}$	$\hat{1}$-$\hat{4}$-$\hat{5}$-$\hat{1}$

(b) The chromatic pitch is: *fi* (♯$\hat{4}$) *te* (♭$\hat{7}$)

(c) The exercise modulates to the key of: V III

(d) The example ends with which progression?

I–V^{8-7}–I I–ii^6_5–V–I i–V^{8-7}–i i–$ii^{ø6}_5$–V–i

(e) Notate the key signature, bass, soprano, and Roman numerals. Indicate the keys with colon notation and the pivot chord at the bent bracket.

I: *m* ($\hat{3}$) ___ ___ ___ ___

___ : ___ ___ ___ ___ ___ ___

d ($\hat{1}$) ___ ___ ___

I: I ___ ___ ___

___ ___ ___ ___ ___ ___

___ : ___ ___ ___ ___ ___ ___

2. (a) The initial progression is:

	I–ii^{6}–V–I	I–V$^{8-7}$–I	i–ii$^{\circ 6}$–V–i	i–V$^{8-7}$–i
Bass:	*d-f-s-d*	*d-s-s-d*	*d-f-s-d*	*d-s-s-d*
	$\hat{1}$-$\hat{4}$-$\hat{5}$-$\hat{1}$	$\hat{1}$-$\hat{5}$-$\hat{5}$-$\hat{1}$	$\hat{1}$-$\hat{4}$-$\hat{5}$-$\hat{1}$	$\hat{1}$-$\hat{5}$-$\hat{5}$-$\hat{1}$

(b) The chromatic pitch is: *di* (♯$\hat{1}$) *fi* (♯$\hat{4}$) *si* (♯$\hat{5}$) *te* (♭$\hat{7}$)

(c) The exercise modulates to the key of: ii IV V vi

(d) The example ends with which progression?

I–ii^{6}–V–I I–V$^{8-7}$–I i–ii$^{\circ 6}$–V–i i–V$^{8-7}$–i

(e) Notate the key signature, bass, soprano, and Roman numerals. Indicate the keys

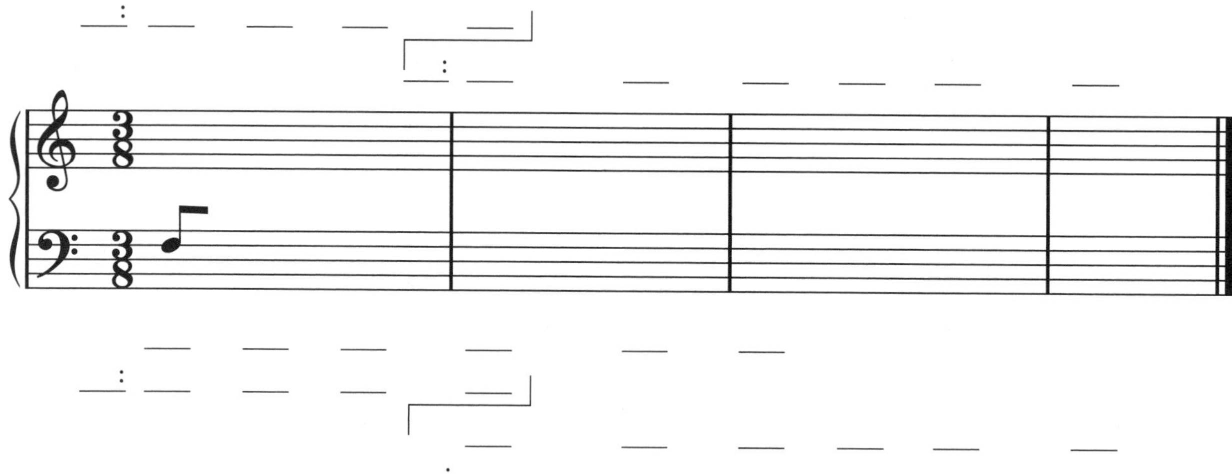

NAME ___________________________

Now, listen to two phrases from a minuet and complete the remaining exercises.

3. Begin with the given items and capture the music in the workspace.
   (a) In the single-line staves, notate the rhythm of the outer parts.
   (b) Below each note, write the syllables or numbers of the pitches.
   (c) In the grand staff, notate the key signature and the pitches and rhythm of the outer parts. Refer to the single-line notation.
   (d) Write the Roman numerals and figures (if needed) that represent the harmony. Indicate the keys with colon notation and the pivot chord with a bent bracket.

Pitches: ___ : ___ ___ ___ ___ ___ ___ ___ ___ ___ ___ ___ ___

Pitches: ___ ___ ___ ___ ___ ___ ___ ___ ___ ___ ___

Chords: ___ : ___ ___ ___ ___ ___ ___ ___ ___ ___

5

Contextual Listening 22.2

Exercises 1–2 begin on tonic and then modulate.

1. (a) The initial progression is: I–V$^{6}_{4}$–I^{6} I–vii$^{\circ 6}$–I^{6} i–V$^{6}_{4}$–i^{6} i–vii$^{\circ 6}$–i^{6}

   Hint: Listen for chord 2's quality.

   (b) The chromatic pitch is: *di* (♯$\hat{1}$)   *fi* (♯$\hat{4}$)   *si* (♯$\hat{5}$)   *te* (♭$\hat{7}$)

   (c) The exercise modulates to the key of: ii   IV   V   vi

   (d) The example ends with which progression? ii–V$^{8-7}$–I   IV–V$^{6-5}_{4-3}$–I   ii$^{\circ}$–V$^{8-7}$–i   iv–V$^{6-5}_{4-3}$–i

   (e) Notate the key signature, bass, soprano, and Roman numerals. Indicate the keys with colon notation and the pivot chord at the bent bracket.

I: *d* ($\hat{1}$) ___ ___ ___ ___ ___ ___ ___ ___

___ : ___ ___ ___ ___

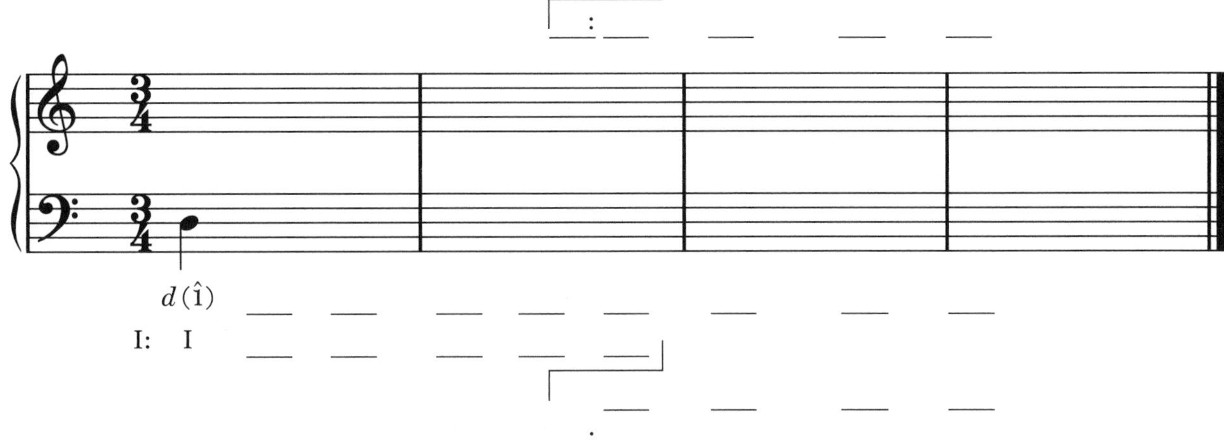

___ : ___ ___ ___ ___

2. (a) The initial progression is: I–V$^4_3$–I^6 I–V$^4_2$–I^6 i–V$^4_3$–i^6 i–V$^4_2$–i^6

Hint: Listen for chord 2's bass pitch.

(b) The chromatic pitch is: *di* ($\sharp\hat{1}$) *fi* ($\sharp\hat{4}$) *si* ($\sharp\hat{5}$) *te* ($\flat\hat{7}$)

(c) The exercise modulates to the key of: ii IV V vi

(d) The example ends with which progression? Hint: Listen to the bass.

	I–ii^6–V^7–I	I–V$^{6-5}_{4-3}$–I	i–ii^{o6}–V^7–i	i–V$^{6-5}_{4-3}$–i
Bass:	*d-f-s-d*	*d-s-s-d*	*d-f-s-d*	*d-s-s-d*
	$\hat{1}$-$\hat{4}$-$\hat{5}$-$\hat{1}$	$\hat{1}$-$\hat{5}$-$\hat{5}$-$\hat{1}$	$\hat{1}$-$\hat{4}$-$\hat{5}$-$\hat{1}$	$\hat{1}$-$\hat{5}$-$\hat{5}$-$\hat{1}$

(e) Notate the key signature, bass, soprano, and Roman numerals. Indicate the keys with colon notation and the pivot chord at the bent bracket.

Now, listen to two phrases from a trio and complete the remaining exercises.

3. Begin with the given items and capture the music in the workspace.

(a) In the single-line staves, notate the rhythm of the outer parts.

(b) Below each note, write the syllables or numbers of the pitches.

(c) In the grand staff, notate the key signature and the pitches and rhythm of the outer parts. Refer to the single-line notation.

(d) Write the Roman numerals and figures (if needed) that represent the harmony.

(e) Near the beginning, indicate the tonicization with bracket, slash, or colon notation.

(f) At the modulation, indicate the keys with colon notation and the pivot chord with a bent bracket.

NAME ______________________________

Pitches: __ : __ __ __ __ __ __ __ __ __ __

Pitches: __ __ __ __ __ __

Chords: __ : __ __ __ __

3

__ __ __ __ __ __ __ __ __

__ __ __ __ __ __

__ __ __ __ __ __

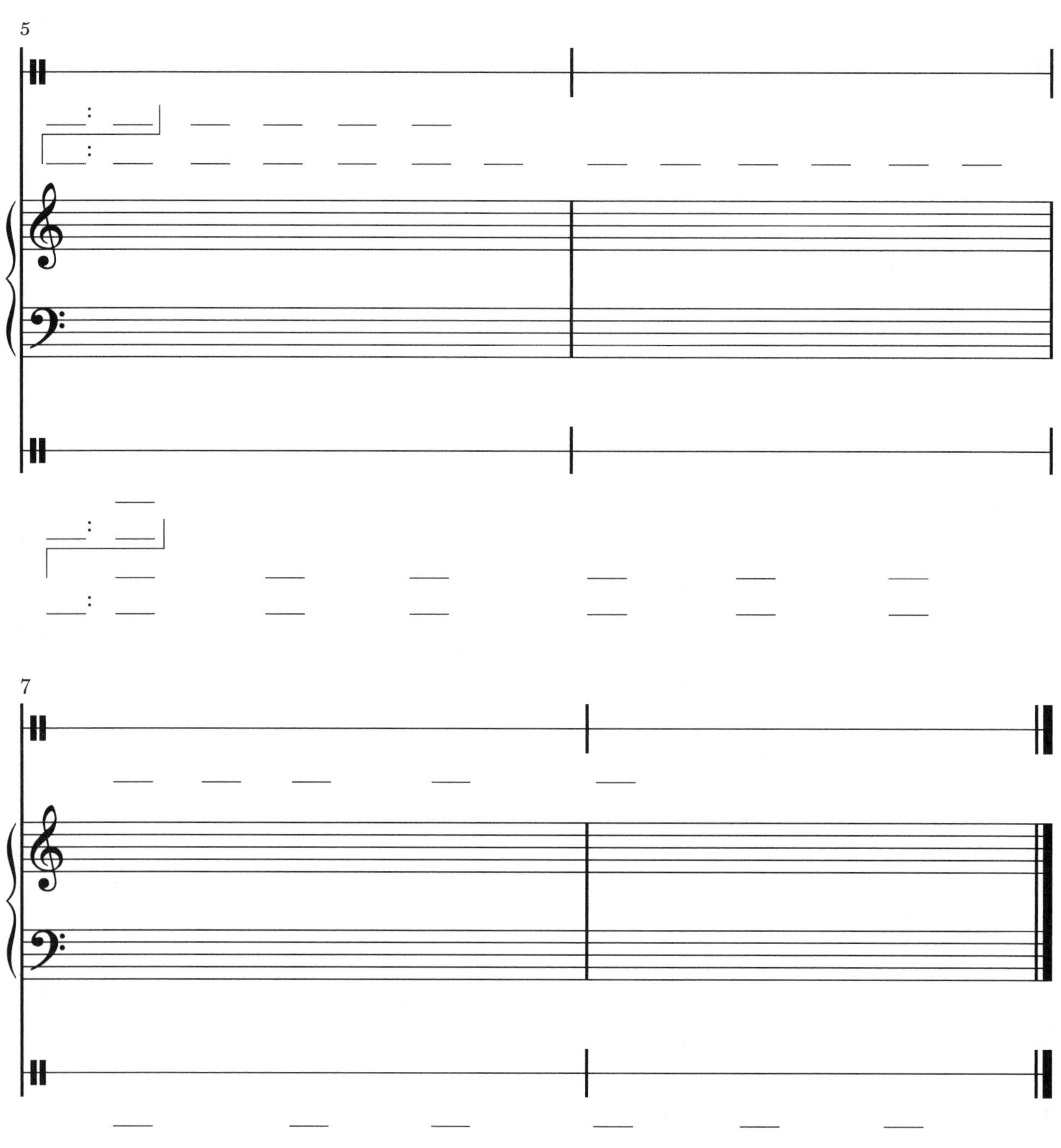
5
7

NAME ______________________________

Contextual Listening 22.3

Exercises 1–2 begin on tonic and then modulate.

1. (a) The chromatic pitches is/are: *ra* (♭$\hat{2}$) *mi* ($\hat{3}$) *fi* (♯$\hat{4}$) *te* (♭$\hat{7}$)

   (b) The exercise modulates to the key of: III iv v VI

   (c) The example ends with which progression?

   I–V8–7–I I–V$^{6-5}_{4-3}$–I i–V8–7–i i–V$^{6-5}_{4-3}$–i

   (d) Notate the key signature, bass, soprano, and Roman numerals. Indicate the keys with colon notation and the pivot chord at the bent bracket.

i: *me* (♭$\hat{3}$) ___ ___ ___ ___ ___

___ : ___ ___ ___ ___ ___ ___

d ($\hat{1}$) ___ ___ ___ ___ ___

i: i ___ ___ ___ ___

___ ___ ___ ___ ___

___ : ___ ___ ___ ___ ___

2. (a) The initial progression is:
   Hint: Listen for chord quality.
   I–V$^{6-5}_{4-3}$–I   i–vii°7–vii°$^{6}_{5}$–i

   (b) The chromatic pitch(es) is/are: *ra* ($\flat\hat{2}$) *mi* ($\hat{3}$) *fi* ($\sharp\hat{4}$) *te* ($\flat\hat{7}$)

   (c) The exercise modulates to the key of: III iv v VI

   (d) The example ends with which progression?
   I–V7–I V$^{6-5}_{4-3}$–I i–V7–i V$^{6-5}_{4-3}$–i

   (e) Notate the key signature, bass, soprano, and Roman numerals. Indicate the keys with colon notation and the pivot chord at the bent bracket.

Now, listen to two phrases from a scherzo and complete the remaining exercises.

3. Begin with the given items and capture the music in the workspace.
   (a) In the single-line staves, notate the rhythm of the outer parts.
   (b) Below each note, write the syllables or numbers of the pitches.
   (c) In the grand staff, notate the key signature and the pitches and rhythm of the outer parts. Refer to the single-line notation.
   (d) Write the Roman numerals and figures (if needed) that represent the harmony.
   - At the modulation, indicate the keys with colon notation and the pivot chord with a bent bracket.
   - After the modulation, indicate the tonicization with bracket, slash, or colon notation.

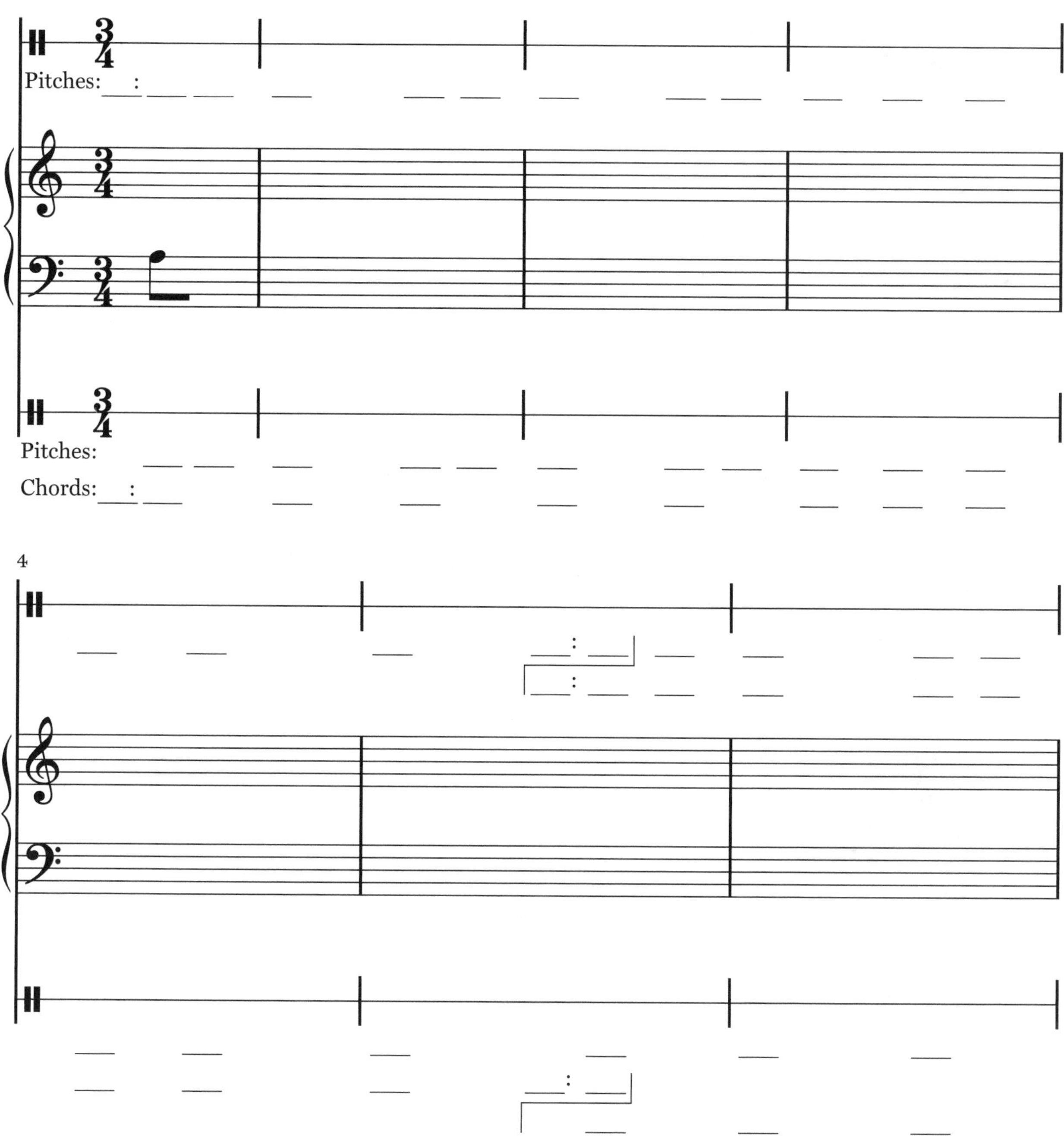
Pitches:
Pitches:
Chords:
4

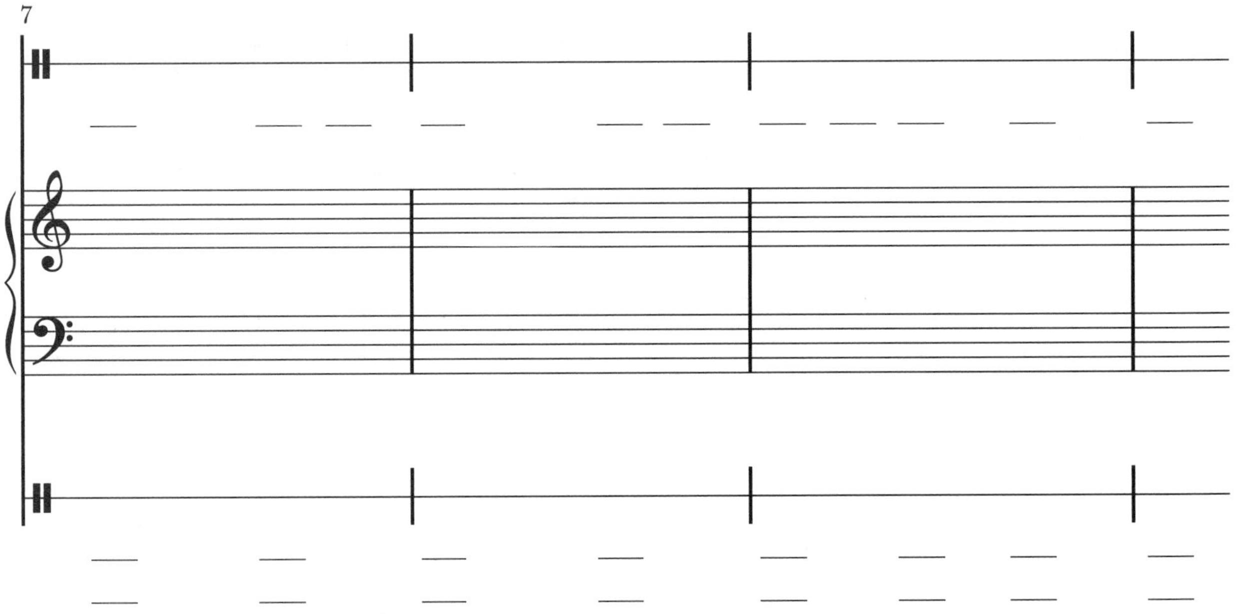
7

NAME ______________________

Modulatory Periods

Modulatory periods begin in one key and end in another. Phrase diagrams indicate each cadence's key in parentheses and include the term "modulatory" in the descriptor.

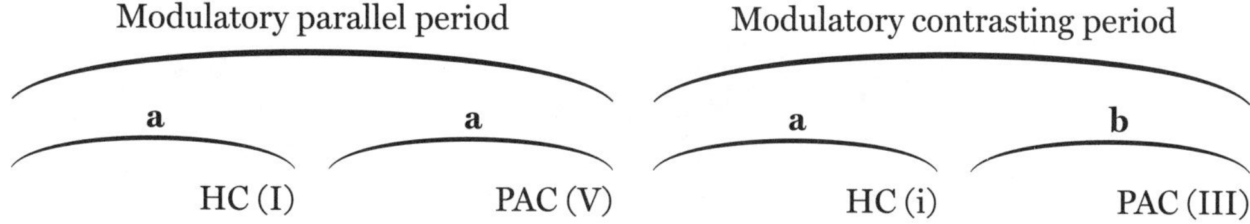

Try it 2

Listen and choose the diagram that matches the phrase structure.

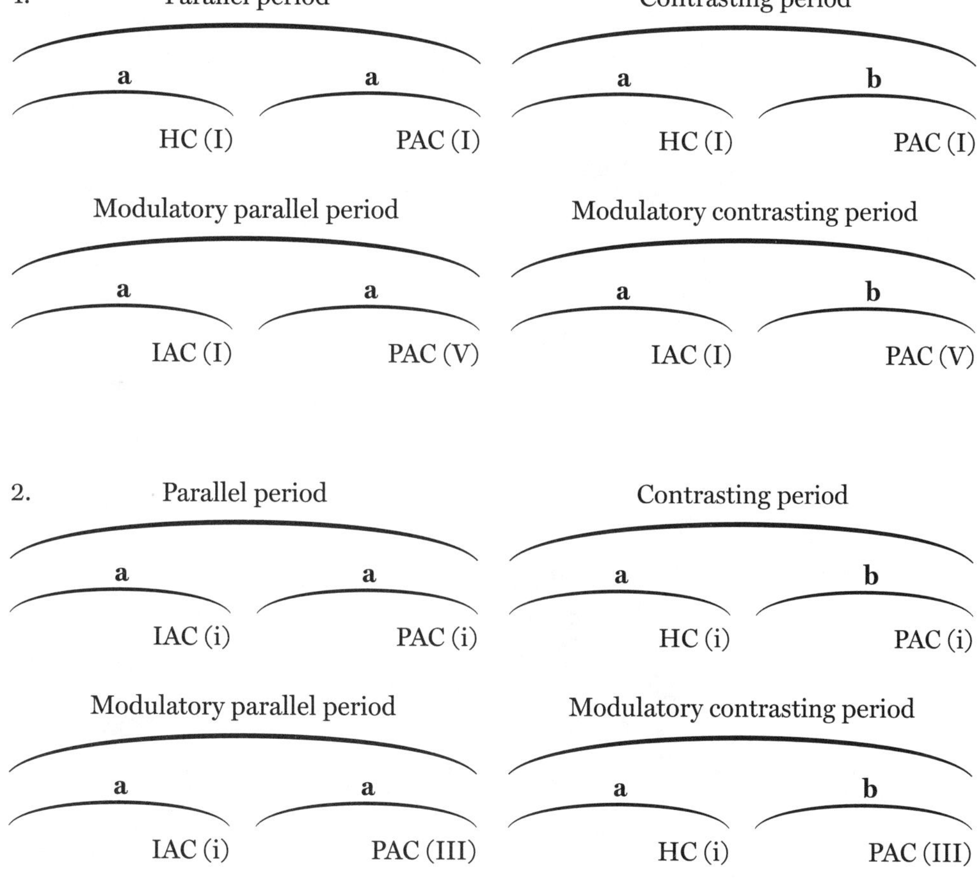

NAME ________________

Contextual Listening 22.4

Listen to two phrases from a chamber work and complete the exercises.

1. In the space below, diagram the excerpt's phrase structure. Draw curves to represent phrases. Write the cadence type and the key in which it occurs (PAC (V), for example). Include design letters and label the entire structure.

2. Begin with the given items and capture the music in the workspace.

   (a) In the single-line staves, notate the rhythm of the outer parts.

   (b) Below each note, write the syllables or numbers of the pitches.

   (c) In the grand staff, notate the key signature and the pitches and rhythm of the outer parts. Refer to the single-line notation.

   (d) Write the Roman numerals and figures (if needed) that represent the harmony. At the modulation, indicate the keys with colon notation and the pivot chord with a bent bracket.

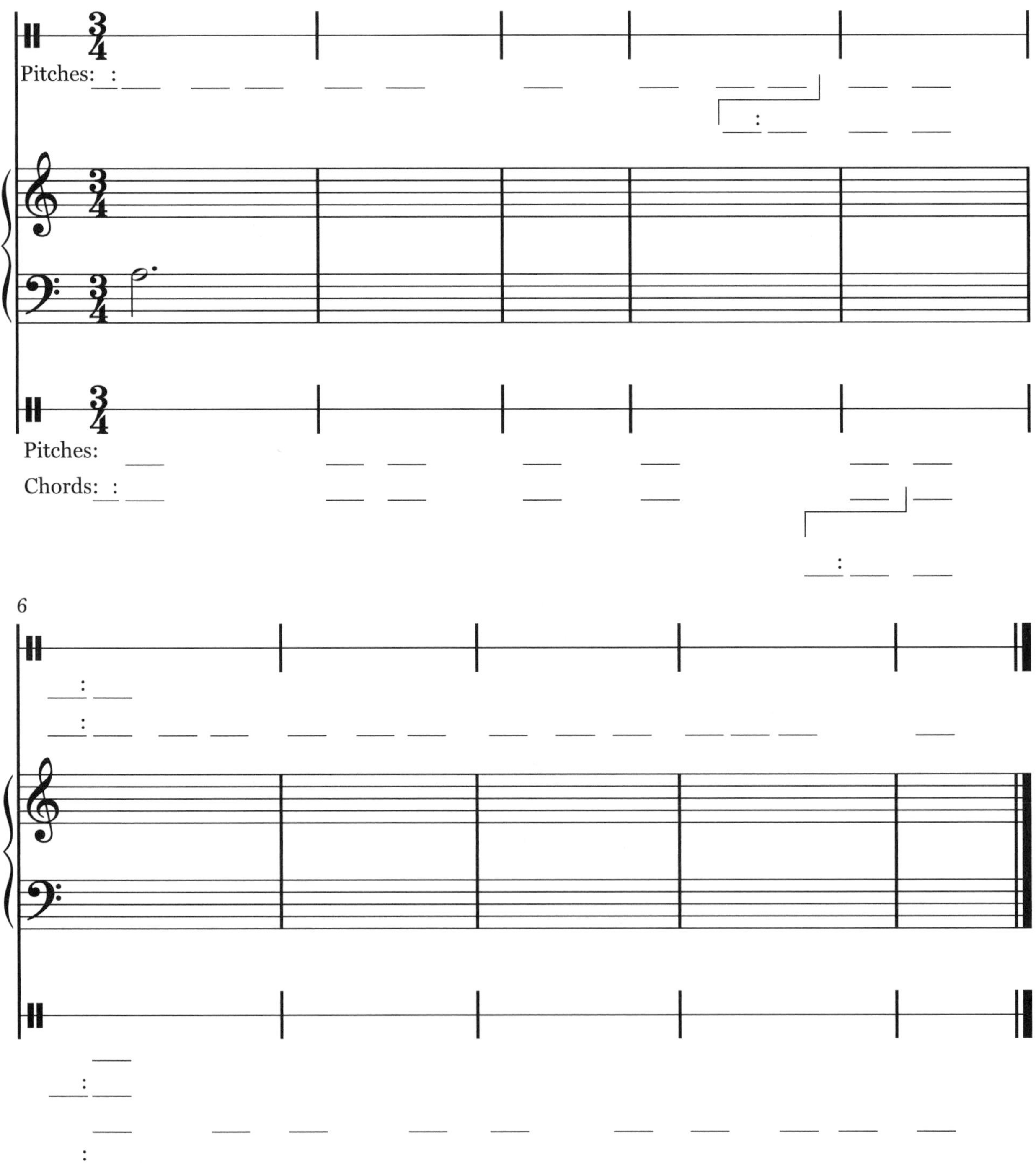

Binary and Ternary Forms

NAME ______________________

In this chapter you'll learn to:

- Identify binary, ternary, and composite forms

Binary Forms

Form is the product of a piece's harmonic structure and melodic design. Two-part forms are called binary. Each part is a repeatable section. Most binary pieces repeat both sections. Several terms distinguish specific binary-form types.

Is the binary form . . .	*Choose option 1 if . . .*	*Choose option 2 if . . .*
(1) rounded or (2) simple?	Section 2 ends with a recapitulation of section 1.	There is no recapitulation of section 1.
(1) sectional or (2) continuous?	Section 1 ends with a PAC in I (or i).	Section 1 ends any other way.
balanced, (1) yes or (2) no?	Both sections conclude similarly.	The sections end differently.

In binary form diagrams, uppercase letters represent section design. Roman numerals show keys. The label may include descriptors, like "simple sectional" or "rounded continuous."

Simple sectional binary

A **B**

‖: I ——— I :‖‖: V ——— I :‖

Rounded continuous binary

A **B** **A′**

‖: i ——— III :‖‖: III — i ——— :‖

Bar form binary repeats section 1, but not section 2.

A **B**

‖: :‖ ‖

Try it 1

1. Listen to section 1 of a string quartet movement. Focus first on the phrases, then the section.

   (a) Which diagram represents the phrase structure?

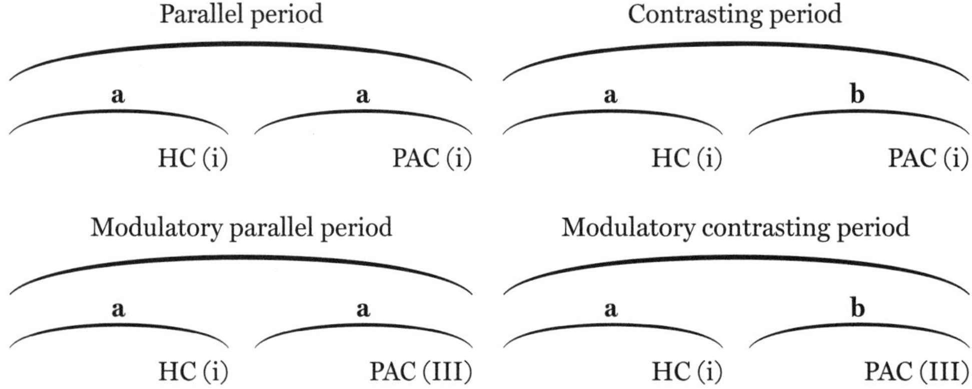

   (b) The excerpt is section 1 of a binary composition. The binary form is:

   sectional continuous

Exercises 2–4 are complete compositions. Focus first on the phrase structure, then the sections, and finally, the overall form.

2. (a) Which is section 1's phrase diagram?

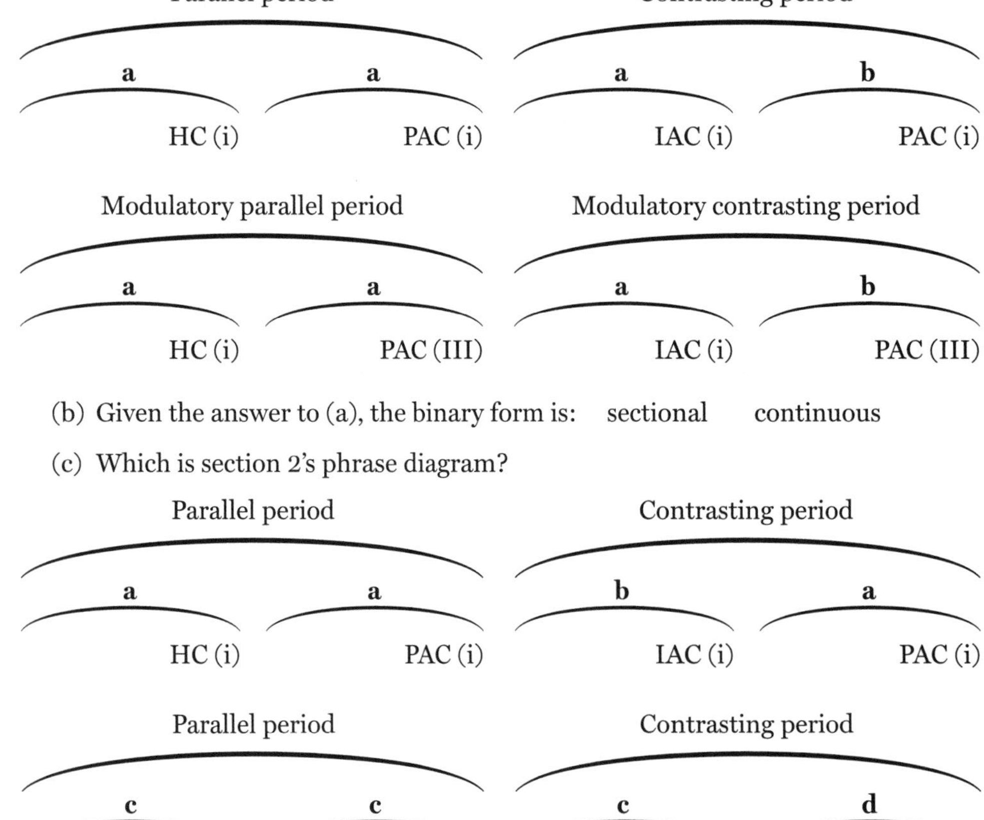

   (b) Given the answer to (a), the binary form is: sectional continuous

   (c) Which is section 2's phrase diagram?

(d) At the end, is there a recapitulation? yes no

(e) Do the sections end with similar melodies? yes no

(f) Which diagram matches the binary form?

Simple sectional binary

A B

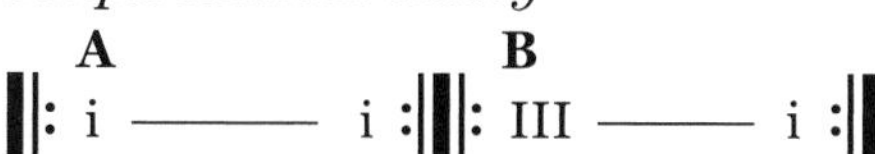

Rounded sectional binary

A B A′

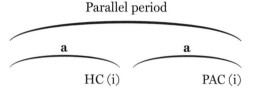

Simple continuous binary

A B

‖: i — III :‖‖: III — i :‖

Rounded continuous binary

A B A′

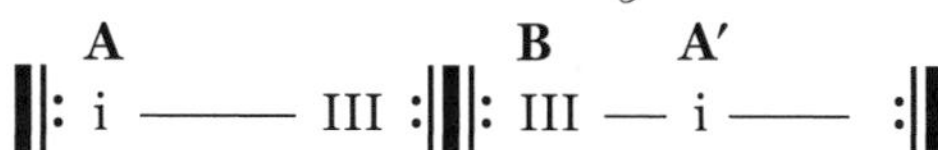

3. (a) Which is section 1's phrase diagram?

Modulatory parallel period

a a

HC (i) PAC (III)

Parallel period

a a

HC (i) PAC (i)

Modulatory contrasting period

Contrasting period

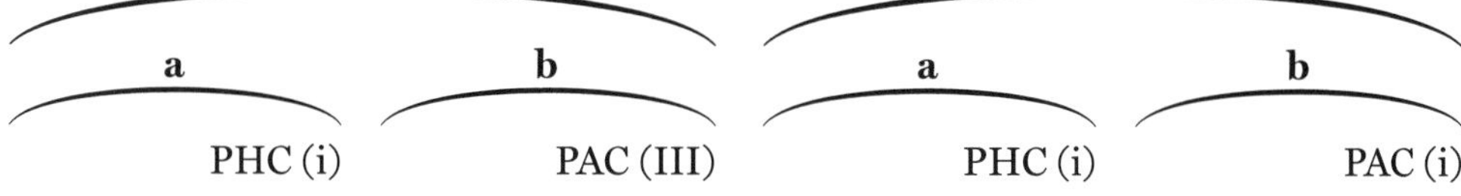

PHC (i) PAC (III) PHC (i) PAC (i)

(b) Given the answer to (a), the binary form is: sectional continuous

(c) Which is section 2's phrase diagram?

Independent phrases

Independent phrases

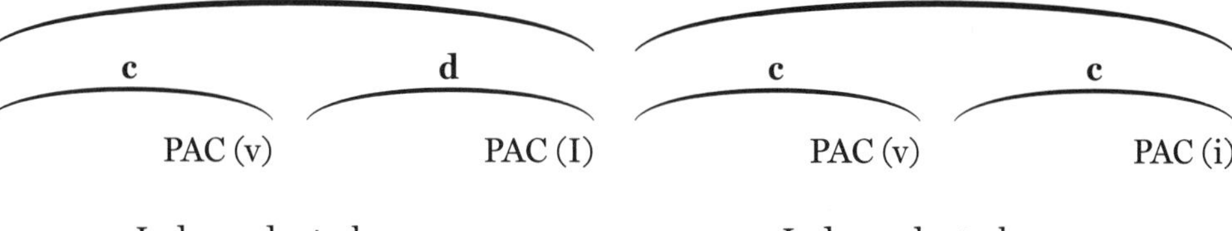

Independent phrases

Independent phrases

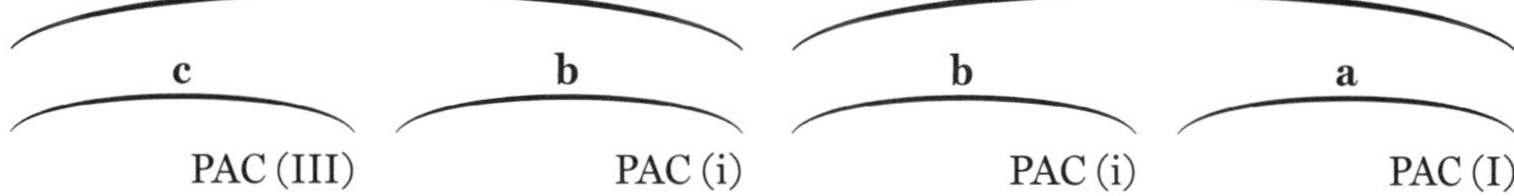

PAC (III) PAC (i) PAC (i) PAC (I)

(d) At the end, is there a recapitulation? yes no

(e) Do the sections end with similar melodies? yes no

(f) Which diagram matches the binary form?

Simple sectional binary

	A		B	
‖:	i ———	i :‖:	III ———	I :‖

Rounded sectional binary

	A		B	A′	
‖:	i ———	i :‖:	III —	i ———	:‖

Simple continuous binary

	A		B	
‖:	i ———	III :‖:	III ———	I :‖

Rounded continuous binary

	A		B	A′	
‖:	i ———	III :‖:	III —	i ———	:‖

4. (a) Diagram and label section 1's phrases and period:

(b) Given the answer to exercise (a), the binary form is: sectional continuous

(c) Diagram and label section 2's phrases and period:
Hint: Periods with odd-numbered phrases are "asymmetrical."

(d) At the end, is there a recapitulation? yes no

(e) Do the sections end with similar melodies? yes no

(f) Incorporating the diagrams from exercises 1 and 3, Diagram and label the form of the entire minuet:

NAME ____________________

Contextual Listening 23.1

Listen to an entire theme, the beginning of which appeared as Contextual Listening 22.1.

1. Which is section 1's phrase diagram?

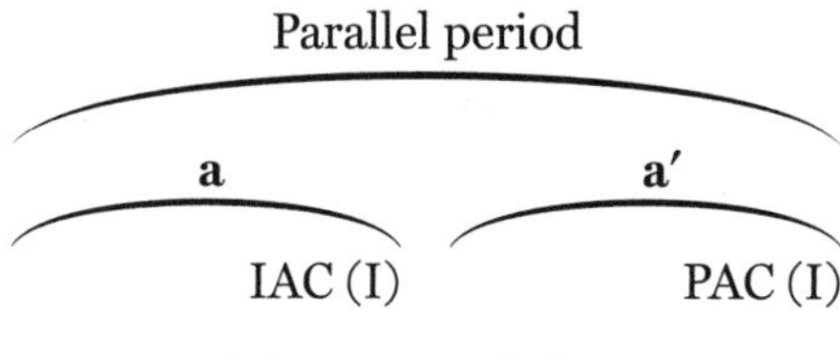

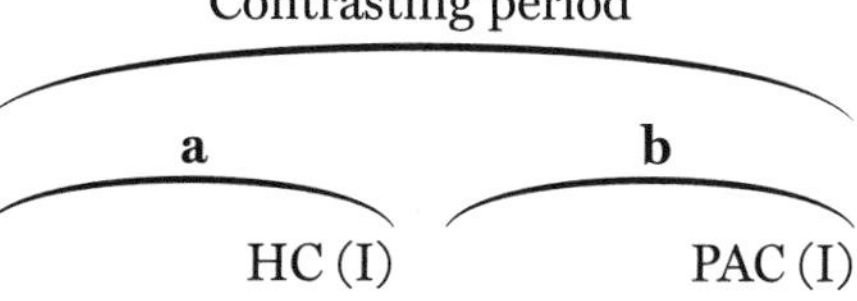

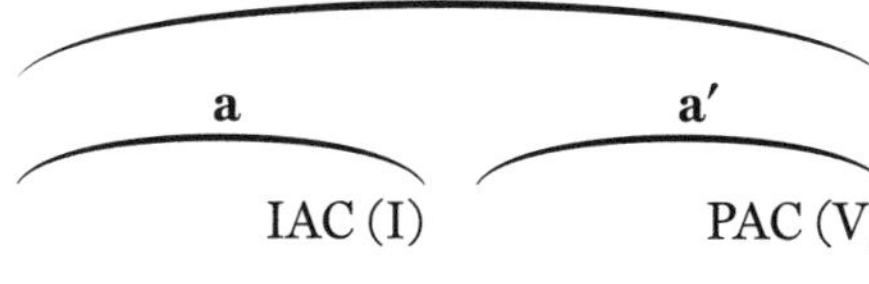

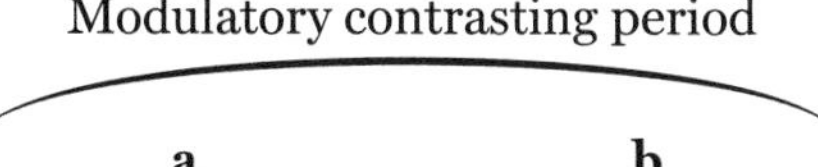

2. Given the answer to exercise 1, the binary form is: sectional continuous

3. Which is section 2's phrase diagram?

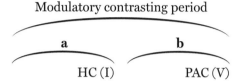

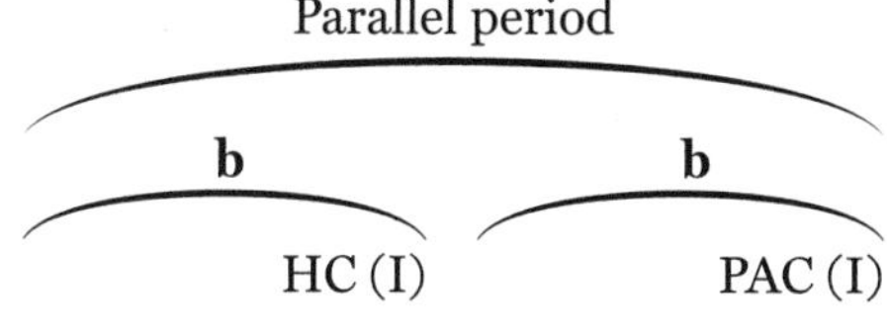

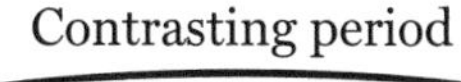

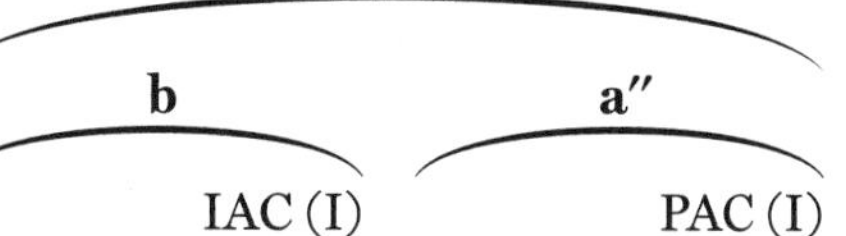

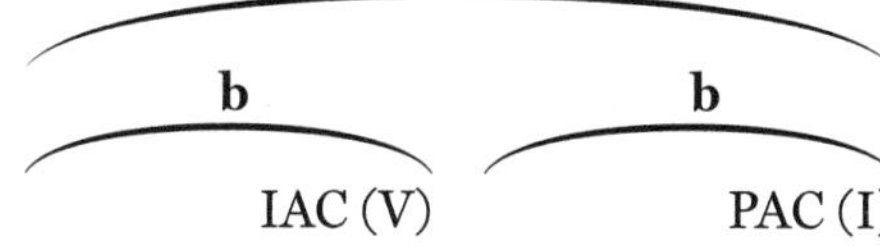

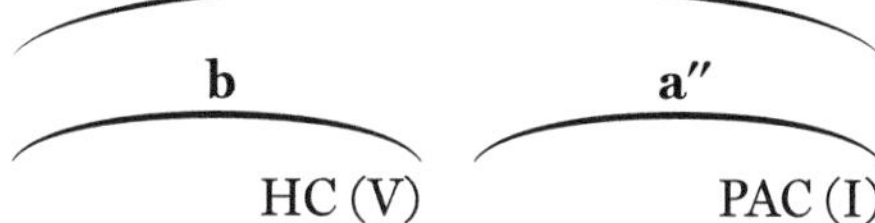

4. At the end, is there a recapitulation? yes no

5. Do the sections end with similar melodies? yes no

6. The $^6_4$ type near each section's end is: passing neighboring cadential

7. Which diagram matches the piece's binary form?

Simple sectional balanced binary

A: ‖: I —— I :‖ B: ‖: V —— I :‖

Rounded sectional binary

A: ‖: I —— I :‖ B: ‖: V —— A′ I :‖

Simple continuous balanced binary

A: ‖: I —— V :‖ B: ‖: V —— I :‖

Rounded continuous binary

A: ‖: I —— V :‖ B: ‖: V —— A′ I :‖

Contextual Listening 23.2

Listen to a chorale and complete the following exercises. Focus first on phrase 1.

1. Use the workspace to capture phrase 1's outer parts and chords. Begin with the given items.
   (a) In the single-line staves, notate the rhythm of the outer parts.
   (b) Below each note, write the syllables or numbers of the pitches.
   (c) In the grand staff, notate the pitches and rhythm of the outer parts. Refer to the single-line notation.
   (d) Write the Roman numerals and figures (if needed) that represent the harmony.

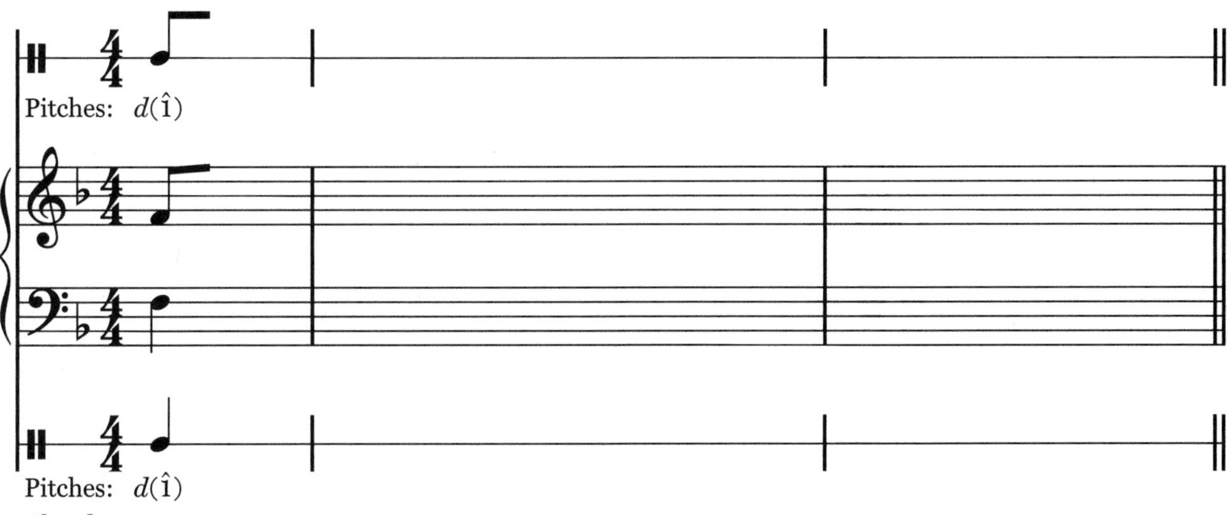

2. Phrase 1's cadence type is: PAC (I) IAC (I) HC (I) PAC (V)

Listen again and focus on all of section 1.

3. Phrase 2's cadence type is: PAC (I) IAC (I) HC (I) PAC (V)
4. Phrase 3 begins by tonicizing which chord? Hint: Listen to bass pitches 1–2.

	ii	IV	V	vi
Bass:	*di-re* (♯$\hat{1}$–$\hat{2}$)	*te-la* (♭$\hat{7}$–$\hat{6}$)	*fi-sol* (♯$\hat{4}$–$\hat{5}$)	*si-la* (♯$\hat{5}$–$\hat{6}$)

5. Phrase 3's cadence type is: PAC (I) IAC (I) HC (I) PAC (V)
6. Diagram section 1's phrase structure. For help, refer to the answers to questions 2–5.

Listen again, focusing on section 2.

7. Section 2, phrase 1 modulates to which key? Hint: Which chromatic pitch sounds near the cadence?

Key:	ii	IV	V	vi
Chromatic pitch:	*di* (♯$\hat{1}$)	*te* (♭$\hat{7}$)	*fi* (♯$\hat{4}$)	*si* (♯$\hat{5}$)

8. Does section 2 repeat? yes no

Now, listen to the entire piece, focusing on the overall form.

9. Which diagram represents the overall form?

Simple sectional bar form

A **B**
‖: I ——— I :‖ I ——— I ‖

Rounded sectional binary

A **B** **A′**
‖: I ——— I :‖‖: V ——— I :‖

Simple continuous bar form

A **B**
‖: I ——— V :‖ V ——— I ‖

Rounded continuous binary

A **B** **A′**
‖: I ——— V :‖‖: V ——— I :‖

Contextual Listening 23.3

Alberti figures prolong a bass line by embellishing it with consonant skips in smaller note values.

Notate the rhythm of the prolonged bass pitches (as opposed to every pitch). Beneath each note, write its syllable or number. Only once per measure, write the Roman numeral and figure(s) of the implied chord. For trills, write the main note and the symbol *tr*.

1.

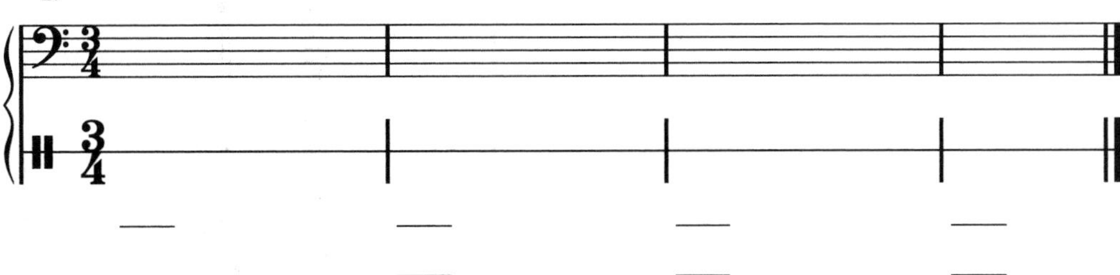

2.

Now, listen to a minuet and complete the remaining exercises.

3. Begin with the given items and capture the music in the workspace.
   (a) In the upper single-line staff, notate the rhythm of the melody. Write *tr* for trill. In the lower single-line staff, the rhythm is given.
   (b) Below each note, write the syllables or numbers of the pitches.
   (c) In the grand staff, notate the pitches and rhythm of the outer parts. Refer to the single-line notation.
   (d) Write the Roman numerals and figures (if needed) that represent the harmony. Indicate the keys with colon notation and the pivot chord with a bent bracket.

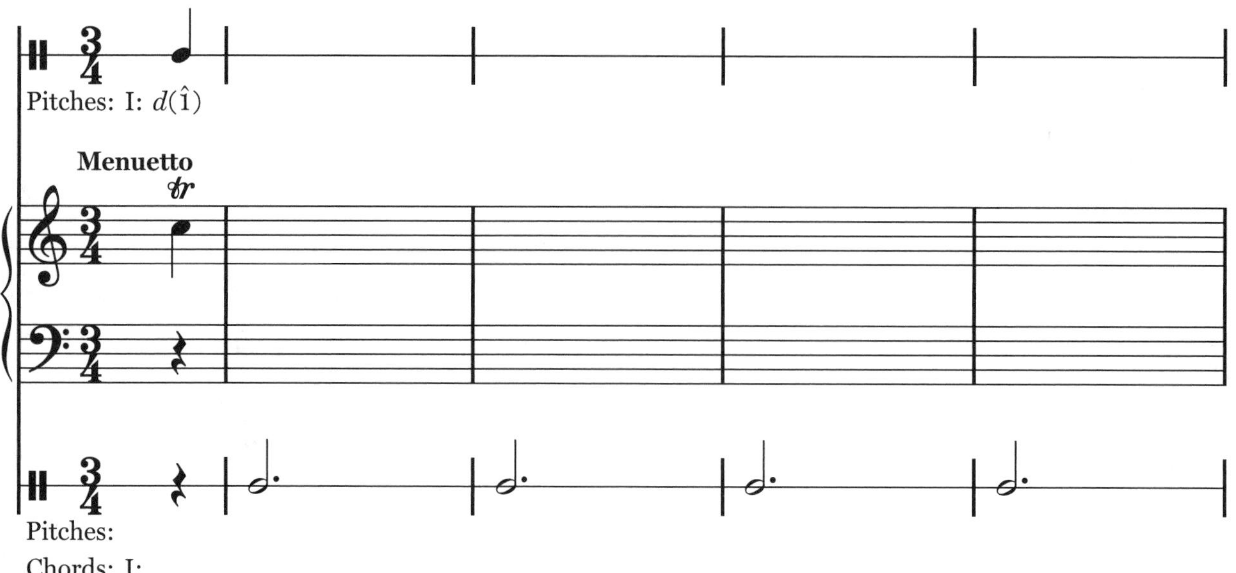
Pitches: I: $d(\hat{1})$
Menuetto
tr
Pitches:
Chords: I:

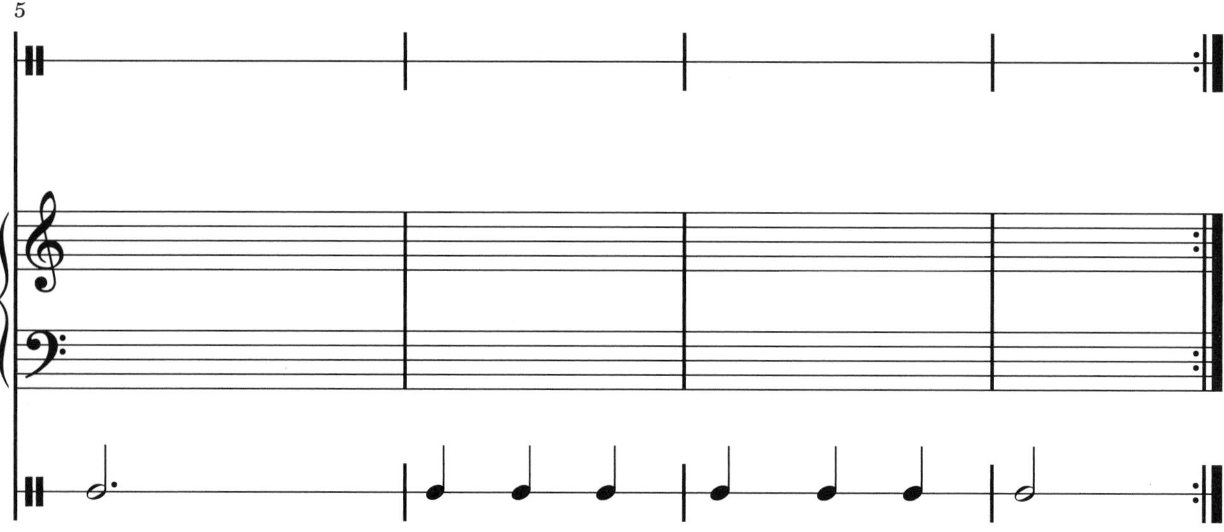
5

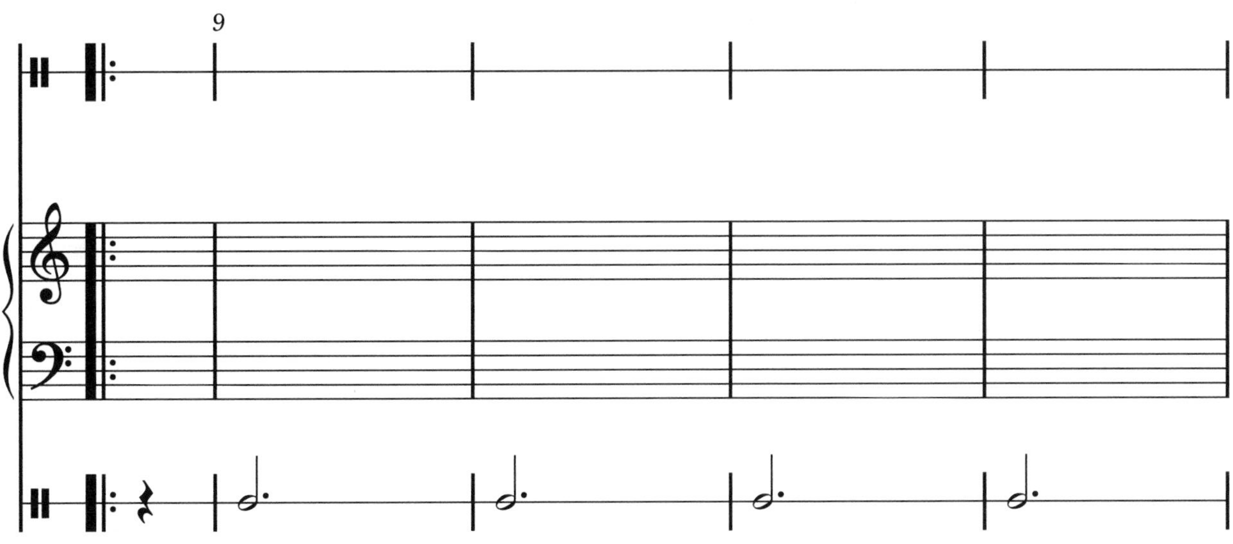
9

13

4. Diagram and label section 1's phrases and period:

5. Given the answer to exercise 4, the binary is: sectional continuous

6. Diagram and label section 2's phrases and period:

7. At the end, is there a recapitulation? yes no

8. Do the sections end with similar melodies? yes no

9. The $^6_4$ type near each section's end is: passing neighboring cadential

10. Incorporating the diagrams from exercises 4 and 6, diagram and label the form of the entire minuet:

Contextual Listening 23.4

Listen to a theme from a piano sonata. Focus first only on phrase 1.

1. Begin with the given items and capture the music in the workspace.
   (a) In the single-line staves, notate the rhythm of the outer parts.
   (b) Below each note, write the syllables or numbers of the pitches.
   (c) In the grand staff, notate the pitches and rhythm of the outer parts. Refer to the single-line notation.
   (d) Write the Roman numerals and figures (if needed) that represent the harmony.

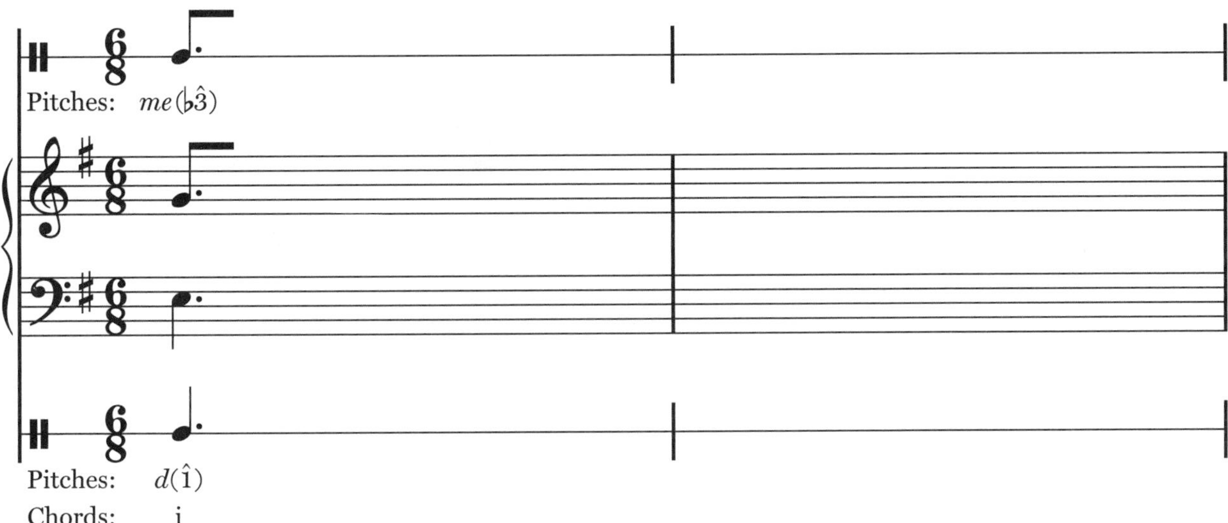

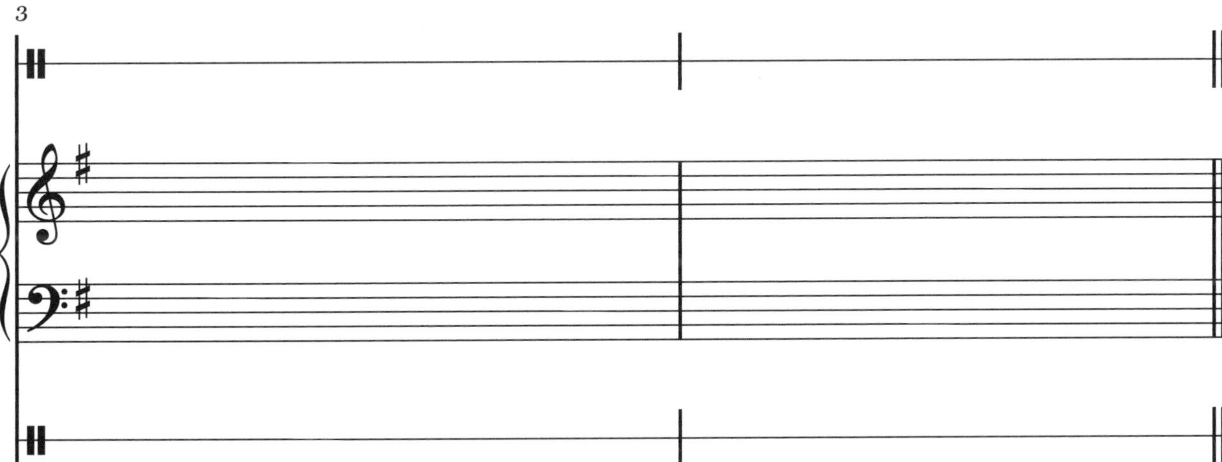

2. Phrase 1's internal organization is a: motive segment sentence section

3. Phrase 1's cadence type is: PAC (i) IAC (i) HC (i) PAC (III)

4. Phrase 2, segment 2 tonicizes which chord? What chromatic pitch(es) are used?

	III	iv	V	VI
pitch(es):	*te* ($\flat\hat{7}$)	*mi* ($\hat{3}$)	*fi* ($\sharp\hat{4}$)	*te* ($\flat\hat{7}$) and *ra* ($\flat\hat{2}$)

5. Phrase 2's cadence type is: PAC (i) IAC (i) HC (i) PAC (III)

6. Phrases 1–2 create which structure?

   parallel period contrasting period

   modulatory parallel period modulatory contrasting period

Now, focus on the entire example.

7. Diagram the form of the entire example:

NAME ________________________________

Ternary Form and Composite Form

Ternary is three-part form, exemplified by *da capo* arias and minuet-trio-minuet movements. Often, ternary forms are sectional, meaning each section ends with a PAC in the key of that section. When a ternary form's **B** section ends with anything besides a PAC in its key, the ternary form is continuous.

Composite form is form within form. Traditional dances, like minuets and trios, are themselves binary. When combined into a single three-section movement, they create composite ternary. Often, trios are in key of the subdominant (IV).

Composite Ternary

A Section 1 / Minuet	**B** Section 2 / Trio	**A** Section 3 / Minuet
Rounded continuous binary	*Simple sectional binary*	*Rounded continuous binary*
A **B** **A′**	**C** **D**	**A** **B** **A′**
‖: I — V :‖‖: V — I — :‖	‖: I — I :‖‖: V — I :‖	‖: I — V :‖‖: V — I — :‖
I: ________	IV: ________	I: ________

Try it 2

Listen to an entire work and diagram its form. Include descriptors for the overall form—binary, ternary, or composite—and phrase-structure diagrams of each section.

Contextual Listening 23.5

Listen to a ragtime piece and diagram its form. As you work, consider these strategies.

- Label each section with a design letter. Section letters are uppercase.
- If a section immediately repeats, use repeat signs (e.g., write **A A** as written **‖: A :‖**).
- If previously heard music recurs *after a contrasting section*, label it with its original design letter (e.g., **A B A**).
- A key change indicates a large-scale structural change. The number of key changes equals the number of large sections.
- If any large section is itself a small form, like binary or ternary, the overall form is a composite form.

APPENDIX

Try it Answers

Chapter 1 *Try it*

1. (a) — / \ (b) — / \ (c) — / \
   (d) — / \ (e) — / \ (f) — / \

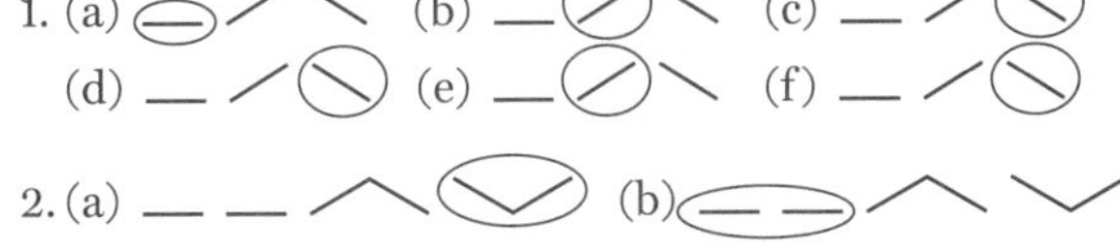

2. (a) — — ^ v (b) — — ^ v
   (c) — — ^ v (d) — — ^ v
   (e) — — ^ v (f) — — ^ v

3.

4. (a) — / \ S H W (b) — / \ S H W
   (c) — / \ S H W (d) — / \ S H W
   (e) — / \ S H W (f) — / \ S H W

Chapter 2 *Try it*

1. (a) 3, 1 (b) 5, 4 (c) 6, 2 (d) 8, 7
2. (a) 2, 5 (b) 3, 4 (c) 7, 1 (d) 6, 8
3. (a) 2, 1 (b) 3, 2 (c) 4, 1 (d) 2, 3
4. (a)

(b)

(c)

(d)

(e)

(f)

Chapter 3 *Try it*

Chapter 4 *Try it*

(f)

Chapter 5 *Try it*

1. (a) harmonic	simple
(b) natural	simple
(c) ascending melodic	compound
(d) harmonic	compound
(e) ascending melodic	simple
(f) natural	compound

2. (a) Dorian	simple
(b) Phrygian	compound
(c) Mixolydian	simple
(d) Dorian	compound
(e) Lydian	compound
(f) Phrygian	simple

3. (a)

(b)

(c)

(d)

Chapter 6 *Try it*

1. Division: simple
   Pitches 1-2 form: P5 *do-sol* ($\hat{1}$-$\hat{5}$)
   Key: major
   Patterns: | 2 6 | 4 1 ||

2. Division: compound
   Pitches 1-2 form: M3 *do-mi* ($\hat{1}$-$\hat{3}$)
   Key: major
   Patterns: | 2 3 | 4 1 ||

3. Division: simple
   Pitches 1-2 form: m3 *do-me* ($\hat{1}$-$\flat\hat{3}$)
   Key: minor
   Patterns: | 2 6 | 4 1 ||

4. Division: simple
   Pitches 1-2 form: M3 *sol-me* ($\hat{5}$-$\flat\hat{3}$)
   Key: minor
   Patterns: | 4 2 | 8 1 ||

5. Division: compound
   Pitches 1-2 form: m6 *sol-me* ($\hat{5}$-$\flat\hat{3}$)
   Key: minor
   Patterns: | 3 3 | 2 1 ||

6. Division: simple
   Pitches 4-5 form: d5 *ti-fa* ($\hat{7}$-$\hat{4}$)
   Key: major
   Patterns: | 4 8 | 2 1 ||

7. Division: simple
   Pitches 1-2 form: M6 *sol-mi* ($\hat{5}$-$\hat{3}$)
   Key: major
   Patterns: ♪| 2 5 | 7 1 ||

8. Division: compound
   Pitches 1-2 form: P5 *sol-do* ($\hat{5}$-$\hat{1}$)
   Key: minor
   Patterns: ♪| 3 5 | 4 1 ||

Chapter 7 *Try it*

1. (a) Triad quality: major
   Last 2 pitches form: P5 *do-sol* ($\hat{1}$-$\hat{5}$)
   Simple or compound: simple
   | 2 6 | 4 1 ||

   (b) Triad quality: major
   Last 2 pitches form: M3 *mi-do* ($\hat{3}$-$\hat{1}$)
   Simple or compound: compound
   | 2 3 | 4 1 ||

   (c) Triad quality: minor
   Last 2 pitches form: m3 *do-me* ($\hat{1}$-$\flat\hat{3}$)
   Simple or compound: simple
   | 2 6 | 4 1 ||

   (d) Triad quality: minor
   Last 2 pitches form: M3 *me-sol* ($\flat\hat{3}$-$\hat{5}$)
   Simple or compound: simple
   | 4 2 | 8 1 ||

   (e) Triad quality: augmented
   Last 2 pitches form: m2 *ti-do* ($\hat{7}$-$\hat{1}$)
   Simple or compound: compound
   | 3 3 | 2 1 ||

   (f) Triad quality: diminished
   Last 2 pitches form: M3 *do-mi* ($\hat{1}$-$\hat{3}$)
   Simple or compound: simple
   | 4 8 | 2 1 ||

   (g) Triad quality: major
   Last 2 pitches form: M6 *do-la* ($\hat{1}$-$\hat{6}$)
   Simple or compound: simple
   ♪ | 2 5 | 7 1 ||

   (h) Triad quality: minor
   Last 2 pitches form: m3 *me-do* ($\flat\hat{3}$-$\hat{1}$)
   Simple or compound: simple
   ♪ | 3 5 | 4 1 ||

2. (a) Chord 1: M Chord 2: M
   (b) Chord 1: m Chord 2: M
   (c) Chord 1: M Chord 2: d
   (d) Chord 1: M Chord 2: m
   (e) Chord 1: m Chord 2: M
   (f) Chord 1: M Chord 2: M
   (g) Chord 1: M Chord 2: M
   (h) Chord 1: m Chord 2: d
   (i) Chord 1: M Chord 2: A
   (j) Chord 1: M Chord 2: M

3. (a) Chord 1: M Chord 2: m Chord 3: M Chord 4: M
   (b) Chord 1: m Chord 2: d Chord 3: M Chord 4: m
   (c) Chord 1: M Chord 2: m Chord 3: m Chord 4: M
   (d) Chord 1: M Chord 2: M Chord 3: m Chord 4: M

Chapter 8 *Try it*

1. (a) MM7 (b) Mm7 (c) mm7 (d) MM7
   (e) mm7 (f) dm7 (g) °7 (h) min7
   (i) 7 (j) 7

2. (a) Chord 1: MM7 Chord 2: dm7
   (b) Chord 1: dm7 Chord 2: Mm7
   (c) Chord 1: mm7 Chord 2: MM7
   (d) Chord 1: min7 Chord 2: min7
   (e) Chord 1: ø7 Chord 2: °7

3. (a)

Chord:	1	2	3	4
Quality:	M	mm7	mm7	Mm7

(b)

Chord:	1	2	3	4
Quality:	m	MM7	mm7	Mm7

(c)

Chord:	1	2	3
Quality:	dd7	m	M

(d)

Chord:	1	2	3
Quality:	dm7	Mm7	mm7

(e)

Chord:	1	2	3	4
Quality:	mm7	mm7	Mm7	MM7
Chord:	5	6	7	8
Quality:	MM7	dm7	Mm7	mm7

4. (a)

Chord:	1	2	3	4
Symbol:	Cmaj	Amin7	Dmin7	G7

(b)

Chord:	1	2	3	4
Symbol:	Cmin	A♭maj7	Fmin7	G7

(c)

Chord:	1	2	3
Symbol:	C♯dim7	Dmin	Amaj

(d)

Chord:	1	2	3
Symbol:	F♯ø7	B7	Emin7

(e)

Chord:	1	2	3	4
Symbol:	Amin7	Dmin7	G7	Cmaj7
Chord:	5	6	7	8
Symbol:	Fmaj7	Bø7	E7	Amin7

Chapter 9 *Try it*

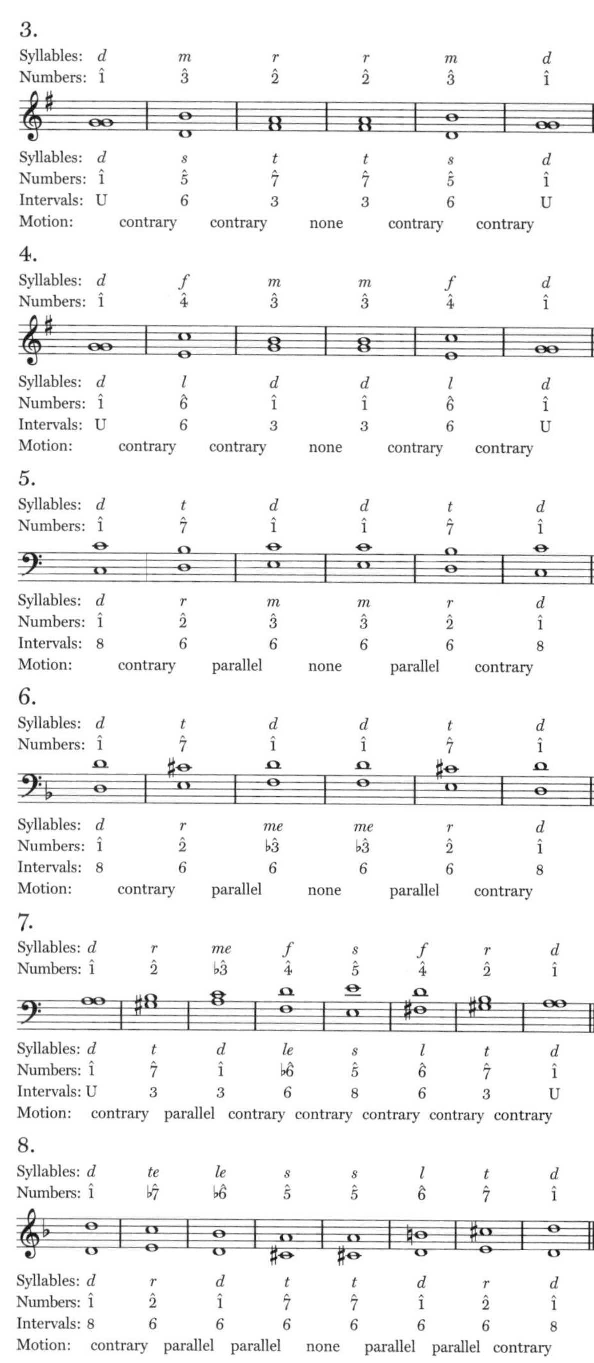

Chapter 10 *Try it*

1. (a) parallel (b) thirds (c) unison
2. (a) lower (b) consonant skip
3. (a) higher (b) neighbor tone
4. (a) higher (b) suspension
5. (a) lower (b) suspension
6. (a) both (b) consonant skip
7. (a) lower (b) passing tone
8. (a) consonant skip (b) neighbor tone
9. (a) parallel (b) sixths (c) octave
10. (a) higher (b) suspension
11. (a) higher (b) incomplete neighbor
12. (a) both (b) voice exchange

Chapter 11 *Try it*

1. The cadence is: conclusive

2. The cadence is: conclusive

3. The cadence is: less conclusive

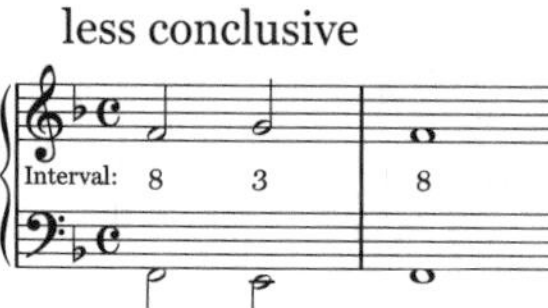

4. The cadence is: less conclusive

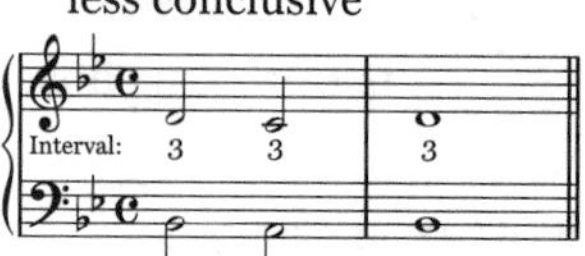

5. The cadence is: less conclusive

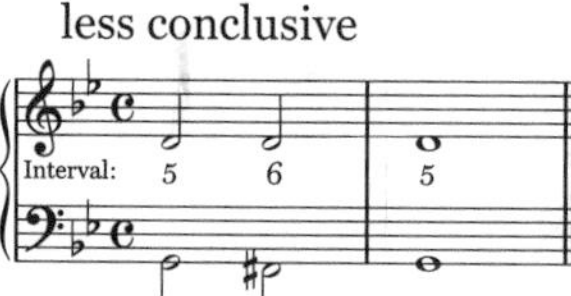

6. The cadence is: less conclusive

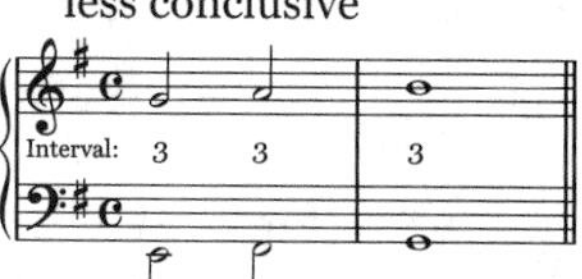

7. The cadence is: less conclusive

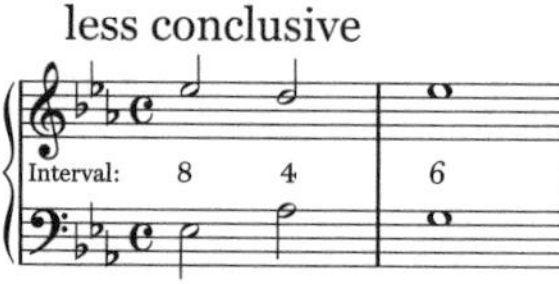

8. The cadence is: less conclusive

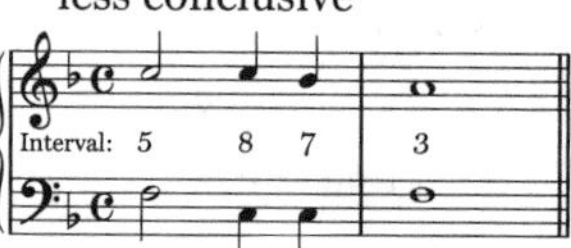

9. The cadence is: conclusive

10. The cadence is: conclusive

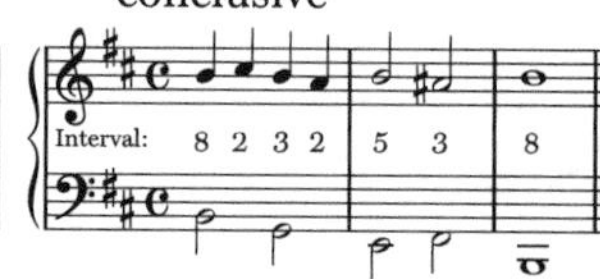

Chapter 12 *Try it*

1. Cadence type: PAC

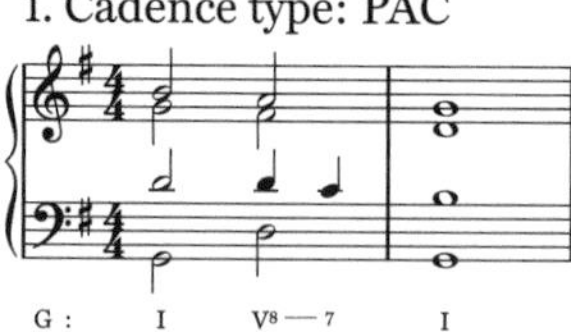

2. Cadence type: IAC

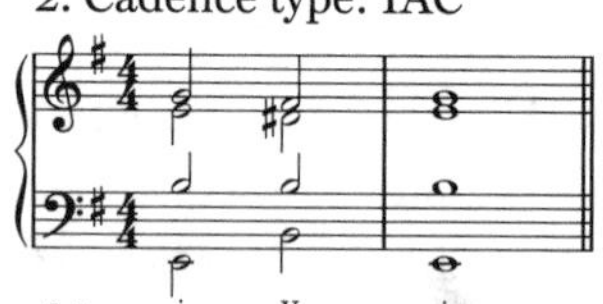

3. Cadence type: PAC

4. Cadence type: HC

5. Cadence type: IAC

6. Cadence type: HC

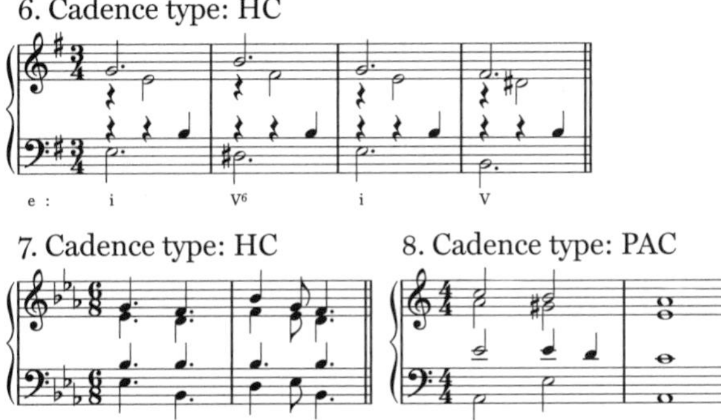

7. Cadence type: HC

8. Cadence type: PAC

Chapter 13 *Try it 1*

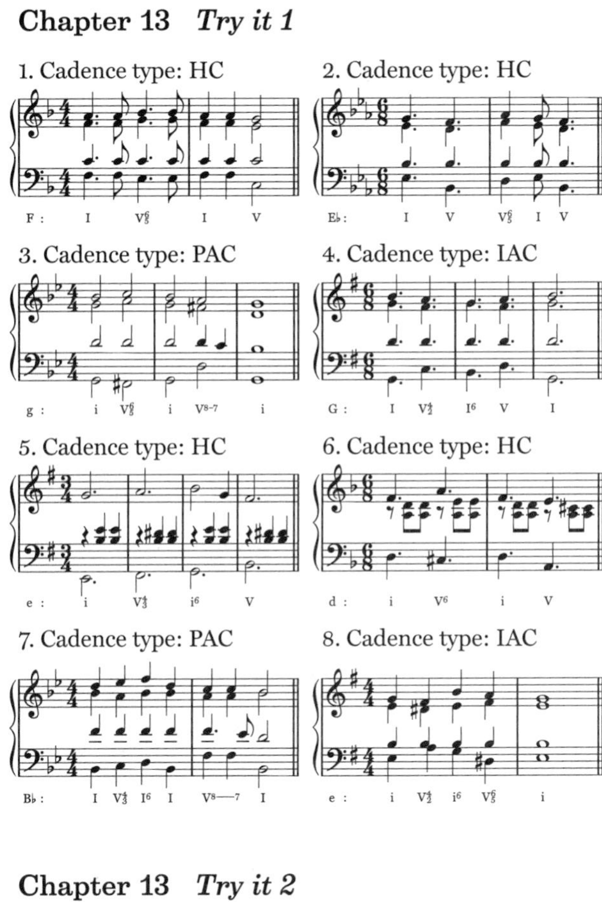

1. Cadence type: HC
2. Cadence type: HC
3. Cadence type: PAC
4. Cadence type: IAC
5. Cadence type: HC
6. Cadence type: HC
7. Cadence type: PAC
8. Cadence type: IAC

Chapter 13 *Try it 2*

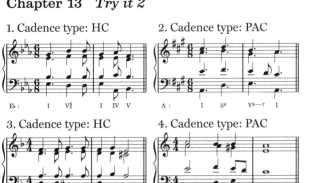

1. Cadence type: HC
2. Cadence type: PAC
3. Cadence type: HC
4. Cadence type: PAC

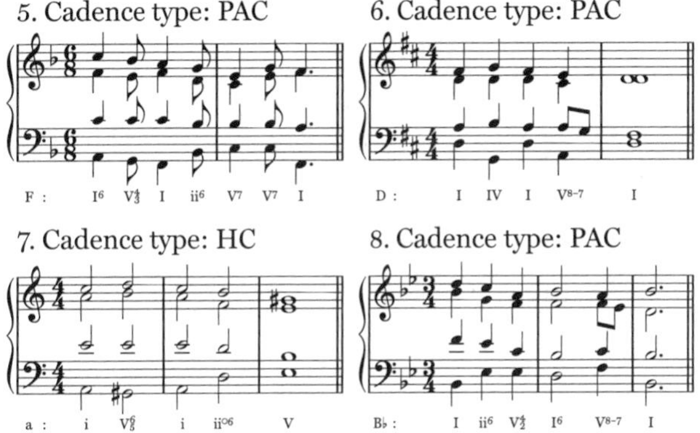

5. Cadence type: PAC
6. Cadence type: PAC
7. Cadence type: HC
8. Cadence type: PAC

Chapter 14 *Try it*

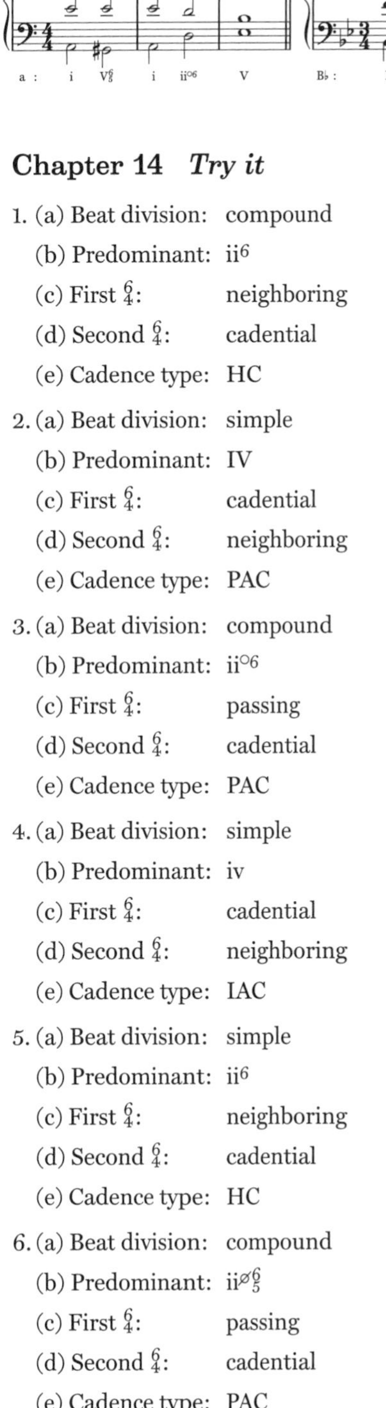

1. (a) Beat division: compound
   (b) Predominant: ii6
   (c) First $^6_4$: neighboring
   (d) Second $^6_4$: cadential
   (e) Cadence type: HC
2. (a) Beat division: simple
   (b) Predominant: IV
   (c) First $^6_4$: cadential
   (d) Second $^6_4$: neighboring
   (e) Cadence type: PAC
3. (a) Beat division: compound
   (b) Predominant: ii°6
   (c) First $^6_4$: passing
   (d) Second $^6_4$: cadential
   (e) Cadence type: PAC
4. (a) Beat division: simple
   (b) Predominant: iv
   (c) First $^6_4$: cadential
   (d) Second $^6_4$: neighboring
   (e) Cadence type: IAC
5. (a) Beat division: simple
   (b) Predominant: ii6
   (c) First $^6_4$: neighboring
   (d) Second $^6_4$: cadential
   (e) Cadence type: HC
6. (a) Beat division: compound
   (b) Predominant: ii$^{ø6}_5$
   (c) First $^6_4$: passing
   (d) Second $^6_4$: cadential
   (e) Cadence type: PAC

7. (a) Beat division: simple
   (b) Predominant: $\text{ii}^{\varnothing 6}_{5}$
   (c) First $^{6}_{4}$: passing
   (d) Second $^{6}_{4}$: neighboring
   (e) Cadence type: PAC

8. (a) Beat division: compound
   (b) Predominant: ii^{6}_{5}
   (c) First $^{6}_{4}$: neighboring
   (d) Second $^{6}_{4}$: cadential
   (e) Cadence type: HC

Chapter 15 *Try it*

1. (a) Beat division: compound
   (b) Predominant: ii^{6}
   (c) $^{6}_{4}$ type: neighboring
   (d) Cadence type: DC

2. (a) Beat division: simple
   (b) Predominant: IV
   (c) $^{6}_{4}$ type: cadential
   (d) Cadence type: DC

3. (a) Beat division: compound
   (b) Predominant: iv^{6}
   (c) $^{6}_{4}$ type: passing
   (d) Cadence type: PHC

4. (a) Beat division: simple
   (b) Predominant: IV
   (c) $^{6}_{4}$ type: neighboring
   (d) Cadence type: PAC

5. (a) Beat division: simple
   (b) Predominant: iv
   (c) Chord 2 is: V^{6}_{5}
   (d) $^{6}_{4}$ type: passing
   (e) Cadence type: PC

6. (a) Beat division: simple
   (b) Predominant: iv^{6}
   (c) Chord 2 is: V^{4}_{3}
   (d) Cadence type: PHC

7. (a) Beat division: compound
   (b) Predominant: ii^{6}
   (c) Chord 2 is: V^{6}_{5}
   (d) $^{6}_{4}$ type: passing
   (e) Cadence type: DC

8. (a) Beat division: simple
   (b) Predominant: iv^{6}
   (c) Chord 4 is: V^{4}_{2}
   (d) $^{6}_{4}$ type: neighboring
   (e) Cadence type: PHC

Chapter 16 *Try it*

1. (a) Beat division: simple
   (b) Predominant: ii^{6}
   (c) Melodic pitches 2 and 4 are: N
   (d) Melodic pitch 6 is an/a: anticipation (A)
   (e) Cadence type: PAC

2. (a) Beat division: simple
   (b) Predominant: iv^{6}
   (c) Melodic pitch 3 is an/a: suspension/retardation (S)
   Choose figure(s): 7-6
   (d) Cadence type: PHC

3. (a) Beat division: simple
   (b) Predominant: iv
   (c) The final measure includes an/a: suspension/retardation (S)
   Choose figure(s): 4-3
   (d) $^{6}_{4}$ type: passing
   (e) Cadence type: PC

4. (a) Beat division: compound
   (b) Predominant: ii^{6}
   (c) Melodic pitch 5 is an/a: suspension/retardation (S)
   Choose figure(s): 4-3, 7-8, 9-8
   (d) $^{6}_{4}$ type: cadential
   (e) Cadence type: PAC

5. (a) Beat division: simple
   (b) Bass pitch 2 is a: P
   (c) Melodic pitch 3 is a: chromatic P
   (d) The final measure includes an/a: suspension/retardation (S)
   Choose figure(s): 4-3
   (e) Cadence type: PHC

Chapter 17 *Try it 1*

1. (a) Chord 2 is: $\text{vii}^{\circ 7}$
   (b) Chord 4 is: V^{4}_{2}
   (c) Predominant: iv
   (d) Cadence type: HC

2. (a) Chord is: V^{6}_{5}
   (b) Chord 4 is: $\text{vii}^{\circ 4}_{3}$
   (c) Predominant: $\text{ii}^{\varnothing 6}_{5}$
   (d) Cadence type: HC

3. (a) Chord 2 is: $\text{vii}^{\circ 6}_{5}$
   (b) Chord 4 is: $\text{vii}^{\circ 7}$
   (c) Predominant: iv^{6}
   (d) Cadence type: PHC

4. (a) Chord is: V^{4}_{3}
   (b) Chord 4 is: V^{6}_{5}
   (c) Predominant: iv
   (d) Cadence type: HC

5. (a) Chord 2 is: $\text{vii}^{\circ 4}_{3}$
   (b) Chord 4 is: $\text{vii}^{\circ 6}_{5}$
   (c) Predominant: iv
   (d) Cadence type: HC

6. (a) Chord is: V^{4}_{2}
   (b) Chord 4 is: V^{4}_{3}
   (c) Predominant: iv^{6}
   (d) Cadence type: PHC

7. The meter type of exercises 1-6 is: compound

Chapter 17 *Try it 2*

1. (a) Chord 2 is: V^{6}_{4}
   (b) Predominant: iv^{6}
   (c) Embellishment: S
   (d) Cadence type: PHC

2. (a) Chord 2 is: $\text{vii}^{\circ 6}$
   (b) Predominant: $\text{ii}^{\circ 6}$
   (c) Embellishment: CS
   (d) Cadence type: HC

3. (a) Chord 2 is: $\text{vii}^{\circ 6}$
   (b) Predominant: iv^{6}
   (c) Embellishment: N
   (d) Cadence type: PHC

4. (a) Chord 2 is: V^{6}_{4}
   (b) Predominant: iv
   (c) Embellishment: S
   (d) Cadence type: HC

Chapter 18 *Try it 1*

1. At the end, the $^{6}_{4}$ chord type is: cadential
2. The next-to-last melodic pitch is which embellishment? retardation
3. The excerpt ends with a/an: PAC
4. Melodic pitches 1-5: motive, subphrase
5. Melodic pitches 6-10: motive, subphrase
6. Melodic pitches 11-end: motive, subphrase
7. The entire excerpt: phrase, sentence, independent phrase

Chapter 18 *Try it 2*

1. (a) (1) Melodic pitches 1-5: motive, subphrase
       (2) Melodic pitches 6-10: motive, subphrase
       (3) Melodic pitches 11-19: motive, subphrase
       (4) Melodic pitches 1-19: phrase, sentence
   (b) Phrase 1 ends with a/an: HC
   (c) Phrase 2 ends with a/an: PAC
   (d) Phrases 1-2 compete which pattern? period
   (e) Compare phrase 2's beginning with that of phrase 1. Phrase 2 begins: the same or similarly (**a** or **a′**)
   (f) Which diagram represents the excerpt's structure?

Parallel period

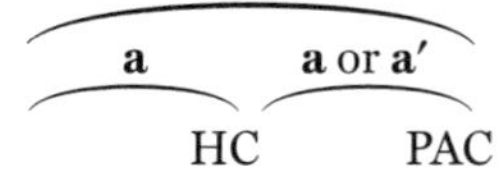

2. (a) Phrase 1 ends with a/an: HC
   (b) Phrase 2 ends with a/an: PAC
   (c) Phrases 1-2 compete which pattern? period
   (d) Compare phrase 2's beginning with that of phrase 1. Phrase 2 begins: differently (**b**)
   (e) Which diagram represents the excerpt's structure?

Contrasting period

3. (a) The beat division is: compound
   (b) The lyrics "It's nine o'clock on a Saturday" complete a: motive, subphrase
   (c) Compare phrase 2's beginning with that of phrase 1. Phrase 2 begins: the same or similarly (**a** or **a′**)
   (d) The excerpt's structure is a: parallel period

Chapter 18 *Try it 3*

1. (a)

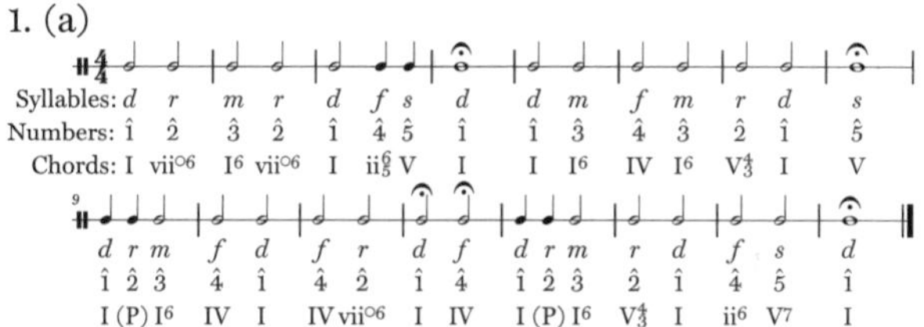

(b) Parallel double period

antecedent phrases | consequent phrases

a | **b** | **a′** | **a′**

IAC | HC | IAC | PAC

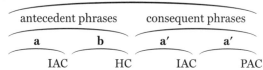

2. Asymmetrical parallel double period

antecedent phrases | consequent phrases

a | **a′** | **a** | **a′** | **a″**

HC | HC | HC | DC | PAC

Chapter 19 *Try it*

1. (a) Meter type: simple
   (b) Chord 2 is: V^{4}_{3}
   (c) Chord 5 is: ii^{6}_{5}
   (d) Chord 6 is: $\text{V}^{6}_{5}\text{/V}$
   (e) Cadence type: HC

2. (a) Meter type: compound
   (b) Chord 2 is: V^{6}_{5}
   (c) Chord 5 is: $\text{ii}^{\varnothing 6}_{5}$
   (d) Chord 6 is: $\text{V}^{6}_{5}\text{/V}$
   (e) Cadence type: HC

3. (a) Meter type: simple
   (b) Chord 2 is: V$^4_2$
   (c) Chord 4 is: vii^{ø7}/V
   (d) $^6_4$ type: cadential
   (e) Cadence type: PAC

4. (a) Meter type: compound
   (b) Chord 2 is: vii^{o7}
   (c) Chord 4 is: vii^{o7}/V
   (d) $^6_4$ type: cadential
   (e) Cadence type: DC

5. (a) Meter type: compound
   (b) Chord 4 is: ii^{o6}
   (c) Chord 5 is: vii^{o7}/V
   (d) $^6_4$ type: passing
   (e) Cadence type: PAC

6. (a) Meter type: simple
   (b) Chord 4 is: iv^6
   (c) Chord 6 is: vii^{o7}/V
   (d) $^6_4$ type: neighboring
   (e) Cadence type: PHC

7. (a) Meter type: simple
   (b) Chord 2 is: V$^4_2$
   (c) Chord 4 is: V^7/V
   (d) Cadence type: IAC

8. (a) Meter type: simple
   (b) Chord 2 is: V$^6_4$
   (c) Chord 5 is: V^6/V
   (d) Cadence type: HC

Chapter 20 *Try it*

1. (a) The initial progression is: I-V$^6_5$-I
   (b) The chromatic pitch is: *si* (♯$\hat{5}$)
   (c) The tonicized chord is: vi
   (d) Tonicization (chords 4–5):

Bracket	*Slash*	*Colon*
V$^6_5$ i (bracket: ii)	V$^6_5$/vi-vi	vi: V$^6_5$-i

2. (a) The initial progression is: I-V$^6_5$-I
   (b) The chromatic pitch is: *di* (♯$\hat{1}$)
   (c) The tonicized chord is: ii
   (d) Tonicization (chords 4–5):

Bracket	*Slash*	*Colon*
V$^6_5$ i (bracket: ii)	V$^6_5$/ii-ii	ii: V$^6_5$-i

3. (a) The initial progression is: I-V$^4_2$-I^6
   (b) The chromatic pitch is: *di* (♯$\hat{1}$)
   (c) The tonicized chord is: ii
   (d) Tonicization (chords 4–5):

Bracket	*Slash*	*Colon*
V$^4_2$ i^6 (bracket: ii)	V$^4_2$/ii-ii^6	ii: V$^4_2$-i^6

4. (a) The initial progression is: I-V$^6_5$-I
   (b) The chromatic pitch is: *te* (♭$\hat{7}$)
   (c) The tonicized chord is: IV
   (d) Tonicization (chords 4–5):

Bracket	*Slash*	*Colon*
V$^6_5$ I (bracket: IV)	V$^6_5$/IV-IV	IV: V$^6_5$-I

5. (a) The initial progression is: i-V$^6_5$-i
   (b) The chromatic pitch(es) is (are): *ra* (♭$\hat{2}$), *te* (♭$\hat{7}$)
   (c) The tonicized chord is: VI
   (d) Tonicization (chords 4–5):

Bracket	*Slash*	*Colon*
V$^6_5$ I (bracket: VI)	V$^6_5$/VI-VI	VI: V$^6_5$-I

6. (a) The initial progression is: i-V-i
   (b) The chromatic pitch(es) is (are): *te* (♭$\hat{7}$)
   (c) The tonicized chord is: III
   (d) Tonicization (chords 4–5):

Bracket	*Slash*	*Colon*
V I (bracket: III)	V/III-III	III: V-I

7. (a) The initial progression is: i-vii$^{o6}_{5}$-i^6
   (b) The chromatic pitch(es) is (are): *ra* (♭$\hat{2}$), *mi* (♮$\hat{3}$)
   (c) The tonicized chord is: iv
   (d) Tonicization (chords 4–5):

Bracket	*Slash*	*Colon*
vii$^{o6}_{5}$ i^6 (bracket: iv)	vii$^{o6}_{5}$/iv-iv^6	iv: vii$^{o6}_{5}$-i^6

Chapter 21 *Try it*

1. (a) In a **major** key, **two**-chord units **ascend** by **second** in **four** reps with a **5-6** LIP to create a(n) **ascending 5-6 sequence.**
   (b) In a **minor** key, **two**-chord units **descend** by **second** in **four** reps with a **10-6** LIP to create a(n) **descending-fifth sequence.**
   (c) In a **major** key, **two**-chord units **descend** by **second** in **four** reps with a **10-8** LIP to create a(n) **descending-fifth sequence.**

(d) In a **minor** key, **two**-chord units **descend** by **third** in **three** reps with a **10-5** LIP to create a(n) **descending-third sequence**.

2. (a) Sequence name: descending fifth

(b) Sequence name: descending third

(c) Sequence name: descending fifth

(d) Sequence name: parallel $^6_3$

(e) Sequence name: ascending 5-6

Chapter 22 *Try it 1*

1. (a) The initial progression is: I-V$^{8\text{-}7}$-I
   Bass: *d-s-s-d* / $\hat{1}$-$\hat{5}$-$\hat{5}$-$\hat{1}$

   (b) The chromatic pitch is: *fi* (♯$\hat{4}$)

   (c) The exercise modulates to the key of: V

   (d) The example ends with which progression?
   I-ii$^6_5$-V-I

2. (a) The initial progression is: i-ii$^{\circ6}$-V$^{8-7}_{\begin{smallmatrix}6-5\\4-3\end{smallmatrix}}$-i
   Bass: *d-f-s-s-d* / $\hat{1}$-$\hat{4}$-$\hat{5}$-$\hat{5}$-$\hat{1}$

   (b) The chromatic pitch is: *te* (♭$\hat{7}$)

   (c) The exercise modulates to the key of: III

   (d) The example ends with which progression?
   I-vi-ii$^6_5$-V$^{8\text{-}7}$-I

3. (a) The initial progression is: I-V$^6_5$-I-ii^6-V$^{6-5}_{4-3}$-I
   Bass: *d-t-d-f-s-s-d* / $\hat{1}$-$\hat{7}$-$\hat{1}$-$\hat{4}$-$\hat{5}$-$\hat{5}$-$\hat{1}$

   (b) The chromatic pitch is: *si* (♯$\hat{5}$)

   (c) The exercise modulates to the key of: vi

   (d) The example ends with which progression?
   i-V$^6_5$-i-ii$^{\circ6}$-V$^{6-5}_{4-3}$-i

4. (a) The initial progression is: I-V$^6_4$-I^6-ii^6-V$^{6-5}_{4-3}$-I
Soprano: *m-r-d . . .* / $\hat{3}$-$\hat{2}$-$\hat{1}$

(b) The chromatic pitch is: *te* (♭$\hat{7}$)

(c) The exercise modulates to the key of: IV

(d) The example ends with which progression?
I-V$^4_3$-I^6-ii^6-V$^{\begin{smallmatrix}8-7\\6-5\\4-3\end{smallmatrix}}$-I

Chapter 22 *Try it 2*

1. Modulatory contrasting period

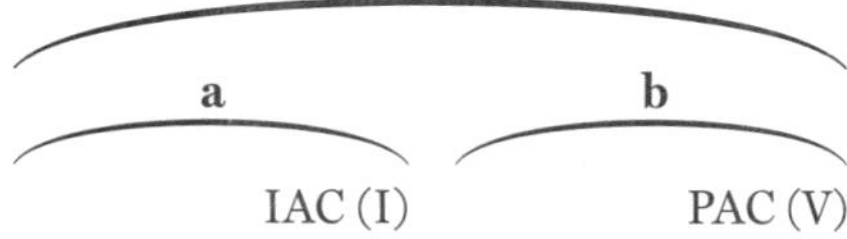

2. Modulatory parallel period

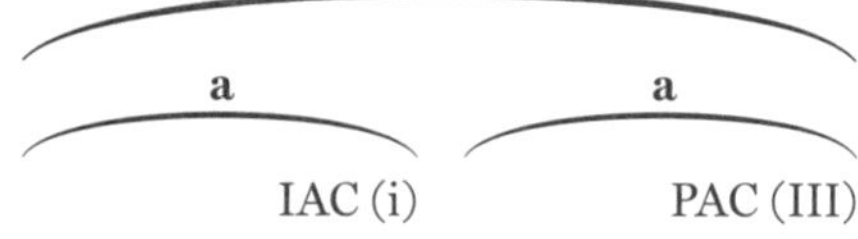

Chapter 23 *Try it 1*

1. (a) Modulatory parallel period

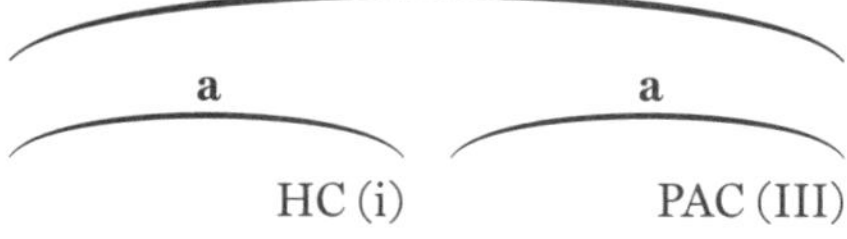

(b) The excerpt is section 1 of a binary composition.
The binary form is: continuous

2. (a) Modulatory contrasting period

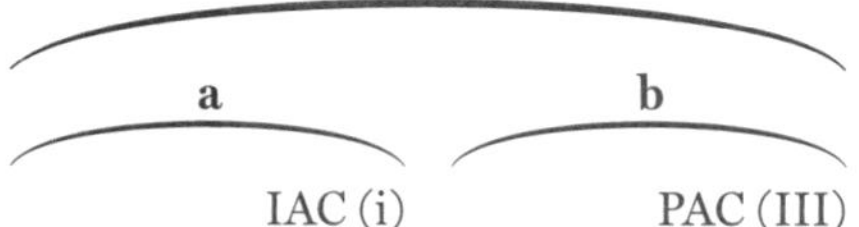

(b) Given the answer to (a), the binary form is: continuous

(c) Contrasting period

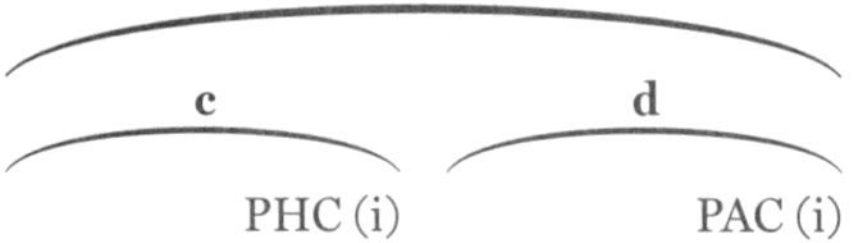

(d) At the end, is there a recapitulation? no

(e) Do the sections end with similar melodies? no

(f) *Simple continuous binary*

A B
‖: i —— III :‖‖: III —— i :‖

3. (a) Modulatory contrasting period

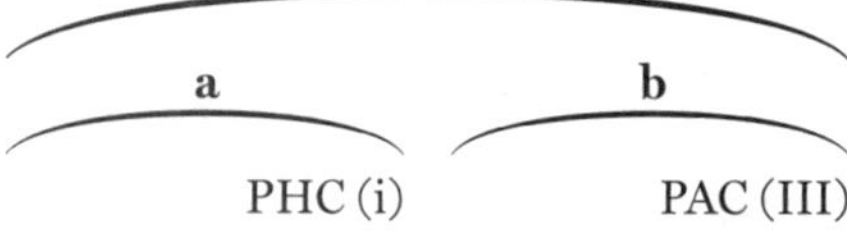

(b) Given the answer to (a), the binary form is: continuous

(c) Independent phrases

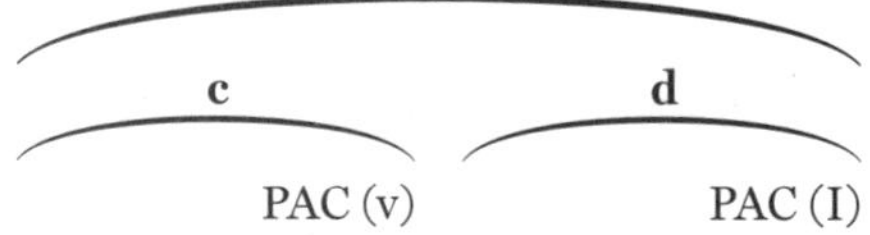

(d) At the end, is there a recapitulation? no

(e) Do the sections end with similar melodies? no

(f) *Simple continuous binary*

A B
‖: i —— III :‖‖: III —— I :‖

4. (a) Parallel period

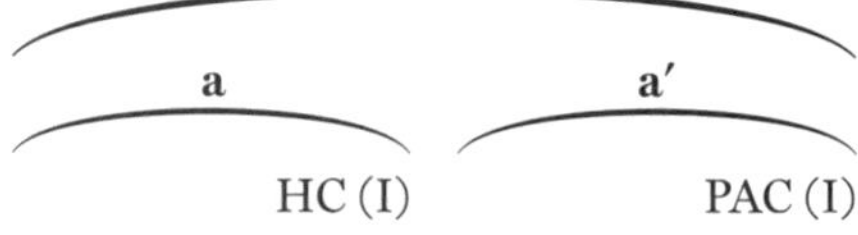

(b) Given the answer to (a), the binary form is: sectional

(c) Contrasting asymmetrical period

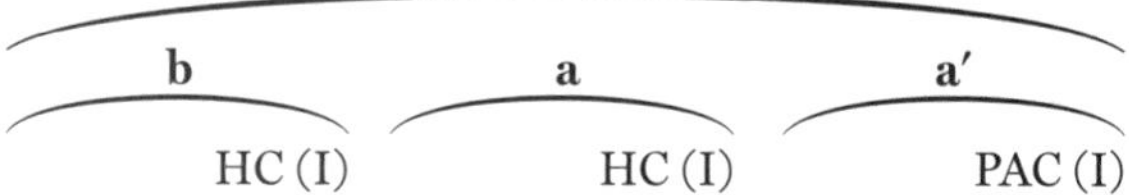

(d) At the end, is there a recapitulation? yes

(e) Do the sections end with similar melodies? yes

(f) *Sectional rounded binary*

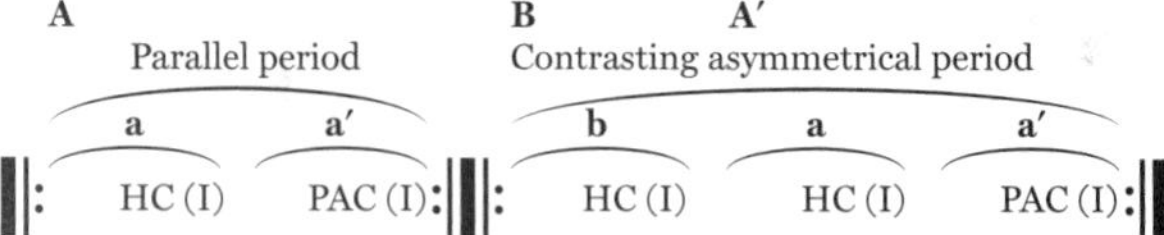

Chapter 23 *Try it 2*

A Section 1 / Minuet
Rounded continuous binary

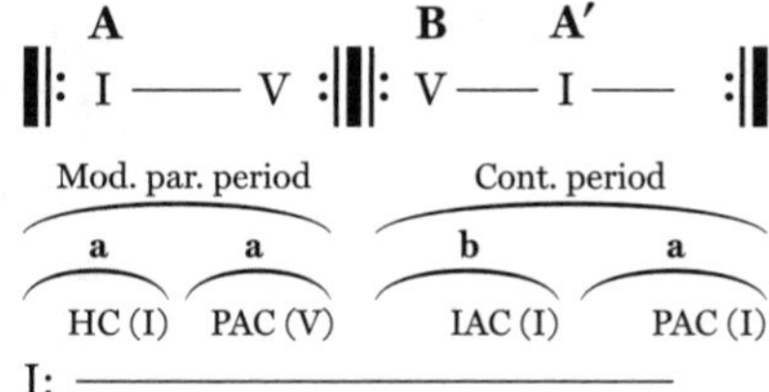

B Section 2 / Trio
Simple sectional binary

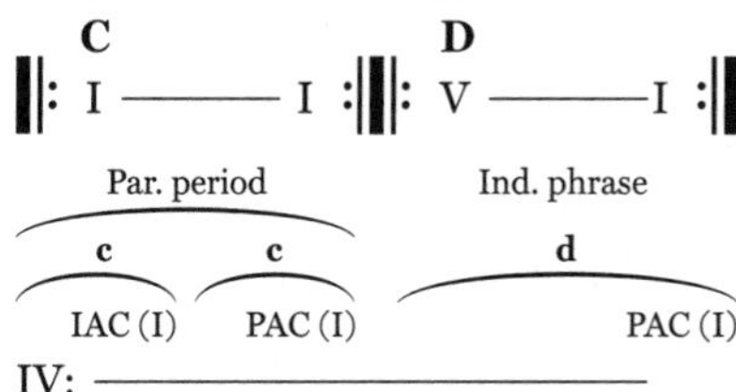

A Section 1 / Minuet
Rounded continuous binary

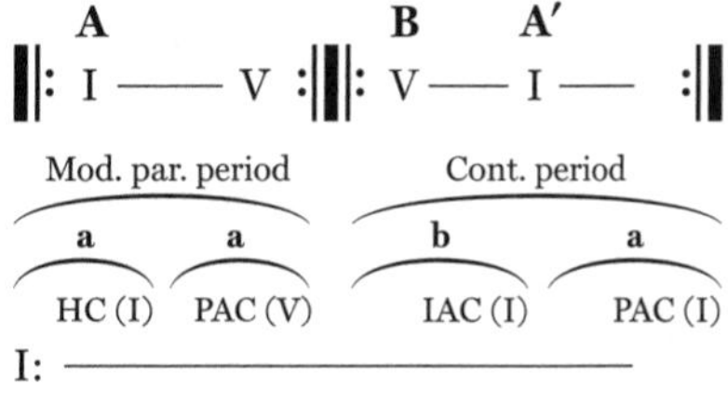

APPENDIX

Set-Class Table

NAME	PCS	IC VECTOR	NAME	PCS	IC VECTOR
3-1(12)	0,1,2	210000	9-1	0,1,2,3,4,5,6,7,8	876663
3-2	0,1,3	111000	9-2	0,1,2,3,4,5,6,7,9	777663
3-3	0,1,4	101100	9-3	0,1,2,3,4,5,6,8,9	767763
3-4	0,1,5	100110	9-4	0,1,2,3,4,5,7,8,9	766773
3-5	0,1,6	100011	9-5	0,1,2,3,4,6,7,8,9	766674
3-6(12)	0,2,4	020100	9-6	0,1,2,3,4,5,6,8,t	686763
3-7	0,2,5	011010	9-7	0,1,2,3,4,5,7,8,t	677673
3-8	0,2,6	010101	9-8	0,1,2,3,4,6,7,8,t	676764
3-9(12)	0,2,7	010020	9-9	0,1,2,3,5,6,7,8,t	676683
3-10(12)	0,3,6	002001	9-10	0,1,2,3,4,6,7,9,t	668664
3-11	0,3,7	001110	9-11	0,1,2,3,5,6,7,9,t	667773
3-12(4)	0,4,8	000300	9-12	0,1,2,4,5,6,8,9,t	666963
4-1(12)	0,1,2,3	321000	8-1	0,1,2,3,4,5,6,7	765442
4-2	0,1,2,4	221100	8-2	0,1,2,3,4,5,6,8	665542
4-3(12)	0,1,3,4	212100	8-3	0,1,2,3,4,5,6,9	656542
4-4	0,1,2,5	211110	8-4	0,1,2,3,4,5,7,8	655552
4-5	01,2,6	210111	8-5	0,1,2,3,4,6,7,8	654553
4-6(12)	0,1,2,7	210021	8-6	0,1,2,3,5,6,7,8	654463
4-7(12)	0,1,4,5	201210	8-7	0,1,2,3,4,5,8,9	645652
4-8(12)	0,1,5,6	200121	8-8	0,1,2,3,4,7,8,9	644563
4-9(6)	0,1,6,7	200022	8-9	0,1,2,3,6,7,8,9	644464
4-10(12)	0,2,3,5	122010	8-10	0,2,3,4,5,6,7,9	566452
4-11	0,1,3,5	121110	8-11	0,1,2,3,4,5,7,9	565552
4-12	0,2,3,6	112101	8-12	0,1,3,4,5,6,7,9	556543
4-13	0,1,3,6	112011	8-13	0,1,2,3,4,6,7,9	556453
4-14	0,2,3,7	111120	8-14	0,1,2,4,5,6,7,9	555562
4-Z15	0,1,4,6	111111	8-Z15	0,1,2,3,4,6,8,9	555553
4-16	0,1,5,7	110121	8-16	0,1,2,3,5,7,8,9	554563
4-17(12)	0,3,4,7	102210	8-17	0,1,3,4,5,6,8,9	546652
4-18	0,1,4,7	102111	8-18	0,1,2,3,5,6,8,9	546553
4-19	0,1,4,8	101310	8-19	0,1,2,4,5,6,8,9	545752
4-20(12)	0,1,5,8	101220	8-20	0,1,2,4,5,7,8,9	545662
4-21(12)	0,2,4,6	030201	8-21	0,1,2,3,4,6,8,t	474643
4-22	0,2,4,7	021120	8-22	0,1,2,3,5,6,8,t	465562
4-23(12)	0,2,5,7	021030	8-23	0,1,2,3,5,7,8,t	465472
4-24(12)	0,2,4,8	020301	8-24	0,1,2,4,5,6,8,t	464743
4-25(6)	0,2,6,8	020202	8-25	0,1,2,4,6,7,8,t	464644
4-26(12)	0,3,5,8	012120	8-26	0,1,2,4,5,7,9,t	456562

NOTE: Numbers in parentheses show the number of distinct sets in the set class if other than 24.
All brackets are eliminated here for ease of reading.

NAME	PCS	IC VECTOR
4-27	0,2,5,8	012111
4-28(3)	0,3,6,9	004002
4-Z29	0,1,3,7	111111
5-1(12)	0,1,2,3,4	432100
5-2	0,1,2,3,5	332110
5-3	0,1,2,4,5	322210
5-4	0,1,2,3,6	322111
5-5	0,1,2,3,7	321121
5-6	0,1,2,5,6	311221
5-7	0,1,2,6,7	310132
5-8(12)	0,2,3,4,6	232201
5-9	0,1,2,4,6	231211
5-10	0,1,3,4,6	223111
5-11	0,2,3,4,7	222220
5-Z12(12)	0,1,3,5,6	222121
5-13	0,1,2,4,8	221311
5-14	0,1,2,5,7	221131
5-15(12)	0,1,2,6,8	220222
5-16	0,1,3,4,7	213211
5-Z17(12)	0,1,3,4,8	212320
5-Z18	0,1,4,5,7	212221
5-19	0,1,3,6,7	212122
5-20	0,1,3,7,8	211231
5-21	0,1,4,5,8	202420
5-22(12)	0,1,4,7,8	202321
5-23	0,2,3,5,7	132130
5-24	0,1,3,5,7	131221
5-25	0,2,3,5,8	123121
5-26	0,2,4,5,8	122311
5-27	0,1,3,5,8	122230
5-28	0,2,3,6,8	122212
5-29	0,1,3,6,8	122131
5-30	0,1,4,6,8	121321
5-31	0,1,3,6,9	114112
5-32	0,1,4,6,9	113221
5-33(12)	0,2,4,6,8	040402
5-34(12)	0,2,4,6,9	032221
5-35(12)	0,2,4,7,9	032140
5-Z36	0,1,2,4,7	222121
5-Z37(12)	0,3,4,5,8	212320
5-Z38	0,1,2,5,8	212221
6-1(12)	0,1,2,3,4,5	543210
6-2	0,1,2,3,4,6	443211
6-Z3	0,1,2,3,5,6	433221
6-Z4(12)	0,1,2,4,5,6	432321
6-5	0,1,2,3,6,7	422232
6-Z6(12)	0,1,2,5,6,7	421242
6-7(6)	0,1,2,6,7,8	420243
6-8(12)	0,2,3,4,5,7	343230
6-9	0,1,2,3,5,7	342231
6-Z10	0,1,3,4,5,7	333321
6-Z11	0,1,2,4,5,7	333231

NAME	PCS	IC VECTOR
8-27	0,1,2,4,5,7,8,t	456553
8-28	0,1,3,4,6,7,9,t	448444
8-Z29	0,1,2,3,5,6,7,9	555553
7-1	0,1,2,3,4,5,6	654321
7-2	0,1,2,3,4,5,7	554331
7-3	0,1,2,3,4,5,8	544431
7-4	0,1,2,3,4,6,7	544332
7-5	0,1,2,3,5,6,7	543342
7-6	0,1,2,3,4,7,8	533442
7-7	0,1,2,3,6,7,8	532353
7-8	0,2,3,4,5,6,8	454422
7-9	0,1,2,3,4,6,8	453432
7-10	0,1,2,3,4,6,9	445332
7-11	0,1,3,4,5,6,8	444441
7-Z12	0,1,2,3,4,7,9	444342
7-13	0,1,2,4,5,6,8	443532
7-14	0,1,2,3,5,7,8	443352
7-15	0,1,2,4,6,7,8	442443
7-16	0,1,2,3,5,6,9	435432
7-Z17	0,1,2,4,5,6,9	434541
7-Z18	0,1,2,3,5,8,9	434442
7-19	0,1,2,3,6,7,9	434343
7-20	0,1,2,4,7,8,9	433452
7-21	0,1,2,4,5,8,9	424641
7-22	0,1,2,5,6,8,9	424542
7-23	0,2,3,4,5,7,9	354351
7-24	0,1,2,3,5,7,9	353442
7-25	0,2,3,4,6,7,9	345342
7-26	0,1,3,4,5,7,9	344532
7-27	0,1,2,4,5,7,9	344451
7-28	0,1,3,5,6,7,9	344433
7-29	0,1,2,4,6,7,9	344352
7-30	0,1,2,4,6,8,9	343542
7-31	0,1,3,4,6,7,9	336333
7-32	0,1,3,4,6,8,9	335442
7-33	0,1,2,4,6,8,t	262623
7-34	0,1,3,4,6,8,t	254442
7-35	0,1,3,5,6,8,t	254361
7-Z36	0,1,2,3,5,6,8	444342
7-Z37	0,1,3,4,5,7,8	434541
7-Z38	0,1,2,4,5,7,8	434442

NAME	PCS	IC VECTOR
6-Z36	0,1,2,3,4,7	*
6-Z37(12)	0,1,2,3,4,8	
6-Z38(12)	0,1,2,3,7,8	
6-Z39	0,2,3,4,5,8	
6-Z40	0,1,2,3,5,8	

*Z-related hexachords share the same ic vector; use vector in the third column

NAME	PCS	IC VECTOR
6-Z12	0,1,2,4,6,7	332232
6-Z13(12)	0,1,3,4,6,7	324222
6-14	0,1,3,4,5,8	323430
6-15	0,1,2,4,5,8	323421
6-16	0,1,4,5,6,8	322431
6-Z17	0,1,2,4,7,8	322332
6-18	0,1,2,5,7,8	322242
6-Z19	0,1,3,4,7,8	313431
6-20(4)	0,1,4,5,8,9	303630
6-21	0,2,3,4,6,8	242412
6-22	0,1,2,4,6,8	241422
6-Z23(12)	0,2,3,5,6,8	234222
6-Z24	0,1,3,4,6,8	233331
6-Z25	0,1,3,5,6,8	233241
6-Z26(12)	0,1,3,5,7,8	232341
6-27	0,1,3,4,6,9	225222
6-Z28(12)	0,1,3,5,6,9	224322
6-Z29(12)	0,1,3,6,8,9	224232
6-30(12)	0,1,3,6,7,9	224223
6-31	0,1,3,5,8,9	223431
6-32(12)	0,2,4,5,7,9	143250
6-33	0,2,3,5,7,9	143241
6-34	0,1,3,5,7,9	142422
6-35(2)	0,2,4,6,8,t	060603

NAME	PCS	IC VECTOR
6-Z41	0,1,2,3,6,8	
6-Z42(12)	0,1,2,3,6,9	
6-Z43	0,1,2,5,6,8	
6-Z44	0,1,2,5,6,9	
6-Z45(12)	0,2,3,4,6,9	
6-Z46	0,1,2,4,6,9	
6-Z47	0,1,2,4,7,9	
6-Z48(12)	0,1,2,5,7,9	
6-Z49(12)	0,1,3,4,7,9	
6-Z50(12)	0,1,4,6,7,9	

SOURCE: Allen Forte, *The Structure of Atonal Music* (New Haven: Yale University Press, 1973) (adapted)